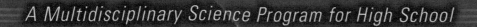

A Multidisciplinary Science Program for High School

Level **1**

BSCS SCIENCE
AN INQUIRY APPROACH

LIFE SCIENCE   PHYSICAL SCIENCE   EARTH/SPACE SCIENCE

EXPLORING THE BUILDING BLOCKS OF THE UNIVERSE

BSCS

KENDALL/HUNT PUBLISHING COMPANY
4050 Westmark Drive   Dubuque, Iowa 52002

BSCS Development Team

Rodger W. Bybee, PhD, *Co-Principal Investigator*
Pamela Van Scotter, *Co-Principal Investigator, Project Director*
Nicole Knapp, *Curriculum Developer, Professional Development Coordinator*
Betty Stennett, *Curriculum Developer, Professional Development Coordinator*
Steve Getty, PhD, *Curriculum Developer, Classroom-Based Research Associate*
K. David Pinkerton, PhD, *Curriculum Developer*
Cyndi Long, *Curriculum Developer, Professional Development Coordinator*
Sandy Smith, *Curriculum Developer*
C. Jane Wilson, *Curriculum Developer*
Debra Hannigan, *Curriculum Developer, Curriculum Coordinator*
David Hanych, PhD, *Curriculum Developer*
Steve Williams, PhD, *Curriculum Developer*
Hedi Baxter, *Curriculum Developer*
Molly McGarrigle, *Internal Evaluator*
Theodore Lamb, PhD, *Co-Director, Center for Research and Evaluation*
Ann Lanari, *Research Assistant*
Raphaela Conner, *Project Assistant*
Terry Redmond, *Project Assistant*
Pamela S. Warren, *Project Assistant*

BSCS Production Team

Barbara Perrin, *Director of Publications*
Dottie Watkins, *Production Coordinator*
Stacey Luce, *Manuscript Specialist, Permissions*
Lisa Rasmussen, *Graphic Artist*
Diane Gionfriddo, *Photo Research*
Angela Paoleti, *Production Assistant*
Jennifer Phonexayphova, *Production Assistant*

BSCS Administration

Rodger W. Bybee, PhD, *Executive Director*
Janet Carlson Powell, PhD, *Associate Director*
Pamela Van Scotter, *Director, The Center for Curriculum Development*
Marcia Mitchell, *Director of Finance*
Carlo Parravano, PhD, *Merck Institute for Science Education, Chairman, BSCS Board of Directors*

Editor

Barbara Resch, Colorado Springs, CO
Fran Sevin, *Education Editor, LLC*, Crestone, CO

External Evaluator

Doug Coulson, PhD, PS International, Arnold, MD

Artists, Designers, Photographers, Photo Research and Permissions

David Ball, Colorado Springs, CO
Laurel Prud'homme, Colorado Springs, CO
Rick Bickhart, Peaceful Solutions Design
Paige Thomas, Colorado Springs, CO
Carlye Calvin, Nederland, CO
Jane McBee, Colorado Springs, CO
Melissa Flamson, Freelance Permissions
LaurelTech Integrated Publishing Services, Manchester, NH

Credits can be found on page 871
Editorial, design, and production services provided by
LaurelTech, New Hampshire

The development of this material was funded by the National Science Foundation under Grant Numbers ESI 9911614 and ESI 0242596. Any opinions, findings, conclusions, or recommendations expressed in this publication are those of the authors and do not necessarily reflect the views of the granting agency.

Printed in the United States of America
2 3 4 5 6 7 8 9 10   10 09 08 07 06

Acknowledgments

Advisory Board Members

Marshall Berman, PhD, New Mexico State Board of Education, NM

Kathy Comfort, PhD, Partnership for the Assessment of Standards-Based Science, WestEd, San Francisco, CA

Ginger Davis, Brevard Public Schools, FL

Melissa DeWitt, East Fairmont High School, Fairmont, WV

Christine Funk, Douglas County High School, Castle Rock, CO

Steve Getty, PhD, Colorado College, Colorado Springs, CO

Michael Hanson, Tahoma High School, Kent, WA

Jerrie Mallicoat, Titusville High School, Titusville, FL

Ronald W. Marx, PhD, University of Arizona, Tucson, AZ

M. Patricia Morse, PhD, University of Washington, Seattle, WA

Susan Mundry, PhD, WestEd, Stoneham, MA

Harold Pratt, PhD, Educational Consultant, Littleton, CO

Rochelle Rubin, PhD, Waterford School District, Waterford, MI

Gary Scott, San Pedro Math, Science, and Technology Center, San Pedro, CA

Ethan Smith, Tahoma High School, Kent, WA

Contributors and Reviewers

Marshall Berman, PhD, New Mexico State Board of Education, NM

Mark Bloom, PhD, BSCS, Colorado Springs, CO

Heidi Carlone, PhD, University of North Carolina, Greensboro, NC

Steven Clemmens, PhD, Brown University, Providence, RI

Rocky Coleman, PhD, Colorado State University, Fort Collins, CO

George Davis, PhD, Minnesota State University, Moorehead, MN

James Garrett Davis, Albuquerque, NM

Edward Drexler, Pius XI High School, Milwaukee, WI

Ellen Friedman, PhD, San Diego, CA

Steve Getty, PhD, Colorado College, Colorado Springs, CO

Anne Haley-Mackenzie, PhD, Miami University of Ohio, Oxford, OH

Mary Kay Hemmenway, PhD, University of Texas, Austin, TX

William Hoyt, PhD, University of Northern Colorado, Greeley, CO

Barbara Hug, PhD, University of Michigan, Ann Arbor, MI

Jay Kauffman, PhD, University of Maryland, College Park, MD

Laura Laughran, PhD, New Directions, Tucson, AZ

Toby Merlin, MD, Centers for Disease Control and Prevention, Atlanta, GA

Samuel Milazzo, University of Colorado, Colorado Springs, CO

Jerry Phillips, PhD, BSCS, Colorado Springs, CO

Harold Pratt, PhD, Educational Consultants, Inc., Littleton, CO

Richard Reynolds, PhD, USDA Forest Service, Rocky Mountain Research Station, Fort Collins, CO

Carol Sheriff, Albuquerque, NM

Ray Tschillard, BSCS, Colorado Springs, CO

Anne Westbrook, PhD, BSCS, Colorado Springs, CO

Lawrence Woolf, PhD, General Atomic, San Diego, CA

Ted Yeshion, Cluefinders, Erie, PA

Field-Test Teachers and Leaders

California

Dlunari Edirisinghe, Narbonne High School, Harbor City, CA

Carolyn Higuchi, Narbonne High School, Harbor City, CA

Roger Mataumoto, Narbonne High School, Harbor City, CA

Gary Scott, San Pedro Math, Science, and Technology Center, San Pedro, CA

Colorado

Kerry Adams, Alamosa High School, Alamosa, CO

Jim Street, Alamosa High School, Alamosa, CO

Dennis Lopez, District Representative, Alamosa High School, Alamosa, CO

Christine Funk, Douglas County High School, Castle Rock, CO

Sharon Harter, Coronado High School, Colorado Springs, CO

Jodi Vine Schlang, University of Denver High School, Denver, CO

Florida

Lori Braga, Melbourne High School, Melbourne, FL

James Meegan, Melbourne High School, Melbourne, FL

Jerri Mallicoat, Titusville High School, Titusville, FL

Jon Nelson, Titusville High School, Titusville, FL

Raul Montes, Cocoa High School, Cocoa, FL

Elizabeth Hickey, Cocoa High School, Cocoa, FL

Cheryl Reve, Cocoa High School, Cocoa, FL

Edward C. Johnson, Cocoa High School, Cocoa, FL

Lisa Wall-Campeau, Eau Gallie High School, Melbourne, FL

Nelson Salazar, Eau Gallie High School, Melbourne, FL

Melindy Myrick-Lupo, Eau Gallie High School, Melbourne, FL

Lisa Scott, Satellite High School, Satellite Beach, FL

Catherine Hoffman, Satellite High School, Satellite Beach, FL

Ginger Davis, Science Supervisor, Brevard Public Schools, FL

Kim Bragg, District Representative, Brevard Public Schools, FL

Illinois

Shannon Edwards, Centennial High School, Champaign, IL

Shirley Ma, Centennial High School, Champaign, IL

Kevin Kuppler, District Representative, Champaign, IL

Massachusetts

Alan Murphy, Pioneer Valley Regional High School, Northfield, MA

Lawrence Poirier, Pioneer Valley Regional High School, Northfield, MA

Jo Anne Pullen, Science Supervisor, Pioneer Valley Region School District, Northfield, MA

Michigan

John Bayerl, Fordson High School, Dearborn, MI

Mary Beth Henry, Dearborn High School, Dearborn, MI

David Mayoros, Edsel Ford High School, Dearborn, MI

Robert Tyler, Dearborn High School, Dearborn, MI

Herm Boatin, Science Supervisor, Dearborn Public Schools, MI

Richard Klee, Science Supervisor, Dearborn Public Schools, MI

Tennessee

Laura Kile, Webb School of Knoxville, Knoxville, TN

Vermont

Bruce Holloway, Brattleboro Union High School, Brattleboro, VT

Scott Noren, Brattleboro Union High School, Brattleboro, VT

Merribelle Coles, Brattleboro Union High School, Brattleboro, VT

Julie Wheeler, Brattleboro Union High School, Brattleboro, VT

Katherine Martin, Brattleboro Union High School, Brattleboro, VT

James Maland, District Representative, Brattleboro Union High School, VT

Washington

Allison Winward, Kamiakin High School, Kennewick, WA

Jim Ramsey, Kamiakin High School, Kennewick, WA

James McLean, Science Supervisor, Kennewick School District, WA

Aanika DeVries, Spring Street School, Friday Harbor, WA

West Virginia

Melissa DeWitt, East Fairmont High School, Fairmont, WV

Mary Lynn Westfall, East Fairmont High School, Fairmont, WV

Sally Morgan, East Fairmont High School, Fairmont, WV

Diane Furman, Science Supervisor, Marion County Schools, WV

Wisconsin

Michael Lyga, Ashwaubenon High School, Green Bay, WI

Joelle Zuengler, Ashwaubenon High School, Green Bay, WI

Kylie Werner, Ashwaubenon High School, Green Bay, WI

Sue Alberti, Science Supervisor, Ashwaubenon School District, WI

Contents

Dear Learners,

Learning—it's important. That's why the staff at BSCS developed *BSCS Science: An Inquiry Approach*. With *you* in mind, we designed a program that puts meaningful learning first.

What's meaningful learning? It's the kind of learning that's fun even though it's a lot of work. It's learning so interesting, relevant, and engaging that you find yourself understanding more and performing better than you ever have. During meaningful learning, it seems like no time passes even though you might spend hours studying difficult subjects. How can that be?

First, this program knows you like *active* learning. You expect direct experiences with nature, not just worksheets and lectures. This is especially true in science. You want to understand through experiments, inquiry, and dialogue. That's what you'll find in these pages, along with the proper rigor so you'll be prepared for a world that needs people who can learn, think, and solve problems.

Second, learning in this book builds on *your* experiences. To do this, this program treats science as a whole, where you use all science disciplines to solve problems. This interdisciplinary approach is the way you think about the natural world when you look at a rainbow. You wonder about the physics of light, the biology of your eye, the earth science of thunderstorms, and the chemistry of rain. It's the natural way to think.

Third, meaningful learning has purpose. And learners with purpose have clear goals—ones that help you focus on what's important. Your book lays out what's important with clear learning goals based on the *National Science Education Standards.* These standards help you understand the big concepts that connect all science subjects. That way, you apply one concept across many disciplines and understand more about nature with less effort. It's a way to honor your time and your commitment to learning.

Finally, the staff at BSCS knows how much learning depends on feedback. Your feedback helps us improve future editions of this program. It's the way we make science books better. So please send us your feedback. It helps us learn. Our mailing address is

BSCS Science: An Inquiry Approach
BSCS
5415 Mark Dabling Boulevard
Colorado Springs, CO 80918-3842

We think learning science is natural and enjoyable, especially when it's done in meaningful ways. That's how we have designed this program. We hope you agree.

Sincerely,
The BSCS Inquiry Approach Team

GETTING TO KNOW *BSCS SCIENCE: AN INQUIRY APPROACH*

BSCS Science: An Inquiry Approach represents a new generation of textbooks for a new generation of high school science students, like you. As with all BSCS materials, *An Inquiry Approach* is an innovative science program that is centered on you, the learner. This program introduces you to the core concepts in science as inquiry, the physical sciences, the life sciences, and the earth & space sciences. In addition, the student book engages you in integration across the disciplines in ways that are relevant to your life. This program provides high school students nationwide like yourself with an important alternative to the traditional sequence of biology, chemistry, and physics.

You will notice that this program is different from other science programs you have used. It emphasizes inquiry, science as a way of knowing about the world, and the big ideas in science. We developed this program with a team of scientists, teachers, science supervisors, and many students in field-test classrooms across the country.

This program supports the following goals for all students:

- To increase your understanding of fundamental concepts in the sciences
- To present science in a context that is relevant to you
- To increase your interest and achievement in science
- To strengthen your critical-thinking and problem-solving skills

Distinguishing Features of the Program

The distinguishing features of *BSCS Science: An Inquiry Approach* include the following:

- Enduring, standards-based content
- Inquiry as the overarching theme
- Activity-centered lessons
- Opportunities for structured and open investigation in areas that are meaningful to you
- Opportunities for you to design and conduct your own investigations
- Opportunities for you to consider recent research in the sciences
- A constructivist, student-centered approach
- Mathematics in the real-world setting of science
- The use of chapter organizers and science notebooks
- The BSCS 5E instructional model
- A collaborative learning environment
- An assessment package with a variety of ways you can demonstrate your learning

The Framework

The framework for *BSCS Science: An Inquiry Approach* presents a logical sequence of concepts through each year and across the years.

Each of the core units includes three chapters that present you with the fundamental concepts in each of the disciplines. The fourth chapter in each core unit allows you to apply what you have learned so far in integrated settings that include at least two different disciplines, such as biology and physics. In this way, we provide you with learning experiences that will help you build and deepen enduring understandings in science.

BSCS Science: An Inquiry Approach Framework for Grades 9–11			
	Major Concepts Addressed at Each Grade Level		
Units	**9**	**10**	**11**
Science As Inquiry	Abilities necessary to do and understandings about scientific inquiry with a focus on:		
	• Questions and concepts that guide scientific investigations	• Design of scientific investigations • Communicating scientific results	• Evidence as the basis for explanations and models • Alternative explanations and models
Physical Science	• Structure and properties of matter • Structure of atoms • Integrating chapter	• Motions and forces • Chemical reactions • Integrating chapter	• Interactions of energy and matter • Conservation of energy and increase in disorder • Integrating chapter
Life Science	• Cell structure and function • Behavior of organisms • Integrating chapter	• Biological evolution • Molecular basis of heredity • Integrating chapter	• Matter, energy, and organization in living systems • Interdependence of organisms • Integrating chapter
Earth-Space Science	• Origin and evolution of the universe • Origin and evolution of the Earth system • Integrating chapter	• Geochemical cycles • Integrating chapter	• Energy in the Earth system • Integrating chapter
Science in a Personal and Social Perspective; Science & Technology	• Personal and community health • Natural and human induced hazards • Abilities of technological design	• Population growth • Natural resources • Environmental quality	• Science and technology in local, national, and global changes • Understandings about science and technology
	History and Nature of Science addressed throughout grade levels and units • Science as a human endeavor • Nature of science • History of science		

Components of the Program

BSCS Science: An Inquiry Approach is a comprehensive program that includes useful resources for you and your teacher. The major components for students include the student book and the Student Resource CD.

Student Book

The student book is designed with students like you in mind. Each chapter and unit draws you into an engaging learning experience. In addition to being conceptually appealing, the book is visually appealing, filled with engaging art and design. Features such as the chapter organizers and openers, special reading sections, FYIs, sidebars, appealing art, and National Science Teachers Association SciLinks help keep your interest and allow you to take charge of your learning journey.

Student Resource CD

The Student Resource CD (SRCD) provides you with concept maps for each chapter. From the concept maps, you can link to additional resources on the SRCD. For example, from a specific concept on a specific map, you might link to an interesting video clip, animation, simulation, reading, or set of images all related to this concept. This visually rich resource is a powerful and convenient learning tool.

Students across the Country Helped Develop This Program

We developed this program with you in mind. Students like yourself and teachers like yours all across the country have used these lessons in their classrooms and their feedback helped us make this program even better. So now we are able to provide you with the innovative, high-quality learning experience in the sciences that you deserve.

A Multidisciplinary Science Program for High School

Level **1**

BSCS SCIENCE
AN INQUIRY APPROACH

LIFE SCIENCE

PHYSICAL SCIENCE

EARTH/SPACE SCIENCE

EXPLORING THE BUILDING BLOCKS OF THE UNIVERSE

CHAPTER 1

The Process of Scientific Inquiry

THE PROCESS OF SCIENTIFIC INQUIRY

A good way to think about science is to think of it as a way of knowing about the natural world—how it works, how it got here, and what it is made of. A good way to understand science is by *doing* science. What do you see the students and scientists doing in these pictures? This year, you will do science in many different ways by participating in activities, completing projects, investigating questions, and discussing interactive readings.

By doing science yourself and taking time to learn what other scientists know about the natural world, you model how scientists do their work. In particular, you see how scientists ask questions and design investigations to answer them. You also see how scientists collect evidence to help them develop sound explanations, consult the historical and current body of scientific knowledge to learn more, use technology and math to enhance their explanations, revise their explanations based on new evidence, and communicate their ideas.

Goals for the Chapter

In chapter 1, The Process of Scientific Inquiry, you will develop a better understanding of the process of scientific inquiry and refine your abilities to do science. When you have completed chapter 1 and have reflected on your experiences, you should be able to answer the following questions:

- How do I conduct a scientific investigation to answer a question about the natural world?
- What is the difference between evidence and inference?
- What characterizes a scientific explanation?
- How do scientists use scientific inquiry to learn about the natural world and communicate explanations? How can their work inform my understanding?

We will introduce you to some important tools and techniques in chapter 1 that will continue to help you in science class every year. These tools and techniques include the following.

1. *Your science book.* Within this book, you will find many tools to help you learn science. Most important, you will find clearly drawn connections that help you understand what you are learning, how

you got there, and where you are going. These connections will be in the form of chapter organizers, chapter introductions, and narrative. The sequence of activities follows a logical progression through concepts so you can build your own understanding.

2. *Chapter organizers.* These diagrams provide a visual overview of the chapter you are about to start. What are the core ideas? How is it organized? What parts are familiar to you? What parts look new? Use the organizers to anticipate what kinds of activities you will be doing.

3. *Your science notebook.* It is critical that you keep track of your results and your growing understanding in a notebook designated for science. In chapter 1, you will learn how to write headings in your notebook before you begin taking notes and answering questions. Continue to use this strategy throughout the remaining chapters in this book to help you keep organized.

4. *Your teammates.* When you work in a team, you combine ideas from multiple minds and learn from your peers.

5. *Investigations.* When you do science, you use the same process of inquiry that scientists use. At the same time, you learn how to ask and answer questions you have about the natural world.

6. *Questions.* When you ask questions of yourself and your classmates, you contribute to your own understanding. When you answer questions posed in your book, you demonstrate your understanding.

7. *Readings.* When you read about the work of other scientists, you learn about their explorations of science. When you combine their knowledge with yours, you understand more.

8. *Scoring rubrics.* Use the scoring rubrics to help you successfully demonstrate what you have learned once you reach the end of a chapter.

To learn about scientific inquiry and to use the tools and techniques of chapter 1, you will participate in the following activities:

ENGAGE	Who Did It?
EXPLORE	What Do You Know for Sure?
EXPLORE	Mystery Sports Drinks
EXPLAIN	What Is Science?
ELABORATE	Back Up That Claim!
EVALUATE	Homemade Sports Drinks

ENGAGE

Who Did It?

Key Idea:
What do you know about scientific inquiry?

EXPLORE

What Do You Know for Sure?

Key Ideas:

- Scientists use evidence and inference to develop scientific explanations.
- Evaluating alternative explanations is an important part of scientific inquiry.

Linking Question

Using what is already known, can I develop a scientifically testable question to guide my investigation of sports drinks?

The Process of Scientific Inquiry

EXPLORE

Mystery Sports Drinks

Key Ideas:

- Scientifically testable questions guide investigations.
- Evaluating what is already known is an important aspect of scientific inquiry.
- Using technology and mathematics contributes to scientific investigation.
- Science includes communicating and defending scientific arguments.

Linking Question

How do these features of inquiry taken together embody science?

6

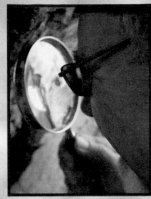

Homemade Sports Drinks

Key Idea:
Scientific inquiry is a rigorous, multifaceted process that includes both skills and understanding.

Linking Question

How can I use what I have learned to demonstrate my understanding of scientific inquiry?

CHAPTER

1 Major Concepts

▶ **The process of scientific inquiry**

▶ **Identifying questions that guide scientific inquiry**

▶ **Using evidence and inference to develop explanations**

ELABORATE

Back Up That Claim!

Key Ideas:
• Analyzing the work of scientists contributes to the discipline and informs specific work.
• Communicating findings is an important feature of the scientific endeavor.

EXPLAIN

What Is Science?

Key Ideas:
• Scientific inquiry is a process that includes using what is known to ask questions, design investigations, collect evidence, develop explanations, analyze alternative explanations, and communicate findings.
• The use of technology can improve the quality of scientific investigations.

Linking Question

▷▶▶

How do scientists communicate their findings and how does this process contribute to the scientific endeavor?

Who Did It?

Often when you do science, you are solving a mystery. Science helps solve mysteries such as why your stomach growls when you are hungry and why leaves turn different colors in the fall. What steps do you take to solve a mystery? What kind of evidence would be important? You will find out as you work with a partner to figure out Who Did It?

Materials

For each team of two students

1 Additional Evidence handout

Process and Procedure

Record all your observations in your notebook under the heading "The Process of Scientific Inquiry." Below it write the heading "Who Did It?"

1. Look at figure 1.1 and describe what you see to your partner.

▲ **Figure 1.1**
Mystery scene. How would you describe this scene?

2. Discuss the following questions with your partner.
    a. What do you see? What is your evidence?
    b. What do you think happened to the store? Why do you think so?
    c. What can you only guess? Why?

3. Imagine that you are part of an investigative team assigned to solve the mystery. Other members of your team have uncovered some important evidence, which is recorded on the evidence sheet in figure 1.2. Study the evidence provided in the figure.

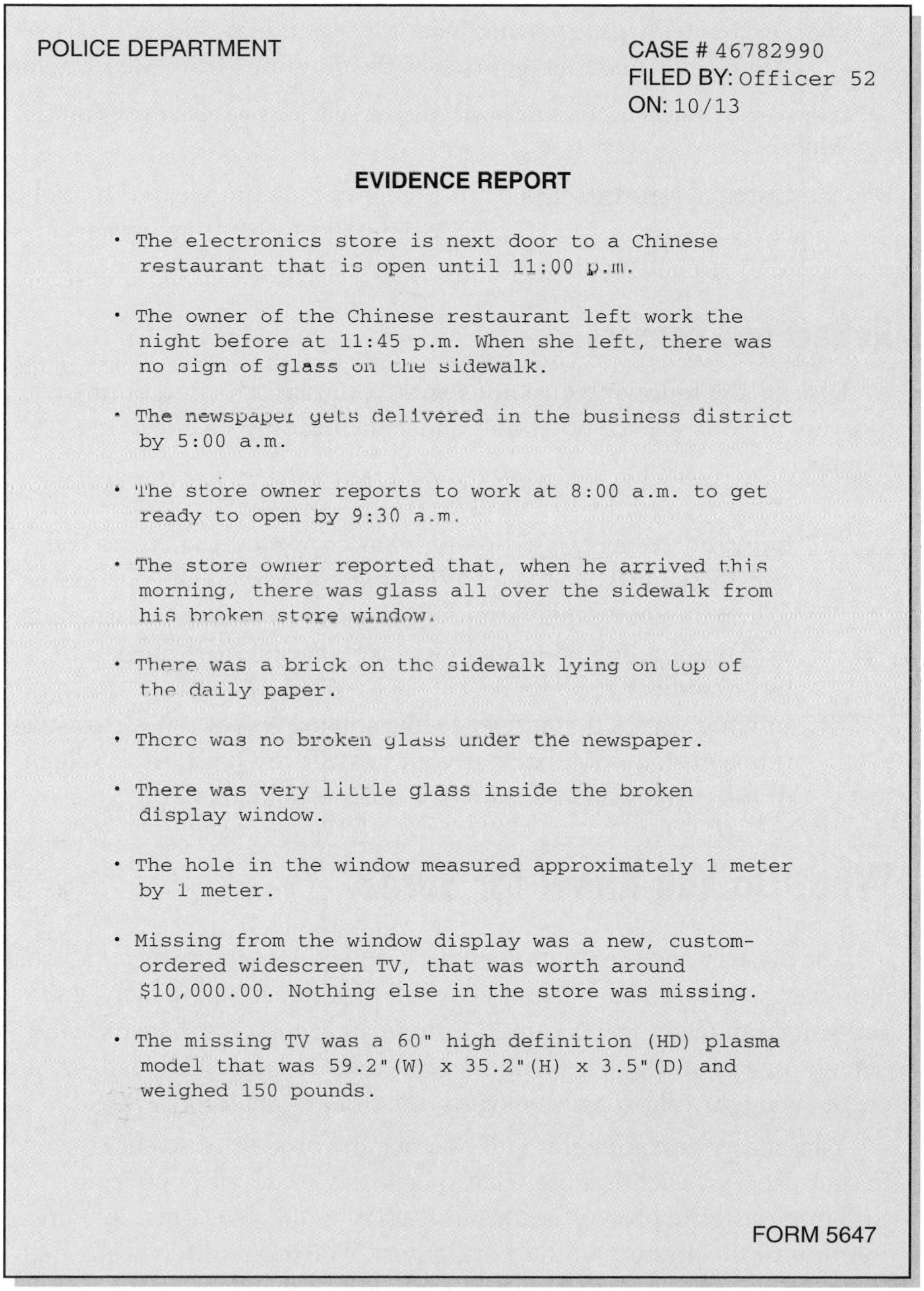

POLICE DEPARTMENT

CASE # 46782990
FILED BY: Officer 52
ON: 10/13

EVIDENCE REPORT

- The electronics store is next door to a Chinese restaurant that is open until 11:00 p.m.

- The owner of the Chinese restaurant left work the night before at 11:45 p.m. When she left, there was no sign of glass on the sidewalk.

- The newspaper gets delivered in the business district by 5:00 a.m.

- The store owner reports to work at 8:00 a.m. to get ready to open by 9:30 a.m.

- The store owner reported that, when he arrived this morning, there was glass all over the sidewalk from his broken store window.

- There was a brick on the sidewalk lying on top of the daily paper.

- There was no broken glass under the newspaper.

- There was very little glass inside the broken display window.

- The hole in the window measured approximately 1 meter by 1 meter.

- Missing from the window display was a new, custom-ordered widescreen TV, that was worth around $10,000.00. Nothing else in the store was missing.

- The missing TV was a 60" high definition (HD) plasma model that was 59.2"(W) x 35.2"(H) x 3.5"(D) and weighed 150 pounds.

FORM 5647

▲ Figure 1.2 **Evidence sheet.** Like any good investigator, you and your teammate have written down every piece of evidence you have gathered so far, even if you don't know if it will be important.

4. Look back at the questions in Step 2. Would you answer any of them differently in light of the new evidence? Discuss any new ideas with your partner.

5. Now get the Additional Evidence handout from your teacher. Read the additional evidence your investigative team has uncovered.

6. Discuss with your partner what the additional evidence tells you about the crime. Ask yourselves the questions from Step 2 again.

Is there more you know for sure now? Are you still guessing about some things? Why?

7. Listen as your teacher reads the news bulletin released by police to local papers. Do you think the police solved the mystery? Why do you think so?

Reflect and Connect

Discuss the following questions with your class. Record your own answers in your science notebook under the heading "Reflect and Connect."

1. What steps did you follow to try to solve the mystery?
2. How did your explanation of what happened change as you considered new evidence? What made you change your ideas?
3. Compare your explanation of the mystery in Step 2 with your explanation in Step 6. In which explanation do you have the most confidence? Why?
4. In what way is doing science like solving a mystery? To answer this question, look back at your answer to Question 1. Which of those steps do you think scientists would also do?

| EXPLORE | # What Do You Know for Sure? |

The mystery and the solution in the Who Did It? activity were fictional. However, scientists study real mysteries all the time. In this activity, you and your teammates will become a team of archaeologists that study the remains of a man who lived long ago, called the Iceman. Although you are only playing the role of archaeologists, the story of the Iceman is real.

You and your teammates will practice the process of science. In that process, scientists use what they know to develop working explanations. The process is a lot like what you did to come up with a solution to the mystery in the first activity. The main difference is that all the mysteries about the Iceman are not yet solved.

Materials

Process and Procedure

Record all your observations in your notebook under the heading "What Do You Know for Sure?"

1. An archaeological society has asked your team to study the remains of a human who died more than 5,000 years ago. You also will study the items that were found with him. Because he was buried in the ice and snow on the Austria-Italy border, his body and his belongings were unusually well preserved.

   To start your investigation, read Iceman by yourself.

READING

Iceman

A man died high in the Alps, above tree line. His body froze into a glacier and remained there for more than 5,000 years. Then, in 1991, hikers who had veered off course discovered the well-preserved corpse. They assumed it was a modern hiker who had been killed the previous winter and they notified authorities. Because the authorities did not realize they were dealing with something very old, they removed the body from the ice carelessly, in a way that resulted in the loss of valuable evidence.

▲ Figure 1.3 **Recovery of the Iceman.** The Iceman is the oldest and best preserved human body ever found.

Imagine the surprise to the authorities when they determined the body was from ancient times, probably 5,300 years ago. He was male, 157 centimeters (5 feet, 2 inches) tall, and 20–30 years old at the time of his death. He had a series of markings on his skin: several sets of blue parallel lines on his lower back, stripes on his right ankle, and a cross behind his left knee. His hair was medium length and had been cut. His physical features were similar to those of humans today.

The Iceman and his possessions are among the most valuable archaeological evidence ever found. Usually, the types of evidence that are preserved from humans who lived 5,000 years ago are hard substances, such as teeth or bones and the stone or metal parts of tools. Pottery, too, might survive, but soft tissues such as skin, hair, plant materials, and leather generally are destroyed by decay. In this case, however, many unusual material remains were recovered with the Iceman. These remains are called **artifacts.** Scientists can use these artifacts to determine how people in ancient times lived.

2. With your team, study figure 1.4, which lists many of the artifacts that authorities and scientists found with the Iceman. Figure 1.5 shows some of these artifacts.

Artifact	Comments
Grass cape	Carefully stitched together; isolated repairs made with grass thread
Arrows and leather quiver (carrying case for arrows)	Oldest leather quiver ever found; some arrows with flint arrowheads; other arrows unfinished
Very long bow	Unstrung
Pouch with worked bits of flint (type of stone that flakes easily into sharp pieces)	
Clothing and boots	Made of leather; grass stuffed inside boots
Copper-bladed axe with wooden handle	One of the oldest axes of its type and first with handle intact; attached by leather ties and glue; copper blade
Mushrooms strung on a leather strip	A type of fungus with medicinal (antibiotic) properties
Flint dagger and grass sheath	Worked flint blade on wooden handle; first sheath of this age recovered
Bone needle	
Grass rope	
Stone disk threaded with a leather strap	
Bits of primitive wheat and wheat pollen	This type of wheat grew only at low altitudes.

▲ **Figure 1.4**
List of Iceman artifacts. What do these artifacts tell you about the life and death of the Iceman?

▶ **Figure 1.5**
Iceman artifacts found with his body. (a) Stone disk threaded on leather strap, (b) flint dagger, (c) copper-bladed axe, (d) fragment of grass cape, (e) leather quiver with arrows, and (f) shoe (top and bottom). The discovery of the Iceman provided new information about the people who lived 5,000 years ago.

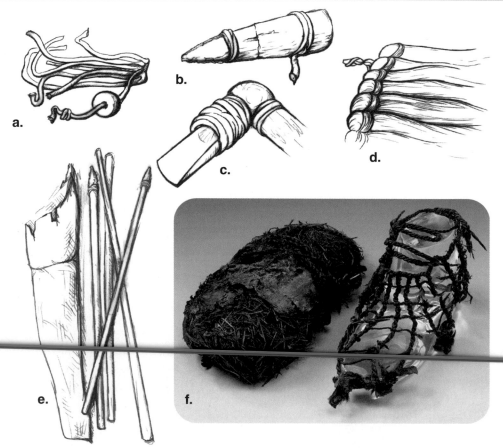

3. Sometimes, scientists must make logical assumptions about things they cannot directly observe. For example, scientists come up with ideas about the skin and outward appearance of a dinosaur from its fossil remains. In the same way, scientists come up with ideas about the appearance or culture of early humans from whatever is preserved. With this in mind, do the following things.

   a. With your team, discuss each artifact, how the Iceman might have used it, and what it might indicate about his way of life.

   b. Record your ideas in a table in your science notebook. Your table should look like figure 1.6.

Artifact	How the Iceman might have used it	What it might indicate about the Iceman's way of life

▲ Figure 1.6
Artifacts table. Write down each of the artifacts in the left column and your ideas in the other two columns.

4. Read the following statements. With your team, decide if the statements are based on **evidence** (observations you can make directly) or **inference** (logical assumptions based on evidence, but which you have not directly observed). Record your ideas in your science notebook and be prepared to explain why you decided the statement is based on evidence or inference.

You observe a person drinking a glass of water. An inference or logical assumption would be that the person is thirsty. An illogical assumption would be that the person is hungry because there is no evidence that indicates the person is hungry.

   a. The Iceman carried arrows made with flint arrowheads.
   b. The Iceman used mushrooms as medicine.
   c. The Iceman spent some time at lower altitudes.
   d. The Iceman had bits of wheat from a lower altitude on his clothing.
   e. The Iceman wore clothing made from animal products.
   f. The Iceman knew how to sew.
   g. The Iceman was a hunter.
   h. The Iceman used grass for several purposes.
   i. The Iceman lived at a time when people knew how to work with metals.

Read the sidebar, An Interview with Mary Leakey, to see how she felt about making inferences from the evidence she uncovered working as an archaeologist.

Topic: inference
Go to: www.scilinks.org
Code: 1Inquiry13

An Interview with Mary Leakey

Mary Leakey and her husband, Louis Leakey, were responsible for finding some of the most significant archaeological and anthropological finds of the 20th century. She was also famous for being unwilling to use these finds to guess about theories of human evolution. In a profession full of people with big egos and the next "correct" interpretation, she was different.

Mary was an exacting, independent person and a very tough woman. When Mary was 17, she began to work on archaeological expeditions in England. She attended lectures on archaeology, prehistory, and geology at University College London, but she never attended college.

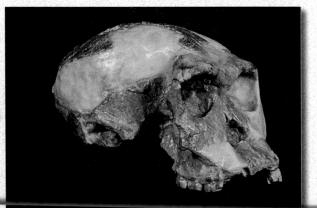

Mary Leakey. Mary Leakey was a renowned archaeologist. She made many discoveries that have contributed to scientists' understanding of human evolution.

After she married, she and her husband searched for the remains of early humans at various sites throughout Kenya and Tanzania. In 1948, Mary found the first perfectly preserved skull and facial bones of a tiny ape that was about 16 to 20 million years old. Anthropologists could see this ape had a bigger brain than other primates that lived at that time. Many felt that Mary had found a "missing link" in primate evolution. But still the Leakeys kept digging.

The Leakeys' big break came one morning in 1959 in Olduvai Gorge, an area of Tanzania near the East African Great Rift Valley (see map). Again it was Mary who made the discovery. Louis was sick, and Mary went out to hunt around. Protruding slightly from one of the exposed sections was a 1.8-million-year-old skull. It was the first hominid (belonging to the human family) skull to be found in East Africa.

How the skull fits into the human family tree is not something Mary was willing to infer from the evidence she had discovered. In fact, she never liked to speculate about the theories that surrounded her findings. "I never felt interpretation was my job. What I came to do was to dig things up and take them out as well as I could," Mary Leakey said in a 1994 interview. "There is so much we do not know, and the more we do know, the more we realize that early

***Homo habilis* skull.** Mary Leakey found a 1.8-million-year-old skull.

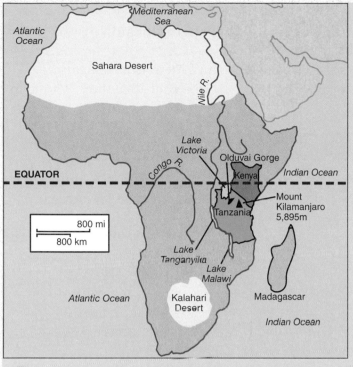

The Leakey's made their discovery in Olduvai Gorge.

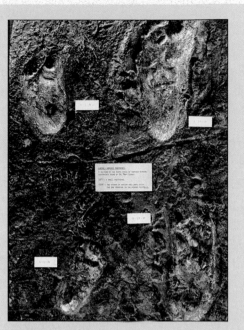

Laetoli trackways. These tracks were preserved in volcanic ash about 3.6 million years ago.

interpretations were completely wrong. It is good mental exercise, but people get so hot and nasty about it, which I think is ridiculous." Such questions are important for understanding humankind, but finding evidence is difficult work.

When asked if humans emerged in Africa or all over the world from different ancestors, Mary started to laugh. "You'll get no fun out of me over these things. If I were Richard [her son], I would talk to you for hours about it, but I just don't think it is worth it. I really like to feel that I am on solid ground, and that is never solid ground."

The discovery that Mary considered most important is the footprints of Laetoli (an area near Olduvai Gorge), which she discovered in 1978. Three hominids and some ancient horses had walked over volcanic ash. Then the ash was buried and hardened like rock, preserving the tracks. The volcanic ash was determined to be about 3.6 million years

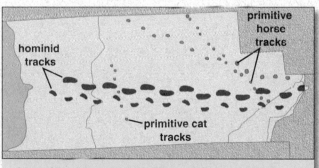

Laetoli trackway map. The map shows tracks of three hominids, some ancient horses, and a primitive cat.

old. The tracks showed that the hominids had walked in an upright position, on two legs, over the ash. Scientists had inferred that human's ancestors walked upright from the structure of leg bones of hominid fossils, but Mary's discovery provided the first solid evidence.

Mary Leakey was one of the world's most renowned seekers of early human fossils. She died in Nairobi, Kenya, on December 9, 1996, at the age of 83.

5. Participate in a class discussion to clarify your understanding of evidence and inference. To prepare for the discussion, do the following tasks.

a. Make a T-table with evidence and inference as headings. List words or phrases that describe each. See the example in figure 1.7.

▶ **Figure 1.7**
Evidence and inference. One example has been provided for you. What words would you use to describe evidence and inference?

Evidence	Inference
observations	logical idea

b. Look back at the ideas you recorded about each artifact in Step 3. Were your ideas about how the Iceman used the items based on evidence, inference, or both?

Reflect and Connect

Discuss the following questions with your class.

1. If you could have 3 more pieces of evidence about the Iceman, what would you want them to be? What information would they give you that would help you explain or describe how the Iceman lived and died?

2. If you could recruit 3 other scientists to help you solve the mystery of the Iceman, what would you like the specialties of those 3 scientists to be? How would their knowledge help you in your work?

3. Think back to your mystery investigation in the previous activity.

a. What did you infer when you first looked at the picture of the crime scene? In other words, what was your logical assumption about what probably happened to the store window?

b. How did the Additional Evidence handout strengthen your explanation of the crime?

c. What would you do if you found new evidence that contradicts the evidence you used to solve the crime?

4. Do you think scientists ever change their explanations about the natural world? Explain your answer.

Mystery Sports Drinks

So far in chapter 1, you are learning how scientists use evidence to form explanations about what they observe in the natural world. The more evidence they have, the better their explanations are. But how do scientists gather evidence? Can you act like a scientist and gather evidence to answer a question about something in your world? In the Mystery Sports Drinks activity, you will work with your class to investigate the answer to a question about beverages many people consume every day: sports drinks.

Process and Procedure

Sports drinks are everywhere. They appeal to active people. Their names imply that after just 1 sip, you will be able to leap tall buildings with a burst of power, or be as strong as a bull. But what if a sports drink were called Wimpy Walrus? Nerd-Ade? Zero Gain? Would you be as interested in drinking it?

Come to think of it, do you really know what you are drinking when you have a sports drink? What is in a sports drink that makes it so great after you have been exercising, working outside, or playing sports on a hot summer day? Is a sports drink really better for you than water? How could you find out?

▲ Figure 1.8
Quench your thirst.
What do you like to drink when you are hot and thirsty? Would you choose a different drink if you knew it was better for you?

Part I: Asking a Testable Question

Record all your observations in your notebook under the heading "Mystery Sports Drinks Part I: Asking a Testable Question."

1. Your teacher will show you a sample of a mystery sports drink. There is no label to read or name to research. Think about what you already know about sports drinks. What questions would you ask about the mysterious sports drink before you would drink it? Contribute your questions and ideas to the list of questions your teacher writes on the classroom board.

2. Now that you have some questions about sports drinks, think about how you would answer the following questions. Then share your answers during a class discussion.

   a. What kinds of things could you do to answer each of the questions on the board?

   b. Which of the questions can be answered based on opinions or beliefs? Would your answers to those questions always be the same as answers other people in your class give?

   c. Which of the questions on the board can be answered by scientific testing? What kinds of tests could you perform to answer questions that can be answered by scientific testing?

Scientific tests involve making observations or conducting experiments.

3. When conducting scientific inquiry, you also need to identify what ideas and knowledge other scientists have about your topic of inquiry. To find out more about sports drinks, read A Powerful Thirst. As you read, think about what scientists say makes a sports drink better than water in some situations.

READING

A Powerful Thirst

In 1958, a sweet-salty beverage named Bengal Punch showed up for the first time at Louisiana State University. It was the first sports drink, followed seven years later by a drink you might have heard of: Gatorade. The rest is history. Today, sports drinks are a booming industry. If you lined up all those brightly colored drinks that are available today, you would end up with more than two dozen different colors and concoctions.

Do sports drinks offer active people any true benefits or are they just advertising hype? Many people drink plain water. Is it just as good?

You need fluids to prevent dehydration when you exercise. Professional athletes know that dehydration is a serious hazard of intense exercise. They know that when you exercise hard, you can lose up to 3 liters of body fluids every

▲ **Figure 1.9 Sports drinks.** The array of different sports drinks is impressive.

hour. If you do not replace the fluids, your body cannot cool itself, your nerves and their pathways do not function, your heart rate increases, and your core body temperature increases above normal. Not only can your athletic performance sink to an all-time low, but you also risk heat exhaustion and potentially fatal heatstroke.

Everyone who exercises should drink lots of water, even when not exercising. The rule of thumb is to try to drink 118–177 milliliters (mL) (4 to 6 ounces) of water every hour you are awake, plus more after you exercise. Fluid replacement before, during, and after exercise helps your body maintain a condition of balance called **homeostasis.** If you don't drink enough water when you exercise, you can seriously disrupt your body's homeostasis. Before long, you will exhibit symptoms of illness.

So what if you don't like drinking water? Drinking tea, coffee, and cola does not help because the caffeine in most of these drinks is a diuretic. **Diuretics** inhibit the absorption of water by your body. Therefore, rather than retaining the necessary fluid from the tea, coffee, or cola, your body eliminates it in the form of urine. The carbonation in colas and other soft drinks gives athletes a full feeling and makes some athletes avoid drinking the additional fluids they need.

This is where sports drinks enter the picture. If you are one of those people who do not drink water because it has little taste, drinking a flavorful sports drink can help. You can keep the necessary fluid going into your body, because a sports drink is mostly water. At the same time, you can enjoy the sweet taste of the sports drink instead of the "ho-hum" taste of water.

But what else are you getting in a sports drink besides water? Sports drinks, as well as orange, grapefruit, and tomato juices, give you water while also fueling you up with **carbohydrates** in the form of sugars. Sugars help the body replace the calories it expends during exercise. Sports drinks also contain electrolytes in the form of salts such as sodium and potassium. **Electrolytes** are salts composed of ions. These salts are found in your body fluids such as blood, plasma, and interstitial fluid (fluid between cells) and are important for bodily functions.

Many people believe they need salt in a sports drink to replace the salt that leaves their bodies through sweat. The amount of salt lost through sweat, however, is negligible. Instead, the salts in the sports drink help the body absorb the water in the drink up to 30 percent faster than when drinking plain water. Sugar also helps with the absorption of water.

Beware, however, of drinks that contain too high a concentration of sugar, such as some sodas and juices. The high sugar content in these drinks actually slows the absorption of fluid. The best concentration of carbohydrates and electrolytes in a sports drink is 6–8 percent by mass of the total mass of the drink.

So the right sports drinks do provide an energy boost and slightly faster fluid absorption than plain water. This combination of energy and fluids in sports drinks helps athletes perform better, whether on the soccer field, in a tennis match, or running a marathon.

▲ **Figure 1.10 Runners.** Drinking the right sports drink can improve an athlete's performance and physical well-being.

4. With your class, discuss your understanding of the ingredients of a sports drink and their purpose.

Part I

Answer the following questions with your class. Make notes of the class discussion of each answer in your science notebook under the heading "Stop and Think—Part I."

1. Based on your reading of A Powerful Thirst, what ingredients in a sports drink can benefit an athlete? Describe what makes them beneficial.

2. How could you find out if the mystery sports drink contains any of these beneficial ingredients? What tests could you perform?

3. How could you test the sports drink to find out how much of the beneficial ingredients are solid and how much are liquid?

Part II: Testing . . . Testing . . . Testing

In Part I, you generated questions about the mystery sports drink. The answers to some of the questions were based on individual opinion, such as, Does the sports drink taste good? An opinion-based question such as this has a range of answers, because everyone has his or her own likes and dislikes.

Other questions that might have come up in your class discussion are, Is the sports drink beneficial to athletes? or Does drinking a sports drink help me run a faster race? These questions rely on science to help answer them. These are testable questions, but they need some focus.

To help you make these questions more focused, you learned what scientists say about the benefits of some sports drinks for athletes. From that information, you suggested tests you could perform to see if your mystery sports drink contains the ingredients required to be beneficial to athletes. Because you have learned about the work of other scientists, you can now ask a more focused testable question such as, Does the mystery sports drink contain ingredients that are beneficial to athletes?

To refine this testable question, you will need to define "beneficial" and identify which ingredients you are looking for. You will have the opportunity to refine this question in the following steps.

Materials

For each team of three students

3 pairs of safety goggles

3 lab aprons

1 set of tongs or mitts

1 evaporating dish

1 graduated cylinder

1 large beaker

3 small beakers or plastic cups

1 test tube

1 test-tube holder

1 dropper

1 centigram balance (can be shared)

1 conductivity probe or conductivity tester (can be shared)

1 heat source (hot plate or Bunsen burner and matches; can be shared)

Benedict's solution (can be shared)

1 sample of a mystery sports drink

heavy-duty aluminum foil (optional)

tap water

distilled water

1 wire gauze square

Cautions

Always use caution when you work with a heat source. Never leave a heat source unattended. If your hair is long, tie it back. Do the same with loose clothing. Use tongs or mitts to handle hot glassware. If you use matches, be sure they are completely out before disposing of them properly. Remember, never taste anything in the science lab.

Process and Procedure

In Part II of this activity, you will get to do some tests to learn more about your sports drink. You will investigate a mystery sports drink using 3 protocols, some of which might be tests that are the same as the tests you thought of. Once you have finished investigating the drink, the contents might no longer be a mystery to you. Record all your observations in your notebook under the heading "Part II: Testing . . . Testing . . . Testing."

1. Read the 3 protocols—Benedict's Test, Electrical Conductivity Test, and Evaporation Test. Then complete the following tasks using the information in A Powerful Thirst and the protocols.

    a. Discuss with your team how each protocol will provide evidence that helps answer the question, Does the mystery sports drink contain ingredients that are beneficial to athletes?

    b. Which ingredients would you say are beneficial to athletes? Are these the ingredients you are testing for in the protocols?

Protocol

Benedict's Test

Benedict's solution is used as a test for the presence of sugar. A positive Benedict's test indicates the presence of a monosaccharide. A **monosaccharide** is a simple sugar. The most common monosaccharides are glucose and fructose, found in honey, fruit juice, and corn syrup.

To perform the test:
1. Put on safety goggles and lab apron.
2. In a clean test tube, place equal amounts of the liquid to be tested and Benedict's solution (a dropper full of each is sufficient).
3. Gently swirl the test tube to mix the contents. The color of the resulting solution will turn a shade of blue from the Benedict's solution.
4. Place the test tube in a hot water bath for 5 minutes.
5. Observe any color changes in the solution.
   - A change from blue to green, yellow, orange, or red occurs if a monosaccharide is present and is considered a positive test.
   - The original blue color will remain after heating if a monosaccharide is not present.
6. Dispose of the liquids as directed by your teacher. Wash and rinse test tubes carefully after each test.

⚠ Caution	Handle hot test tubes with test-tube holders.

Electrical Conductivity Test

Use an electrical conductivity tester to test the electrical conductivity of solutions. An electrical conductivity tester tests for the flow of electrical charge through a material. You can use this test to draw conclusions about the presence of electrolytes in solutions. Electrolytes are substances, such as salts like sodium and potassium, that dissolve in water to produce a solution that conducts an electrical current. When these substances dissolve, their ions carry the current through the solution.

To run the test:
1. Put on safety goggles and a lab apron.
2. Obtain an electrical conductivity probe or another electrical conductivity tester.
3. Place both probes into the solution to be tested.

An electrical conductivity probe might look like a single probe, but it has two probes within its tip. Because the battery is a low voltage (9 volt), you do not need to be concerned about getting an electrical shock when you test the liquid materials.

4. Observe the resulting reading on the tester and record the reading in a data table.

   An electrical conductivity probe provides a reading on a calculator or computer. Other electrical conductivity testers provide information through a light-emitting diode (LED). When the light is on, the solution contains dissolved ions. Some testers will provide information about the concentration of ions, such as high or low, by providing a green and a red LED. The green LED requires more voltage than the red LED. A scale is usually attached to the meter to help you judge between low conductivity and high conductivity.

5. Thoroughly rinse the tips of the probes with distilled water and dry them between tests, especially when using liquids. Do not touch the electrode with your fingers. This will prevent contamination and results that might be misleading.

6. When you finish using the meter, be sure to turn it off or disconnect the battery. This will prevent draining the charge from the battery.

Evaporation Test

The process of evaporation separates liquids from solids in a solution. The mass of solids in a solution can be determined once the liquid has evaporated. This figure can be compared with the mass of the entire volume of solution to determine the percentage (by mass) of the solution that is solid.

To run the test:
1. Put on safety goggles and a lab apron.
2. Determine the mass of the solution you will be testing. To do this, follow these steps.
   a. Using a balance, measure the mass of an evaporating dish.
   b. Pour a small sample (about 10 mL) of the solution to be tested into the evaporating dish.
   c. Measure the mass of the evaporating dish and the solution.
   d. Calculate the mass of the solution alone.
3. Slowly heat the solution in the evaporating dish. When all the liquid has boiled off, turn off the heat source. Let the evaporating dish cool before handling it.

Caution

Always use caution when you work with a heat source. Never leave a heat source unattended. If your hair is long, tie it back. Do the same with loose clothing. Use tongs or mitts to handle hot glassware.

4. Measure the mass of the evaporating dish and any remaining residue from the solution.

5. Using your original measurement of the mass of the evaporating dish (see Step 2a), calculate the mass of the remaining residue alone.

6. Compare the mass of the solution you had at the start with the mass of the residue you have at the end. Describe what percentage of the original solution was made up of solids.

2. Rewrite the testable question, Does the mystery sports drink contain ingredients that are beneficial to athletes? Your revised question should specify the ingredients and the amount of ingredients that make a drink beneficial. Record this question in your science notebook.

Scientists design investigations based on testable questions they have developed. Therefore, their testable questions list the specific items that will be involved in their investigation.

3. Make a data table (or several data tables) in your science notebook to record the data and results from each test described in the protocols. Include the following headings in your data table(s): "Benedict's Test," "Conductivity Test," and "Evaporation Test."

You can decide if it is easier for you to keep the results of each protocol organized in a separate data table or if you want to record all your data from the three protocols in one data table.

4. Write a statement that predicts the outcome of your investigation. This is your **hypothesis**. Write it in your science notebook.

Hypotheses are tentative explanations that are testable. An example of a hypothesis is, Runners who drink water will run a race faster than runners who drink a sports drink. You could test this hypothesis by comparing the times of runners competing in the same race who drank either water or a sports drink.

Topic: hypothesis
Go to: www.scilinks.org
Code: 1Inquiry24

5. Obtain a sample of a mystery sports drink. Divide the sample equally into 3 small beakers, 1 to use with each protocol.

6. Discuss with your team what you need to keep in mind as you use the protocols to investigate your question.
   - What will you collect as evidence to answer your question?
   - Do you need to control any variables? Is it important to test samples from the same source? Do you think the temperature of the sample should be the same? Can you test the samples

several times to make sure that your Benedict's solution and conductivity testers are giving you the same results?

- Could you compare your results with a **control**, such as a known beverage like distilled water? What could that tell you?

If you need to refresh your memory about variables and controls, read the sidebar, Background on Controlled Experiments.

7. Test the samples using the procedures outlined in each protocol, 1 sample per protocol. Be sure to make careful observations and record your data in a data table.

8. To help you begin summarizing and interpreting your results, do the following tasks.

    a. Create graphs, charts, or both to help you compare the samples you tested in your investigation.

    b. Look at the hypothesis you wrote in Step 4. Are the results what you expected? Describe how closely your hypothesis did or did not match the results you obtained.

    c. Discuss some possible sources of error in your investigation. (What could have affected your results?)

    d. List 1 new question you have about sports drinks after conducting your investigation.

9. Discuss the results of your investigation with your team. Use evidence from the investigation to propose an explanation about the sports drinks you investigated. Your explanation should help answer the question you recorded in Step 1d. Write your explanation in your science notebook.

Your explanation should be based on evidence and inference. Remember that inferences are logical assumptions based on evidence. Use the data you collected as well as the information you learned from other scientists' work in A Powerful Thirst.

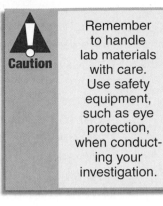

Caution — Remember to handle lab materials with care. Use safety equipment, such as eye protection, when conducting your investigation.

▲ Figure 1.11
Students conducting an investigation. What do you think will happen when Benedict's solution is added to the sports drink?

Topic: scientific explanation
Go to: www.scilinks.org
Code: 1Inquiry25

Reflect and Connect

Answer the following questions in your science notebook under the heading "Reflect and Connect."

1. How certain are you of the explanation you wrote in Step 8? Why?

2. How was the process you followed like what scientists do to answer questions about the natural world? For example, how was your investigation similar to how scientists investigate tornadoes or sports injuries?

Background on Controlled Experiments

The process of science includes asking questions, gathering information, and proposing explanations. You know that science can answer testable questions, but how can scientists design an experiment to gather information to answer their questions?

When scientists want to understand how some factor or event influences a system, they test that factor in an experiment that focuses on one measurable or observable aspect of their question. For this evidence to be meaningful, the scientists must control (keep constant) all other factors that could affect the results of the experiment. These other factors are called variables. Only by controlling all other variables can scientists be certain that the results they see depend on the one factor they are testing.

For example, if scientists want to find out if fertilizer helps houseplants grow, they would need to identify all the variables that might affect plant growth. Some possible variables might be the type of plant, the amount of water the plant gets, the soil the plant is growing in, and the amount of light the plant gets. Unless the scientists control all of these variables, they cannot know for sure if a plant grew better because of fertilizer or because of other factors.

An effective setup for a controlled experiment to test the effectiveness of fertilizer would be to choose at least two plants of the same type. Place them in identical clay pots, each filled with 250 grams of potting soil from the same bag of soil. Place both of them on the same win- dowsill. Water them at the same time with the same amount of water. Add fertilizer to only one

pot and do not treat the other pot. The untreated pot becomes your control. You can compare the growth in the pot with the fertilizer with the growth in the pot under normal conditions. Why do you need a control? Without a control, you might not know what usually happens, so you might not recognize results related to the fertilizer treatment.

If you observe differences in the growth of each plant, you would be correct to think that the fertilizer was the cause of the differences because you controlled all other variables. You could check your results by repeating the same controlled experiment with multiple plants to see if you could make the same observations. Scientists repeat their controlled experiments many times to increase their confidence in their data and develop more complete explanations.

Potted plants control and treatment. More than one plant should be used for the control (C) and treatment (T) groups because growth varies among plants.

3. Imagine that other scientists discovered, by performing further tests, that sports drinks need less than 3 percent carbohydrate or electrolyte contents to be beneficial to athletes. How would that new information affect your results? How would it affect your conclusion?

4. How might you use scientific inquiry to investigate the claim that using Mighty Might Power Drink will increase your energy level 100 percent?

What Is Science?

What do you think science is? Is it a series of questions and investigations? Or is it a set of facts and ideas? In this activity, you will work in a team to look at a way to describe the process of science and apply the methods to your own investigation.

a.

b.

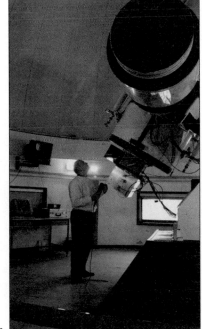

c.

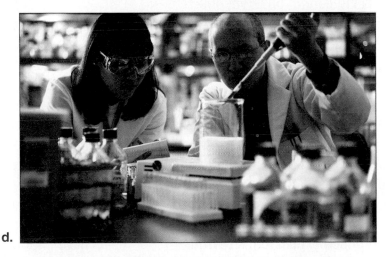

d.

▲ **Figure 1.12 Scientists.** Scientists study the natural world in a variety of ways including (a) by making models, (b) by making observations and describing organisms, (c) by discovering new objects and phenomena, and (d) through experiments. How have you been investigating the natural world?

Process and Procedure

Part I: The Process of Scientific Inquiry

Record all your observations in your notebook under the heading "What Is Science? Part I: The Process of Scientific Inquiry."

1. Read Science as Inquiry to learn about how scientists talk about the methods they follow to investigate questions. In particular, study the "road map" in figure 1.13 and discuss your understanding with your class.

READING

Science as Inquiry

Many people have the mistaken idea that science is a body of facts relating to the natural world. More accurately, science is a way of knowing about the natural world. It includes the doing of science as well as the knowledge that results from the work. In your investigation of the mystery sports drink, you used the fundamental processes of scientific inquiry. These processes included

- making careful observations,
- asking questions that can be answered by scientific inquiry,
- checking your current knowledge and that of other scientists,
- making predictions based on evidence,
- proposing explanations based on evidence,
- considering alternative explanations,
- testing explanations by gathering more evidence or seeing if new predictions based on the explanation are supported, and
- communicating your findings and proposed explanations to others.

Notice that the processes in the list above are not numbered. There is no specified order of steps in which scientific inquiry occurs. In fact, the process of scientific inquiry can be illustrated using the idea of a road trip.

How is inquiry like a road trip? When you wonder about things in the natural world, you might come up with a scientifically testable question. You can design and conduct an investigation to answer your question. If all goes well, your evidence will help you propose an answer and an explanation and you can communicate that explanation. In other words, you have followed the straightest road to your destination with no detours.

Sometimes in an investigation, however, you need to circle back. Sometimes, you need to adjust the design for more accurate results. Perhaps your investigation did not produce the evidence you expected. Perhaps there are other ways to explain what you observed. You might need to run more tests to see which of several explanations makes the most sense. Now your road trip becomes longer, with unexpected turns and new scenery. Perhaps you learn that other scientists have traveled the same highway and have important information that might change how you continue on your journey.

Sometimes, scientists decide to discontinue an investigation if the results are not convincing. On a journey, you might have car trouble and return home instead of continuing on the trip.

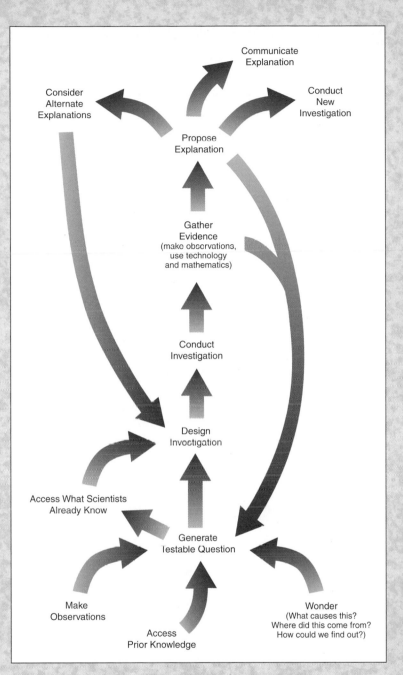

Communicate
Explanation

Consider
Alternate
Explanations

Conduct
New
Investigation

Propose
Explanation

Gather
Evidence
(make observations,
use technology
and mathematics)

Conduct
Investigation

Design
Investigation

Access What Scientists
Already Know

Generate
Testable Question

Make
Observations

Access
Prior Knowledge

Wonder
(What causes this?
Where did this come from?
How could we find out?)

Sometimes, scientists abandon a certain question when a new and more important question emerges. During your road trip, you might decide to go to a different destination instead of the one you had originally planned.

As a result of your sports drink investigation, you answered your original question, but you probably came up with new questions, too. Maybe you wondered how much of the residue is carbohydrates and how much is electrolytes. You might have tried to think of a test you could use to find out. If you had time, you might have continued your inquiry journey until you could identify all the ingredients in the sports drink or could answer other testable questions. In the process, you would be doing science.

◀ **Figure 1.13 Scientific inquiry.** The process of scientific inquiry can be like a road trip. Sometimes, you can get where you want to go in one straight line (up the middle). But often, you might circle back to get things you forgot, make a few wrong turns, encounter detours, or try a different route to see different sights. From each experience on your journey, you learn something new.

2. Identify the stages in your sports drink investigation that correlate with the processes of scientific inquiry that you just read about. Describe what you did in your investigation to address each of the processes you identify. Record your answers in your science notebook.

As an alternative, you could create a labeled diagram or series of sketches.

3. Read Essential Features of Scientific Inquiry to learn more about scientific inquiry.

Topic: scientific inquiry
Go to: www.scilinks.org
Code: 1Inquiry29

a.

Topic: scientific investigations
Go to: www.scilinks.org
Code: 1Inquiry30

In the practice of science there are particular ways of learning about and coming to understand the natural world. Scientists make observations. They ask questions they can answer using the processes we described in Science as Inquiry. They design and conduct investigations and use technology and other techniques to collect, analyze, and interpret the data that result. Scientists develop descriptions, explanations, predictions, and models based on evidence. Scientists also communicate their procedures, findings, and conclusions to others through books, journal articles, or lectures. Scientists evaluate each other's work by reviewing experimental procedures, examining evidence, identifying faulty reasoning, and suggesting alternative explanations.

In science, different types of questions call for different types of investigations. Some questions lead to investigations that involve observing and describing objects, organisms, or events. Other questions lead to investigations that involve collecting specimens in their natural settings in different locations across the world, or even in space. Still others lead to investigations in which scientists set up carefully designed experiments in laboratories to get evidence about a specific process or event.

Remember, not all questions can be answered through scientific inquiry. Some questions are questions of opinion or

b.

preference, such as, Do you like reading fiction or nonfiction? Other questions, such as Is it okay to cheat on a test if everyone else is? are questions of ethics. These types of questions are interesting and important, but they are not scientifically testable questions. Ethics in doing science, of course, is very important.

Scientists' current knowledge and understanding provide a starting point for scientific investigations. Investigations provide evidence or data that is compared with existing explanations. Sometimes, the new evidence supports the current explanations, and sometimes the new evidence suggests a different one. Investigations sometimes result in new ideas altogether. These new ideas, procedures, or techniques often lead to new investigations.

Science is a human activity conducted by women and men of different social and ethnic backgrounds. Different types of people may ask different types of scientific questions, which in turn advance science in ways that might not occur if the same types of people are always asking the same types of questions. Some scientists work in teams, while others mostly work alone. All scientists rely on critical thinking, evidence, inference, scientific abilities, and creativity to accomplish their work. They also rely on intellectual honesty and openness to new ideas. When scientists carefully review each other's work, skepticism plays an important part in the process as well. Sometimes, other scientists can see a flaw in the design or in the analysis of the data that the team performing the work hasn't noticed. This, too, is very important in science. Because science continues to adjust to reflect new evidence, it keeps getting more accurate.

▲ Figure 1.14 **Communicating results.**
Scientists communicate their results in a variety of ways including through (a) books, (b) journal articles, and (c) lectures.

Sometimes, the language of scientific inquiry confuses people. This is because the meanings of certain words in science differ from their meanings in everyday life. As you probably know, a hypothesis is a testable statement about the natural world. It is not pulled out of thin air, but rather is based on a thoughtful analysis of as many observations as possible. Scientists support or reject hypotheses through investigation and observation. The process of scientific inquiry takes a long time, and scientists reject many more hypotheses than they support. From each experience, though, scientists make new observations that help them make new hypotheses.

Even though people often think of science as a bunch of facts, scientists rarely use the word *fact*. **Facts** are observations that have been repeatedly confirmed. Because observations can change with better technology and ways of looking at data, scientists are open to the idea that new observations might change a current explanation. For example, scientists once observed that human cells had 24 pairs of chromosomes. Students at the time learned this as a fact. Later, more powerful microscopes revealed that human cells have only 23 pairs of chromosomes. As a result of new observations, facts and explanations are subject to change.

In science, the term **law** describes how the natural world behaves in specific circumstances. For example, scientists have repeatedly observed that an object that is dropped from some height accelerates as it falls to the ground. Across time, scientists have tested numerous objects of many sizes and masses to establish this fact. Newton's second law uses this fact to explain what can happen to any object that is accelerated. Laws typically use mathematics in their descriptions: the mathematical description for Newton's second law is $F = ma$. This means that the net force (F) on an object is equal to the mass (m) of the object multiplied by its acceleration (a). Because of this relationship, when the mass of an object is greater, the force of gravity on the object also is greater and thus weighs more. As with all aspects of science, laws can be modified to reflect new information.

A **theory** explains an aspect of the natural world using tested hypotheses, scientific facts, laws, and logical inferences. A theory explains how the natural world works, but a law describes what happens in the natural

◄ Figure 1.15 **Stephen Hawking changes his view of black holes.** For 30 years, physicist Stephen Hawking argued that black holes destroy information. In July 2004, Hawking changed his position. Using a mathematical technique, he concluded that information is not destroyed when it falls into a black hole. Many scientists question the validity of the mathematical technique Hawking used to come to this conclusion. What happens in a black hole remains one of the biggest mysteries in physics. Hawking is a well-known theoretical physicist who has spent his life studying the laws that govern the universe. He has done much of his work from a wheelchair because he suffers from Lou Gehrig's disease.

world under certain conditions. Theories do not become laws, instead, theories and laws do different things and have different roles in science. Some examples of powerful theories in science include the theory of evolution (that hereditary characteristics change over the course of generations) and cell theory (that all living things are composed of cells).

All too often, people assume "theory" means wild guess. How many times have you heard someone dismiss an idea with the comment, Well, that is only a theory? In science, theories are supported by so much evidence and so many observations that they are universally accepted in the scientific community. For example, the facts about gravity and the law of gravitation accurately describe what scientists see in the natural world. Gravity also effectively explains things that are harder to observe beyond our world and out into the solar system and universe. Because of this, scientists have developed the theory of gravitation that applies to all bodies in the universe that have mass.

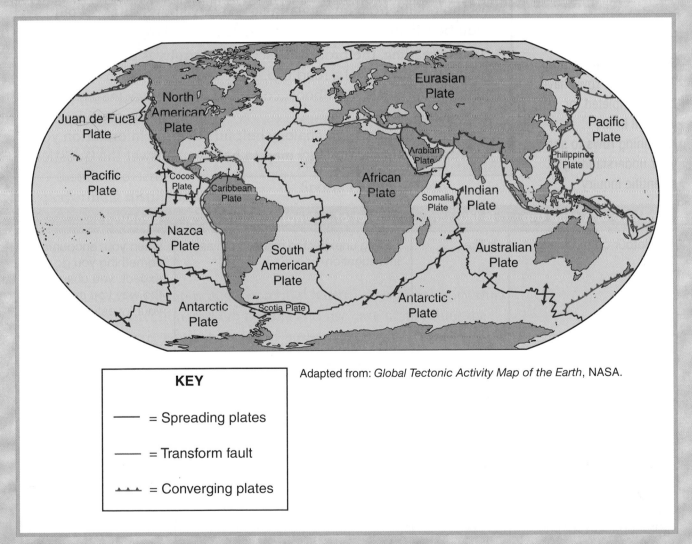

Adapted from: *Global Tectonic Activity Map of the Earth*, NASA.

KEY

——— = Spreading plates

——— = Transform fault

▲▲▲ = Converging plates

△ **Figure 1.16 Theory of plate tectonics.** The theory of plate tectonics states that Earth's outer layer is made of 12 main plates that move slowly over the surface of Earth. The size and position of the plates have changed throughout Earth's history. Sites of intense activity, such as earthquakes, volcanoes, and mountain building, are concentrated along the edges of the plates, where they move against each other.

b. What evidence would you want to collect if you were to determine the identity of the liquid part of a sports drink? How could you collect it?

2. Observe a setup for the process of **distillation**. Discuss with your class these questions.

   a. How is distillation like 1 of the processes you used in your sports drink investigation? How is it different?

   b. How could you use the process of distillation to determine the identity of the liquid in a sports drink?

3. Follow your teacher's directions to distill a small amount of the sports drink.

Topic: distillation
Go to: www.scilinks.org
Code: 1Inquiry36

You can do this with your team if your teacher has enough equipment, or you can watch as your teacher demonstrates this process called *distillation.*

As you watch the distillation process (which takes some time), actively think about what is happening by doing these things.

   a. Predict what you will see remaining in the flask that held the sports drink after most of the liquid has boiled away.

   b. Watch as the mystery sports drink boils. Observe the flask. Was your prediction correct?

   c. Observe the distillate that collects from the condenser. The **distillate** is the liquid that you collect as the result of the distillation process. What does the distillate look like? How is it the same as the original sports drink? How is it different?

   d. Do you think the distillate is purified water? How could you prove your prediction?

4. Discuss with your classmates how you would test the collected liquid to confirm that it is water. With your class, make a list of tests you can perform using materials available in your lab.

5. Divide into teams and decide which of the tests your team would like to perform using a small amount of the distillate.

6. Design a procedure so that you can collect evidence that helps you decide if the distillate is (or is not) water. Write your procedure in your science notebook. Be sure to think about the following things.

   a. What do you know?

   b. What do you want to know?

   c. What tools do you need?

   d. Can the investigation be done in the classroom in a reasonable amount of time?

   e. What steps do you need to take to produce measurable results?

   f. Do you need a control for comparison?

   g. Will the evidence you collect answer your question?

7. Have your teacher approve your procedure and make any changes as necessary.
8. Conduct the test, make your observations, and record the results of the test in your science notebook.
9. Contribute your data to a chart of data that includes all the results of the teams' tests. Contribute your conclusions to the chart, too. Discuss the combined results of all the tests with your class.

Part II

Discuss these questions with your class. Write your answers under the "Stop and Think—Part II" heading in your notebook.

1. Did other teams that performed your test reach the same conclusions? Why or why not?
2. How certain are you about the identity of the distillate after only your team's test?
3. How certain are you about the identity of the distillate after hearing about the results of all the tests in your class?
4. How was the process of collaborating as a class to reach a conclusion similar to what scientists do? Use what you learned from the readings in Part I.

▼ **Figure 1.18**
Sports drink label.
How much can you learn about a sports drink by looking at the label?

Part III: It's All on the Label

You might be wondering why you went to all the trouble to test for ingredients in a sports drink when all sports drinks disclose their ingredients on their labels. Wouldn't it have been easier to read the label to see if the sports drink is beneficial to athletes?

The answer to this question can be both yes and no. Reading the label would have been an easier way to establish what ingredients are in a sports drink, but it would not have given you as much practice solving a mystery using the methods of scientific inquiry. Your understanding about how to find out what is in a sports drink would have been limited: you could only figure out the ingredients of sports drinks with labels. You would not have learned how to conduct your own tests to identify the key ingredients.

Labels do provide one way to investigate sports drinks, however. In this part, you work individually to use a sports drink label to establish whether it has the beneficial concentration of carbohydrates and electrolytes for athletes. You also see that sports drinks can contain ingredients for which you have never tested.

Materials

For each student

1 sports drink with label

1 It's All on the Label handout

1 calculator

Process and Procedure

Record all your observations in your notebook under the heading "Part III: It's All on the Label."

1. Obtain a label from a sports drink of your choice. Among all the members of your class, try to cover a wide variety of sports drinks, from fitness waters, to recovery drinks, to energy drinks.
2. Work through the procedures on the It's All on the Label handout.
3. Share the results of your calculations with the rest of the class. Discuss the following questions with your class.
   a. Did the sports drink you analyzed contain the beneficial concentration of carbohydrates and electrolytes?
   b. Would you recommend your sports drink to an athlete? Why?

Reflect and Connect

Answer these questions in your science notebook under the heading "Reflect and Connect."

1. Describe why the results of the distillation investigation strengthened your explanation of the benefits of the sports drink.
2. Refer to the diagram of the water cycle in figure 1.19 to describe how distillation and the water cycle are related. Which parts of the water cycle relate to specific parts of the distillation process?
3. You might have heard that the water on Earth today is the same water that has been on Earth for billions of years. In fact, you could have fun grossing out your friends by saying that the water we drink is the same water that dinosaurs drank and then eliminated as urine! Use your knowledge of evaporation and condensation to explain why this idea should not disgust you.
4. Describe the variety of ways that scientists can investigate the natural world. Why are the different methods important to building good scientific explanations?

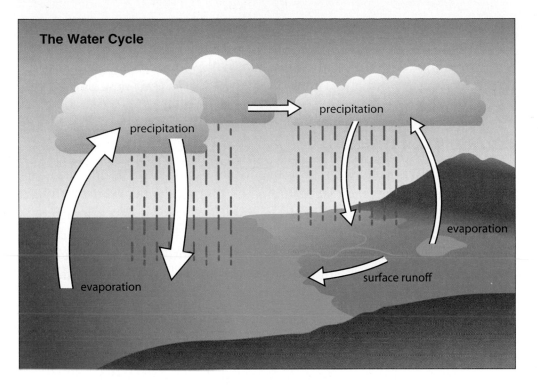

The Water Cycle

precipitation

precipitation

evaporation

evaporation

surface runoff

◀ **Figure 1.19**
Water cycle. How are the water cycle and the distillation process related?

Back Up That Claim!

ELABORATE

After all your investigations, you are probably pretty sure that the sports drink you tested is made of carbohydrates, electrolytes, and water. You confirmed your ideas by reading the label. And you have been able to figure out whether the drink you tested would be beneficial to an athlete. You did this by determining the percentage of the drink that is carbohydrates and electrolytes.

There's one problem. Do you believe everything you read? For example, do you believe that 6–8 percent carbohydrate-electrolyte drinks make athletes better performers? If you thought like a scientist, you would ask for the evidence that this claim is true. If the claim is true, then data would support the claim. You would want to see the data.

Luckily, there are scientific studies on the benefits of sports drinks. Exercise physiologists, nutritionists, and sports medicine doctors all have contributed to the growing body of knowledge about sports drinks. Their studies appear in scientific journals for their peers to review. Scientists must report the results of their scientific inquiry logically and completely. They do this so that other scientists can offer critical comments. Reporting results also gives other scientists the opportunity to investigate the same question to see if they get the same results.

In this activity, you will work with your team to review a study of sports drinks. You will determine the claims the scientists could make with the evidence in the study. Then you will write a paragraph to add to the reading A Powerful Thirst on pages 18–19. Your new paragraph should summarize the study and back up the article's claims.

Process and Procedure

It is not always easy to read a scientific research report. Often, scientists use language and measurements that students are not familiar with. In this activity, you will read a simplified version of a scientific research report. With your team, you will work through the report 1 section at a time to learn what a group of scientists discovered about sports drinks. Record all your observations in your notebook under the heading "Back Up That Claim!"

1. Get into teams of 3. Then read the Sports Study Document in figure 1.20 and answer the questions in Steps 2–6. Record your answers to the questions in your science notebook.
2. Look at the title of the study. What do you think the researchers meant by "improve performance"? How could you measure improved performance in a running event? Discuss your answers with your team.
3. Read the Abstract and Introduction sections to learn about the study. Discuss your answers to the following questions.

In scientific journal articles, abstracts describe a study and the results from a study without providing specific details. The introduction describes the problem researchers are addressing and how the research will contribute to our understanding of the natural world.

   a. Why were researchers interested in conducting their study in the heat?
   b. What did researchers know about how sports drinks (carbohydrate-electrolyte beverages) help runners who exercise in the heat for less than 1 hour? For more than 2 hours?
4. Read the Methods section to learn more about how the study was conducted and how the data collected were analyzed. Discuss your answers to the following questions.
   a. How many subjects did the researchers study? What was similar about all of them? What was different?
   b. Describe how the researchers controlled variables in this study.
5. Read the Results section to review the data the researchers collected. Discuss your answers to the following questions.
   a. What did the researchers measure? How do these data help answer their question?
   b. Can you think of anything else they could have measured?

6. Read the Discussion and Conclusion sections to learn what inferences the researchers made based on the data they collected. Discuss your answers to the following questions.
   a. What conclusions did the researchers draw? What evidence did they use to draw those conclusions?
   b. What questions do they still have?
   c. Do you think this is a strong study? Why?
7. You might have noticed names and dates appear in several places in the document. These names and dates appear when the work of other scientists is being referenced. The complete references are provided in the Reference section of a scientific journal article. Describe why you think it is important to reference the work of other scientists.
8. Read the Acknowledgments section. Companies like Coca-Cola and organizations such as the American Dairy Association often fund scientific research. Do you think the source of funding might affect the results that scientists publish in journal articles? Why or why not?
9. On your own, write a paragraph that uses evidence to back up the final claim in the reading, A Powerful Thirst on pages 18–19: "[T]he right sports drinks do provide an energy boost and slightly faster fluid absorption than plain water. This combination of energy and fluids in sports drinks helps athletes perform better, whether on the soccer field, in a tennis match, or running a marathon." To write the paragraph, do the following.
   a. Imagine that you are being asked to add a paragraph to the original reading so that it contains more information. You need to convince the reader that the claim made at the end of the reading is based on scientific research.
   b. Educate runners about the benefits of sports drinks under certain conditions using the evidence from the Sports Study Document.
   c. Be creative, but be scientifically accurate.

Reflect and Connect

Answer the following questions in your science notebook under the heading "Reflect and Connect." Discuss your answers with your class.
1. In what way is the paragraph you wrote in Step 9 more effective at answering the question, Are sports drinks beneficial to athletes? than the reading, A Powerful Thirst?
2. What if the researchers from the Sports Study Document had found out that there was no difference in athletic performance when an athlete drank a sports drink? Would they have failed

Do Sports Drinks Improve Performance During a 15-km Run in the Heat?

M. Lindgren-Shaw
A. Ramirez
S. J. Conner

Abstract

Twelve highly-trained runners ran 15 kilometers (km) on a treadmill in warm conditions. Runners consumed water, a 6%, or 8% carbohydrate/electrolyte beverage before and during the run. The run times were compared for runners consuming the three beverages. Runners consumed similar amounts of each beverage. During the first 13.4 km of the race, run times were not different. However, consumption of carbohydrate/electrolyte beverages improved performance during the last 1.6 km of the race compared to water.

Introduction

Major athletic competitions are often held in warm, humid environments (Sparling, 1995). For example, the Summer Olympics took place in Atlanta in 1996 and Athens, Greece in 2004. Few studies have investigated the effect of drinking a carbohydrate/electrolyte beverage during competitive running of less than 1 hour in the heat (El-Sayed et al., 1995; Ventura et al., 1994). However, some research shows that carbohydrate/electrolyte beverages can improve endurance performance when administered regularly to athletes running more than 2 hours in the heat (Millard-Stafford, 1992). Researchers are curious whether drinking a carbohydrate/electrolyte beverage (prior to and during exercise) could improve performance at the end of a 15-km run in warm, humid conditions.

Methods

Twelve highly-trained male runners volunteered to participate in the study. The runners ranged in age from 23 to 36 years old. All trained more than 65 km per week for the previous 12 weeks and had similar "best times" of about 32 minutes in a 10-km race.

Researchers conducted three 15-km timed trials with each athlete. They had the athlete drink a different beverage before each 15-km run. Then, they compared the results of each run to see if the runners completed the run faster after drinking water or carbohydrate/electrolyte beverages.

The runners completed a practice run on the treadmill 1 week prior to the test trials. This practice session helped runners set their pace for the subsequent trials.

Runners recorded diet and training for the week before their three tests. They were asked to follow the same diet and training pattern for the week preceding each of the other two trials. Runners were not allowed to train in the 24 hours preceding each test.

Each runner completed three 15-km runs, separated by at least 1 week. They started each trial at 8 a.m. after fasting for 10 hours. They ran at a self-selected pace on a motorized treadmill in an environmentally controlled room to simulate heat conditions. The room temperature and humidity varied throughout the tests from 27.2 °C to 28 °C and from 62% to 76% relative humidity. There were fans that cooled the runners during their runs.

Runners could vary their speed as they wanted and select their own pace for each run. Rest breaks were scheduled for each runner at 7.5 km (for 3 minutes) and 13.4 km (for 5 minutes). Following the second break, runners were asked to give all-out maximum effort as they completed the final 1.6 km of the run. Prize money was used to motivate the runners to run their fastest. Prize money was awarded in two categories. One category was for the best cumulative times for all three 15-km runs and the other for the best cumulative times for the three final 1.6-km runs.

Each time a runner did a trial, he drank a different beverage 1 hour before running:
- 1 liter of distilled water; or
- 1 liter of a 6% carbohydrate/electrolyte sports drink (Gatorade®) with 60 g of combined carbohydrates, sodium, and potassium; or
- 1 liter of an 8% carbohydrate/electrolyte sports drink (PowerAde®) with 80 g of combined carbohydrates, sodium, and potassium.

The carbohydrate/electrolyte beverages both were lemon-lime flavor. All beverages were held at a temperature of 10 °C. The runner could continue to drink as much of the beverage as he wanted during the run, during scheduled rest breaks, and during a 30-minute recovery period.

Results

The average* amount of each beverage consumed during the runs by all runners was not significantly different** (Table 1, Figure 1). The time to complete the first 13.4 km was not significantly different between the trials of the two sports drinks and water (Figure 2). The time to complete the final 1.6 km was significantly faster for the two sports drinks compared to water (Figure 3). The ± symbol followed by a value (for example, ±52) indicates the variability of the average. The variability is shown on Figures 1, 2, and 3 as bars above and below the average.

Table 1. Results from the 15 km run.

Beverage	Average drink consumed (mL)	Average run time for initial 13.4 km (minutes)	Average run time for final 1.6 km (minutes)
Water	301 (±52)	55.9 (±1.1)	5.8 (±0.1)
6% carbohydrate/electrolyte sports drink	282 (±55)	55.4 (±1.4)	5.6 (±0.07)
8% carbohydrate/electrolyte sports drink	298 (±56)	55.4 (±1.3)	5.5 (±0.07)

*To calculate the average beverage consumed, the total liquid of each type that each athlete drank during or after exercise (they all drank 1 liter before exercise) was divided by the total number of athletes (12). Similarly, the average run time was calculated by dividing the total run times of all the athletes by the total number of athletes (12).

**Results were compared between the three beverages to determine which results were significant. A significant result indicates the probability that 95% of the time the same result would be found and by chance only 5% of the time.

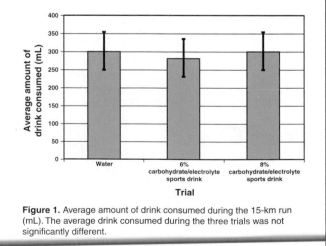

Figure 1. Average amount of drink consumed during the 15-km run (mL). The average drink consumed during the three trials was not significantly different.

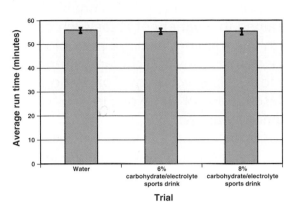
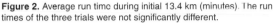

Figure 2. Average run time during initial 13.4 km (minutes). The run times of the three trials were not significantly different.

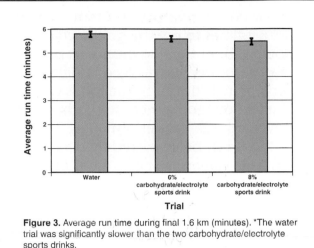

Figure 3. Average run time during final 1.6 km (minutes). *The water trial was significantly slower than the two carbohydrate/electrolyte sports drinks.

Discussion

The research indicates that the 1.6-km run performance after 13.4 km of running was better when the athlete consumed 1 liter of a carbohydrate/electrolyte beverage. The beverage provided 60 to 80 grams of carbohydrates with additional salt and potassium. The performance improvement over water was about 4–5%.

One limitation of this study was the lack of a control trial with a lemon-lime flavor drink containing no carbohydrates or electrolytes in addition to a water trial. The strongest research design is when subjects cannot identify the drink being tested. It was difficult to schedule 12 athletes for a total of 36 trials. Additional trials would have been even more difficult. As a result, there was a lack of a fourth trial: subjects knew when they were drinking water as compared to sports drinks. The researchers did not add artificial sweeteners, flavoring, or color to the water to mask its identity. However, since water remains the most widely available and consumed beverage in race settings, it provided a meaningful comparison to the sports drinks. Most subjects also rated water as the preferred fluid replacement beverage during training and competition. The money incentives based on all 3 run times combined were devised to prevent runners from giving less effort on any one trial. Therefore, the investigators felt confident that subjects gave equal effort on all 3 trials despite knowledge that they were drinking water during one trial.

This research does not answer the question of why runners ran faster after consuming carbohydrate/electrolyte beverages, but provides evidence that drinking these beverages in the hour before exercise may be beneficial, not harmful to performance. Some research has suggested that the carbohydrates in these beverages increase blood glucose levels. Other studies, however, suggest that increased performance was not associated with increased blood glucose levels (Below et al.,1995). More research needs to be done to determine the underlying cause of the improvement in performance of events less than 1 hour in duration for athletes who drink sports drink beverages.

Conclusion

When compared to water, drinking 6% or 8% carbohydrate/electrolyte beverages both before and during exercise significantly improved performance for the final 1.6 km of a 15-km run in a warm, humid environment.

References

Below, P. R., Mora-Rodriguez, R., Gonzalez-Alonso, J., & Coyle, E. F. (1995). Fluid and carbohydrate ingestion independently improve performance during 1 h of intense exercise. *Medicine and Science in Sports and Exercise, 27,* 200–210.

El-Sayed, M. S., Raitu, A. J. M., & Roberts, I. (1995). Effects of carbohydrate feeding before and during prolonged exercise on subsequent maximal exercise performance capacity. *International Journal of Sports Nutrition, 5,* 215–224.

Millard-Stafford, M. L., Sparling, P. B., Rosskopf, L. R., & DiCarlo, L. J. (1992). Carbohydrate-electrolyte replacement improves distance running performance in the heat. *Medicine and Science in Sports and Exercise, 24,* 934–940.

Sparling, P. B. (1995). Expected conditions for the 1996 Summer Olympic Games in Atlanta. *Clinical Journal of Sports Medicine, 5,* 220–222.

Ventura, J. L., Estruch, A., Rodas, G., & Segura, R. (1994). Effect of prior ingestion of glucose or fructose on the performance of exercise of intermediate duration. *European Journal of Applied Physiology, 63,* 345–349.

Acknowledgements

This study was supported by a grant from the Coca-Cola Company.

From M. Millard-Stafford, "Water Versus Carbohydrate – Electrolyte Ingestion Before and During a 15-km Run in the Heat," in the Internal Journal of Sport Nutrition, 7(1), 26–38. ©1997 by Human Kinetics. Adapted with permission from Human Kinetics (Champaign, IL).

The Science of Sports and Fitness

How do Olympic athletes trim seconds off their times to get the gold medal? Should weight training programs be different for people involved in different sports or activities? Can the foods we eat affect our endurance, strength, speed, or even our mental performance? These questions can be answered by people who have careers in sports medicine.

The goal of sports medicine is to help everyone, whether an athlete or someone involved in any physical activity, reach optimal health and peak performance. Sports medicine is increasing our understanding of how the body responds to all forms of physical activity and is being used to help people of all ages and abilities. For example, sports medicine might help reduce the chance of a repetitive stress injury for a worker on an assembly line or help determine the best exercise program for a competitive athlete.

Sports medicine professionals are trained in a variety of areas such as athletic training, exercise physiology, biomechanics, physical therapy, nutrition, and sports psychology. Following are descriptions of some of the specialty areas:

- Athletic trainers work with athletes at the high school, college, and professional level in the physical conditioning of the athlete and in the prevention of illness and injury related to sports and exercise.
- Exercise physiologists study the body's physiological responses to physical activity.
- Biomechanical engineers apply the laws of physics to physical activity to learn how muscles, bones, and joints function together. They use this information to design sports equipment and rehabilitation devices.
- Physical therapists help rehabilitate people with injuries to muscles, bones, and joints.
- Nutritionists or dieticians prepare diets that provide complete nutrition for optimal health and physical condition.
- Sports psychologists work with athletes to overcome psychological obstacles that prevent them from performing their best.

Physical therapists help patients overcome injuries through exercise and other treatments.

in their study? Would they have had nothing to report? Explain your answer.

3. Why do scientists communicate the results of their inquiries? What can other scientists do when they learn of a scientist's research?

Homemade Sports Drinks

Now that you know what goes into a beneficial sports drink, do you think you could make one that would be just as good? What would you put in it? Would your own sports drink have the same benefits? Would anyone want to drink it? How might you go about answering questions like these, using the process of scientific inquiry?

In this activity, you will have an opportunity to demonstrate what you have learned about scientific inquiry. You will work as a team to design a homemade sports drink, test it to see if it is as beneficial as some commercial sports drinks, and present your drink to the class.

Materials
For each team of three students

3 pairs of safety goggles

several sets of common measuring utensils such as measuring spoons and cups

laboratory materials from Mystery Sports Drinks and What Is Science?

1 Scoring Rubric for Homemade Sports Drinks handout

Cautions

Remember to exercise caution when working in the lab. Wear safety goggles. Remember, it is not safe to taste anything you work with in a science lab, including foods. If you want to taste your sports drink, make a sample at home using your own ingredients.

Process and Procedure

Record all your observations in your notebook under the heading "Homemade Sports Drinks."

1. Review the Homemade Sports Drinks Scoring Rubric for this activity to see what your teacher expects you to accomplish and how you will demonstrate your understanding as you design your own sports drink.

Notice the process of inquiry that provides evidence that your sports drink is beneficial is as important as the creative marketing of your sports drink. The best project will reflect the scientific and creative efforts of all team members.

2. Meet with your team. Discuss the components of a beneficial sports drink. In particular, answer the following questions.
   a. What ingredients make up a beneficial sports drink? What variety of substances can you use to provide these ingredients in your sports drink?
   b. In what concentration should each of the ingredients be?
   c. What other factors besides the concentration of ingredients make athletes often prefer sports drinks over water or other drinks such as colas?

3. What kind of recipes for homemade sports drinks exist? Conduct some research to find out what other people have created for homemade sports drinks. Record ideas you get from your research in your science notebook.

4. Review the sports drink labels from your team's It's All on the Label handouts from the last activity to determine some possible ingredients and quantities of ingredients.

5. Plan a recipe for your team's homemade sports drink based on your knowledge from Step 2 and your findings from Steps 3 and 4. Write your recipe in your science notebook. Include an explanation of why you included each ingredient.

Get your teacher's approval for your recipe before you move to Step 6.

6. Make a batch of the sports drink using ingredients your team has brought from home or your teacher has supplied. Follow your recipe exactly.

You should make only a small batch to start, because you need to test it to see if it has the qualities of a beneficial sports drink. If it does not, you will need to alter your recipe. By making small batches, you will not waste ingredients.

7. Conduct tests on your homemade sports drink to provide evidence that it is beneficial according to the description of beneficial sports drinks in the scientific literature. Record the results of your tests in your science notebook.

8. Adjust your recipe until you can provide evidence that the sports drink has the necessary qualities to be beneficial to athletes. Record the final recipe in your science notebook.

Remember, do not taste the sports drink in the lab. Once you have settled on a recipe that works, you can make up a batch of your sports drink at home to taste it. With your batch at home, you might want to conduct a taste test among family members or friends. How would a taste test help support your marketing claim that the sports drink is a good product?

9. Design a label that includes information about the contents of your sports drink. Look at the label of a commercial sports drink for ideas.

10. Design a fun advertisement that convinces an athlete that your sports drink is beneficial. Be sure to be specific and scientifically accurate.

How do real advertisements include information from scientific studies? Look in magazines for advertisements for medicines or nutrition products to find some examples.

11. Present your sports drink, label, and advertisement to the class. Provide copies of the recipe for each class member.

UNIT 1

Matter Is Marvelous

Matter Is Marvelous

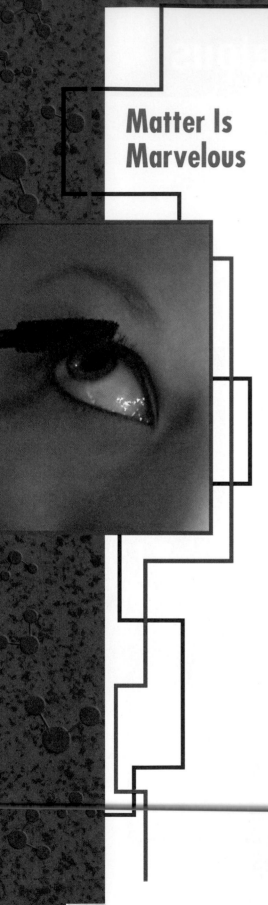

Look around. You are surrounded by different materials—in school, at home, at work—every-where. As you go about your daily life, advertisements bombard you with information about more materials—new and improved materials. Try to recall the most recent advertisement you have seen or heard for a new product. Was it a TV commercial for the latest line of athletic shoes, a radio ad about the newest flavor of soft drink, or perhaps a magazine ad for a faster computer? Think about a new and improved product that you have acquired recently. For example, what makes one stereo speaker better than another one? Are the materials different? How are those differences important in our everyday world—the material world?

In the Matter Is Marvelous unit, you will explore the material world we live in from two viewpoints—*macroscopic* and *microscopic*. Your senses allow you to observe matter that is macroscopic. You can touch a football, see a grain of sand, and hear a waterfall. However, a microscopic viewpoint focuses on particles so small they are invisible to the unaided eye. Both viewpoints help you understand a unifying principle of science: *form* and *function*.

You will think about how the underlying microscopic form of matter helps you understand the unique properties of matter. That way you can explain how matter functions at the macroscopic level. Exploring the observable properties of matter and models of its underlying structure will help you understand why the best product is better than others.

Goals for the Unit

By the end of unit 1, Matter Is Marvelous, you should understand the following:

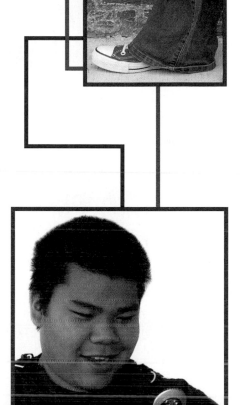

- Matter has characteristic physical and chemical properties, which result in unique qualities you can see and measure—its macroscopic behavior.

- Properties are a result of the underlying structure of matter at the invisible level—its microscopic form.

- When properties are used to arrange elements, repeating patterns emerge that are related to the underlying structure of matter at the microscopic level. The Periodic Table of the Elements expresses these patterns by its unique layout of elements in rows and columns.

- At the microscopic level, all matter is made up of tiny particles, called atoms, in constant motion. Atoms are composed of even smaller components.

- Atoms interact with one another by transferring or sharing electrons to make other tiny particles, called molecules, which are held together by forces of attraction sometimes called bonds.

CHAPTER 2

The Material World

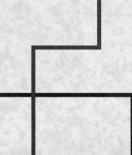

The Material World

ook at the wave toy pictured in the opener. What is so captivating about it? Why does the little penguin ride on one fluid and not the other? How can *both* fluids be transparent yet one have color and the other no color? Would the toy be as fun if it were made from only one material? Which substances would *you* use to make the toy function in the most entertaining way? What happens if the materials react chemically with each other?

Certainly, toy makers ask themselves these questions and more. Why? Because the properties of materials determine how well toys function. Moreover, proper function makes for a better product, and that is an important part of everyday life.

Goals for the Chapter

In chapter 2, The Material World, you will investigate the properties that help you distinguish one material from another material. As you think about what you see, you might become curious about why matter behaves in certain ways. To answer *why* questions requires you to wonder about things you cannot see. You will begin to build a mental model for the microscopic structure that underlies all macroscopic properties. When you finish chapter 2, you should be able to answer the following questions:

- What are some characteristic properties of matter and how are they used to identify matter?

- What is the underlying structure of matter and how do the properties we observe relate to this underlying structure?

You will be better able to answer these questions by participating in the following activities:

ENGAGE	Toying with Matter
EXPLORE	Materials Make the Toy
EXPLAIN	Sink or Float
EXPLAIN	Mind over Matter
ELABORATE	Reacting to Density
EVALUATE	Properties "Я" Us!

Your chapter organizer plays an important role in your learning. Bring it to class every day. Look at it before and after *each* activity. Think about where you are in its flow and organization. Use the organizer to help you monitor your understanding. If at any point you are confused, consult with your teacher.

Can I design a wave toy?

Toying with Matter

Key Idea:
Wave toys are made
of different materials.

EXPLORE

Materials Make the Toy

Key Idea:
Wave toy design
depends on characteristic
properties of materials.

Linking Question

How are the materials in a
wave toy different?

The Material World

EXPLAIN

Sink or Float ▶▶

Key Idea:
Wave toy design depends on differences in density.

Linking Question

What is the underlying reason
for differences in materials that
compose a wave toy?

Properties "Я" Us

Key Idea:

The particle model explains how the wave toy and other matter function.

Do changes in physical and chemical properties explain how other matter behaves?

ELABORATE

Reacting to Density

Key Idea:

Atoms interact with each other. Atomic interactions sometimes lead to changes in physical properties, chemical properties, or both.

CHAPTER 2 Major Concepts

Particle Model
- Atoms are microscopic-sized particles.
- Atoms compose all matter.
- Atoms interact with each other.
- Physical properties change.
- Materials change chemically.
  - For all physical and chemical change, the total amount of matter in the universe remains constant.

Mind over Matter

Key Idea:

Microscopically sized particles called atoms make up all matter and explain the characteristic properties of all materials in the wave toy.

Do chemical reactions occur in the wave toy?

Toying with Matter

Toy manufacturers must understand the properties of matter. Otherwise, their toys do not function as designed. What properties of matter are important to how a wave toy functions? How do those properties differ among the materials used in the toy? What do you already know about density, solubility, and reactivity? What else do you need to learn in order to understand how the wave toy works?

▶ **Figure 2.1**
What happens to the way products function when the materials are not right?

In the Toying with Matter activity, you will use what you already know about matter and determine if that knowledge matches what you see. If you see something unusual, your curiosity will prompt you to generate new questions to explore. You will be working alone, with a partner, and with the entire class.

▼ **Figure 2.2**
Consumer products. All these products are made of materials. Do you know the names of any of these materials?

Materials

Process and Procedure

Work individually initially, then with others as instructed. Keep a careful record of what you see and what you are thinking. Use both sketches and written notes. Place all observations in your science notebook under the heading, "Toying with Matter."

1. Study the liquids in figure 2.3. Your teacher will have the same 2 substances in the room for you to view from your seat.
   a. Are they made of the same matter? What macroscopic observations lead you to your answer?
   b. How could you determine if these materials would be right for a wave toy of your own design?

Write answers to both questions in your notebook.

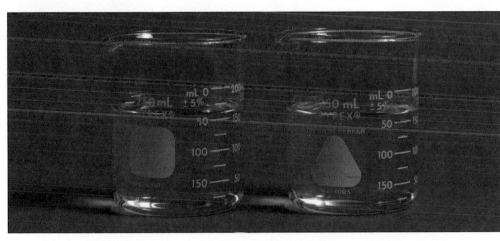

◄ **Figure 2.3**
Beakers with possibly different substances. These substances look the same. Are they? Do they remind you of any substances that you have seen before? Which ones?

2. Find a partner and read your answers from your notebook. Communicate your ideas clearly.

One way to learn more is to listen to what others say.

◄ **Figure 2.4**
In the past, have you learned something important by listening?

a. Determine if your partner is confused.

b. Respond to any questions your partner may have about what you read.

3. Switch roles and listen to what your partner reads. Ask questions to clarify anything you do not understand.

4. Add to your answers anything you feel your partner helped you learn. Your partner should do the same.

5. Decide what is different between figure 2.3 and figure 2.5.

Your teacher will mimic figure 2.5 in front of the class.

a. Draw a sketch of what you see.

b. Label each important part.

▶ **Figure 2.5**
What happens when each candle falls into the liquid?

6. Use what you wrote and learned from Steps 2–4 to predict what will happen to *each* candle.

You don't know what the substances are, so use your previous experiences.

a. Show what you think will happen in 2 sketches.

b. Answer *why* you think it will happen under each sketch.

Use science concepts and words you may have learned at other times like *density, mass,* and *volume.*

▶ **Figure 2.6**
Sample student notebook. Predictions help you make sense of the results of an activity.

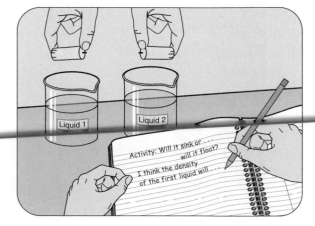

7. Repeat Steps 2–4 with your predictions.

Don't forget to ask each other questions and to learn from your partner.

8. Participate as your teacher asks the class what it thinks.
   a. Does everyone have the same prediction?
   b. What do differences in predictions tell you about what individuals think about the material world?
9. Sketch in your notebook what you see when your teacher drops candles into each liquid.
   a. How do your predictions compare with what you see?
   b. How do class predictions compare?
10. Think of at least 1 situation from your experiences in or out of school that is similar to what you just saw.

Likely situations include the material some people place on salads, a tree branch falling through air into a river, or people swimming in water.

   a. Make a sketch of what you remember.
   b. Label the names of each material.
   c. Underneath the sketch, write how your new sketch is like what you observed in class.
11. Show your sketch to your partner. Use Steps 2–4 to learn from his or her sketch.

Reflect and Connect

Think about the following questions and record your best ideas in your science notebook. Place the heading, "Reflect and Connect," at the beginning of your responses. When you have finished, find at least 2 classmates not on your team. Compare your answers. Include what you learned from your classmates and teacher in your notebook.

1. What features of this activity could toy designers use to produce an entertaining wave toy?
2. What might happen to a candle placed in a *mixture* of the 2 pure substances used in this activity? What property of matter must be different in order for your answer to be accurate?
3. Which properties of matter, other than the one you mentioned in Question 2, are important for the little penguin in the wave toy to function properly?
4. How would a penguin function that is 1/10 the size of the one pictured in the chapter opener? One-millionth? Is there a limit to how small a wave toy could be made and still behave the same way? Justify your answer.

▼ **Figure 2.7**
Nesting dolls. These dolls are getting smaller. Does their small form affect the way they function as dolls?

Materials Make the Toy

In the previous activity, Toying with Matter, you considered which properties of matter help toy designers create entertaining and durable toys like the wave toy. Density is a physical property you probably decided was important. Perhaps you learned about density in earlier grades. This property of matter helps explain why a hot-air balloon rises in cool air.

▶ **Figure 2.8**

Density differences cause objects to float or sink. Which substance has the greatest density? Would hot air be a good material to use for the little penguin? What properties other than density must toy designers consider when making a best-selling wave toy? What if the penguin dissolved in one of the wave toy liquids? What if it reacted chemically with one or both of the liquids?

In the Materials Make the Toy activity, you will start with what you learned about how candles behaved in different clear, colorless liquids. Then you will explore how to use what you learned about properties of matter to design your own wave toy. Who knows, you might invent the next hottest-selling toy!

Your teacher will show you two wave bottles, which are constructed using the same principles as wave toys. Each bottle has four materials inside, *but not the same four*. Your challenge will be to work in teams to design wave bottles that function the same way with the substances provided. Then your curiosity will demand an explanation for the microscopic nature of the materials that is responsible for what you observe.

Materials

For each team of two or three students

3 pairs of safety goggles	isopropyl alcohol (C_3H_7OH)
3 lab aprons	water (H_2O)
1 100-mL graduated cylinder	dye #1
3 droppers	dye #2
1 well plate	clear containers with tight-fitting lids
baby oil or mineral oil ($C_{12}H_{26}$)	cotton swabs

Cautions

Wear your safety goggles at all times. Isopropyl alcohol is flammable. Do not conduct this investigation near an open flame or heat source. Avoid direct skin contact with the materials. Although the materials in this lab are common household or laboratory materials, it is still important to exercise caution when handling materials in the lab. If you spill a substance on the floor or desk, tell your teacher so he or she can let you know how to clean it up safely.

Process and Procedure

1. Your teacher will show you 2 wave bottles: A and B. Observe each one carefully as the teacher moves them about.

Write the heading, "Materials Make the Toy," in your notebook. Under the activity title, generate a T-table with the headings "Similarities" and "Differences."

◀ Figure 2.9
T-table in student notebook. Organized notebooks help you spend the least amount of time getting the most out of an activity.

2. Compare the 2 wave bottles. List as many similarities and differences as you can under the proper headings of your T-table.
3. Read to all team members what you wrote in your table. Add to your table what you learn from your partners.
4. Study the substances set out by your teacher. They are labeled "isopropyl alcohol," "water," "baby oil," "dye #1," and "dye #2."

These are the *only* substances you can use to design your wave bottle. Each wave bottle has a different combination of these four substances.

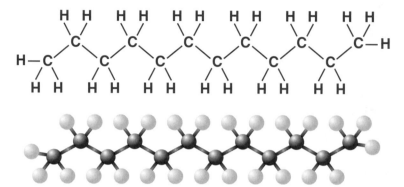

▶ **Figure 2.10**

Ball-and-stick model of baby oil. Atoms of carbon bond to other carbon atoms and to hydrogen atoms to make one of the representative molecules of baby oil. Other molecules in baby oil are very similar. The long connection of carbon atoms is called a chain.

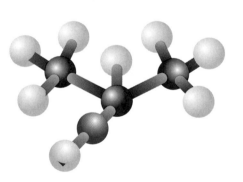

▶ **Figure 2.11**

Ball-and-stick model of isopropyl alcohol. Atoms of carbon bond to other carbon atoms, and to hydrogen and oxygen atoms, to make isopropyl alcohol, also called rubbing alcohol.

5. Consider with your lab team how to observe interactions among *all* pairs of substances.

You want to find out how certain properties cause the desired interactions among these materials.

6. Decide on the best format for a data table. Keep efficiency in mind, exerting the least effort for the most benefit.

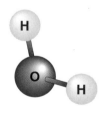

▶ **Figure 2.12**

Ball-and-stick model of water. An oxygen atom bonds with two hydrogen atoms to make dihydrogen oxide, also called water.

Writing observations in random, disorganized places in your notebook makes understanding those observations very difficult. In the long term, it wastes your valuable time.

Using droppers and well plates allows you to investigate with small amounts of each substance, minimizing waste and mess, and improving your efficiency in doing experiments.

7. Conduct your tests to determine the interactions among materials. All team members should record **all** observations in their notebooks.

Caution Wear safety goggles and lab aprons.

Don't forget to test *mixtures* of substances to determine if their properties change, depending on the proportions in the mixture.

8. Find another team to work with.
   a. Decide which wave bottle each team will attempt to reproduce.
   b. Study your observations from Step 7 and create a precise recipe for *your* wave bottle.

Decide which substances and what quantities to add to your container.

   c. Write your recipe in your notebook. Follow the recipe carefully and make your wave bottle.

First, determine the volume of your container by using water and a graduated cylinder. Then figure out how much of each substance is needed and in what order to add substances to the container.

9. Compare your wave bottle with the original your teacher made and the other team's bottle.
   a. How did each bottle function?
   b. Make sketches that show the relative sizes of each wave bottle and proportions of materials inside.
   c. Label the material in each layer.
   d. Underneath your sketches, suggest what properties of the matter in each layer are most important for understanding how each layer functions. Explain your answer.

Reflect and Connect

Meet with the team that made the other wave bottle. Compare your answers. Write answers to the following questions in your notebook under the heading, "Reflect and Connect." Include what you learned from your classmates and teacher in your notebook.

1. What are the similarities and differences between your team's recipe and the other team's recipe?

Use a T-table to report your findings.

2. There were 4 substances in each bottle. Why were there only 2 layers? Explain your reasoning by referring to the labeled diagrams you generated in Step 9.
3. Did dye #1 and dye #2 dissolve the same way in all substances? What effect did any differences have on your recipe?

Remember to use the proper name for each material discussed.

4. Think of a situation other than the wave toy in which the concept of recipe is important. Describe how the properties of the materials used in the recipe affect the resulting wave toy.

Sink or Float

In the activity, Materials Make the Toy, you observed what happened to a candle when it was placed in liquids with different densities. Water has a greater density than paraffin so paraffin floats in water. As a result, the candle floats. Understanding density helps explain what happens in nature, from deep ocean currents to thinning bones among the elderly. Density is important to businesspeople. Toy manufacturers must be able to determine the density of any solid *or* liquid they intend to use in a wave toy. Otherwise, the toy will not function as designed. Sales will suffer.

▶ **Figure 2.13**

Plastic toy boat in water. This plastic has a greater density than water. Then why does the toy boat float?

In the Sink or Float investigation, you will learn how the physical property density explains part of the wave toy's function. To determine the density of materials, you will use tools that are important in science—including mathematics. In this activity, you will work in teams of three.

Part I: Determining the Density of a Liquid

Materials
For each team of three students

3 pairs of safety goggles

3 lab aprons

1 100-mL graduated cylinder

1 plastic pipette

1 balance

colored pencils

approximately 100 mL each of water, isopropyl alcohol, and baby oil

1 calculator (Teams can share calculators.)

Cautions

Wear safety goggles at all times. Avoid direct skin contact with the materials. Although the materials in this lab are common household or laboratory materials, it is still important to exercise caution when handling materials in the lab. If you spill a substance on the floor or desk, tell your teacher so he or she can let you know how to clean it up safely.

Process and Procedure

Is the density of candle wax the same as the density of water? Are the densities of isopropyl alcohol and baby oil the same? How do you know? Would the same volume of each of these substances read the same value on a laboratory scale? Why? You are about to measure 2 values required to calculate density—mass and volume. Density is the ratio of these 2 values given by the following mathematical relationship:

$$\text{density} = \frac{\text{mass}}{\text{volume}} \text{ or } D = \frac{m}{v}$$

When one material is more massive than another for the same amount of volume, then it has a greater density. Steel for bridges has a high density. Air that we breathe has a low density.

Once you calculate density, you can use this derived result to predict how substances will interact with each other, as in a wave toy.

1. Develop a step-by-step procedure to determine the density of 3 *different* amounts of the liquids supplied by your teacher and record this procedure in your notebook under the heading "Sink or Float—Part I" to help accomplish 1a–e.

   a. Meet with your team to discuss appropriate steps and agree on those steps before proceeding.

   Consult with your teacher if the team cannot reach consensus.

   b. Decide how to measure mass and volume for liquid samples using the equipment provided.

   The mass of a liquid sample *inside* your graduated cylinder is what you use to calculate density. Therefore, incorporating the graduated cylinder's mass with the liquid would give you a false value for density.

   c. Include steps for collecting 3 sample sizes of *each* liquid with volumes varying from 20 to 100 milliliters (mL).

   This step eventually gives you feedback on how reliable your measurement technique is.

   d. Write the procedure in numbered steps in your notebook.

   e. Have your teacher approve your procedure *before* collecting data.

   Scientists are responsible for recording their own data. That way they can review their data away from the lab.

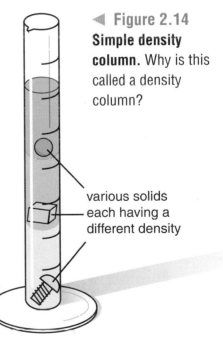

◀ **Figure 2.14**
Simple density column. Why is this called a density column?

various solids each having a different density

Caution Wear safety goggles and lab aprons.

▼ **Figure 2.15**

Graphing mass and volume data. Make your graph large enough to add information as you understand more.

▼ **Figure 2.16**

Sample mass versus volume scatter plot. Draw best-fit lines with about as many points above the line as below. Leave room for highlight comments.

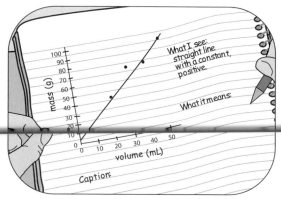

2. Construct a data table in your notebook that has a space for each important observation, for *each* liquid.
   a. Include columns and rows with informative headings and proper measurement units.
   b. Leave spaces for the calculated density of each sample.
   c. Record the mass of a clean, dry graduated cylinder.
3. Collect data efficiently and return all liquids as instructed by your teacher.

Gather your materials.

4. Graph your mass and volume data in your notebook or on graph paper as instructed by your teacher.

Graphs help you picture differences in density.

   a. Place your graph axes in the upper two-thirds of a page. Reserve the bottom third for a caption.
   b. Use mass in grams (g) for the dependent variable (vertical axis) and volume in mL for the independent variable (horizontal axis).
   c. Create scales for both axes that will include data for *all 3 liquids*.

Inspect your data for the largest mass and volume value. Create scale numbers large enough to incorporate these values. There should be three points for each liquid.

5. Draw a best-fit line for each liquid.
   a. Use different colored pencils for each liquid.
   b. Place a key on your graph, explaining what each color represents.

A best-fit line places approximately as many data points above the line as below it. It represents a type of average.

Remember, simply "connecting the dots" will not give you the real picture of density.

6. Look carefully at the best-fit line for water. Consider the key features or *highlights* of what you see and what it means.

   a. Think of a few words that you have learned in other science and mathematics classes to describe what you see.
   b. Write the phrase "What I see:" by the best-fit line for water. Following this phrase, write your short description. This forms half of your highlight comments.

Consider if the line is curved or straight, flat or sloped, positively sloped or negatively sloped. Include those considerations in your description.

7. Repeat Steps 5 and 6 for *each* liquid.

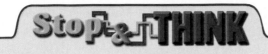

Part I

Wave toys depend, in part, on differences in density. Graphs show those differences. They help you understand, because they help you see what the numbers mean. Answer the following questions in your notebook under the heading, "Stop and Think—Part I."

1. Compare the highlight comments you wrote beside *each* "What I See" entry with others in your team. Modify your comments based on what you learned from others. Include those modifications in your notebook.

2. Write "What it means" under each "What I see" comment. This phrase is the other half of your highlight comments. Explain what a constant positive slope means about the density of *each* liquid.

   Remember from math class that constant slope means constant $\frac{rise}{run}$. For this graph, $\frac{rise}{run}$ is the same as $\frac{mass}{volume}$ if the line passes through the origin. Both ratios have the same numerical value.

3. Are the slopes of all three lines the same? What does that mean?

   Write your highlight comments about the relative sizes of slopes in a "What I see," "What it means" format on the graph.

4. Meet with your team and share what you have written for each comment on your graph. Decide as a team what to write as a caption under the graph.

   Think back to other graphs and charts you have read. Captions often told you, in sentence format, what you were looking at, what it meant, and why it was important. Include these features in your caption.

5. Calculate the slopes of *each* best-fit line and show all your work with proper units and labels.
   a. Find your calculated densities for each sample (you will have 9 calculations in your data table).
   b. Compare those values with the slopes you just calculated.
   c. What does it mean if they are very close to each other? What does it mean if they are very far apart?

6. Decide as a team the best way to explain how graphs help you "see" density differences.

Part II: Determining the Density of a Solid

Materials

3 pairs of safety goggles

1 100-mL graduated cylinder

1 balance

1 strainer

water

candles (3 different sizes)

1 calculator (Teams can share calculators.)

colored pencils (optional)

For each team of three students

Cautions

Always wear safety goggles and lab aprons in the lab, particularly when you are investigating chemical reactions.

Process and Procedure

Inside the wave toy are 2 liquids of different densities. Density helps determine what is unique about a substance. We call these unique attributes **characteristic properties**. Such properties help us pick and choose materials for specialized uses. But what about the little penguin? It is a solid, not liquid. How do we determine its density? You are right. We still need to measure mass and volume, and we need to use mathematics to *calculate* density.

1. Meet with your team and talk about the best way to determine the mass and volume of 3 different-sized samples of paraffin.

If you submerge an object in water, the object displaces water in a volume equal to the object. That causes the water level in a graduated cylinder to rise.

2. When your team agrees on the best way to determine the mass and volume, ask your teacher to approve your procedure. Then carry out your procedure. Record all observations in your notebook under the heading "Sink or Float—Part II."

a. Construct a data table in your notebook with proper headings, including measurement units.

These tables help you spend the least amount of time collecting the best possible data.

Don't forget columns for the water level in your graduated cylinder before *and* after you place a solid sample in it.

b. Record your observations.

Topic: characteristic properties of matter
Go to: www.scilinks.org
Code: 1Inquiry70

▼ **Figure 2.17**

Irregularly shaped object submerged in liquid. The object displaces water, making the fluid level rise. How does the change in fluid level relate to the volume of the object?

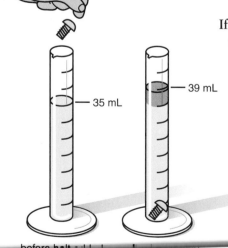

35 mL

39 mL

before bolt added   after bolt added

The volume of the bolt in this illustration is 4 mL, or 4 cm³.

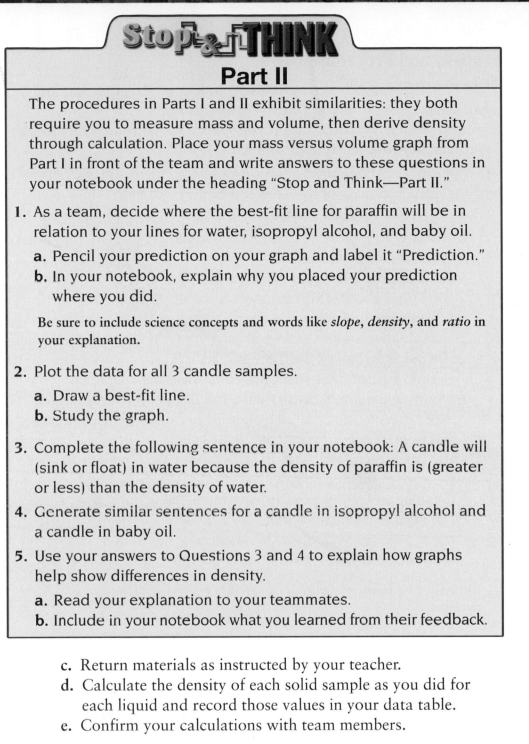

Stop & THINK

Part II

The procedures in Parts I and II exhibit similarities: they both require you to measure mass and volume, then derive density through calculation. Place your mass versus volume graph from Part I in front of the team and write answers to these questions in your notebook under the heading "Stop and Think—Part II."

1. As a team, decide where the best-fit line for paraffin will be in relation to your lines for water, isopropyl alcohol, and baby oil.
   a. Pencil your prediction on your graph and label it "Prediction."
   b. In your notebook, explain why you placed your prediction where you did.

   Be sure to include science concepts and words like *slope*, *density*, and *ratio* in your explanation.

2. Plot the data for all 3 candle samples.
   a. Draw a best-fit line.
   b. Study the graph.

3. Complete the following sentence in your notebook: A candle will (sink or float) in water because the density of paraffin is (greater or less) than the density of water.

4. Generate similar sentences for a candle in isopropyl alcohol and a candle in baby oil.

5. Use your answers to Questions 3 and 4 to explain how graphs help show differences in density.
   a. Read your explanation to your teammates.
   b. Include in your notebook what you learned from their feedback.

   c. Return materials as instructed by your teacher.
   d. Calculate the density of each solid sample as you did for each liquid and record those values in your data table.
   e. Confirm your calculations with team members.

Part III: Deciphering a Density Column

Materials

For each team of three students

1 Density of Various Materials handout

colored pencils

Process and Procedure

In Part III, you will use your understanding of density to explain what you see as your teacher slowly mixes substances of different densities. Keep a careful record in your notebook of what happens by using sketches with labels and comments.

Your wave bottles have several substances in them. What happens when *many* substances, both solids and liquids, are placed in a glass cylinder? Density is key to the answer.

▼ **Figure 2.18**
Density column with liquids. Will the solid object sink through each layer? What information do you need to make a prediction?

liquid layers of different densities

1. Meet with your team and review the data in the handout that your teacher provides.
   a. Look for differences in density.
   b. Think about which substances would sink or float in another substance.
2. Check your understanding of the data with one other teammate by quizzing him or her. Discuss which pairs of substances would sink or float when placed in the same container.
3. Analyze the liquid density data and decide what will happen if your teacher mixes all these liquids in a clear glass cylinder.
   a. Represent your prediction in a sketch.
   b. Label each layer with the substance name and density. Be sure to include units.
4. Watch carefully as your teacher mixes the liquids. Make changes to your predictions as needed.
   a. If your prediction was incorrect, explain why.
   b. Use the concept word *density* in your explanation.

Focus on the relationship between the densities of two liquids in your explanation.

5. Analyze the data for various solids. Imagine dropping each solid into the same density column before you.
   a. Make a prediction for each solid. Where will it float? How many layers will it sink through?
   b. Draw a labeled sketch to represent your prediction.
6. Repeat Step 4 except focus on solids.

Reflect and Connect

Answer the following questions individually. Record your answers in your science notebook under the heading "Reflect and Connect." After you have finished, read your answers to a class member who is *not* part of your team. Listen to his or her answers. How similar or different are your answers? Check with another team if you cannot resolve differences. Include what you learned in your notebook.

1. Your teacher needs your help. Several students from another class failed to clean up their unlabeled liquid samples. Your teacher needs you to determine the identity of each of the unlabeled samples. She labeled the samples "A," "B," and "C."

   a. Use the data in the table in figure 2.19 and the data in your science notebook to determine the identity of the unlabeled samples. Explain how you got your answers.

Material	Volume of liquid sample (mL)	Mass of cylinder with liquid sample (g)	Mass of cylinder alone (g)
Sample A	100	142.54	2.54
Sample B	100	93.21	2.54
Sample C	100	83.44	2.54

▲ **Figure 2.19**
Volume and mass for samples. What is the density of each of these samples?

   b. Is it possible to determine the identity of an unknown sample using only mass or volume data? Explain.

   c. What other information about the unlabeled samples would be helpful as you try to identify them? Explain why that new information would be helpful.

   d. If 2 samples have the same density, are they the same material? Explain your answer by using an example from outside school.

2. Density is a characteristic *physical* property of a material. Use your recent experiences to describe what that means.

3. Use your graph from Part I and Part II to answer the following question. What would you predict is the density of 1 liter (L, or 1,000 mL) of isopropyl alcohol? Of 1.35 kilograms (kg) of paraffin? Explain your answers using the concept words *slope* and *density*.

Mind over Matter

Differences in density result in differences in the way substances behave—how they function. You can *see* density differences when a candle floats in isopropyl alcohol and sinks in water or when two liquids in a wave toy form layers between them. You can also see density differences on a graph. But what is it about the underlying nature of matter that makes one substance denser than another? Is there something about *all* matter, that is invisible, that explains density? If there is, then you need a special part of your brain to answer these questions—your imagination.

In this investigation, you will imagine what might be true about matter at a level you cannot see—the microscopic level. Afterward, your mind will have a complete explanation of how different

▼ **Figure 2.20** **Student looking at abstract art.** Imagination helps you understand art *and* science concepts.

materials can have different densities. To accomplish this, you will work individually and in teams.

Materials

Process and Procedure

Density is one property of matter that is responsible for how the wave toy functions. But what makes the density of a material constant for a given temperature and pressure? Why are densities different for most substances? The answers have to do with the structure of a substance—its microscopic form. And to see that, your mind is very important.

Write answers to the following questions in your notebook under the heading "Mind over Matter." If you have difficulty, use some of the learning techniques that you practiced throughout the previous activity.

1. Check your current understanding by reading Density.
   a. Make a T-table in your notebook with the headings "Fact or Idea I Read" and "Question I have about the Fact or Idea."
   b. Fill out *both* sides of the table as you read.
   c. Share any questions you still have about density with your team or teacher and write what you learned in your notebook.

READING

Density

As you investigated different solids and liquids, you probably noticed that you were not able to measure directly the density of *any* substance. That is because density is a *derived quantity*. What does this mean? **Density** is the ratio of the material's mass to the volume it occupies. You cannot directly measure the ratio. Instead, you need to find the values for the mass and volume and use them to calculate the ratio. You can obtain a ratio by dividing the two quantities.

Because you derive density from two measurements, you express the calculated ratio as a relationship using units. If you measured a solid to be 32 g in mass and it displaced 16 mL of water in volume, you would express its density (or ratio of mass to volume) as 2.0 grams per milliliter, or 2.0 g/mL. This means that there are 2.0 g for *each* milliliter of material. If you measured a liquid to be 45 g in mass and 90 mL in volume, you could express its density as 0.5 grams per milliliter, or 0.5 g/mL. In math class, you expressed this calculation as a fraction.

The table in figure 2.21 shows the density for some of the materials commonly used in making jewelry. Notice that the table reports units for density as grams per cubic centimeter (g/cm³) instead of g/mL.

Often, scientists report density in the units grams per cubic centimeter. How are grams per milliliter related to grams per cubic centimeter?

▼ Figure 2.21 Density of precious metals and gemstones. How does the density of these precious metals and gemstones compare with the density of some of the common materials you have worked with?

Precious metal	Density (g/cm³)	Gemstone	Density (g/cm³)
Silver	10.5	Diamond	3.5
Platinum	21.1	Cubic zirconia	5.8

At room temperature and pressure, they are approximately the same: 1 milliliter = 1 cubic centimeter. For convention, however, scientists usually report the density of both liquids and solids in grams per cubic centimeter.

You have seen that mass and volume can be different for different amounts of a given material. When the volume of a material increases, the mass also increases. What happens, then, to the ratio of those two quantities (the density)? In the previous activity, you saw in graphs that the ratio of mass to volume, or the density, is the same no matter how much of the material is measured. You can see what happens with water by looking at figure 2.22.

Density is a characteristic physical property. Density is characteristic because it is useful in determining the identity of a sample of matter. Density is a physical property because you can determine it without changing the identity of the material. Scientists also call density an **intensive property** because its value does not depend on the amount of material tested. Mass and volume are also physical properties, but you would not consider them characteristic properties because they change depending on how much material you have. Scientists call properties that depend on amount **extensive properties**. Mass and volume are examples of extensive properties.

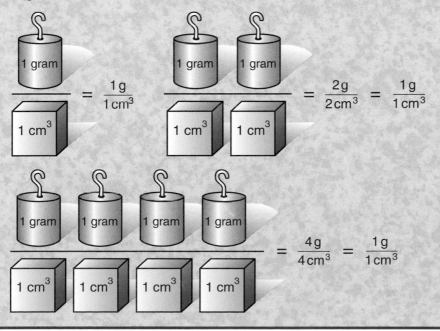

◀ **Figure 2.22 Density calculations for samples of water.** One gram of water takes up 1 cubic centimeter of volume, so the ratio of mass to volume, and therefore the density, of water is 1 g/1 cm³. As the mass and volume of water increases to 2 g/2 cm³ and then to 4 g/4 cm³, the ratio of mass to volume remains the same and the density remains 1 g/1 cm³.

Topic: extensive property of matter
Go to: www.scilinks.org
Code: 1Inquiry75

2. Use the information in the Density reading to answer the following questions in your science notebook.

a. Imagine you are looking at 2 chains that are the same in every respect except that one is made of silver and the other is made of platinum. Which would have a greater mass? Why?

b. Jewelers measure the mass of gemstones in carats. One carat is equal to 200 milligrams (mg). Which would look bigger, a 1-carat diamond or a 1-carat cubic zirconia? Why?

c. A silver ring has a density of 10.5 g/cm^3. A polished aluminum copy looks the same, but a ring with a volume of 2 mL (measured by displacement) has a mass of only 5.4 g. Compare the densities of the metals that make up the 2 rings. Record any calculations you make.

3. Listen as your teacher reads the following paragraph aloud:

You have seen in your work with solids and liquids that, regardless of how much of the material you have, the density of the material remains constant. So, theoretically, if you cut a 1 cm cube in half, then in half again, and keep cutting it repeatedly, each piece would have a smaller size but the same density as the original cube. About 400 BC a Greek scientist and philosopher named Democritus thought about this and what it meant about the fundamental composition of matter. Imagine what would happen if you could go back in history to interview him.

4. To understand more about Democritus and his thinking, read An Interview with Democritus as instructed by your teacher.

READING

An Interview with Democritus

▶ **Figure 2.23**
Ancient Greek amphitheater. Theater productions help you imagine times long past. How does imagination help scientists "see" the invisible world of atoms and molecules?

STUDENT 1: Wow! This is an incredible place. Is it always this busy in Athens?

DEMOCRITUS: Yes, it is. This is the most exciting time to be living in Greece. We are at the center of a great civilization. With our seaport, we have many people coming and going. People are busy trading raw materials, designing new products, producing artwork, and thinking up new ideas.

STUDENT 2: It must have been exciting growing up in such a powerful place.

DEMOCRITUS: Actually, I grew up in a small place called Abdera. I was not from one of the richest families in Greece, and I didn't live in a prestigious and powerful place like Athens or Sparta. But life wasn't too tough for me. We were wealthy enough that I got to travel and study philosophy and science without having to worry about making a living.

STUDENT 1: Why did you study both philosophy and science? Aren't they very different subjects?

DEMOCRITUS: Well, people around here are asking many questions about things that are too large, too distant, or too small for us to see. In Greece, we are only just starting to do experiments to find out things about the natural world. So, instead, we come up with ideas by thinking about what we already know. My background in philosophy and science really helps.

STUDENT 2: You would be amazed at some of the equipment and technology we have in the future to study nature. How do the Greeks study nature if they don't perform many experiments?

DEMOCRITUS: We use models to help us understand our ideas, even when we do not have any way to test them.

STUDENT 1: Can you give us an example?

DEMOCRITUS: Well, I have spent a lot of time thinking about the properties of substances. I know that some properties of a substance are characteristic no matter how much or how little of the substance there is. For example, alcohol always smells funny, iron always rusts, and lead is much denser than air, even when there is only a little of each substance. I have been thinking about what would happen if I kept splitting a sample of a substance. With a sharp knife (and a steady hand), I figure a sample could be split many times.

STUDENT 2: Have you ever tried it?

DEMOCRITUS: I have tried it with big samples of substances, and I see no reason why the splitting could not continue beyond that which could be done by hand. I imagine the splitting process continuing, resulting in smaller and smaller pieces.

STUDENT 1: So you could continue to split a sample of a substance forever?

DEMOCRITUS: I don't know for sure. I can't see anything that small, but I do not think the process could go on forever. I believe there is a limit to how small something can be to keep the characteristic properties it has as a larger piece. I have decided to call these fundamentally small particles of a substance *atomos*, which means "cannot be further divided." I have based my model for matter on these small particles.

STUDENT 2: Today, we call those small particles **atoms**.

DEMOCRITUS: So I was right?

STUDENT 2: Atoms, just as you imagined, are so small that we can only see them with the help of our modern technology. We have performed enough tests on substances to know that your idea about atoms makes sense. Our modern atomic theory is based on your ideas.

DEMOCRITUS: I knew it! You see, some substances are heavier than others, even in very small amounts. Substances differ from each other in many additional ways, such as color, hardness, melting point, and freezing point. I have always thought that the particles that make up these substances, or what you call atoms, must be unique in some way to account for these characteristic differences. A water atom, for instance, is very different from a lead atom.

STUDENT 1: Ah! That is where our modern technology has advanced our understanding of matter beyond your ideas. We now know that

Topic: element
Go to: www.scilinks.org
Code: 1Inquiry78a

there are fewer than 100 naturally occurring **elements**. The smallest particle of an element is an atom of that element. So you can have an atom of lead. But you can't have an atom of water.

DEMOCRITUS: Why not? Water is a fundamental substance.

STUDENT 1: You are right there. But the basic unit that makes up water is not an atom, but a molecule. When atoms of different elements combine, a **compound** is formed. Water is a compound, whose smallest unit is a **molecule**.

Topic: molecule
Go to: www.scilinks.org
Code: 1Inquiry78b

In the case of water, two hydrogen atoms combine with one oxygen atom to form a molecule of water. If you break the molecule apart, water no longer exists.

DEMOCRITUS: So my ideas still work for water, but I must think of the fundamental particle of water as a molecule rather than an atom.

STUDENT 2: That's right. A water molecule is unique. When you get many, many of them together, you have enough water to observe. Water has many observable characteristic properties. A drop of water has the same characteristic properties as a liter of water and a bathtub full of water.

DEMOCRITUS: I could have told you that! My ideas still work, even though I was confused about water.

STUDENT 1: Yes. Your ideas apply equally to elements that can be divided down to one atom and compounds that can be divided down to one molecule. We call these materials **pure substances**. Pure substances are different from mixtures, which are physical combinations of substances. Pure substances always have the same characteristic properties. **Mixtures** might have some of the same properties, but often have new properties. For example, when we combine iron, nickel,

Topic: mixture of substances
Go to: www.scilinks.org
Code: 1Inquiry78c

carbon, and other metals, we make a mixture called steel. The mixture is harder than any of the pure substances.

DEMOCRITUS: I am excited to learn that my ideas and models have had lasting influence on science.

STUDENT 2: Not only that, but your name is still important to modern Greek people. They have named a major university and an important nuclear research facility after you. They even put you on their 100 dracma banknote.

DEMOCRITUS: And I thought that only Aristotle and his teacher Plato would be famous. It just shows you what a simple man from a small town can do.

5. Check your understanding of this reading by discussing these questions with your team and recording your answers in your notebook.

   a. According to the ideas of Democritus, what might account for 1 cm³ of one substance being heavier than 1 cm³ of another substance?

   b. If a large piece of iron has a density of 7.9 g/cm³, then what is the density of a small piece of iron? How do you know without measurements and calculations?

Reflect and Connect

Write answers to the following questions in your notebook under the heading "Reflect and Connect."

1. Read the following information and use it to answer Questions 1a–d.

Water has a density of 1 g/cm³. Graphite, used to make pencil lead, has a density of 2.25 g/cm³. The wood portion of a pencil is typically cedar, which has a density around 0.5 g/cm³.

    a. What would a mass versus volume graph showing the density of these 3 materials look like? Make a quick sketch to illustrate your answer. Include highlight comments and a caption.

    b. Draw a diagram showing how a piece of graphite and a piece of cedar would be positioned in a large container of water.

    c. Describe how the lines on your graph support your placement of the graphite, cedar, and water in your diagram.

    d. Is this enough data to predict whether an actual pencil would float or sink in water? Explain your answer.

2. As shown in figure 2.24, the densities of most woods are reported as a range of values. The densities of most pure metals, such as silver and platinum, are reported as a single value. Explain why this is so.

▼ **Figure 2.24**
Density of various woods. Why are the densities of most woods reported as a range of values instead of a single value?

Wood (seasoned)	Density (g/cm³)	Wood (seasoned)	Density (g/cm³)
Balsa	0.11–0.14	Maple	0.62–0.75
Cedar	0.49–0.57	Oak	0.60–0.90
Cherry	0.70–0.90	Pine, white	0.35–0.50
Ebony	1.11–1.33	Teak, Indian	0.66–0.88

3. A student observes that an ice cube floats in water, but sinks in rubbing alcohol. Draw 2 sketches representing these observations at the microscopic level. Use dots made by your pen or pencil to represent the microscopic particles Democritus imagined. Use 50 dots to represent the ice cube and 100 dots to represent each liquid. Include highlight comments in the "What I See," "What it Means" format in each sketch.

Don't forget that you can represent the amount of space between particles by changing the distance between dots.

4. Describe a situation where a consumer uses characteristic properties to make informed decisions (optional).

Read the sidebar, Genuine Gemstones, to learn how you can use characteristic properties to determine if a gemstone is genuine.

Genuine Gemstones

You just got a new ring. It sparkles like a diamond. But is it a diamond? How can you tell? Right now, there are three diamond-like gemstones available in the market: diamonds, cubic zirconia, and moissanite. Gemstones can be natural or they can be synthetic. **Synthetic** gemstones are manufactured stones.

Diamonds are made of carbon, the same element found in pencil lead and charcoal. Most diamonds are natural, formed by pressure and heat far below Earth's surface. Synthetic diamonds do exist, but jewelers do not use them because of their high cost. Also they are typically smaller and used for industrial purposes such as diamond coatings on drills. Synthetic diamonds have the same properties as natural diamonds.

You might be familiar with other synthetic gemstones that look much like diamonds. Cubic zirconia is a popular synthetic gemstone made of zirconium oxide. Because cubic zirconia looks like a diamond, jewelers consider it a diamond simulant. Cubic zirconia is popular because it is much less expensive than diamond. The cost of a one-carat cubic zirconia is about 1/1000 the cost of a one-carat diamond.

Moissanite is another diamond simulant. It is made of silicon carbide. Jewelry containing synthetic moissanite first appeared in 1998. Until that time, the semiconductor industry was the principal user of synthetic moissanite. Natural moissanite does exist. Henri Moissan, a Nobel Prize–winning scientist, first discovered natural moissanite in 1893. He found it hidden within the fragments of an ancient meteorite found in Diablo Canyon, Arizona. Because the supply of natural moissanite is so limited, the jewelry industry does not use it. Instead, the jewelry industry uses the synthetic stone. The cost of a one-carat synthetic moissanite is about 1/10 the cost of a one-carat diamond.

So how can a jeweler tell the diamond from the diamond look-alikes? The chart in figure 2.25 summarizes some of the physical properties jewelers use to distinguish one gemstone from another. Jewelers use a thermal probe to identify diamonds. The probe detects how well the gemstone conducts heat. When a jeweler touches a diamond with the thermal probe, it registers green. When the probe touches a cubic zirconia, it registers red. What about moissanite? The chart shows it conducts heat just like diamond. The thermal probe cannot distinguish between the diamond and the moissanite. However, a jeweler can take a closer look at the stones through a microscope. Under magnification, the cut edges of a moissanite appear as double edges, while those of a diamond appear as single edges. In addition, a moissanite does not have any of the natural flaws that a diamond does. When in doubt, jewelers can do added tests based on other physical properties of the gemstones.

▼ Figure 2.25 **Physical properties of diamond and diamond-like gemstones.**
How can physical properties help you tell the difference between three sparkling gemstones?

Gemstone	Density (g/cm^3)	Thermal conductivity	Hardness	Refractive index
Diamond (C)	3.52	high	10.0	2.42 singly refractive
Cubic zirconia (ZrO$_2$)	5.65–5.95	low	8.50	2.17 singly refractive
Moissante (SiC)	3.1–3.20	high	9.25	2.6–2.7 doubly refractive

Reacting to Density

By now, you understand how density plays a part in designing a properly functioning wave toy. What would happen to the wave toy if the materials reacted chemically? Would the wave toy keep its original appearance? Would it function the same way?

In the Reacting to Density activity, you will apply what you know about physical properties to understanding some important features of chemical properties. **Chemical properties** describe how a material reacts or fails to react in the presence of another material to form new materials. To accomplish this, you will try to understand chemical properties from two viewpoints, macroscopic and microscopic. Together, these two viewpoints will help you form a more complete understanding of matter. What might this understanding do? You will be able to put all sorts of matter to better use, both for your benefit and the benefit of others. You will work with partners, teams of four, and your entire class during this investigation.

Part I: Antacid Tablets and Water

Materials
For each team of two students

2 pairs of safety goggles

2 lab aprons

1 25-mL graduated cylinder

1 250-mL beaker

1 balance

1 antacid tablet (broken in half)

25 mL of water

1 balloon

1 empty 20-ounce plastic soda bottle with cap

1 piece of paper towel

1 short candle with a small piece of clay on bottom

matches or lighter with long barrel

▲ **Figure 2.26**
Chemical reaction of materials. Some nail polish removers can dissolve plastics. Do toy manufacturers use fingernail polish remover in wave toys?

Cautions

Always wear safety goggles in the lab, particularly when you are investigating chemical reactions. Be careful around an open flame. Make sure you have water available to put out the flame and that you tie back long hair.

Process and Procedure

In Part I of this activity, your goal is to capture all the products of the reaction between an antacid tablet and water. The reaction will take place in a plastic soda bottle. You will use what you already know about the particle nature of atoms and molecules to understand the macroscopic behavior you observe resulting from this chemical reaction. Record your observations and answer questions under the heading "Reacting to Density."

Caution Wear safety goggles and lab aprons.

1. Put on your safety goggles and lab aprons and gather all your materials at a location where your teacher tells you to conduct this investigation.
2. Combine 2 teams of 2 students each to form teams of 4.
3. Decide at least 2 ways to trap *all* reaction products in the soda bottle when you drop 1/2 of an antacid tablet into the bottle that already has 25 mL of water in it.

One team of two will try one of these methods. The other team will try the other.

What if one of the products is a gas? How could the balloon trap the gas? How could a bottle cap trap the gas?

   a. Draw a sketch of your setup and label all the parts, including the names of any chemical substances you know.
   b. Sketch the other teams' setup in your notebook and include labels.

Each team will use a different method of capturing all the reaction products.

4. Determine a way to monitor whether the soda bottle lost *any* material during the reaction and write this procedure under each sketch.

Pretend you measured your body mass by standing on a bathroom scale before *and* after taking off your shoes. How could you tell if you lost mass?

5. Ask your teacher to approve your procedure.
6. Conduct your experiment and record observations of the bottles from *both* teams. Use carefully labeled sketches.

Did you note any changes in the shape of the bottle? The balloon? Did you observe any changes in the antacid tablet? The water? Was there a difference in the mass of the bottle and its contents, including either the cap or balloon?

7. Determine whether both teams were successful in capturing *all* the materials from the reaction between an antacid tablet and water.
8. Remove the cap and balloon and record what you see, hear, and feel.

9. Determine if the material that exited the balloon or bottle had any mass.

Don't forget to place either the balloon or cap back on the balance.

10. Decide how to determine if the gas produced by the reaction will extinguish a candle flame.

You do not need to know which gas this is in order to complete this step. Place a candle in the bottom of a dry 250-mL beaker and light it. If you tip the bottle gently, the gas remaining in the soda bottle will pour out of the bottle as though it were a liquid—*if* you tip the bottle *gently*.

11. Create labeled *before* and *after* sketches showing what happened.

12. Read the following paragraph and use the information to accomplish 12a–d:

You learned in earlier grades that chemical reactions produce products with different physical *and* chemical properties than the original reactants. In this reaction, antacid tablets, mostly sodium bicarbonate, and water were reactants, and carbon dioxide gas was one of the products. Democritus might say the invisible particles that compose the product materials must be different in some ways from the reactant particles. These differences result in observations such as the production of gases, color changes, formation of a solid when there was none, and release or absorption of heat. Regardless of these changes, the tiniest particles Democritus imagined, atoms, retain their characteristic mass. They recombine to form new molecules, but every atom of reactant matter becomes an atom of product matter. In previous science classes, you probably called this idea, the **law of conservation of matter.**

Topic: law of conservation of matter
Go to: www.scilinks.org
Code: 1Inquiry83

   a. Make a double T-table with the following headings at the top of each column: "What I Observed," "Evidence For or Against," and "How I Know."
   b. List each important observation from both bottles in the first column.
   c. Write in column 2 whether the observation is evidence *for* or *against* a chemical reaction taking place.
   d. Explain in the final column how you know your answer to 12c is correct.

13. Use a double T-table as in Step 12a to answer the following question: What evidence from this activity supports the idea that this chemical reaction demonstrates the law of conservation of matter?

Stop & THINK

Part I

Meet with at least one other team and discuss the following tasks and questions. Consult with your teacher if you cannot reach agreement. Write answers in your notebook under the heading "Stop and Think—Part I."

1. The gas produced was carbon dioxide, the same gas we exhale during breathing. Suppose both the cap and balloon methods captured exactly 50 particles (molecules) of carbon dioxide (there were actually vastly more).

   a. Sketch these gas particles for both methods (balloon and cap) and include highlight comments and captions for each sketch.

   Consider how far apart your dots are, how many there are, and if they should be grouped in one place inside the bottle or distributed evenly.

   b. Why should there be the same number of gas particles in each bottle, provided the amount of water and the size of the tablet were the same?

   c. Are the carbon dioxide particles moving or stationary? How do you know?

   Reflect on your observations from Step 6. What prevents the balloon from collapsing due to the room's air pressure?

   d. Illustrate your answer to 1c on the drawings you made in 1a.

2. In which method is the pressure inside the bottle the greatest? What evidence supports your answer?

3. In which method is the density of the carbon dioxide gas the greatest? What evidence supports your answer?

4. In light of your answers to Questions 1, 2, and 3, show with a sketch graph the relationship between density and pressure for a gas like carbon dioxide at a constant temperature. Include highlight comments and a caption as you have done in prior activities.

   Note: Place density on the vertical axis and pressure on the horizontal axis.

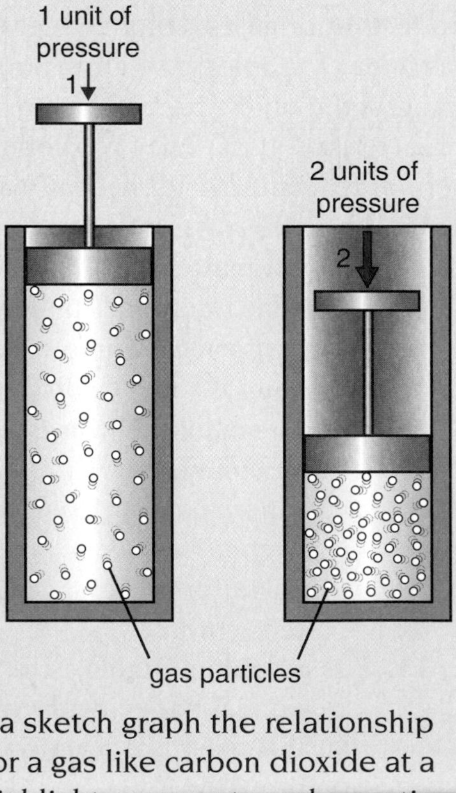

▶ **Figure 2.27**
Piston with gas particles in cylinder. Particles collide with each other and the cylinder walls in random motion to create pressure. Is the pressure inside (caused by the captured gas) and outside (caused by air *and* the piston) the piston equal? How do you know? What should happen if it weren't?

1 unit of pressure

2 units of pressure

gas particles

Part II: Candle Combustion

Materials
For each team of two students

2 pairs of safety goggles

2 lab aprons

1 balance

1 candle

matches (several)

ball-and-stick molecule kit or student-made models

Cautions

Always wear safety goggles in the lab, particularly when you are investigating chemical reactions. Be careful around an open flame. Make sure you have water available to put out the flame and that you tie back long hair.

Process and Procedure

Candle wax burns in air in a process called *combustion*. This reaction fuels much of our modern lifestyle. Gasoline in cars and coal in electrical generating plants burn by combining chemically with oxygen in the air to produce mostly carbon dioxide and water. What is happening at the microscopic level?

In this part of the activity, you will work with a partner to observe a common combustion reaction, and then use your imagination to picture what might be happening to the tiny particles that participate in combustion. To help, you will use models to represent atoms and molecules that you cannot see.

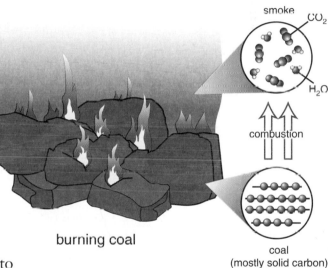

▼ **Figure 2.28**
Lump of coal burning.
Scientists think that microscopic particles of coal interact with particles in the air to make combustion products and heat energy. But what does the reaction really look like?

1. Decide with your partner how to *demonstrate* that a candle burning for 2 minutes represents a chemical reaction.
   a. Apply what you have learned in this chapter and discuss some ideas with teammates.
   b. Record your procedure in your notebook.
   c. Have your teacher approve your procedure.

Don't forget to include conservation of matter along with observations of changes of physical and chemical properties and temperature changes.

2. Conduct your experiment.
   a. Draw detailed sketches of the candle *before* and *after* burning.

Caution — Wear safety goggles and lab aprons.

b. Label both sketches using *at least* the following words: *solid, liquid, gas, wick, flame, temperature change,* and *mass.*

3. Take turns and read the following paragraphs to each other aloud:

In nature, every atom remains the same throughout its existence in everyday chemical reactions, even though it might combine with different atoms to make new molecules as in combustion. But you cannot see an atom. Models and symbols help. For example, natural gas, also called methane, is a fuel similar in some ways to coal or gasoline. Its molecule has 1 carbon atom and 4 hydrogen atoms. The symbols CH_4 represent this molecule, where C stands for carbon, *H* for hydrogen, and *4* means 4 hydrogen atoms.

Physical models allow you to imagine what atoms and molecules look like. Scientists sometimes picture atoms as hard spheres of different diameters and masses. Forces of attraction called chemical bonds hold atoms close to each other to form molecules. With this model, methane has 1 carbon atom surrounded by 4 hydrogen atoms to make 1 methane molecule. Bonds hold hydrogen to the carbon atom. Methane is an example of a saturated hydrocarbon fuel because it has the maximum amount of hydrogen possible for carbon. Other common saturated hydrocarbons include propane and butane.

4. Build physical models of the reactant and product molecules for the combustion of methane as instructed by your teacher.

Remember that reactants for this combustion reaction are methane, CH_4, and oxygen gas, O_2. Product molecules for complete combustion are carbon dioxide, CO_2, and water, H_2O.

5. Consider with your team how you could use a balance to help you model conservation of matter with the molecules you constructed.

Models often make atoms of carbon, oxygen, and hydrogen the same size and mass, but different colors. For actual atoms, size and mass differ.

a. Sketch each molecule in your notebook.
b. Label each atom with its proper symbol and state whether it is part of a reactant or product molecule.

Small sticks can represent bonds. At the microscopic level, bonds have no mass. They are only forces of attraction.

c. Build more of any molecule required in order to demonstrate conservation of matter at the atomic level.
d. Make a detailed sketch of *all* your model molecules once you have the mass of the reactants and products in the relationship you desire.
e. Write the correct symbols for each molecule under its appropriate sketch.

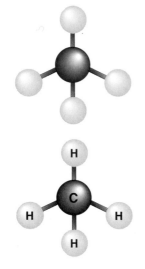

▲ **Figure 2.29**
Ball-and-stick model of methane. This physical model represents one molecule of methane.

Stop & THINK

Part II

Discuss these questions with 1 or 2 teams. Write answers in your notebook that reflect your best understanding of what the group decided. Place those answers under the heading "Stop and Think—Part II." Consult with your teacher if the discussion leaves you feeling unsure of any answers.

1. Which half of the reaction, reactant or product, had a greater mass when you constructed only 1 molecule each of methane, oxygen, carbon dioxide, and water? Explain why, using the correct symbols for each atom and the law of conservation and matter.

2. Which molecules did you have to build more of in order to show conservation of matter? Explain how you selected which molecules and how many.

3. Explain why the mass of your candle changed after 2 minutes of combustion, considering the law of conservation of matter and the procedure you used.

4. What steps did you take in the antacid tablet in water reaction that were different from the candle burning reaction in regard to conservation of matter? Explain why those steps worked or didn't work.

▼ **Figure 2.30**
Steaming tea kettle and clouds. Steam is actually liquid water condensed on tiny dust particles in the air. Water vapor, the gas phase of water, is colorless and transparent, therefore invisible to you. How does this fact relate to clouds?

Part III: Phases of Matter

Materials
For each team of two students

2 pairs of safety goggles

2 lab aprons

candle

matches

Process and Procedure

You will work with your partner to look carefully for different phases of matter. Everyday experience reminds you of 3 phases: solid, liquid, and gas. How do these phases of matter differ at the microscopic level? The energy of a burning candle can help you answer that question. Keep a record of your observations under the heading "Part III: Phases of Matter."

▲ **Figure 2.31**
Fuel system in car engine. Gasoline changes to vapor inside the piston and combusts to form exhaust products. The piston is made of metal. The combustion chamber is where gasoline changes to vapor.

▶ **Figure 2.32**
Paint thinner and hot water heater. Liquid paint thinner molecules change to gaseous paint thinner molecules even at room temperature. Gas can travel to the flame under the hot water heater. Why is this a safety hazard?

1. Study a burning candle.
2. Sketch a close-up of the parts of the candle you think are solid and liquid.
   a. What is required to change candle wax from the solid phase to the liquid phase?
   b. In which phase of matter, solid, liquid, or gas, do particles move about most freely?
   c. Next to the appropriate part of the candle drawing, sketch a *microscopic* view of candle wax particles in the solid and liquid phases.

How will you illustrate what you answered in 2a–b?

   d. Include highlight comments for both sketches in the "What I see," "What it means" format.
3. Blow out the candle and determine if there is a white trail of particles rising from the extinguished wick.
4. Decide how to test if the white trail observed in Step 3 is made of fuel particles (candle wax) or not.

Fuel will ignite easily if it is in the gas phase, just like gasoline in the fuel injectors of automobile engines or paint thinner left too close to a hot water heater.

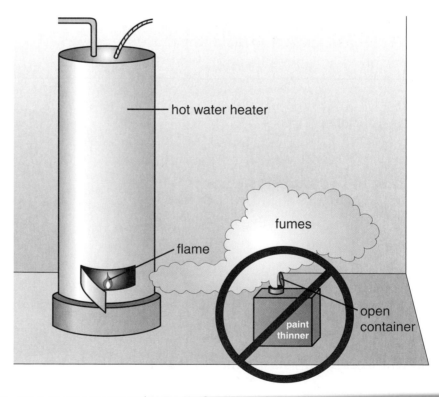

hot water heater

fumes

flame

paint thinner

open container

5. Repeat Steps 2a–d except focus on the transition from liquid to gas, not the transition from solid to liquid.

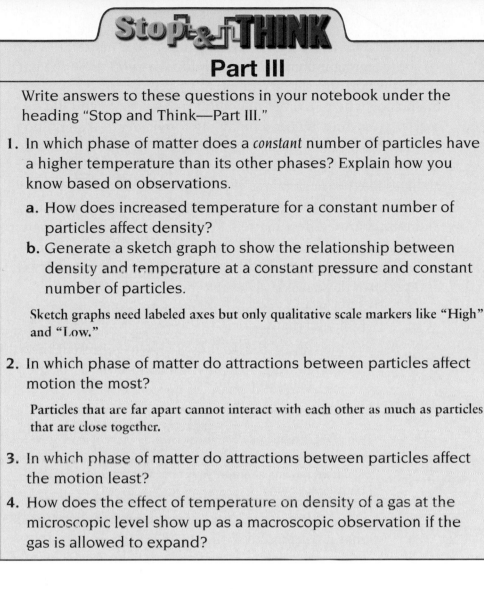

Stop & THINK

Part III

Write answers to these questions in your notebook under the heading "Stop and Think—Part III."

1. In which phase of matter does a *constant* number of particles have a higher temperature than its other phases? Explain how you know based on observations.

   a. How does increased temperature for a constant number of particles affect density?

   b. Generate a sketch graph to show the relationship between density and temperature at a constant pressure and constant number of particles.

   Sketch graphs need labeled axes but only qualitative scale markers like "High" and "Low."

2. In which phase of matter do attractions between particles affect motion the most?

   Particles that are far apart cannot interact with each other as much as particles that are close together.

3. In which phase of matter do attractions between particles affect the motion least?

4. How does the effect of temperature on density of a gas at the microscopic level show up as a macroscopic observation if the gas is allowed to expand?

Reflect and Connect

Write answers to these questions in your science notebook under the heading "Reflect and Connect." Consult with your teacher or classmates when you are not certain of an answer.

1. Decide whether each of the following is a physical change or a chemical change. Explain your reasoning based on your past observations and experiences.
   a. An egg frying, but not burning
   b. A piggy bank breaking
   c. A cake baking
   d. Milk spoiling
   e. Hydrogen peroxide bubbling when poured over a wound
   f. Table salt dissolving

2. Hydrogen peroxide (H_2O_2) particles decompose into water (H_2O) and oxygen gas (O_2) particles. Represent this chemical reaction at the microscopic level with a drawing.

a. Under *each* microscopic representation of a material, write a short highlight comment explaining why you drew the particle the size and shape you did.

b. Include why you drew the *number* of particles you did.

c. Use your drawings and highlight comments to explain how your drawings represent the law of conservation of matter.

3. Does the law of conservation of matter apply to physical changes like phase changes? If so, demonstrate this in a sketch.

4. Figure 2.33 is called a phase diagram. It shows how pressure and temperature affect matter. Notice how the phase of matter changes depending on temperature and pressure. Use your observations from Parts I, II, and III to answer these questions and perform these tasks.

> **a.** Sketch this figure in your notebook.
>
> **b.** Label the figure with the correct phase name for the section that is most likely to represent the temperature and pressure conditions associated with the solid phase of matter.
>
> **c.** Include highlight comments for that section.

> **Don't forget to include comments stating if the temperature and pressure are relatively high or low in the "What I see" part. Include comments about microscopic and macroscopic viewpoints in the "What it means" part.**

5. Draw a horizontal line across the phase diagram so that it touches all 3 phases of matter.

> **a.** Imagine being a particle experiencing the temperatures and pressures indicated by your line.

b. Describe what you would see and feel from the macroscopic and microscopic viewpoints.

▼ **Figure 2.33**

Phase diagram. A phase diagram shows what kind of pressure and temperature conditions exist for each phase.

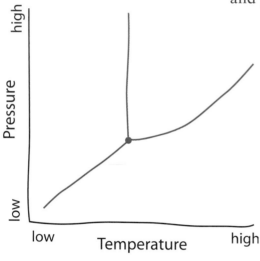

Properties "Я" Us!

Knowing about characteristic properties is vital to people who want to understand why products like wave toys function as they do. What about a product you haven't seen yet? Can you use your knowledge about physical and chemical properties to decipher how it behaves? If you can, you will have strong evidence of how much you have learned in this chapter.

Figure 2.34 shows a unique science toy available for sale in many specialty shops. It is a thermometer. Several glass balls, partially filled with materials of different colors, float in a clear, colorless liquid. How does it work? What aspects of your knowledge of characteristic properties help you understand a product you haven't seen before? Figure 2.35 shows what happens to the small glass balls inside the glass cylinder when a hair dryer blows hot air on the outside glass tube.

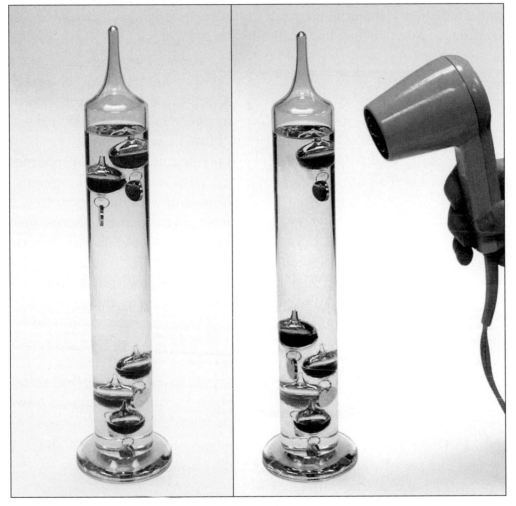

◀ **Figure 2.34**
Galilean thermometer. The balls move up and down as a function of temperature. Why? What characteristic properties change?

◀ **Figure 2.35**
Galilean thermometer with hair dryer. What properties are important to understand in order to determine how this thermometer functions when it is heated? Are there chemical reactions taking place?

In this evaluate activity, you will work alone, in small groups, and with your teacher to demonstrate how well you understand characteristic properties. From their feedback, you will pinpoint what you understood from chapter 2 and learn how to clarify any lingering confusion.

Review the scoring rubric *before you start*. It will help you get the best performance for the least amount of your time.

Part I: Sales Pitch

Materials
For each team of four students

pen or pencil

4 copies of the Properties "Я" Us! Scoring Rubric

Process and Procedures

Many successful businesspeople understand chemical and physical properties. What they know helps them explain their products to potential clients. Imagine their sales performance when clients have confidence in what they know and understand.

You will be a top salesperson making a sales pitch to sell the thermometers shown in figure 2.34. The client asks, "How does it work?" Fortunately, you have prepared a 1-page handout that explains how your product functions from 2 viewpoints: macroscopic *and* microscopic. In Part I, your teacher will perform a demonstration to help you understand why the thermometers shown in figures 2.34 and 2.35 behave as they do. Then you will make a 1-page sales handout that helps your customer understand how the thermometer functions.

▲ **Figure 2.36**
Sales meeting presentation. An understanding of science concepts and knowledge helps you make effective presentations.

1. Draw a sketch of the spring scale and object suspended above a beaker of water as demonstrated by your teacher.
   a. Label all the parts.
   b. Record the mass of the object dangling from the scale.
2. Predict what the apparatus will look like when your teacher lowers the mass into the water.
   a. Draw a detailed sketch to represent your prediction.
   b. Include a short caption, detailing why you think your prediction is correct.

Don't forget to predict what will happen to the scale's reading.

3. Turn and talk about your prediction to a nearby classmate.
   a. Point to each feature of your prediction drawing and explain what it means.
   b. Listen to what your classmate says.
4. Observe what happens when your teacher lowers the mass into the water.

Be certain to modify your sketch to reflect anything that was different than your prediction.

Stop & THINK

Part I

1. Turn and discuss the following questions with a classmate. Consult with your teacher if both of you are unsure of an answer.

   a. Did the density of the dangling object change? How do you know?

   b. What happened to the mass and volume of the object? Use numbers based on your observations.

   c. How does the volume of water displaced by the object compare with the volume of the object?

   Write your answer as a ratio of one number divided by another with proper labels and units. Explain what your ratio means.

   d. What is the relationship between the mass of water displaced by the object and the *change* in the scale's reading?

   Express your answer as a ratio with proper units and labels. Explain what the ratio means.

   e. How does the mass of air displaced by the object compare with the mass of water displaced?

   Write your answer as a ratio of the largest number divided by the smallest number, using proper units and labels. Explain what your ratio means about the relative densities of the solid material and air.

2. Use the thermometer shown in figure 2.34 to answer Questions 2a–b.

   a. In which condition, cool or warm, is the liquid *outside* the balls more dense than the balls?

   b. Explain your reasoning with a sketch at microscopic scale. Include a caption explaining what the sketch shows.

   Remember how temperature affects the density of solid, liquid, and gas phases.

3. Draw a double T-table and place the headings "feature," "similarities," and "differences" at the top of each column.

   a. Under "feature," list "materials suspended in fluid," "fluid," and "temperature." Write all the similarities and differences you can think of between the demonstration you just saw and the unique thermometer shown in figures 2.34 and 2.35.

   b. Compare your table with a classmate's from the opposite side of the room.

   c. Make additions to your chart based on what you learn.

4. Now, on your own, you are ready to make your sales pitch. It will be in the form of a 1-page handout on unlined paper. Your handout

Part I continued

will explain how the thermometer functions macroscopically based on microscopic form. Think of modern advertisements. Sketches and captions are more important than long paragraphs of text. Your handout should have the following features:

- Two large sketches of the thermometer at 2 different temperatures
- Enlargements of 1 ball and the surrounding fluid at both temperatures; these drawings should show what is happening at the microscopic level, including the motion and distribution associated with particles
- Labels and captions for all significant features of the thermometer

Part II: What's Wrong with the Competition?

Materials
For each team of two or three students

unlined notebook paper

pencil

colored pencils (optional)

2–3 copies of What's Wrong with the Competition? handout

Process and Procedure

One of your competitors offers your client an alternative handout. Only your thorough understanding of physical and chemical properties will help you spot the mistakes. How will noticing flaws in your competitor's explanation affect your sales performance?

1. Form a team of 2 or 3 students to evaluate the sales handout your teacher gives you.
   a. Look for features that are correct *and* incorrect.
   b. Consult with another group if the team cannot reach consensus.
2. Draw a double T-table in your notebook and place the headings "feature," "correct," and "incorrect" at the top of each column.
   a. List all the important features of the handout in the "feature" column.
   b. Write what is correct and what is incorrect about each feature in the appropriate column.

Part III: More Questions

Materials
For each student

pen or pencil

Process and Procedure

The differences between your explanation and your competitor's explanation make the client ask more questions. Your answers will determine whom your client selects.

1. Consider the air pocket at the top of the thermometer.
   a. What is the purpose of the air pocket at the top of the glass column?
   b. What would happen if it were not there?

Explain your understanding with sketches of the air pocket under cool and warm conditions. Include captions.

2. Are the masses dangling from each ball the same number of grams? If not, what is the trend from top to bottom? Explain the trend.
3. How does the density of each ball vary with temperature? How do you know?
4. What type of characteristic property must toy designers consider besides physical properties? Explain how this other type of property of matter affects the reliability of your thermometer's performance. Give a specific example.
5. Sketch a graph of density as a function of temperature by completing 5a–b.
   a. Draw a line that represents the relationship between density and temperature *for the liquid* outside the floating balls.
   b. Perform the same task for the balls.

Include all the materials that make up the ball including glass, liquid, and the small weight which dangles from each ball.

Include highlight comments and captions under each graph.

6. Which of the materials used in chapter 2 would be best to use for the *outside* liquid of your thermometer?

Use your understanding of characteristic properties to explain why.

7. Repeat Step 5a for the liquid *inside* the balls and the matter dangling from each ball.

CHAPTER 3

Get a Charge Out of Matter

Get a Charge Out of Matter

There is something wonderful about understanding matter. You can design successful products such as wave toys and thermometers. Does your understanding include why some liquids in your wave bottle are mutually soluble and others are not? Is density the only reason for layers? Remember how a candle floats in water, but not in isopropyl alcohol. What about the little penguin in the wave toy? Why doesn't it dissolve? Did any solids dissolve in water or in the isopropyl alcohol and baby oil that you used in the wave bottle activity?

You have more to learn about physical and chemical properties. It seems that the invisible particles Democritus theorized about are more complex than anyone first imagined. These microscopic particles interact, forming invisible connections. The result sometimes leads to one substance dissolving in another. What is it about particles that makes some of them interact to form new particles? Do new particles exhibit the same physical and chemical properties as the original ones? Why or why not?

Interactions between microscopically sized particles are called bonds in some circumstances and intermolecular forces in other situations. These interactions explain why some liquids mix together to form solutions and other liquids separate into layers. Atomic-sized interactions also explain why some solids seem to disappear when placed in water while others keep their form for a long time. Bonding explains why certain compounds form and others do not. Bonding even helps explain how the electricity in lightning conducts through a tree, as shown in the this photograph.

Do trees ordinarily conduct electricity? Is it the wood or the water inside the tree that conducts electricity?

Goals for the Chapter

It is natural to be curious about these interactions. Understanding the nature of these interactions gives you a more complete picture of how everyday objects, such as wave toys, function. When you have completed chapter 3, Get a Charge Out of Matter, you will be able to apply your knowledge to new products and processes. To accomplish this, you will seek answers to the following questions:

- What happens when atoms interact with other atoms?
- How does chemical bonding explain properties of different compounds?
- How does bonding *within* molecules affect interactions between molecules?
- How can different models of microscopic behavior help explain the macroscopic behavior of compounds?

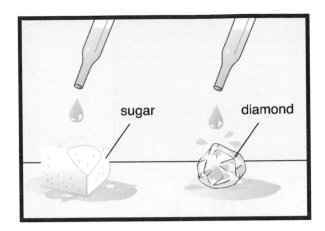

▲ Figure 3.1 **Differences in dissolving.** A cube of sugar easily dissolves in water, but a diamond does not. What is different about their microscopic interactions?

You will answer those questions by participating in the following activities:

ENGAGE	What's Shocking?
EXPLORE	Particular Properties
EXPLAIN	The Solution to Solutions
EXPLAIN	Charge Those Particles
ELABORATE	Caffeine Full or Caffeine Free?
EVALUATE	A Clean Performance

Your chapter organizer helps you monitor what you are learning. Look at it every day before class. Think about where you are with regard to its flow and organization. If you think you are falling behind or you are confused, consult with your teacher immediately. Your feelings represent important data. Successful people use those data to monitor their understanding. They seek help when they are falling behind or are not sure what to do next.

Linking Question

How does the property of electrical conductivity sort materials into categories?

ENGAGE

What's Shocking?

Key Idea:

Pure water doesn't conduct electricity; some water solutions do.

EXPLORE

Particular Properties

Key Idea:

Characteristics of the charge of materials help classify matter.

Linking Question

How do the characteristics of the charge of particles explain why some materials dissolve in water and others do not?

Get a Charge Out of Matter

EXPLAIN

The Solution to Solutions

Key Idea:

The way and extent that particles become charged affects how they interact with water.

Linking Question

Is there a way to predict the distribution of charge in particles?

A Clean Performance

Key Idea:
Plus-minus interactions explain the
dry cleaning process at the microscopic level.

How do the substances used
in the dry cleaning process
demonstrate interactions
between charges?

ELABORATE

CHAPTER	
3	**Major Concepts**

Caffeine Full or Caffeine Free?

Key Idea:
The way a charge
distributes in caffeine
affects how it is removed
from drinks.

▶ **Bonding**
- **Atoms interact due to forces between plus and minus charges.**
- **Forces of interaction inside molecules result in different types of chemical bonds.**
- **Forces of interaction between molecules result in differences in physical properties.**

▶ **Scientific Communication**
- **Writing, speaking, diagrams, and mathematics are required for effective communication.**

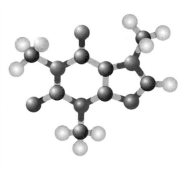

EXPLAIN

Linking Question

Charge Those Particles

Key Idea:
The strength of attraction between electrons and
protons helps predict the characteristics of the charge of an
atom or molecule.

How does the distribution
of charge affect the way
complex molecules interact
with other particles?

What's Shocking?

Many common substances appear to be similar but are actually very different. At a glance, water and vinegar look similar, but you would not want to take a big sip of vinegar! Baby oil might look like light corn syrup, but you would not use baby oil in your pecan pie recipe. Why might substances seem so similar yet be so different?

You often depend on your senses to distinguish between similar substances. You could smell vinegar and sense that it was not pure water. Sometimes the sense of smell does not provide you with enough information. For example, would pure water appear different from water that contains dissolved table salt?

Your teacher will show you pure water and three solutions: acetic acid ($C_2H_4O_2$) in water (also called vinegar), sodium chloride (NaCl) in water, and sucrose ($C_{12}H_{22}O_{11}$) in water. All solution concentrations are approximately equal. In the What's Shocking? investigation, you work alone and with classmates to think about these similar-looking solutions of water; then you compare them with pure water. Your scientific curiosity leads you to ask how to tell them apart *without tasting*.

Materials

Process and Procedure

1. Carefully observe the material in *each* container.
   a. Sketch each container in your notebook.
   b. Label the name of the material in each beaker, including symbols for microscopic particles.

Remember from chapter 2, The Material World, how the symbol CH_4 can represent microscopic methane particles and that it is called the chemical formula.

   c. List your observations under each sketch.
2. Make predictions about differences in these substances by responding to Steps 2a and b in your notebook.
   a. Pretend you are sitting in a tub filled with the material from 1 of the containers when a plugged-in hair dryer, which is running, falls into the tub. Predict in which tubs you would get shocked.

In the previous chapter, you investigated the electrical conductivity properties of sports drinks.

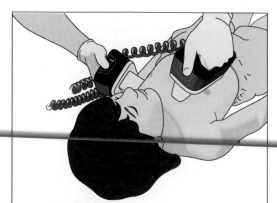

▼ **Figure 3.2**

Monstrous shock!
Does all matter conduct electricity the same way? Why is that question important?

b. Explain your predictions in writing based on what you know from past experiences.

Movies and books are important experiences, as are direct encounters with electrical appliances in water.

3. Check your understanding with a classmate near you.
   a. Read your predictions, including your explanations.
   b. Ask your classmate if he or she understands what you read and monitor the response.
   c. Change roles and discuss any differences you hear in the explanations.
4. Make careful observations as your teacher demonstrates an instrument called a conductivity meter.

A conductivity meter tests for the flow of electrical charge through a material. The light glows when both probes touch a material that conducts electricity.

   a. Sketch the instrument.
   b. Label the parts while your teacher names them.
   c. Record how the conductivity meter behaves when its probes touch common substances such as copper wire, glass, Styrofoam, and air.

Materials that conduct electricity well are called electrical conductors. Materials that do not conduct electricity well are called electrical insulators.

5. Make a list of as many conductors and insulators as you can and compare your list with another classmate's list.
6. Repeat Steps 2 and 3 for your prediction of the conductivity test for pure water.
7. Observe what happens when your teacher uses the conductivity meter to test whether electricity flows easily through pure water.
   a. Record your observations in your notebook.
   b. Include whether you were surprised by your observations and, if so, why.
8. Predict what will happen to the conductivity meter in a new situation.
   a. Imagine a tub filled with pure water. A volunteer handles a few salty potato chips and then dips his or her fingers into the water.
   b. Use Steps 2 and 3 as a general guide for making and sharing your prediction.

Reflect and Connect

Form a team of 2 or 3 and discuss the answers to the following questions. When your team agrees, write your answers in your notebook.

1. Reread your observations. Record questions you have regarding any observations that were unusual, unexpected, or contrary to your past experiences.

Often, you learn the most when something unusual happens.

2. Write what you know about the reason for *each* observation.
   a. Draw a T-table in your notebook.
   b. Place the headings "What I see" and "What it means" at the top of each column.
   c. Use what you know at this point about the science concept words *dissolve, soluble, electricity, charge, plus, minus,* and *movement* to fill out the right-hand column.

3. Which aspect, if any, of this activity represents a violation of the law of conservation of matter? Why?

Remember that solid sodium chloride and sucrose dissolve in water to make solutions.

Use particle-level sketches to show your current idea of what might be happening during the dissolving process.

4. What will happen if you place the conductivity probes (electrodes) in a small pile of solid sodium chloride? In sucrose?

Don't forget to link what you see in this activity to what you think it means.

EXPLORE

Particular Properties

In the engage activity, What's Shocking?, you focused on the similarities and differences in four chemical compounds—water, acetic acid, salt, and sugar. But you have lingering questions. Does *dissolve* always mean "conduct"? Is the molecule that makes up the compound called water responsible for the conductivity meter glowing? What is it about the particles that compose sodium chloride and acetic acid that cause them to conduct electricity when dissolved in water? How does water interact with each substance?

Curious people pursue lingering questions. If you explored the properties of more common substances, perhaps you could place them in categories according to likenesses and differences. From that information, you might see trends in behavior. Eventually, understanding those trends might help you explain why microscopic

◄ **Figure 3.3**
Spot of tar on car.
Will soapy water
dissolve the blob
of tar on this car?

particles interact the way they do. Then you would have the full story
behind solubility. And that information is important because designing
a successful wave toy depends on solubility.

In the Particular Properties activity, you work in teams to
investigate the properties of several common chemical compounds. You
then organize the compounds based on the results of your investigation.
Throughout the activity, you ask yourself what is true about the
microscopic form of particles that eventually explains the macroscopic
categories you discover in this activity.

Your team uses information from six tests of eight compounds to
form groups of substances that behave similarly. Those tests are physical
appearance, relative hardness, conductivity of the solid compound,
solubility in distilled water, conductivity in solution, and relative melting
point, in that order. If you are not sure how to conduct certain tests, read
the protocols included in this activity. Record all of your observations in
your notebook under the heading "Particular Properties."

Materials

For each student

1 pair of safety goggles

1 lab apron

1 electrical conductivity meter

1 Bunsen burner

access to water bath station

For each team of three students

1 test tube

1 test-tube holder

1 scoop

1 well plate

1 metal spatula

1 pair of forceps

1 medicine dropper

1 set of 8 compounds (aspirin, cornstarch, deicer, Epsom salts, paraffin wax, sugar, table salt, vitamin C) in transparent, labeled containers

distilled water

paper towels

8 toothpicks

Cautions

Wear your safety goggles at all times during this investigation. In this procedure, you use a Bunsen burner to heat a substance in a test tube. Therefore, tie back loose hair and keep loose clothing away from the flame. When heating the contents of the test tube, point the open end away from people. Do not apply heat directly to the test-tube holder or your hand. Although the test tube might not look hot, it will be. Do not touch hot glassware without protection.

Process and Procedure

1. Discuss with your team the best way to conduct and record the results of 8 tests on 8 compounds.

   a. In your notebook, create a data table in the shape of a grid (rows and columns) and print appropriate headings in the top row and left-most column.

   Remember to make grid boxes large enough for informative observations.

   b. Decide as a team how to perform *each* test on *each* compound so that *each* team member sees what happens and records observations in his or her notebook.

   Review the protocols regarding hardness, conductivity, solubility, and melting point on pages 108–109 to get ideas on what tests to perform. You used one of these tests in The Process of Scientific Inquiry.

2. Conduct all tests and fill in your data table carefully.

3. Compare your results with teams around you and repeat tests if you notice confusing differences between teams.

   If you are unsure about a procedure, consult with your teacher before proceeding.

> **⚠ Caution**
> Wear safety goggles and lab aprons when using laboratory materials.

4. Dispose of materials as directed by your teacher and clean the well plate by rinsing its contents down the sink.

Use forceps to remove the paraffin wax from its well.

5. Categorize tested compounds and make a chart or diagram that includes the following:
   a. Name for each category
   b. List of the compounds that belong to each category
   c. List of the properties that are common to that category

Label the diagram "Macroscopic Categories of Compounds." You will use this diagram in the next investigation.

6. Determine whether other teams categorized the compounds the same way.
   a. Compare your diagram with those of other teams and ask questions to clarify your observations.
   b. Work with your teacher to reach consensus on the category names and placement of compounds in categories.

Reflect and Connect

Discuss with your team the following questions and tasks and record your best thinking in your science notebook.

1. Answer the following questions about the term *relative*.
   a. What does the word *relative* in the phrases *relative hardness, relative melting point*, and *relative solubility* mean?
   b. Does collecting relative versus numerical data prevent you from generating useful categories? Explain your reasoning.

2. Read the following information and use it to answer this question: To which of your categories would you add the 3 compounds listed in figure 3.4? Justify your answer based on observations.

   An independent investigator collected the following information (see figure 3.4) about 3 additional compounds—artificial sweetener; petroleum jelly; and calcium oxide (quicklime),

▼ Figure 3.4

Various tests on three compounds. How would you classify these compounds?

Compound	Appearance	Hardness	Conductivity (as solid)	Solubility in water	Conductivity (as liquid or solution)	Melting point
Artificial sweetener	White powder	Soft	None	Soluble	None	Medium
Petroleum jelly	Greasy solid	Soft	None	None	Not applicable	Low
Calcium oxide	White crystal	Hard brittle	None	Yes	Strong	High

an important industrial chemical that has a variety of uses, from making glass to enriching soils.

3. Decide in which category to place water and list your reasons for your decision.

Remember the demonstration that your teacher performed with distilled water during the previous activity.

4. In which category would you place baby oil and isopropyl alcohol from your wave bottle? Where would you place vinegar? Explain your reasoning.

Protocol

Testing Appearance and Relative Hardness

> **Caution** — Wear safety goggles and lab aprons during this test.

1. Place a small amount of each compound in a separate well in a well plate. Use enough to fill the well about 1/4 full.
2. In your data table, record your observations about the general appearance of each of the compounds.
3. Use a metal spatula to press against the compound to see if it crushes easily. What is the relative hardness of each sample? Record your findings on your data table.

   Use a paper towel to clean the spatula after testing each substance.

Testing Electrical Conductivity

> **Caution** — Wear safety goggles and lab aprons during this test.

1. Obtain an electrical conductivity meter.
2. Place both probes into the substance to be tested. Make sure both probes are touching the same continuous piece of material.

   An electrical conductivity probe might look like a single probe, but it has 2 probes within its tip. Because the probe uses a low voltage battery (9 volts), you do not need to be concerned about getting an electrical shock when you test the liquid materials.

3. Observe the resulting reading on the meter and record the reading in your data table.
4. To prevent contamination and results that might be misleading, thoroughly rinse the tips of the probes with distilled water and dry them between tests, especially when using liquids. Also, do not touch the electrode with your fingers.
5. When you finish using the meter, turn it off or disconnect the battery. This prevents draining the charge from the battery.

Determining Relative Solubility

1. Do not allow any substance to come in contact with your skin.
2. Place small amounts of the solid to be tested in the small depression of your well plate.
3. Use a medicine dropper to add distilled water to each compound that you placed in a well. Add enough water to fill each well about 3/4 full.
4. Stir the resulting mixture using a clean toothpick for each well. Record whether the compound is soluble, partially soluble, or insoluble in water.

Caution Wear safety goggles and lab aprons during this test.

Determining Relative Melting Points

1. You are working close to an open flame. Tie back long hair and loose clothing. Never point the open end of a test tube you are heating toward another person. Heat all substances slowly.
2. Place 1 gram (g) of the compound in a labeled test tube. Place the test tube in the hot water bath prepared by your teacher.
3. Check the contents of the test tube after 2-3 minutes. If the compound has melted, record "low" melting point in your data table and discard the compound as your teacher directs.
4. If the compound in your test tube did not melt, remove it from the hot water bath using a test-tube holder. Carefully dry the outside of the test tube. (Remember, it is hot!)
5. Using the proper heating technique shown in the figure, heat the test tube gently with the flame of a Bunsen burner. Remove the test tube from the flame once the compound inside begins to melt or as soon as 3 minutes have passed, whichever comes first. Once the compound has melted, remove it from the flame and turn off the Bunsen burner. If the compound has not melted within 3 minutes, remove the test tube from the flame and turn off the Bunsen burner.

   Do not continue to heat a melted compound.
6. Record "medium" melting point for compounds that melt in the Bunsen burner flame within 3 minutes. Record "high" melting point for those compounds that do not melt in the flame within 3 minutes.
7. Dispose of the compounds as your teacher directs.

Caution Wear safety goggles and lab aprons during this test.

Proper heating technique. Always point the test tube away from you and wave the bottom gently in the flame.

Electrical Conductivity

In this investigation and in chapter 1, The Process of Scientific Inquiry, you tested for electrical conductivity. What exactly does it mean when something is an electrical conductor? You have probably heard of conductors and insulators. Materials that allow an electric current to flow are **conductors**. Copper wire is a good conductor. Materials that do not allow electric current to flow are **insulators**. Rubber is a good insulator. **Electrical conductivity** is a physical property that involves the flow of electrical charges through a solid or liquid. This flow of charges is called an **electric current**.

Electrical conductivity is a property of substances that cannot be detected by observation alone. How can you tell whether a material is an electrical conductor? One way is to use a simple device called a conductivity meter. A **conductivity meter** is a tool that measures electrical conductivity. The diagram shows a simple conductivity meter.

Notice that the conductivity meter has a source of power (a low voltage battery) and a way to show the flow of electric current (with an LED, or light-emitting diode). The conductivity meter also has two probes that are not connected. The spacing between the probes prevents the flow of charges, making this simple circuit incomplete.

For the electric current to flow, you need to make a connection between the probes. This is where the test material comes in. If you place the two probes in contact with a conductive material, the charges are able to flow, and the LED lights up. If the material you place between the two probes is an insulator, the current is unable to flow. The LED remains unlit.

For electric current to flow, there also must be **movement** of electric charges. A conductor provides the charged particles

and provides a pathway for them to move. A metal, such as copper, has negatively charged electrons that are free to move about. The movement of electrons supplies the electric power used in homes and schools. All metals are conductors, but not all conductors are metals. Some conductors work through the movement of **ions,** which are also charged particles. The movement of ions in batteries provides the electric current necessary to power cars, watches, and portable radios.

Substances that produce ions in water solution are **electrolytes**. These substances do not conduct an electric current as solids because their ions are not free to move in a solid. If the substance dissolves in water, the moving electrical

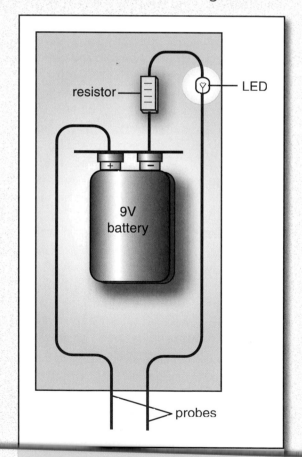

Conductivity meter. The LED glows when electrical charges flow between probes.

charges constituting the current are the dissolved ions. Electrolytes can vary in the degree to which they conduct current. Some are strong conductors, and others are weak. Depending on the particular conductivity meter you use, you may be able to determine whether the material has low, medium, or high conductivity. What level of conductivity would you expect sports drinks to have? You might recall from The Process of Scientific Inquiry that many sports drinks contain electrolytes. Therefore, they are excellent conductors of electric current.

The Solution to Solutions

You can place different chemical compounds into groups based on tests such as relative hardness, electrical conductivity, and solubility in water. Groups of chemical compounds share macroscopic similarities. For example, many hard, crystalline solids with high melting points do not conduct electricity as solids, but test positive with a conductivity meter when dissolved in water. Soft, oily materials with low melting points do not conduct electricity and are not soluble in water. Medium hard, powdery substances with medium melting points sometimes dissolve in water partially, but conduct electricity poorly, if at all. What is the underlying microscopic form that explains the way these compounds function macroscopically?

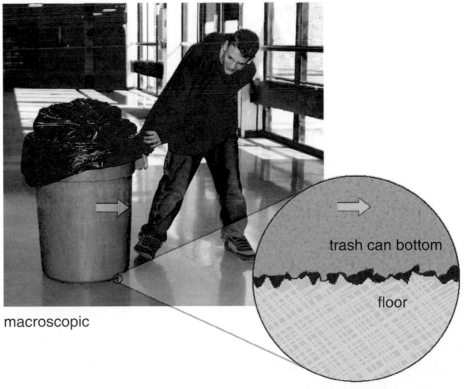

macroscopic

trash can bottom

floor

microscopic

◀ **Figure 3.5 Two views of friction.** In a macroscopic view of friction, you experience friction. In a microscopic view, you imagine things that you cannot ordinarily see. Considering both microscopic and macroscopic views of matter helps you understand the dissolving process.

Evidence from a conductivity meter suggests that electricity is involved. When charges are free to move, a material conducts electricity. Something about matter at the microscopic level involves electrical charges. This electrical nature of *all* matter explains solubility trends and the formation of compounds that can be grouped into categories with shared properties. What causes the electrical nature of microscopic particles? Why is the effect of this electrical nature stronger between some materials than others? What is it about the molecular structure of certain families of compounds that makes them behave in similar ways?

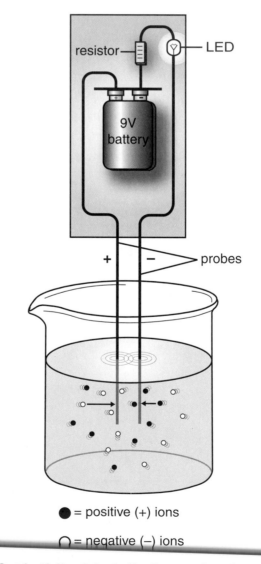

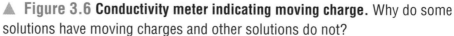

▲ **Figure 3.6 Conductivity meter indicating moving charge.** Why do some solutions have moving charges and other solutions do not?

In the Solution to Solutions activity, you work individually, in groups, and with your teacher to investigate the electrical nature of common substances, especially water, and to make your particle model of matter more complete. To accomplish this, you blend your previous knowledge of particles with a new understanding of the electrical nature of matter.

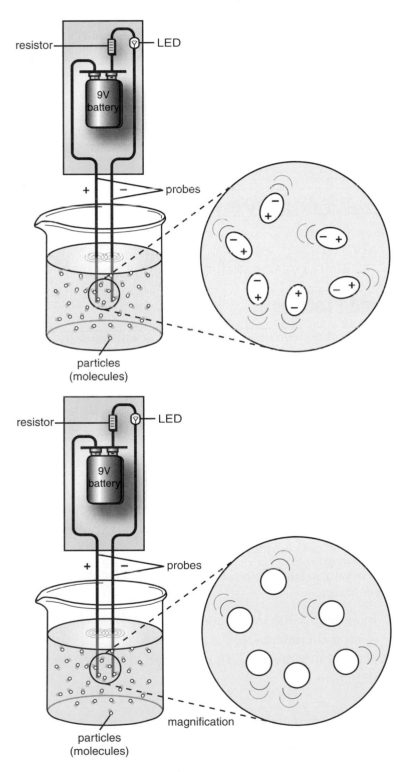

◀ **Figure 3.7 Two liquids with different electrical properties.** Which particles represent water? Baby oil? How does a conductivity meter help you find out?

Part I: Different Charges

In Part I, you observe a device that can demonstrate which charge, positive or negative, an object exhibits. The device is called an **electroscope**. Record all observations under the heading "Part I: Different Charges."

Materials
For each team of three students

3 pairs of safety goggles

1 test tube or Erlenmeyer flask

1 plastic picnic knife

paper from recycle bin

1 pair of scissors

access to small trickle of water

Cautions

Wear your safety goggles at all times during this investigation.

Process and Procedure

1. Observe the electroscope that your teacher demonstrates and look for evidence of electrical properties.
   a. Sketch the electroscope in your notebook.
   b. Label each part and its function (how it operates).
2. Predict what will happen when your teacher uses the electroscope to demonstrate charge on a plastic knife.

Your teacher will rub a plastic knife with paper, then touch the knife to one of the metal pins. Your teacher will remove the knife, then bring it close to the pin.

   a. Make a sketch of what you think will happen at the macroscopic level and write a short caption explaining why you think it will happen.

Remember what you know about charged particles. Like charges repel, and opposite charges attract.

   b. Include in your sketch ideas about what you think will happen on the microscopic level to cause what you observe.
3. Explain your drawing to a classmate and listen to his or her explanation.

4. Observe what happens to the electroscope during the demonstration and write an explanation in your notebook using the words *conduction*, *charge*, and *repel*.

Remember from other courses that *conduction* in this context means "to move or transfer charge from one place to another." Metals, such as copper, are good conductors of electricity. Insulators, such as foam cups, do not conduct electricity.

5. Repeat Steps 2–4, but replace the plastic knife with glassware, such as a test tube or flask, in your sketch, prediction, and explanation.

Part I

Individually answer the following questions in your notebook under the heading "Stop and Think—Part I." Compare your answers with those of someone else in the class and incorporate important things that you learned.

1. When did you first learn that certain objects can exhibit plus and minus charges?

2. How did the electroscope demonstrate the rules you remember about how charges interact?

3. How does the separation distance affect the amount of force a charged object can exert on another charged object?

   State evidence from this demonstration to form a complete answer.

4. What happened at the microscopic level for the plastic knife and glass to begin the demonstration neutral and then acquire a charge?

   Remember, you can drag your feet over many types of floor materials and still acquire a static charge, even though both you and the floor were initially electrically neutral.

5. Is *neutral* a third type of charge? Support your answer with examples from a microscopic view.

Part II: Paper Charges

In Part I, you saw how common objects can exhibit electrical properties. Do other common substances show evidence of plus and minus charges? What about paper? Does paper exhibit both plus and minus charges? That is the question to keep asking yourself during Part II of this investigation into the electrical nature of matter.

Materials

For each team of three students

3 pairs of safety goggles

1 test tube or Erlenmeyer flask

paper from recycle bin

1 pair of scissors

access to small trickle of water

glassware

Cautions

Wear your safety goggles at all times during this investigation.

Process and Procedure

Form a team of 3 students and record observations in your notebook under the heading "Part II: Paper Charges."

1. Meet with your team and decide on the best way to determine how a charged plastic knife interacts with tiny bits of paper.

Be sure to observe with your eyes at the same level as the top of the mound of paper.

2. Ask your teacher to approve your method of testing charge.
3. Conduct your experiment and record the results.
4. Repeat Steps 1–3 with glassware instead of the plastic knife.

Stop & THINK

Part II

Discuss with your team answers to the following questions and write your best thinking in your notebook under the heading "Stop and Think—Part II."

1. How did the pieces of paper interact with differently charged objects?

   Report your answer in a T-table with headings "What I see macroscopically" and "What it means microscopically."

2. How would your observations change if you could cut up the pieces of paper to the size of Democritus's particles?

Part III: Bending the Rules

In Part II, you observed how paper attracts both kinds of charge. This observation suggests that little pieces of paper have both kinds of charge. Is this true for the microscopic particles that make up paper? Do the particles that make up other substances have both positive and negative parts?

Part III helps you answer this question by investigating water. You will see in Part IV how the electrical properties of water molecules help explain the process of dissolving.

Materials
For each team of three students

3 pairs of safety goggles

1 test tube or Erlenmeyer flask

1 plastic picnic knife

paper from recycle bin

1 pair of scissors

access to small trickle of water

Cautions

Wear your safety goggles at all times during this investigation.

Process and Procedure

Work with your team to accomplish the following tasks. Record all observations in your notebook under the heading "Part III: Bendin the Rules."

1. Investigate the electrical properties of a narrow stream of wat falling from a faucet.
    a. Predict how a charged plastic knife affects the stream of water macroscopically.

Look back at figure 3.7. Which particle in figure 3.7 best represents a water molecule? Does water have a charge? If so, does it attract or repel other charged objects?

A sketch and short caption is an efficient way to record your prediction for future consideration.

    b. Sketch what you think is happening at the microscopic level. Your sketch will explain your macroscopic prediction.

Use + and - symbols to represent charged particles, just as Benjamin Franklin did.

▲ **Figure 3.8**
Benjamin Franklin represents charges.
Benjamin Franklin began the tradition of using plus and minus symbols for the two types of charges.

    c. Show your sketches to team members and read your captions to them.

    d. Check your prediction by performing an experiment and recording observations.

2. Repeat Steps 1a–d, but replace the plastic knife with the same piece of glassware you used in Part II.

3. Write in your notebook what unexpected things happened and why they were unexpected.

4. Represent your best ideas of the microscopic form of nature by performing Steps 4a–d.

    a. In your notebook, draw the microscopic view of 2 falling streams of water, one falling past a charged plastic knife and the other falling past a charged piece of glassware.

Represent water molecules with a simple shape. Include symbols for charge if you think your observations suggest that water molecules exhibit electrical properties.

    b. Show with sketches what might be happening at the microscopic level. Your sketches should show how water molecules attract *both* positively and negatively charged objects.

    c. Illustrate in your drawings how liquid water molecules are free to rotate.

    d. Write short captions under both drawings. The captions should explain how you have demonstrated the electrical nature of matter.

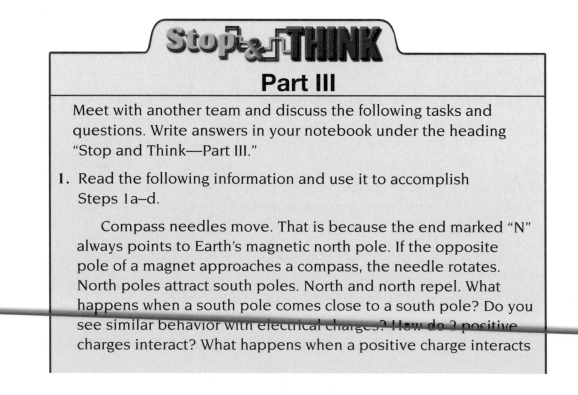

Part III

Meet with another team and discuss the following tasks and questions. Write answers in your notebook under the heading "Stop and Think—Part III."

1. Read the following information and use it to accomplish Steps 1a–d.

    Compass needles move. That is because the end marked "N" always points to Earth's magnetic north pole. If the opposite pole of a magnet approaches a compass, the needle rotates. North poles attract south poles. North and north repel. What happens when a south pole comes close to a south pole? Do you see similar behavior with electrical charges? How do 2 positive charges interact? What happens when a positive charge interacts

Part III

with a negative charge? Magnetic poles are not electrically charged, but the way poles interact with each other is similar to the way charges interact with each other.

a. In your notebook, draw representations of a water molecule and a compass needle.

b. Include +, –, N, and S where you think they belong.

c. Draw a double T-table in your notebook with the headings "Feature of Water Molecule," "Feature of Compass Needle," and "Why They Are Like Each Other."

d. Complete the T-table based on your best idea of the similarities between water molecules and a compass needle.

2. What might scientists mean when they call water a *polar* molecule?

3. Based on what you recorded in your Macroscopic Categories of Compounds chart from the previous activity, what materials are not polar molecules (like water)? Explain your reasoning.

Polar refers to any molecule that behaves like a compass needle except that the "poles" are not due to north and south magnetic poles. The poles are due to a pair of plus and minus charges, which can interact with other plus and minus charges.

Part IV: Resolving Dissolving

In Part III, you formed a picture in your mind. You pictured a water molecule with a positive end and a negative end. Those plus and minus ends affect how water interacts with other substances. For example, you might ask how the polelike nature of water molecules explains why sodium chloride dissolves in water and baby oil does not.

Part IV helps answer this question. Keep a record of your thinking in your notebook under the heading "Part IV: Resolving Dissolving."

Materials

Process and Procedure

1. Read Solvation Process and use the information to perform Steps 1a–c.

    a. Draw a T-table in your notebook with the headings "Fact or Idea" and "Questions I Have about the Fact or Idea."

b. Complete the T-table as you read.

c. Share your questions with your team and consult with your teacher regarding any unresolved questions you still have.

READING

Solvation Process

All matter demonstrates electrical properties. What does this mean? At the macroscopic level, it means you can observe what matter does. It attracts and repels. What does it mean at the microscopic level? It means plus and minus charges make up all matter.

But not all matter demonstrates electrical properties in exactly the same way or to the same extent. For example, some solids dissolve in water. That is because those solids have similar electrical properties to water. However, water and baby oil do not interact electrically. Their molecules are not similar.

The result is something you saw in previous activities. An entire category of compounds share similar properties. For example, hard, crystalline solids with high melting points tend to dissolve in water to form solutions. A compound in this category is sodium chloride. Solutions of these compounds conduct electricity.

Baby oil does not have similar electrical properties to water. Baby oil is in a different category of compounds. These compounds do not dissolve in water, and they do not conduct electricity.

A microscopic view of matter helps explain these differences. Figure 3.9 shows charges in solid sodium chloride. The name for these charged particles is **ions.** Solids made of ions are called **ionic compounds.**

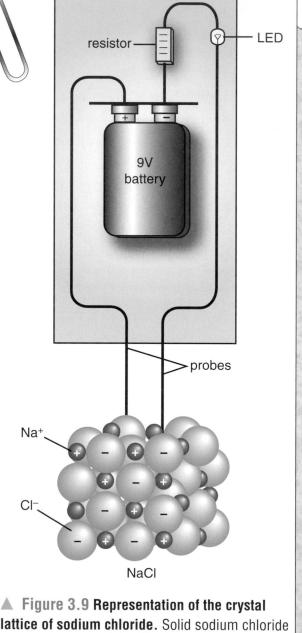

▲ **Figure 3.9 Representation of the crystal lattice of sodium chloride.** Solid sodium chloride does not conduct electricity because charged particles that are locked in place are not mobile.

SCiLINKS®
NSTA

Topic: ionic compounds
Go to: www.scilinks.org
Code: 1Inquiry120

Notice how the ions in figure 3.9 are not mobile. They cannot move about freely like dust particles in air. Instead, plus and minus attractions lock them in place. The name for the orderly microscopic structure of solids is the **crystal lattice.** In figure 3.9, the ions in the crystal lattice are not free to move between the probes of a conductivity meter. When charges are not mobile, no electricity flows.

Ionic solids such as sodium chloride interact with water at the microscopic level. That is because of the electrical nature of water molecules. Do you remember Part III of this activity? How did a stream of water interact with a positively charged object? A negatively charged object? Water bent toward both. That means water demonstrated characteristics of *both* plus and minus charges.

The part of a molecule that demonstrates both plus and minus charges is called a **dipole.** *Di* means "two," and *pole* refers

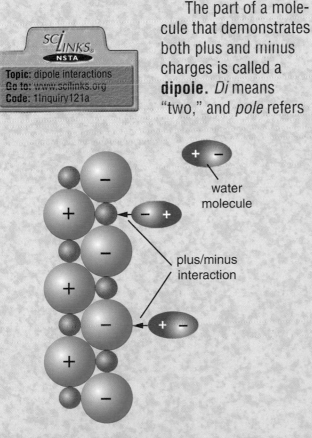

Figure 3.10

water molecule

plus/minus interaction

to either plus or minus charge. Molecules with dipoles frequently fall into the category of compounds called polar molecules. **Polar** refers to the similarity between dipoles and compass needles you investigated in Part III.

Imagine an ionic solid in water. Figure 3.10 shows what that might look like. Find the plus and minus charges on the water molecules. Those plus and minus symbols represent one way to illustrate a dipole.

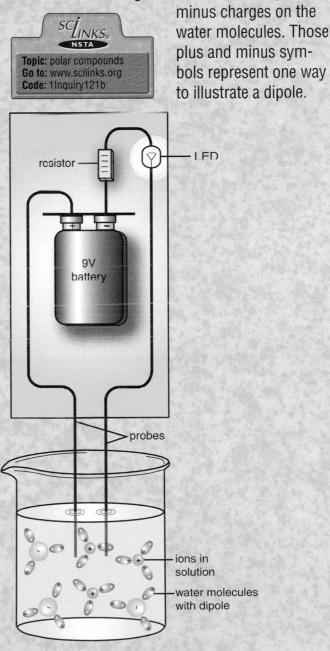

resistor

LED

9V battery

probes

ions in solution

water molecules with dipole

▲ **Figure 3.10 Representation of a sodium chloride crystal in water.** Dipole ends of water interact with ions in sodium chloride strongly enough to free ions from the crystal.

▲ **Figure 3.11 Representation of solvation.** Dipole ends of water interact with ions in sodium chloride strongly enough to free ions from the crystal lattice.

The charged ends of water molecules attract sodium chloride ions. The plus end of water's dipole attracts negative chloride ions. Similarly, the negative end of water's dipole attracts positive sodium ions.

Water molecules pull ions free from their crystal lattice. Soon sodium and chloride ions are in solution. Once in solution, water molecules surround each ion. One result is that these ions are free to move about in the solution along with the water molecules.

As a result, the solution conducts electricity. Why does the solution conduct electricity? The answer is because now there are charged particles, positively charged sodium ions and negatively charged chloride ions, free to move in the solution.

Dipoles of water molecules interact with ions in sodium chloride. The result is a solution of dissolved sodium chloride. The process is called **solvation** (figure 3.11). As a general rule, substances with similar electrical properties to water molecules dissolve in water. The rule is sometimes stated "like dissolves like."

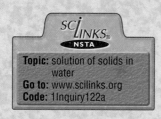

Topic: solution of solids in water
Go to: www.scilinks.org
Code: 1Inquiry122a

Molecules in the same category as baby oil and paraffin are not like water. Baby oil and paraffin are made of molecules with different electrical properties from water. They have few or no dipoles. What does that mean? It means molecules of baby oil and paraffin do not have plus and minus sections like water molecules do, nor are they made of ions like sodium chloride. Molecules such as baby oil and paraffin are typically called **covalent** molecules.

Atoms with similar attraction for plus and minus charges, such as carbon and hydrogen, make up the covalent molecules in paraffin and baby oil. Ionic compounds are made from atoms with strongly opposite charges. Sodium chloride is an example of an ionic compound.

Topic: covalent compounds
Go to: www.scilinks.org
Code: 1Inquiry122b

Polar molecules are somewhere in the middle. They are made of atoms with electrical properties whose difference lies somewhere between ionic and covalent molecules. As you know by now, water is an example of a polar molecule. Therefore, polar molecules demonstrate certain characteristics of *both* ionic and covalent substances.

2. Use your knowledge of covalent and polar molecules from the reading you just completed to draw a series of sketches. These sketches should show why water does *not* dissolve paraffin.
   a. Include + and – symbols if and where appropriate.
   b. Include captions explaining each sketch.
3. Read the passage Other Polar Covalent Molecules and repeat Steps 1 and 2. Use sketches to explain why molecules such as sugar *are* soluble in water.

Other Polar Covalent Molecules

Hydrogen and oxygen form a polar bond in water molecules. That is because hydrogen and oxygen atoms have different electrical properties. This difference is due to the oxygen end being negative and the hydrogen end being positive. But molecules other than water also contain dipoles. Nonetheless, differences in the plus-minus nature of atoms are responsible for the dipole.

When dipoles form in molecules, carbon and oxygen atoms are frequently involved. These two atoms have different electrical properties. That is, when carbon and oxygen bond, carbon is slightly positive and oxygen is slightly negative. These atoms form a dipole. But the dipole isn't as strong as the dipole in water. Why? The electrical properties of carbon and oxygen atoms must be more similar to each other than the electrical properties of hydrogen and oxygen atoms are to each other.

Yet dipoles of *any* strength have plus and minus ends. What does that mean? It means molecules with dipoles can attract each other. The strength of attraction depends on the strength of the dipoles involved, just as the strength of attraction between magnets depends on the strength of the magnets. Without dipoles, little attraction occurs.

How does this relate to solvation? The answer involves the principle "like dissolves like." Molecules with dipoles interact because of their plus and minus parts. The process is similar to the way water molecules pull plus and minus ions from an ionic crystal such as sodium chloride.

In a sense, all molecules with dipoles are alike. Why are they alike? They are alike because they have plus and minus parts, just not all of the same strength. As a result, molecules with dipoles are alike. They should dissolve in each other.

Sucrose, $C_{12}H_{22}O_{11}$, is common table sugar. It provides an example of the principle "like dissolves like." Sucrose is an organic compound made of carbon atoms bonded to other carbon atoms to form rings. Bonded to these carbon rings are oxygen and hydrogen atoms.

Figure 3.12 represents a way to visualize a molecule of sucrose. Carbon and hydrogen attract charged particles with similar strengths, though their charges are different signs. What does that suggest? It suggests that no strong dipole forms between carbon and hydrogen. If these bonds were the only ones in sucrose, table sugar would not dissolve in water.

But you know that sucrose *does* dissolve in water. Why? Sucrose dissolves because parts of it *do* show a dipole. Which parts? They are the parts involving oxygen and hydrogen. These parts have a dipole that is similar to the dipole in water. If that is the case, sucrose is like water. Sucrose and water both have dipoles. And the dipoles are strong enough to attract each other. Therefore, sucrose should dissolve in water.

Many compounds show macroscopic behavior between ionic and covalent molecules. These compounds generally have carbon atoms bonded together in long chains. Frequently, the ends of these long chains connect to form circular structures called rings. The hydrogen atoms bonded to carbon atoms in these compounds do not form strong dipoles.

But atoms other than hydrogen bond to carbon. Oxygen, nitrogen, and sulfur are

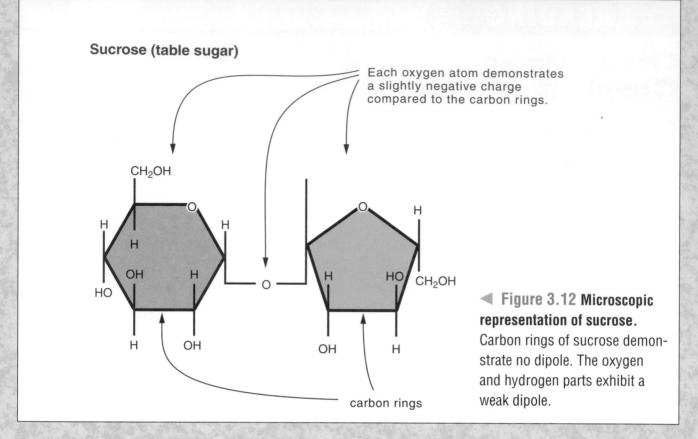

Sucrose (table sugar)

Each oxygen atom demonstrates a slightly negative charge compared to the carbon rings.

CH₂OH

carbon rings

◀ **Figure 3.12 Microscopic representation of sucrose.** Carbon rings of sucrose demonstrate no dipole. The oxygen and hydrogen parts exhibit a weak dipole.

common examples in nature. When this happens, the molecule can have plus and minus parts. Do you remember what that part of the molecule is called?

That small section of plus and minus charge is a dipole. Molecules with strong dipoles tend to dissolve in water. Why is that fact important? It is important because many ingredients of the foods you eat contain molecules with dipoles of varying strength. Ingredients you have heard about—vitamins, proteins, and carbohydrates—are good examples. What does this suggest about the solubility of many foods in water? As you have experienced, many foods are soluble in water.

Reflect and Connect

Work with your team to answer these questions. Write your answers in your notebook under the heading "Reflect and Connect."

1. Does the statement *All matter exhibits electrical properties* mean that all matter conducts electricity? Does the statement *All matter exhibits electrical properties* mean that all matter is soluble in water? Explain by comparing how dipoles can vary in strength to whether dipoles exist at all in a compound.

2. The table in figure 3.13 provides the chemical names and formulas of the substances you grouped in the previous investigation. Use this information to accomplish 2a and b.

Samples	Chemical name	Chemical formula
Aspirin	Acetylsalicylic acid	$C_9H_7O_4$
Cornstarch	Amylose	$(C_6H_9O_5)n$
Deicer	Calcium chloride or potassium chloride	$CaCl_2$ or KCl
Epsom salts	Magnesium sulfate	$MgSO_4$
Paraffin wax	Paraffin wax	$C_{20}H_{42}$
Sugar	Sucrose	$C_{12}H_{22}O_{11}$
Table salt	Sodium Chloride	NaCl
Vitamin C	Asorbic acid	$C_6H_8O_6$

▲ Figure 3.13 **Results from various tests on three compounds.** You can classify these substances by their microscopic electrical form. Cornstarch is a chain of molecules of varying lengths. The symbol n refers to the number of molecules in the chain.

    a. Fill in the column "Microscopic Type" based on your understanding of the terms *covalent, ionic,* and *polar.*

    b. Write an explanation of why you chose each type.

3. When a material such as a plastic knife changes from a noncharged to charged, does it mean particles have changed in fundamental ways? Explain your answer with sketches and science concepts that you have learned in this activity.

Charge Those Particles

EXPLAIN

    In the last explain activity, you saw how important plus and minus charges were. Do you remember how the dipole in water attracts sodium chloride ions? Forces between plus and minus charges help you understand solubility and bond type. Properties such as solubility and bond type help you place compounds into categories of similar behavior. From this knowledge, you can make good decisions about the kinds of compounds you want for any given task you are interested in—such as designing a great wave toy.

    But how do atoms and molecules become charged in the first place? In this explain activity, Charge Those Particles, you work individually and in teams. You explain how microscopic particles become charged. Once you understand how they become charged, you can predict what kind of bond holds atoms together in a molecule. That knowledge then helps you predict how molecules interact to explain properties such as solubility.

Part I: Getting Charged

You know from previous activities that atoms and molecules become charged. How do they become charged? It depends on the charged particles that make up atoms. Do you remember what those particles are? The *charged* particles in an atom are electrons and protons. In Part I, keep asking yourself the following question as you work: How do atoms become charged?

Materials

Process and Procedure

1. Read Getting Charged to determine what happens to atoms and molecules when they become charged.

    a. As you read, arrange in your notebook the following concept words in an importance pyramid: *proton, ion, neutral, charged, electron, periodic table, forces,* and *bond.*

    Each concept word above helps you answer the focus question, how do atoms become charged? But some words are more important than others. Put the most important word at the top of the pyramid. Arrange the remaining words in decreasing order of importance.

    b. Place your importance pyramid next to a teammate's importance pyramid and look for similarities and differences.

    c. Modify your importance pyramid based on what you learned from your partner.

▶ **Figure 3.14**
Importance pyramid.
Which concept is *most* important in answering the question, How do atoms become charged? Place *all* of the keywords from your reading on the pyramid.

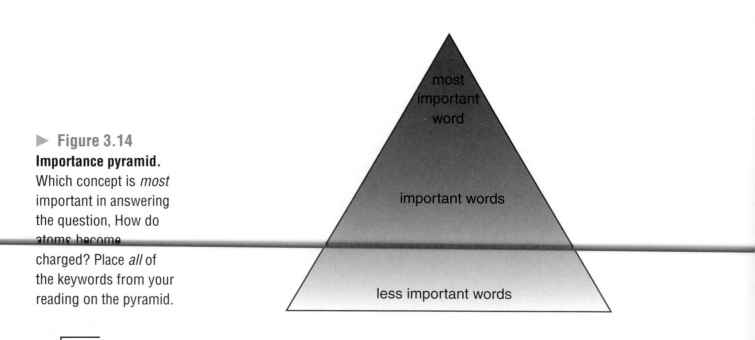

most important word

important words

less important words

Getting Charged

Electrical forces play an important role in how atoms and molecules interact. Those forces are due to plus and minus charges. Remember from previous activities that when an entire atom or molecule is charged, you call it an ion. When a section of a molecule is charged positive on one part and negative on another part, you call that section a dipole.

But how do particles as small as atoms and molecules become charged in the first place? What makes the amount of charge large in one particle and small in another?

The answers have to do with parts of atoms. You might have learned about those parts in previous courses. Atoms are composed of charged particles called electrons and protons. There are other particles, but you will learn about them later.

If atoms have charged parts, how can they ever be neutral? Neutral atoms must have equal numbers of plus and minus charges. What does this mean about the *sum* of all positive and negative charges in a neutral atom? As you predicted, the sum is zero.

This means that a neutral sodium atom has as many protons as electrons. How many? You can find that number on the periodic table of the elements shown in figure 3.15.

▲ Figure 3.15 **Periodic table of known elements.** The periodic table arranges elements in rows called periods and columns called families, or groups. The atomic number represents the number of protons or electrons in a neutral atom. Metals are generally on the left and nonmetals on the right.

A sodium ion, Na^{1+}, has one more positive charge than it has negative charges. The extra positive charge makes the entire atom charged. Since protons do not leave the atom in everyday chemical reactions, a sodium ion of charge 1+ has 11 protons and 10 electrons. How many protons and electrons make up a chloride ion, Cl^{1-}? How about a calcium ion, Ca^{2+}?

Once you understand how atoms and molecules become charged, you can predict what kind of bond holds atoms together. Knowing the bond type helps you make predictions about how molecules will interact. When you know how molecules will interact, you can explain properties such as solubility and conductivity.

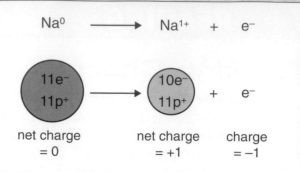

▲ **Figure 3.16 Neutral sodium becomes a sodium 1+ ion.** A sodium ion, Na^{1+}, forms when the balance between the number of protons and electrons changes. In this case, neutral sodium loses an electron. The p^+ stands for a proton, and the e^- stands for an electron.

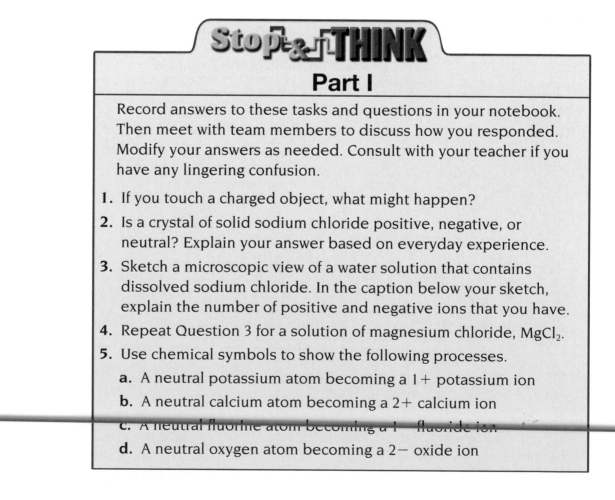

Stop & THINK

Part I

Record answers to these tasks and questions in your notebook. Then meet with team members to discuss how you responded. Modify your answers as needed. Consult with your teacher if you have any lingering confusion.

1. If you touch a charged object, what might happen?

2. Is a crystal of solid sodium chloride positive, negative, or neutral? Explain your answer based on everyday experience.

3. Sketch a microscopic view of a water solution that contains dissolved sodium chloride. In the caption below your sketch, explain the number of positive and negative ions that you have.

4. Repeat Question 3 for a solution of magnesium chloride, MgCl$_2$.

5. Use chemical symbols to show the following processes.

   a. A neutral potassium atom becoming a 1+ potassium ion

   b. A neutral calcium atom becoming a 2+ calcium ion

   c. A neutral fluorine atom becoming a 1− fluoride ion

   d. A neutral oxygen atom becoming a 2− oxide ion

Part II: Ionization versus Dissociation

Part I helped you understand how electrons and protons are involved in making charged particles. How are charged particles important in properties such as solubility? First, charged particles have to be made from neutral atoms or molecules. This involves interactions *within* an atom or molecule. The result is often an ion. Next, charged particles interact with other charged particles. This involves interactions *between* particles. The result is often a solution.

In Part II, you work with your partner to explain the differences and similarities between forming ions and forming solutions. You consider only solutions that conduct electricity. Record your best thinking under the heading "Part II: Ionization versus Dissociation."

Materials

Process and Procedure

1. Make a T-table in your notebook with the headings "Fact or Idea I Read" and "Questions I Have about the Fact or Idea."
2. Read Ionization versus Dissociation with your partner and complete the T-table.

SCiLINKS®
NSTA
Topic: dissociation of ionic compounds
Go to: www.scilinks.org
Code: 1Inquiry129

READING

Ionization versus Dissociation

Energy is needed to remove a negative charge from a positive charge. Anyone who has experienced static cling knows this property of charged matter. When the charged particles that are being separated are electrons and protons, the process is called **ionization**.

Something very similar happens in ionic solids. When the ions in a crystal lattice are separated, the process is called **dissociation**. Ionization depends on forces *inside* the atom, like the force between electrons and

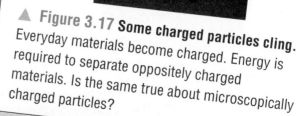

▲ Figure 3.17 **Some charged particles cling.** Everyday materials become charged. Energy is required to separate oppositely charged materials. Is the same true about microscopically charged particles?

protons. Dissociation depends on forces *outside* atoms. You can think of the outside forces as interactions between two or more compounds.

In ionic compounds, ionization took place to form the solid ionic crystal. Sodium chloride is an example with its positive sodium ions and negative chloride ions. Ionic crystals can then interact with water molecules to dissociate. As you remember from previous activities, the result is a solution that conducts electricity.

You can represent the microscopic view of ionization with simple symbols. Figure 3.18 shows one way. Notice how energy must be *added* to the neutral atom to remove an electron from protons. As you might expect, the amount of energy depends on the type of atom. That means each element has a characteristic **ionization energy.** For example, the ionization

energy for chlorine is 2.5 times greater than that for sodium. Notice on the periodic table

$$NaCl_{(s)} \longrightarrow Na^{1+}_{(aq)} + Cl^{1-}_{(aq)}$$

▲ **Figure 3.19 Symbol representation of dissociation.** Sodium chloride solid (NaCl) dissociates in water to form sodium ions (Na^{1+}) and chloride ions (Cl^{1-}) in an aqueous (aq) solution.

where sodium and chlorine reside. In contrast, the ionization energy for oxygen is only 1.2 times that of carbon. Notice the position of these elements on the periodic table in figure 3.15.

Dissociation also involves separating oppositely charged particles. The particles are ions, not parts of atoms like protons and electrons. For example, you can represent dissociation of sodium chloride in water with different symbols than you used for ionization. Dissociation occurs because of solvation, which requires interaction of charged particles with similar electrical properties.

Ionization depends on factors *inside* the atom. Dissociation depends on factors *between* molecules. Together these factors help explain important macroscopic properties such as solubility, hardness, and conductivity.

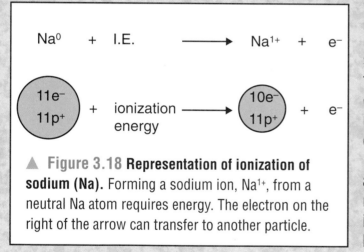

▲ **Figure 3.18 Representation of ionization of sodium (Na).** Forming a sodium ion, Na^{1+}, from a neutral Na atom requires energy. The electron on the right of the arrow can transfer to another particle.

3. Share the contents of your T-table with your partner and add to your table what you learned from your partner.

Consult with another team or your teacher regarding any unanswered questions.

4. Make a Venn diagram in your notebook to illustrate the similarities and differences between ionization and dissociation.

Use your previous T-table to complete this new diagram. Remember to place similarities in the overlapping section of your Venn diagram.

5. Use your understanding of ionization and dissociation to accomplish Steps 5a–c.
   a. Predict the relative ionization energies associated with ionic, covalent, and polar bonds.

Remember that chlorine's relative ionization energy was 2.5 times greater than sodium's.

   b. Predict what type of bonding (covalent, ionic, or polar) occurs between hydrogen atoms in the elemental compound H_2.

Represent your explanation with particle-level sketches and include symbols for charges where appropriate.

   c. Draw a series of molecular level sketches to show whether hydrogen gas, H_2, is highly soluble in water.

Part III: Sharing Electrons

In Getting Charged and Ionization versus Dissociation, you learned how atoms and molecules become charged and what the difference is between ionization and dissociation. Your knowledge helped you think about properties of matter, such as solubility. You pictured what happens to atoms and molecules when they interact to make solutions.

Your knowledge also helps you understand bonding. Remember that bond type depends on differences in electrical properties. One way to picture those differences is ionization energy. But there is another way. It's called electronegativity.

In Part III, you work with your partner to explain the differences and similarities between ionization energy and electronegativity. Understanding both tools gives you the increased ability to predict the type of bonds found in compounds. In turn, this knowledge helps you predict important properties of materials.

Record your best thinking under the heading "Part III: Sharing Electrons."

Materials

Process and Procedure

1. Repeat Steps 1–4 of Part II, but read Electronegativity and look for similarities and differences between ionization energy and electronegativity.

Electronegativity

In the previous activity, you learned about covalent bonds. They form when atoms have similar electrical properties. Ionization energy is one way to characterize and quantify those electrical properties. Electronegativity is another way.

When two atoms of the *same* element bond, they form a covalent molecule. The molecule is covalent because its atoms share electrons equally. However, when two different atoms share electrons, the sharing may not be "equal."

Why don't some atoms share their electrons equally? The answer to this question lies in atomic structure. Based on atomic structure, some atoms are better than others at attracting electrons. This ability to attract electrons is characterized by a property called **electronegativity.**

Topic: electronegativity
Go to: www.scilinks.org
Code: 1Inquiry132

Linus Pauling, an American chemist, devised the electronegativity scale. He assigned fluorine an arbitrary value of 4.0. Fluorine is the most electronegative element because it is able to attract an electron better than any other element on the periodic table.

Pauling calculated electronegativity values for the other elements compared with that of fluorine. Figure 3.15 provides the electronegativity values for most elements. Electronegativity values can tell you the types of bonds that form between atoms. How? To answer this question, you need a way to represent electronegativity.

One way to represent electronegativity is to imagine a tug-of-war game with one atom on each side of the rope. The rope represents one or more electrons. If the atoms have the same or similar strength (electronegativity), there will be a tie—neither will win. When two hydrogen

atoms share electrons with one another, they share electrons equally. The bond that is formed is called a covalent bond (see figure 3.20).

If the atoms are somewhat different in strength (electronegativity), one atom pulls the rope more than the other. Neither wins, but more of the rope is to one side. Which side wins? The side with the greatest electronegativity wins.

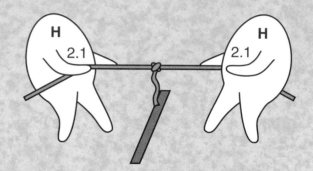

▲ **Figure 3.20 Representation of hydrogen atoms competing for electrons.** Two hydrogen atoms compete for electrons in a sort of tug-of-war. Which atom wins and why?

This unequal sharing of electrons represents a *polar covalent bond*. A polar covalent bond results in a molecule that has regions of positive charge, +, and negative charge, −. Do you remember what this separation of charge within a molecule is called? For instance, when a hydrogen atom and a chlorine atom combine, the region around the hydrogen atom has some positive charge. The region around the chlorine atom has some negative charge (see figure 3.21).

If the atoms have drastically different values of electronegativity, the atom with the greater electronegativity will win the electron. The electron is essentially transferred from the atom with the low electronegativity to the atom with the high electronegativity. This results in the formation of

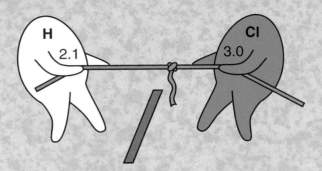

▲ **Figure 3.21 Unequal electronegativity leads to dipole.** Chlorine and hydrogen compete for electrons in a tug-of-war. This time chlorine attracts electrons better than hydrogen does. How does this affect the molecule?

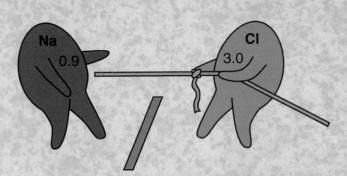

▲ **Figure 3.22 Ions result from large electronegativity differences.** Chlorine wins the tug-of-war for electrons over sodium. How does this affect the properties of sodium chloride?

two ions, one positive and one negative. The attraction between the two oppositely charged ions is an ionic bond (see figure 3.22).

You are probably wondering where the lines are drawn between the various types of bonds. What difference in electronegativity values results in a nonpolar (no dipole) covalent bond? What about a polar covalent bond and an ionic bond? The table in figure 3.23 indicates the values that chemists commonly use to predict bond type based on electronegativity differences.

As you study bonding, you may notice that the terms *molecule* and *compound* are sometimes

used interchangeably. Both terms refer to the same concept. A molecule is the smallest unit of a covalently bonded compound. Whenever you see the term *molecule,* you know that the bonds between atoms within that molecule are formed through covalent bonding. Covalently bonded substances can be called molecules or compounds. Substances formed from ionic bonds, on the other hand, are simply called *ionic compounds* since there are no individual molecules in an ionic crystal.

Type of bond	Nonpolar covalent	Polar covalent	Ionic
Electronegativity difference	< 0.4	0.4–2.1	> 2.1
Diagram	H– – ÷ – – H	H$^{\delta+}$– – – ÷ –$^{\delta-}$ $\overset{..}{\underset{..}{C}}$l:	Na$^+$– – – – ÷ $\overset{..}{\underset{..}{C}}$l:$^-$
Electrons	Shared equally	Shared unequally	Transferred

▲ **Figure 3.23 Electronegativity differences and bond types.** How does bonding relate to electronegativity values?

2. Use your T-table to answer Questions 2a–c in your science notebook.

Inspect figure 3.15 for any electronegativity values you might need.

a. What trends do you see in electronegativity values?

How do the trends relate to the number of protons and electrons in an atom? What happens to electronegativity values as you move down a group (column)? Across a period (row)? Compare electronegativity values of metals, such as copper, with nonmetals, such as fluorine.

b. When atoms with similar electronegativities bond to form molecules, what type of bond forms? Are the differences in electronegativity small, medium, or large?

c. What type of bond forms when atoms from *opposite* sides of the periodic table form a compound?

What are some typical differences in electronegativity values between two elements from opposite sides of the periodic table? Think about the formation of sodium chloride (NaCl) or lithium fluoride (LiF).

3. Complete the following tasks and answer the related questions with your partner. Record your answers in your science notebook.

Consult with your teacher if you and your partner cannot reach consensus.

a. Make a diagram to show how each pair of atoms listed below shares or transfers electrons and determine the type of bond:
- Hydrogen-oxygen in water (H_2O)
- Carbon-oxygen in carbon dioxide (CO_2)
- Potassium-fluorine in potassium fluoride (KF)
- Carbon-hydrogen in methane (CH_4)
- Bromine-bromine in bromine (Br_2)

Show your calculation of electronegativity differences.

Whenever you determine electronegativity differences, subtract the smaller electronegativity value from the larger one. Differences in electronegativity are never negative.

b. How does electronegativity relate to bond type?

4. This reading used the tug-of-war model and electronegativity to describe the way that atoms can share electrons. Develop another way to describe 3 types of bonding.

Remember that *removing* electrons gives you important information about the likely type of bond formed.

5. Both ionization energy and electronegativity help you understand the electrical properties of matter, but from different perspectives. Use your notebook to write about other situations in which viewing something from multiple perspectives helps you understand better.

Reflect and Connect

Work with your team to answer these questions. Record your answers in your science notebook. Be prepared to share answers during a class discussion.

1. Predict the type of molecule (or compound) each of the following might be. Justify your prediction.
   a. $CaCl_2$
   b. N_2
   c. CO_2

Remember the model of carbon dioxide you constructed when you studied combustion in chapter 2. The atoms of carbon and oxygen formed a straight line.

2. Describe in your own words how bonding between atoms contributes to the characteristics of an entire molecule or group of atoms.

Read the sidebars, Water Works! and Mysterious Metals, for some hints.

Water Works!

Water flows. Water freezes. Water evaporates. Water is important on both local and global levels. The human body is made up of 55–75 percent water. People use water to cook, bathe, and drink. Water is the focal point of many sports and hobbies—swimming, hockey, figure skating, water polo, fishing, boating, and snow skiing. On a global level, the water in, on, and around Earth plays a pivotal role in Earth's climate and in shaping the land.

So what is so special about water? How can it serve so many functions? Take a closer look—a much closer look. No, closer. Okay, there you go. Now that you're at the molecular level, what do you see? You know that the formula for water is H_2O. One molecule of water is made up of two hydrogen atoms and one oxygen atom. As you know, water is a polar covalent compound. Each bond between the oxygen and hydrogen atoms is covalent. Because the sharing of the electrons is unequal, there is a partial negative charge near the oxygen atom and a partial positive charge near each of the hydrogen atoms. As shown in the three-dimensional water molecule illustration, water is a bent molecule. Sometimes water is called the Mickey Mouse molecule. Can you see why?

Imagine water in its three phases: as a gas in the atmosphere, as a liquid in a lake, and as ice covering that same lake in the winter. What is different about the water molecules? Aren't the water molecules the same in the gaseous atmosphere, the liquid lake, and the frozen lake? Yes, the molecules are the same. However, the interactions between the molecules are different. Water molecules in the gas phase move fast and are too far apart to have much interaction. Once the water molecules slow down enough to form a liquid, they are close enough for hydrogen bonding to become a factor in holding them together. Recall that hydrogen bonding occurs when the partially positive charge of a hydrogen atom within a water molecule is attracted to the oppositely charged oxygen atom of another water molecule. The hydrogen bonding in liquid water is somewhat disorganized. Water molecules form loose groups of four to eight molecules. As water cools and forms ice, the molecules arrange themselves in an organized lattice structure arranged in hexagons with large holes. Water molecules in the lattice are actually farther apart than they are in their liquid phase. The more links there are, the less fluid the water becomes. As the water becomes less fluid, it becomes ice! The diagram shows the structure of liquid water and ice.

Because of these intermolecular properties, water molecules interact with other water molecules in ways that contribute to water's amazing properties.

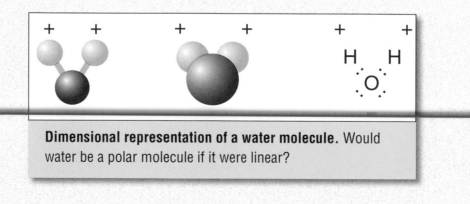

Dimensional representation of a water molecule. Would water be a polar molecule if it were linear?

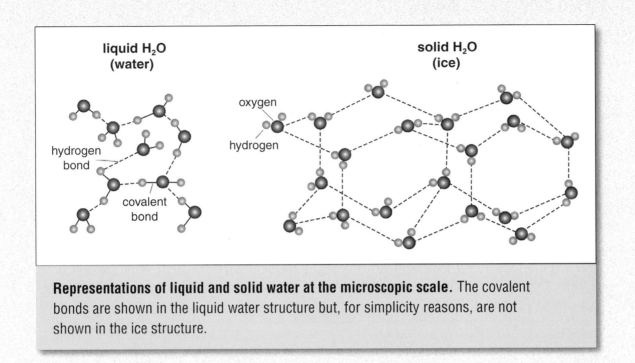

Representations of liquid and solid water at the microscopic scale. The covalent bonds are shown in the liquid water structure but, for simplicity reasons, are not shown in the ice structure.

One amazing property of water is its surface tension. **Surface tension** is the overall inward pull of molecules. Intermolecular forces pull the water molecules inward, forming a smooth surface. You can observe the surface tension of water when you slightly over-fill a cup with water. The water does not spill over because the molecules of water are tightly packed together (see the illustration) and held together by strong hydrogen bonds.

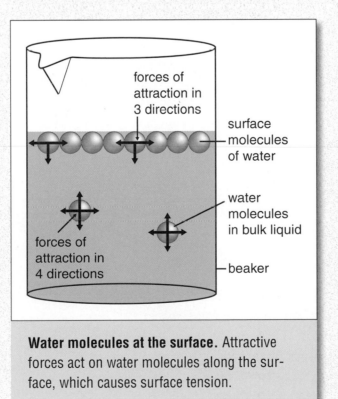

Water molecules at the surface. Attractive forces act on water molecules along the surface, which causes surface tension.

Mysterious Metals

All of the objects in this figure are made of copper. What are some properties of copper metal? First, consider its appearance. Copper is shiny. What about its shape? Copper can be easily reshaped. It can be drawn into wire, pounded into sheets, formed into tubing, and stamped to make coins. What else do you know about copper? What makes it useful in cookware and electrical wiring? Copper conducts heat and has high melting and boiling points. Copper also conducts electricity better than most materials. Copper's properties are shared by a number of other substances, such as silver, gold, and iron. Elements that are shiny, are easy to reshape into wires and sheets, and are good conductors of heat and electricity are metals.

The properties of metals sound very different from the properties of the materials you have been studying in this chapter. You have been focusing on the different types of bonds that hold atoms together in compounds. You have learned about atoms that share electrons to form compounds with covalent bonds and atoms that transfer electrons to form

Copper metal in use. What properties do these copper objects have in common?

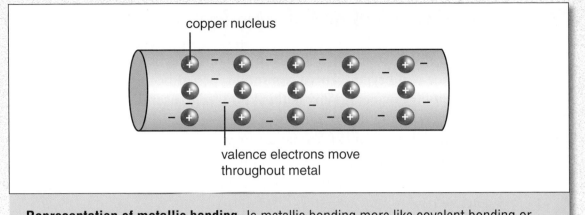

copper nucleus

valence electrons move
throughout metal

Representation of metallic bonding. Is metallic bonding more like covalent bonding or ionic bonding? Consider common tests of physical properties.

compounds with ionic bonds. You have also learned how the type of bond can be used to explain the observed properties of compounds. Because the properties of metals are very different from the properties of covalent and ionic compounds, it is reasonable to assume that there is another type of bond that holds atoms of metals together—a *metallic* bond.

You will note that metals are typically found on the left side of the periodic table. They tend to hold electrons loosely. Why? Inspect the illustration of metallic bonding. Note the relative size of first ionization energies for metals versus nonmetals. How does low ionization energy relate to electronegativity?

When metal atoms are packed very closely to one another, their outermost electrons often move freely from one atom to another. For this reason, metals are often described as positive metal ions immersed in a sea of electrons. The forces of attraction between the electrons and positive metal ions are called metallic bonding.

The "sea of electrons" model of metallic bonding accounts for many of the characteristic properties of metals. Metals are excellent conductors of electricity and heat because their loosely held electrons are free to move about. Because the positive metal ions are attracted to all of the free electrons nearby, there is no directional nature to the bonds. Bonds are uniform throughout the solid, allowing one plane of metal ions to slide past another. This makes metals easy to bend and shape into sheets and wires. Metals have high melting and boiling points because of the strength of the uniform metallic bonding. The electrons in a metal are involved in giving them a shiny appearance.

3. What kind of bonding was present in each of the compounds you studied in the activity, Particular Properties? Explain your selections.

4. In a wave toy, what type of bonding do you want in the liquids that should *not* mix? In the little penguin? In the container? Why?

Caffeine Full or Caffeine Free?

In the previous activity, Charge Those Particles, you learned how to predict bond types. Three common types of bonds are covalent, ionic, and polar covalent. Why is this knowledge useful? When you know bond type, you can predict properties of materials. You can determine whether two liquids form layers or whether they mix.

Do you remember when you first wanted to know whether liquids mixed? It was at the beginning of the unit. Do you remember the wave toy?

You have learned a lot about the material world from a simple wave toy. You appreciate how toy manufacturers need to understand the material world. They want to understand *both* the macroscopic function and the microscopic form of materials. Otherwise, they could not produce successful products.

Not only toy manufacturers need to keep learning about the material world. Civil engineers want to know about better materials for bridges, home owners want to determine the best stain remover for carpets, and food companies want to learn how to include or exclude additives to the foods they sell. All of the answers depend on how molecules bond.

In this activity, Caffeine Full or Caffeine Free?, you apply your understanding of bonding *within* and *between* molecules to help you understand more about an important food ingredient—caffeine. You work in a team of two students as well as with your entire class.

Materials
For the class

1 molecular model of caffeine

For each team of two students

1 molecular model kit

Process and Procedure

1. Talk with a classmate about the following questions regarding caffeine.
   a. What popular beverages contain large amounts of caffeine? Contain little or no caffeine?
   b. Is caffeine a natural part of beverages?
   c. Can caffeine be added or removed from foods?
   d. Why do some people drink beverages with caffeine?
   e. Is caffeine found in products other than beverages? If so, what other products?

2. Take turns reading the following paragraphs aloud and quiz each other on the contents.

Beverages containing caffeine have been around for thousands of years throughout the world. Chinese emperor Shen Nung brewed the first pot of tea over 4,700 years ago (around 2700 BC). Coffee originated as a drink in Africa around AD 575. In 1519, the Aztec emperor Montezuma treated his guests, Spanish conquistadors exploring the New World, to a chocolate drink. The first caffeinated soft drinks appeared in the 1880s.

So what exactly is caffeine? Caffeine is a naturally occurring substance found in over 60 plant species worldwide. It is typically concentrated in the seeds, leaves, or fruits of certain plants. Beans provide the caffeine for coffee, and leaves deliver the caffeine in tea. How do soft drinks get their caffeine? Some soft drinks get their caffeine as part of their natural flavoring. The kola nut from Africa provides flavoring for a number of colas. Other soft drink companies specifically add caffeine to enhance flavor. Most root beers do not contain caffeine. However, the makers of some root beers intentionally add caffeine to give the soft drink a distinct "bite." (Caffeine itself has a bitter taste.) Much of the caffeine added to soft drinks comes from the decaffeination of coffee beans and tea leaves.

Extracted and purified caffeine is a white crystalline powder. Caffeine's formula is $C_8H_{10}N_4O_2$, and its name is 1,3,7-trimethylxanthine. (Go ahead, try to pronounce the name! You will probably be happier just calling it caffeine.) Figure 3.24 shows the structural formula for caffeine. Take a close look.

3. In your science notebook, draw a large representation of a caffeine molecule and include the information requested in Steps 3a–c.
   a. Number of atoms of *each* element that are present within the molecule
   b. Location of any dipoles between pairs of atoms

An arrow can represent a dipole. The arrow points from positive to negative charge. Thicker or longer arrows indicate stronger dipoles.

   c. Labels naming the type of bond between pairs of atoms

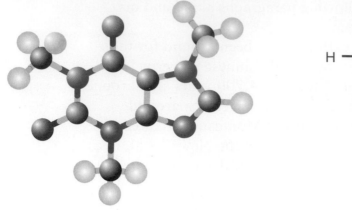
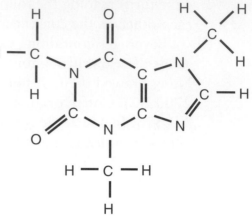

▲ **Figure 3.24 Structural model of caffeine.** The caffeine molecule (formula: $C_8H_{10}N_4O_2$, name: 1,3,7-trimethylxanthine) contains many bonds. Note how carbon bonds to other carbon atoms as well as to oxygen, nitrogen, and hydrogen.

Electronegativity values for elements in caffeine are in figure 3.15.

4. Make a T-table with the headings "Property" and "How I Know" and use it in Steps 4a–c for a caffeine molecule.
   a. List the properties *hardness, solubility, conductivity,* and *melting point* in the first column.
   b. Complete the second column based on your knowledge of the electrical interactions between pairs of atoms.
   c. Use your T-table to determine whether the *entire* caffeine molecule is ionic, covalent, or polar covalent. Include a justification for your answer under your chart.

5. Read the following paragraphs and use the information to perform Steps 5a–b.
   a. Construct models of methylene chloride and carbon dioxide based on the sketches your teacher shows you and study their differences.
   b. Repeat Steps 3 and 4 for those solvent molecules.

What's the Best Solvent?

Through the years, many consumers continued to seek out their favorite caffeinated beverages. Other consumers became concerned about the side effects of caffeine. They called for the removal of caffeine from some of their favorite beverages. Consumers wanted the same taste without the caffeine. Companies turned to chemists for a way to decaffeinate the plants used to make popular beverages. Chemists searched for a solvent that would dissolve the caffeine, leaving the other components behind. They found that soaking plant parts (leaves and seeds) in a small nonpolar solvent was an effective way to remove the caffeine.

Companies used trichloroethylene (C_2HCl_3) as a solvent until scientists identified it as a possible cancer-causing substance in the late 1970s. Companies switched to other solvents, including methylene chloride (CH_2Cl_2). However, it was not long before consumers raised questions about possible side effects of methylene chloride. The search for a different solvent molecule continued.

Carbon dioxide (CO_2) is the latest solvent that companies use to remove caffeine. You might not think of carbon dioxide as a solvent because it is a gas under normal pressure. However, carbon dioxide is a liquid in higher-pressure conditions. Liquid carbon dioxide dissolves caffeine in plant parts, leaving the flavor components behind. Any leftover carbon dioxide vaporizes when the operator decreases the pressure.

Reflect and Connect

Based on what you know about decaffeination, do you think water could be used for this process? Work with your partner to answer the following questions and write your answers in your science notebook.

1. Compare the molecules of methylene chloride and carbon dioxide with a molecule of water and answer Questions 1a and b.
   a. Is caffeine soluble in water? What evidence do you have?
   b. Could water be used to remove the caffeine? Why or why not?
2. What role does the principle "like dissolves like" play in decaffeinating beverages?
3. Write a paragraph explaining the decaffeination process from a microscopic viewpoint. Use the words *interaction*, *electrical*, *bond*, *charge*, *dipole*, *dissociation*, *ionization*, and *solvation* in your paragraph.

A Clean Performance

In this chapter, you have explored the electrical properties of various substances at a molecular level. You can explain why salt and sugar dissolve in water but oil does not. You know why saltwater conducts electricity but sugar water does not. You can relate the properties of substances to the interactions *within* and *between* molecules. You understand how properties can make a product successful or guarantee its failure in the marketplace.

In whatever job you may have, you will encounter materials. And as you continue to make use of the material world, you will need to learn more to ensure your success. The concepts you learned in this chapter provide the foundation for that success.

In the Clean Performance investigation, you have an opportunity to work on a team to demonstrate your understanding of those concepts as they apply to a process that has become a fixture in the modern world: dry cleaning. Your task is to develop a resource that explains how and why the dry cleaning process works—*down to the molecular level*. To help you, your teacher has identified the information you need to include in your guide. Review the following essential components:

1. Describe *why* garments must be dry-cleaned.
2. *Compare* and *contrast* (at the molecular level) the solvents used in the traditional dry cleaning process and in the newer type of dry cleaning process. Include a detailed description, including diagrams, of the bonding that occurs inside molecules and the interactions that occur between molecules.
3. Describe how the dry cleaning process removes stains that contain grease and how it deals with stains that contain salts or sugars.
4. Include a section called "Frequently Asked Questions" to answer the following questions:
   - What are the advantages of using the new carbon dioxide dry cleaning process?
   - What are the disadvantages of the new carbon dioxide dry cleaning process?
   - Where does the carbon dioxide come from, and where does it end up?
   - Add a question you generated (with approval from your teacher).

Materials

For the class

reference materials (books, encyclopedias, articles, the Internet)

art supplies

molecular model kits

For each student

1 copy of the Evaluate Scoring Rubric: Dry Cleaning handout

Process and Procedure

1. Review the Evaluate Scoring Rubric handout that your teacher provides to see what is expected of you as you complete the assignment.

2. Read the staging paragraphs below and use the information to accomplish Steps 2a–b.

   a. Discuss with your class the *type* of information you need to research to answer the band director's questions.

   b. Discuss with your class *where* you can find the information you need to answer the band director's questions.

3. Conduct your research, taking notes in your science notebook as needed. Make sure you have all of the information you need.

Remember, you need to address what happens both *within* and *between* molecules. It is unlikely that common references will help you with this aspect of the information guide. You need to use what you have learned in this chapter to address what happens at the molecular level.

4. Prepare a rough draft of the guide and ask yourself Questions 4a–c before finishing your guide.

   a. Is the information organized visually such that the dry cleaner owner can use it conveniently?

   b. Have you included *all* of the required components listed in the introduction?

   c. Have you provided enough detail at the molecular level to demonstrate your understanding of the science concepts that you learned in this chapter?

The scoring rubric will help you determine the level of detail to include.

5. Develop your final resource and submit it to your teacher.

Read the sidebar, An Amazing Chemist, to learn more about the person who introduced carbon dioxide to the dry cleaning market.

Positives and Negatives of Dry Cleaning

The band director at your school has asked your science teacher for some help. Because the band director wants the band to look sharp for the homecoming parade, he needs to get the uniforms cleaned. He noticed that the tags on the uniforms say "Dry-clean only." He looked in the phone book for dry cleaning companies and found several to choose from. One company claims to have a new and better dry cleaning method. The ad boasts that this method uses carbon dioxide instead of the traditional method of a commonly used solvent.

At this point, the band director has numerous questions. Can he save money by washing the uniforms in a washing machine? How does the dry cleaning process work? Why does the new company use carbon dioxide? Does one method work better than another? What are the advantages to each method? What are the disadvantages? Band members in the Environmental Club have expressed concerns about dry cleaning. Is dry cleaning harmful to the environment? The band director has many questions and hopes the science teacher can help.

After listening to the band director's dilemma, your insightful science teacher realizes that this is an opportunity for your class to help the band director as well as to educate others about dry cleaning. Your teacher would like you to develop an information guide to educate others about dry cleaning. The information guide can be a brochure, a flyer, a poster, or even a mock-up for a Web page. Since this is a science class, you will educate others about the science behind dry cleaning.

An Amazing Chemist

Dry cleaning is a dirty business, in many ways. The solvents used in traditional forms of dry cleaning are plagued with safety concerns. The original solvents were highly flammable and toxic. Current solvents are considered a risk to health and the environment. The search for viable alternatives is on! Leading the pack is the dry cleaning method that uses carbon dioxide as a solvent. Although the idea for using carbon dioxide as a solvent has been around since the early 1970s, it took an amazing chemist, Joseph DeSimone, to bring the idea to dry cleaning reality. So who is Joseph DeSimone, and how did he get involved in the dry cleaning business?

DeSimone's interest in the environment started during his childhood. He grew up in Collegeville, Pennsylvania. His father was a tailor, and his mother was an accountant. Every Friday he made a trip to a remote site to fill containers with drinking water for his family. A metal degreasing facility had contaminated the water in his neighborhood, making it unfit to drink. This early experience, along with a good high school chemistry teacher, inspired DeSimone to become a scientist.

DeSimone studied at Ursinus College, where he earned a bachelor of science degree in chemistry. He went on to earn a PhD in chemistry from Virginia Tech in 1990. DeSimone's early research was not about dry cleaning. Originally, he worked on ways to make polymers (plastics) in carbon dioxide. In doing this work, researchers in his lab discovered a number of detergents that worked with carbon dioxide.

Traditional detergents that work with water have two parts. One part of the detergent is attracted to water, and the other part is attracted to oil and grease. Detergent molecules cluster around dirt particles and form little spheres called micelles. The part of the detergent molecule that is attracted to oil forms the inside of the micelle, sticking to the grease particles. The other end of the detergent molecule that is attracted to water forms the outer shell of the micelle. Water carries away the micelle containing the grease particles.

The detergents DeSimone's research group discovered also had two parts. One part attracted carbon dioxide, and the other part attracted oil and grease. The group realized that many types of cleaning processes could use these detergents. In 1995, DeSimone and two fellow scientists patented the process and established the company Micell Technologies. The company uses liquid carbon dioxide for degreasing metals and for dry cleaning.

DeSimone talked with business professionals and decided that creating a franchise would be the best way to market his product. Dry cleaners interested in the Hangers Cleaners franchise buy DeSimon's MICARE system and give a portion of their profits to Micell Technologies. In return, Micell Technologies provides training, advertising, and other benefits to each franchise location. At one dry cleaning store in Wisconsin, sales have increased by about 20 percent since converting to the Hangers Cleaners franchise.

DeSimone's work has the potential to revolutionize the dry cleaning industry. He believes that using liquid carbon dioxide can make dry cleaning a business that is both profitable and environmentally friendly. Many people agree with him. They have recognized his contributions with awards and grants. DeSimone received an R & D [Research and Development] 100 Award in 1998 for one of the most technologically significant products of the year. DeSimone has also received the Presidential Green Chemistry Challenge Award, the North Carolina Governor's Award for Excellence, and the National Science Foundation's Young Investigator Award. He also received a $20 million grant to fund a new science and technology center that supports new technologies that prevent pollution. What is really amazing is that he has accomplished all of this before he turned forty, and he is not planning to slow down any time soon.

CHAPTER 4

Organizing the Elements: The Periodic Table

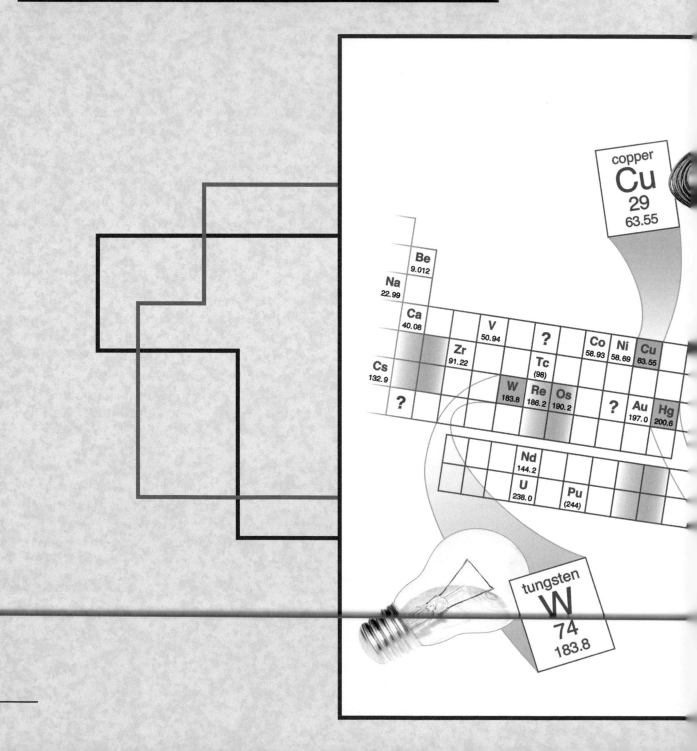

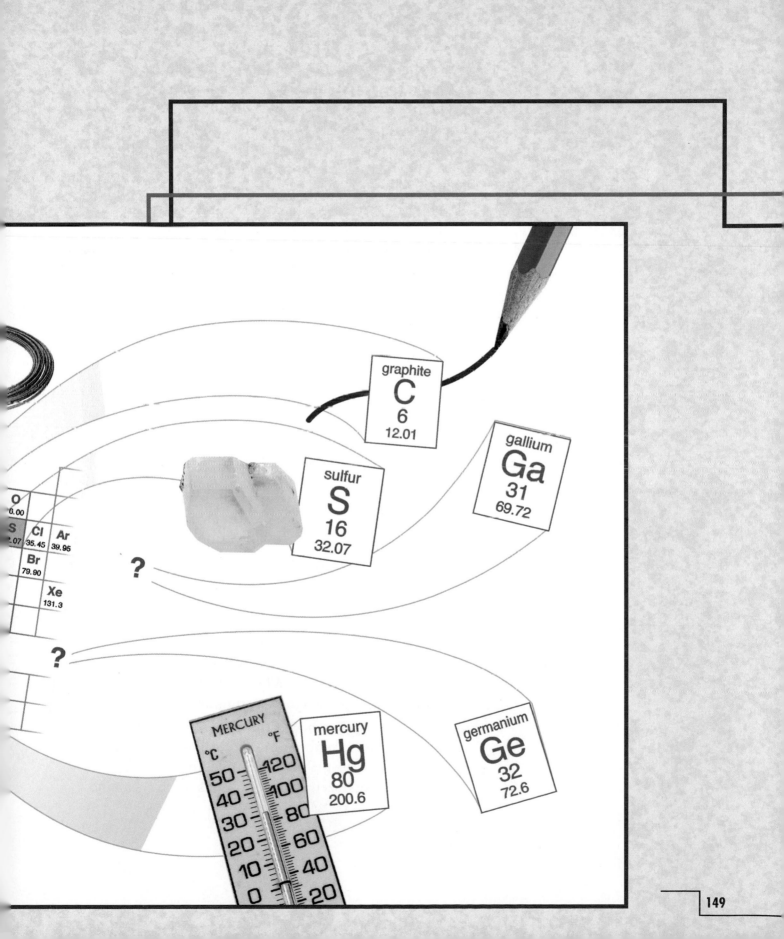

graphite
C
6
12.01

gallium
Ga
31
69.72

sulfur
S
16
32.07

O
6.00

S
.07

Cl
35.45

Ar
39.95

Br
79.90

Xe
131.3

?

?

MERCURY
°C   °F

50 120
40 100
30   80
20   60
10   40
0   20

mercury
Hg
80
200.6

germanium
Ge
32
72.6

Organizing the Elements: The Periodic Table

Matter is marvelous. Why? Just look at the marvelous knowledge you have learned about matter.

In chapter 2, The Material World, and chapter 3, Get a Charge Out of Matter, you started with characteristic properties such as density and solubility. Then you learned about the microscopic reasons that explain those properties. You kept learning when you studied bonding. That knowledge helped you predict how compounds interact. Scientists need to know how compounds interact. Why? They need to be able to pick and choose the compound that is most useful to them.

But there is so much more to learn and understand. Sometimes it can be confusing, which is why scientists organize information. Organizing information makes knowledge easier to use and remember. Ultimately, quality organization helps you spend less time getting what you want out of information. In fact, organization saves you valuable time.

You have learned about characteristic properties, solubility, ionization energy, and bonding for just a few elements and compounds. But there are many more elements and millions of compounds. And successful scientists expand knowledge *daily*. That way they can make discoveries and increase people's understanding of the natural world. How do scientists keep up with all of that new information? How can you make sense of it all?

Organizing information about the material world is the key. For example, you did this in chapter 2 by categorizing compounds based on covalent, ionic, and polar bonds. When you finished, you could make better decisions about the best materials to use in a wave toy. What about those elements *not* used in the wave toy? What kind of materials can you make with them? What sort of compounds might they form? How will the new compounds interact?

In chapter 4, Organizing the Elements: The Periodic Table, you will learn about the world's most famous graphic organizer—the periodic table. In the table, elements are organized based on trends in physical and chemical properties. When that happens, you see patterns of behavior that are easy to remember and understand. Those patterns depend on the microscopic form of atoms. As you have learned, microscopic form leads to macroscopic function, such as solubility and chemical reactivity. Deciding where to place an element in the periodic table is an important decision. It is a decision that helps you understand the material world in an efficient and organized way.

Goals for the Chapter

When you finish chapter 4, you should be able to answer the following questions:

- What is the underlying structure of the atom? How do you know?
- How has the model of the atom changed across time?
- How does the underlying structure of the atom relate to patterns in macroscopic and microscopic properties of the elements?

You will be better able to answer those questions by participating in the following activities:

ENGAGE	Creating Color
EXPLORE	Emitting to the Truth
EXPLAIN	Super Model
EXPLAIN	Noble-ity
ELABORATE	All in the Cards
EVALUATE	Testing Pattern

Your chapter organizer helps you monitor what you are learning. Look at it every day before class and think about where you are in its flow and organization. If at any point you are confused or think you are behind, consult with your teacher. Remember, monitoring what you understand helps you learn. And what you learn helps you become more successful.

How does atomic structure relate to different colors in flame tests?

◄◄ *Creating Color*

Key Idea:
Not all elements generate color when placed in a flame.

EXPLORE

Emitting to the Truth

Key Idea:
Electrons are responsible for spectral lines seen in flame tests.

Linking Question

How are protons and electrons arranged in atoms?

Organizing the Elements: The Periodic Table

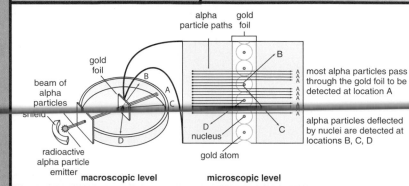

alpha particle paths   gold foil

gold foil

beam of alpha particles

shield

radioactive alpha particle emitter

macroscopic level

B
A
C
D

D nucleus

gold atom

B

C

microscopic level

most alpha particles pass through the gold foil to be detected at location A

alpha particles deflected by nuclei are detected at locations B, C, D

Testing Pattern

Key Idea:
Scientists learn from their
mistakes. The same is true for students.

How does the periodic
table demonstrate
atomic theory?

ELABORATE

All in the Cards

Key Idea:
Repeating patterns of
physical and chemical
properties are due
to atomic structure.

Linking Question

How does electronic
configuration apply to
trends on the
periodic table?

CHAPTER 4

Major Concepts

▶ **Atomic Structure**
- **Scientists infer atomic structure from indirect evidence.**
- **Atoms are mostly empty space.**
- **Electrons exist only in discrete energy states.**

▶ **Periodic Table Trends**
- **Atomic structure explains all trends on the periodic table.**
- **Noble gases are stable because of the configuration of their electrons.**
- **Stable compounds and noble gases have similar electron configurations.**

▶ **Models**
- **Models can be physical, conceptual, or mathematical.**
- **Logic, evidence, and critical analysis help select effective models.**

EXPLAIN

Super Model

▶▶

Key Idea:
Models help us make sense
of indirect evidence.

Linking Question

How do chemists
design stable
compounds?

EXPLAIN

Noble-ity

Key Idea:
Stable compounds acquire noble
gas electron configurations.

Creating Color

Think about the wave toy from chapter 2, The Material World. Would it be as entertaining if both layers were colorless? As a toy designer, you would investigate ways to make one layer colored. That way your product would sell better. Remember how you made a colored layer in the wave bottle activity? Is adding a dye the only way to create color?

▲ **Figure 4.1**
Fireworks create color. Colors give information about the elements inside the fireworks. What do atoms do to create color?

Now think about fireworks exploding in the night sky. What makes them so entertaining? Certainly, much of the joy of watching fireworks comes from color. And though the way dyes and fireworks produce color is different, color provides important information about the nature of elements and molecules.

For example, in the wave bottle activity, one dye was soluble in a polar liquid, but not in a nonpolar liquid. What would color tell you about the bonding *inside* dye molecules? *Between* dye molecules? Could color give you clues about the microscopic nature of matter? How could you organize this new information?

In the Creating Color activity, you will work by yourself and with others as your teacher creates color. Throughout the activity, ask yourself this question: What does color tell me about the nature of matter at the microscopic level? When you find out, you will understand another important way to organize what you know about the material world.

Materials

Process and Procedure

1. Carefully observe each solution displayed by your teacher and record what you see using Steps 1a–d as a guide.
   a. Sketch in your science notebook all 5 *salt* solutions.

Salt is a generic term used as a category name for many ionic solids. Not all salts are equally soluble in water.

    b. Include the chemical name for each salt.

    c. Include the chemical formula for each salt.

    d. Include the proper symbols to represent *dissociation* of each salt in water.

Remember how you represented dissociation in chapter 3. Sodium chloride dissolved in water by $NaCl_{(s)} \longrightarrow Na^+_{(aq)} + Cl^-_{(aq)}$. Don't forget to account for the law of conservation of matter with $SrCl_2$, $CaCl_2$, and $CuCl_2$.]

    2. Connect what you have already learned to what you see in each beaker by completing the following statements in your science notebook.

        a. I think each salt forms an ionic solid because _____.

        b. I can test to determine whether each solution contains ions by _____.

        c. I think ionic crystals dissolve in water because at the microscopic level, _____.

        d. Positive ions in each salt solution are generally organized on the _____ side of the periodic table (see figure 3.15) and are classified as _____.

        e. Negative ions in each salt solution are organized on the _____ side of the stair-step line on the periodic table and are classified as _____.

    3. Check your understanding of ions with a classmate by completing 3a–c.

        a. Read your answers slowly to your partner.

        b. Listen to what your partner reads.

        c. Modify your answers based on what you learned from your partner.

Don't forget to consult with your teacher if you and your partner cannot reach consensus or you are still confused. Successful students refuse to be confused.

    4. Carefully observe what happens when your teacher places small amounts of *each* salt solution in the flame.

        a. Make a sketch of the flame test apparatus and include the following labels where appropriate: "Bunsen Burner," "Hottest Part of Flame," "Coolest Part of Flame," "Flame Test Wire," and "Cleaning Solution."

        b. Record the color you see from each flame test.

5. Complete the following statements. Then repeat Step 3.
   a. I think the colors *are not* due to dissociation because

   _____.

   b. I think the colors *are not* due to negative ions because

   _____.

   c. I think the colors *are not* due to combustion because

   _____.

   d. I think the colors *are* due to positive ions because

   _____.

6. Answer 6a and perform 6b–c. Then repeat Step 3.
   a. Based on your knowledge of atoms, what part of the atom is most likely to be involved in the creation of color when your teacher places metal ions in a flame? Base your answer on what you learned about ionization in chapter 3.

   Think about bonding. What part of the atom moved about the most in bonding—electrons or protons?

   b. Sketch representations of 2 strontium ions (Sr^{2+}) with the proper number of protons and electrons, one *before* it enters the flame and another *after* it enters the flame.

   Think about the amount of heat energy *outside* versus *inside* the flame. In which location will strontium most likely experience some sort of change to a part of the atom? Your sketch should reflect that change.

   c. Using your best thinking, record what you suspect is happening in Sr^{2+} ions that produce color.

   Use your answer from Step 6a and the fact that Sr^{2+} does *not* lose or gain electrons in the flame to produce color.

Reflect and Connect

Form a team of 3 students and discuss the following questions. After the team reaches consensus, write your answers in your science notebook.

1. How are flame tests similar to fireworks? How are they different?

   Read the sidebar, The Chemistry of Fireworks, to delve deeper into the science of fireworks.

The Chemistry of Fireworks

On the Fourth of July, chemistry is probably the last thing on your mind. But if you plan to enjoy the fireworks display in your town, you should be glad that someone had his or her mind on chemistry.

What do fireworks and chemistry have in common? Chemistry explains what makes fireworks so spectacular. Sparklers, big booms, and colorful starbursts that you enjoy in the sky—chemistry makes them all possible.

The Chinese first made black powder during the ninth century, using it to drive away evil spirits. When ignited, black powder produces very hot gases, but does not produce the spectacular colors associated with fireworks today. In the 1830s, the Italians made a discovery. They began to add potassium chlorate to black powder, causing the powder to burn hotter and brighter. Once people found that they could create colors with black powder mixtures to produce fireworks, they began using them for entertainment.

Colors in fireworks are produced by the emission of energy from atoms and molecules. As black powder burns, energy from the fuel source transfers to certain chemicals in the fireworks. The chemicals absorb the heat energy and then release some of that energy in the form of light. Each chemical produces a distinct color of light. Strontium is red, barium is green, sodium is yellow, and copper is green blue. A mixture of colors is possible. For example, strontium and copper give off a purple color.

The brilliant white flashes in some fireworks are the result of chemical reactions. Magnesium, a very reactive metal, reacts with oxygen and burns at high temperatures. The energy given off heats the resulting compound (magnesium oxide), making it glow white hot. The process of giving off light due to increased temperature is called incandescence. You have probably observed this process in an incandescent lightbulb. As electricity passes through the filament, its temperature increases until it glows white hot. A similar process occurs in some fireworks. You also see shimmering sparks of metal when you light sparklers.

Pyrotechnicians are specialists trained to handle fireworks. They make small pellets of colorant out of compounds and mix them with fuel. The pellets can be as small as peas or as large as strawberries, depending on the desired display. Pyrotechnicians add titanium for sparks and loud booms and zinc for clouds of smoke.

2. How could you use flame test colors to organize *metallic* elements found on Earth?
3. What differences among the atoms of sodium, potassium, strontium, calcium, and copper could lead to differences in flame test colors?
4. Why doesn't water produce color in a flame test?
5. What questions do you still have regarding how some atoms produce color in a flame?

Emitting to the Truth

In Creating Color, you observed a different way to produce color. Your teacher used a flame test. Did your teacher use a *dye* to make different colors? Remember how dyes can make one layer of a wave toy very colorful.

You have been studying properties of matter. Is color a *characteristic* property of matter, like density or solubility? Does color help you understand the material world? You can answer those questions by connecting what you see to what it means.

For example, in the previous activity, you saw different metal ions emitting colors in a flame test. What do your observations mean? Do they suggest how protons and electrons behave in metal ions? If so, the macroscopic way materials function depends on the underlying microscopic form of matter. When have you heard this guiding principle before?

In Emitting to the Truth, you explore how color reveals important information about the microscopic particles that make up all matter.

Materials
For each team of three students

3 pairs of safety goggles

3 lab aprons

1 handheld spectroscope

access to various light sources

colored pencils

Cautions

Never look directly at the Sun, even through a spectroscope. Doing so can damage your eyes and may cause blindness. Do not touch or in any way disturb the light sources. The element tubes and their power supplies are expensive and require special handling. Do not touch them unless directed to do so by your teacher. Wear safety goggles and a lab apron.

Process and Procedure

A wave toy's color is due to a process that is different from the process that produces colors in the flame test. How do you know? You know because of what you see every day.

You have seen materials that are very hot produce color. Think of the phrases *white hot* and *red hot*. Does a red-hot heating coil on your stove produce color the same way copper ions produce color in a flame test? What explains how different metals in a flame of the *same temperature* produce different colors?

Could the answers be due to something that is happening at the atomic level? Could differences in atoms be responsible for differences in flame test colors? Are the differences due to characteristic properties? Why else would strontium always produce a characteristic scarlet flame test color? In this activity, see if you can discover answers to those questions.

Topic: spectra of elements
Go to: www.scilinks.org
Code: 1Inquiry159

You work individually and in teams to explore the behavior of 3 sources of light: **incandescent** lightbulbs, **fluorescent** tubes, and **element** tubes. To help, you will use an instrument called a spectroscope. The spectroscope helps you study different colors in the 3 sources of light. Those colors, in turn, will make you think about colors in flame tests.

A spectroscope is an instrument that takes light from any source and produces details you cannot see with your eyes alone. Those details are characteristic of the light source. They reveal clues about the atomic-level behavior of matter.

Scientists call those details **spectra**. Each spectrum of a substance is unique. In a way, spectra are like fingerprints. Spectra can be used to identify a substance.

Focus your exploration with this question: How does what I see at the macroscopic level connect to what occurs at the microscopic level?

1. Learn the proper technique for using a spectroscope by accomplishing Steps 1a–c.
   a. Observe your teacher's technique.
   b. Sketch the arrangement of teacher, eye, light source, spectroscope, slit, and distance between the eye and the light source.
   c. Label each feature listed in Step 1b.
2. Design an experiment to observe and record spectra from 3 light sources (incandescent lightbulb, fluorescent tube, and element tube) by considering Questions 2a–c.
   a. How will you record *exactly* what each spectrum looks like?
   b. How will you confirm observations among team members?
   c. How will you connect the type of source with its spectrum?
   d. How will you record your experimental procedure and results in your science notebook?
3. Record ideas about your design and develop your procedure.

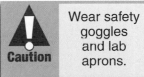

Wear safety goggles and lab aprons.

Caution

Ask your teacher to approve your procedure *before* you begin collecting data.

4. Carry out your experiment and record your results according to your plan.

5. In your science notebook, generate a list of important features of spectra by considering the following questions.
   a. Were all spectra continuous?

Continuous in this context means colors were spread out as in a rainbow with no distinct bands of blackness between colors.

   b. Did all spectra produce thin lines of color?
   c. Did all spectra show bands of black space with no color?
   d. Were thin lines of color always separated by the same amount of black space?
   e. Were thin lines always located in the same place when comparing 2 different sources?

6. Organize your list into similarities and differences by performing 6a–b.
   a. Draw 3 overlapping circles in your notebook that are large enough to occupy an entire page.

Your teacher will demonstrate the approximate proportions of each circle and label what each circle represents. Together the circles are sometimes called a Venn diagram.

   b. Analyze the list of important features that you produced in Step 5 and place each feature in the appropriate section of your 3-circle diagram.

Place only those features that are common to all 3 spectra in the part of your diagram where the 3 circles overlap. Continue this process for parts of your diagram where only 2 circles overlap.

7. Think about the Venn diagram of each team member by considering Steps 7a–d.
   a. Switch notebooks with a partner and study carefully your partner's 3-circle diagram.
   b. Inspect the diagram for the placement of features with which you agree.
   c. Discuss why you agree.
   d. Repeat Steps 7b–c, but focus on features with which you disagree.

Reflect and Connect

Discuss the following questions with your team. Consult with your teacher if you cannot reach consensus. Then write your answers in your science notebook.

1. What function does energy serve in flame tests? What function does energy serve in the 3 light sources?

2. Think about the spectra you might see when viewing light from flame tests. Now remember the spectra from the light sources in this activity. Should spectra from flame tests be similar to any of the 3 light source spectra? If so, which one or ones and why?

3. Think about the spectrum you might see when viewing a white-hot campfire. Should the spectrum from a campfire be similar to any of the 3 light source spectra? If so, which one or ones and why?

4. Light is a form of energy. Otherwise, oceans would not warm and skin would not sunburn. Is every color of light emitted from a light source associated with exactly the same amount of energy? Connect your answer to evidence from flame tests and spectra.

Energy: The Ultimate Quick-Change Artist

Energy is probably a familiar term to you. You may have used it by saying, "I just don't have any energy today." Or you may have heard someone say, "He has just too much energy!" You have also read about energy in this book. Energy will come up repeatedly as you continue your studies in science. But what is energy? Where does it come from? What does it do? What does it explain?

During your journey through science this year, you will have the opportunity to study several different disciplines of science, such as physical science, life science, and earth science. In each of those subjects, you will see macroscopic and microscopic examples of how changes in energy are important. For example, in physical science, you already studied how energy is involved on a microscopic level. You learned about the energy required to remove an electron from an atom to produce a positive ion. You learned that this is

Hummingbird and flower. What are the changes in energy that you see in this photograph?

called ionization energy. In your study of life science this year, you will study energy changes through a food web (the macroscopic level) from producers to consumers. As you study stars this year, you will learn how nuclear energy on the microscopic level is changed to observable heat and light energy. In the last unit, Perspectives on Science and Technology in Your World, you will see at the macroscopic level how the energy released in a fire can destroy a forest.

Energy is often defined as the ability to do work. You will study that idea of energy in depth in chapter 9, Life's Work. Although that definition may not mean much to you right now, one way to think about energy is as part of a cause-and-effect principle. For example, energy is a cause that exhibits many effects. Energy can be measured only by what it does—the actions or changes it causes in nature. It cannot be placed in a measuring cup like flour, be consumed like a slice of bread, or give off smoke like a fire. Energy is not a thing; it is abstract. You cannot see it, but you can detect it. You can detect the presence of energy only by the changes it effects.

Energy can cause changes in temperature, height, velocity, bonds in a molecule, and the state of an electron around an atom. The Sun heats up the surface of Earth, changing its temperature. Lifting a backpack from the floor to your shoulders to change the height of the backpack takes energy. Burning the gasoline in a car more rapidly to change the speed of the car also takes energy. When you studied the bonds in methane that break and form new bonds in water during combustion, you saw changes that were a result of applying energy. When your teacher performed a flame test earlier, you saw how energy caused change when atoms were heated and, as a result, electrons moved to different energy levels. The evidence you saw to indicate this change was the colored light that was produced.

All of your studies in science have energy as part of the focus, and you should keep some things in mind. First, energy is not something you can put on a balance or in a beaker to measure. You measure the changes that energy causes. The ways these changes are measured are different for various disciplines. You will learn some of these this year. Second, energy is not created or destroyed—it just changes forms. You witness this as you turn on a light switch in a room. At this level, you witness electrical energy changing

to light. Would you expect that the bulb is warm? If so, then some of that energy must also convert to heat. In the process, no energy is lost or gained.

As you continue your learning throughout the rest of the year, think about the changes that you observe when energy transfers occur. Your observations are evidence. You need observations to make conclusions. And the conclusions you make about energy involve how it is distributed, not whether it is made or lost. This knowledge will help you make connections and better understand one of the most central concepts that underlies all of science—energy.

Skiers on a chairlift. This chairlift will take these skiers to a high mountaintop. The skiers use this additional energy to have fun on the mountain. Can you name the changes in energy that are involved in taking the skiers to the top of the mountain to their final position as they finish their run at the bottom of the mountain?

EXPLAIN

Super Model

The Emitting to the Truth activity made you think about colored spectral lines as a characteristic property. Spectra are unique for every element. Differences in spectra depend on differences in the atoms that produce those spectra. But specifically, how are the tiny particles that Democritus imagined different? How does the structure of an atom vary from element to element?

You know that the number of protons and electrons differ from element to element. But how are protons and electrons arranged in atoms to give atoms their overall structure? It seems the more you

Topic: model of the atom
Go to: www.scilinks.org
Code: 1Inquiry162

explore about atoms and molecules, the more information there is to organize.

You probably guessed how important it is to know the structure of atoms. That knowledge increases your understanding of the material world. Unfortunately, the most powerful microscopes produce only fuzzy pictures of atoms. How can you determine the structure of something you cannot see?

Over the years, scientists have produced experimental results that help others infer what must be true about the structure of atoms. Scientists have put together evidence and have created a mental picture of atoms. Those mental pictures are sometimes called models. Models function a lot like analogies in English class. Models help scientists, teachers, *and* students visualize and better understand atoms.

In Super Model, you work individually and in teams to build a mental picture of atoms. You accomplish this task using two types of models—conceptual and mathematical. Both approaches lead you to a working understanding of the structure of atoms. To guide your work, ask yourself this question at each step of the procedure: What does this step reveal about the structure of atoms?

Part I: The Rutherford Atom: A Conceptual Model

Materials
For each team of four students

4 pairs of safety goggles

4 lab aprons

1 beaker (250 or 500 mL)

1 Rutherford model apparatus

1 toy marble

Cautions

Wear safety goggles and a lab apron. Do not throw marbles.

In Part I, you think about the structure of atoms. The picture of atoms you form in your mind will be based on experiments conducted by the famous scientist Ernest Rutherford. He analyzed his data and inferred what atoms might look like at the microscopic level. His analysis led to a conceptual model of atoms.

Process and Procedure

1. Try to picture Rutherford's model of the atom by reading Ernest Rutherford (1871–1937).

Ernest Rutherford (1871-1937)

Ernest Rutherford was a highly educated man. He worked under another scientist, Joseph John Thomson, a professor of experimental physics who had discovered electrons in 1897. Rutherford was anxious to probe the atom for more information. In 1911, Rutherford did just that. He learned more about the interior structure of an atom by shooting positively charged particles at very thin gold foil.

Rutherford had the idea to take a very thin gold foil and bombard it with high-energy, lightweight, positively charged particles (called alpha particles). He surrounded the foil target with detectors that would show where the alpha particles ended up after hitting the gold foil. The foil was only a few atoms thick, and most of the particles blasted through it, just as Rutherford expected. However, on rare occasions, an alpha particle would bounce from the target straight back in the direction from which it came. Rutherford was astonished. To him, this observation was similar to "firing cannonballs at tissue paper and having one come back and hit you."

What were the particles hitting? Rutherford knew that the electrons in the atoms were much less massive than the bombarding particles and that the electrons were negatively charged—opposite from the bombarding positively charged particles. Bombarding particles would be attracted to the electrons, not repelled. Further, if a direct collision did occur, the electrons would be too small and light to cause the

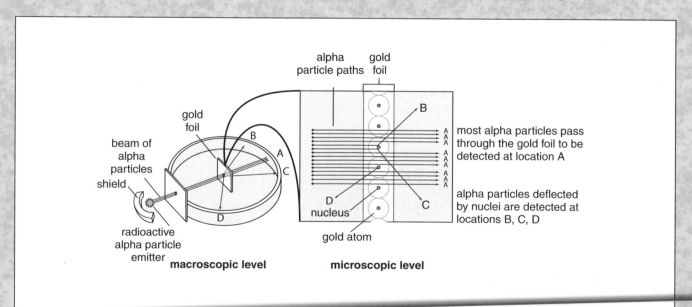

▲ **Figure 4.2 Schematic diagram of Rutherford's experiment.** When Rutherford shot alpha particles through gold foil, most ended up at point A. What surprised him was that some alpha particles were deflected to points B and C while others bounced back to points like D.

much heavier bombarding particles to rebound. So Rutherford concluded that the particles were not ricocheting off electrons.

Rutherford decided that the particles he was firing into the gold foil were hitting something that was more massive than the bombarding particles and that was positively charged. He knew that like charges would repel one another and that only heavier particles would cause the lighter particles to rebound. Rutherford also concluded that this positively charged part of the atom that was causing the rebound contained almost all of the mass of the atom, but it was very small compared with the size of the atom itself. He deduced this from how seldom the rebound events occurred. Most of the time, the particles he fired went straight through the foil, hitting nothing.

As a result of his observations, Rutherford proposed a new model of the atom (figure 4.3), one with a small, dense core (**nucleus**) that was made of positively charged particles called **protons.** Rutherford's atom was mostly empty space, with the nucleus at the center surrounded by electrons. Most of his bombarding particles penetrated the empty space of the atoms in the gold foil without coming near enough to a nucleus to rebound. Rutherford concluded that a rebound of

Topic: proton in the atom
Go to: www.scilinks.org
Code: 1Inquiry165

bombarding particles occurred only when the particles directly hit the nucleus of an atom in the gold foil.

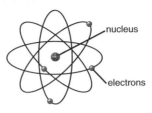

(nucleus not shown to scale)

▲ **Figure 4.3 Rutherford model of the atom.** The Rutherford model of the atom has a very small, dense, and positively charged nucleus surrounded by negatively charged electrons of very small mass.

▲ **Figure 4.4 Uses of gold.** The precious metal, gold, is used in some sophisticated electrical circuits.

2. Arrange the words *gold foil, alpha particles, nucleus, empty space, rebound, target,* and *astonished* in an importance pyramid. Use what you learned from the Ernest Rutherford reading to make this arrangement.

Remember that the importance pyramid asks you to place the most important words at the top of the pyramid. Then you place the other words underneath in decreasing order of importance in order to explain Rutherford's model. Some words may have the same level of importance.

3. Compare your understanding of the Rutherford reading with that of your teammates by performing Steps 3a–d.
   a. Exchange importance pyramids with a teammate.
   b. Review your teammate's arrangement of words.
   c. Rearrange your pyramid based on discussions with your partner.
   d. Exchange your pyramid with your other teammates and repeat Steps 3a–c.
4. Study figure 4.2 and use it to complete the analogy map in figure 4.5.

▼ **Figure 4.5**
Analogy map for Rutherford's experiment. Analogy maps help you create connections between models and experiments.

Feature of figure 4.2	Is like . . .	Piece of evidence from Rutherford experiment . . .	Because . . .
The red dot	is like	an alpha particle	because it "shoots" toward atoms in gold foil.
A red line	is like	the path of an alpha particle through gold foil	because it traces how the alpha particle started and where it ended up.
A black circle	is like	the nucleus of a gold atom	
A gold circle	is like		
The space between black dots	is like		
Continue based on Rutherford reading			
Continue based on team discussions			

The analogy map rows have not yet accounted for all of the evidence from Rutherford's experiment. Be sure to incorporate *all* of the evidence.

5. Design an experiment similar to the Rutherford experiment by considering Steps 5a–e.

You are making a conceptual model. Read the sidebar, What Is a Model?, for more details about models.

What Is a Model?

You have seen models before. You may have even built one. When most people hear the word *model,* they think of physical models, such as a model airplane or a model of the solar system. A **physical model** reproduces an object on a different scale, often a scale that allows you to handle the model. A model airplane looks like a real airplane, but the model is much smaller. A model of a cell looks like a real cell, but the model is much bigger than a real cell. You can compare a physical model with the actual object. The more accurate the physical model, the more it looks like the real object.

When scientists consider models, they often think of conceptual models. A **conceptual model** describes a system, not an object. A tornado, for example, is best described by a conceptual model. Such a model shows how the various components of the system interact. The components of a tornado include atmospheric pressure, humidity, temperature, and air currents. The more accurate the conceptual model, the better the scientist can predict the behavior of the system.

Like a tornado, the atom is a complex system and is best described using a conceptual model. The atomic model is not a re-creation of the actual atom. It is a symbolic representation of atomic behavior. A model of an atom provides an idea about atomic structure. Unlike the model airplane, however, no one knows if the model actually looks like the atom.

With current technology, scientists have not been able to see the inside structure of an atom because an atom is so small. Scanning tunneling microscopes have provided the best and most direct image of an atom so far. These microscopes are not like the kind you use in school: you cannot look through an eyepiece and see an atom. Instead, the microscope prepares an image on a computer screen. The image is a contour map of charge densities that a probe tip generates by moving across the surface of a substance. Each hill represents a charged area on the surface that scientists interpret to be the electron cloud of an atom. The valleys are the spaces between the atoms.

Because scientists are not able to see the interior of an atom, they develop conceptual models to aid their understanding. Scientists build atomic models from **inferences**—conclusions that follow logically from evidence. You learned about inference in chapter 1. In the case of atoms, the evidence includes laboratory data from investigations using technology such as X-rays, particle accelerators (machines that bombard materials with particles), scanning tunneling microscopes, and computers. As scientists learn more about atoms, they change and improve the model so it is consistent with the new information. Much current research in this area works toward an improved understanding of the nature of the particles that make up protons and neutrons, called quarks. The value of an atomic model lies in its ability to explain why atoms behave the way they do and to predict their behavior.

A subset of conceptual models is a mathematical model. It uses values derived from mathematical relationships to picture systems. Often, scientists and businesspeople find mathematical models to be very useful in making exact quantitative predictions of a system's behavior. For example, stockbrokers might use a mathematical model to predict the effect of increased oil prices on certain stocks. If their model is successful, they tend to be successful.

  a. Meet with your team to decide how to use the materials provided by your teacher. Specifically, decide how to represent
   the space between gold atoms with the cloth-over-frame
   apparatus, the alpha particles with the marbles, and the
   nucleus of a gold atom with a beaker under the cloth.

Check your design with your teacher before proceeding.

  b. Write your procedure in your notebook.
  c. Reproduce each alpha particle path shown in figure 4.2,
   using your marble.
  d. Sketch your model and draw each path that the marble takes
   during your investigations.
  e. Record how often each path occurs.

6. Construct an analogy map in your notebook similar to the one
 in Step 4. Use the headings "Feature of My Model," "Is Like,"
 "Evidence from Rutherford Experiment," and "Because."
 Complete the map using Step 4 as a guide.

7. Check your understanding of the analogy between your model
 and Rutherford's idea of the structure of an atom by performing
 Steps 7a–c.

  a. Compare your analogy map with teammates' maps and
   modify yours based on what you learned.
  b. Contribute your ideas to a class discussion.
  c. Make final additions and deletions to your map if your ideas
   change based on class discussion.

Caution — Do not throw marbles.

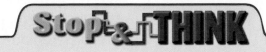

Part I

Write answers to each question in your science notebook and consult with teammates after you have finished your first attempt. Complete your answers after your conversations.

1. What are some characteristics of a *poor* model?

   Sometimes knowing what *does not* work helps you understand what *does*.

2. Why are models especially important to your understanding of the structure of atoms?

3. Think about what it would look like if you placed *all* of the cloth-over-frame structures in the classroom edge to edge in a line. Use the image in your mind to answer Steps 3a–f.

   a. What does this new arrangement represent? Answer using a sketch and caption for your explanation.

   b. Why is it easy for the marble to pass between the hills made by beakers? What does this model?

   c. Approximately where would electrons be located in your line-of-atoms model?

   d. Why don't positive alpha particles "bounce back," away from negative electrons? Why don't they "hit and stick"?

   Read the sidebar, Joseph John Thomson (1856–1940), to understand how surprisingly small the mass of an electron is.

   e. What does it mean when all of the beakers are the same height?

   f. How might the macroscopic properties of the foil change if different-sized beakers were used in the model?

   Beakers of different heights model nuclei with different numbers of protons. Different numbers of protons are one way to distinguish one element from another. For example, gold nuclei have 79 protons and silver nuclei have 47 protons.

Joseph John Thomson (1856–1940)

In 1897, an English physicist named Joseph John (J. J.) Thomson performed an experiment that shed light on the structure of the atom.

Like many scientists of his time, he was experimenting with electricity, trying to understand what was happening when electricity flowed through a wire. He performed an experiment that other scientists also were performing. He replaced a section of wire that was connected to batteries with a sealed glass tube. The ends of the wire extended into the tube, but there was a long gap between them that scientists believed would break the circuit and prevent electricity from flowing.

However, when scientists began pumping air out of the tube, current did flow, even though it looked as though the circuit was open. The electricity was getting across the open gap. Scientists observed an odd, faint glow in the tube, like a ray of energy crossing between the two wires. Scientists called the glowing rays **cathode rays,** and the big push in physics was to figure out what they were.

Scientists wanted to find out how the electric current was bridging the gap, so they performed more experiments. In one experiment, they placed positively and negatively charged plates inside the glass tube.

Thomson repeated all of the experiments, changing small parts of them in the hope of observing something new. He tried many changes, finally getting a result when he used more voltage than other scientists had used. When the cathode ray traveled between the two charged plates, the glow seemed to bend toward the positively charged plate.

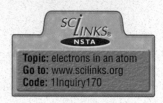

Topic: electrons in an atom
Go to: www.scilinks.org
Code: 1Inquiry170

This was an exciting observation to Thomson. Because of the bend of the glow, he knew that whatever was causing the electric current was behaving as particles usually did in response to positive and negative charges. He knew that like charges repel each other and unlike charges attract each other. Therefore, he concluded that the particles causing the electric current must be negatively charged because they were attracted to the positively charged plate.

Based on what the strength of the electrically charged plates was and how much the glow bent in the tube, Thomson calculated how massive these particles must be. He was shocked when he did the calculation. The mass of the particles carrying the current in the tube was tiny—1/2,000 of the mass of the hydrogen atom, the lightest element known.

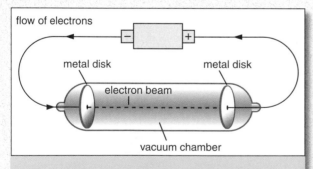

Cathode-ray tube. Joseph John Thomson's cathode-ray tube helped him calculate the charge-to-mass ratio for electrons.

"Could anything at first sight seem more impractical than a body which is so small that its mass is an insignificant fraction of the mass of an atom of hydrogen?" Thomson wondered.

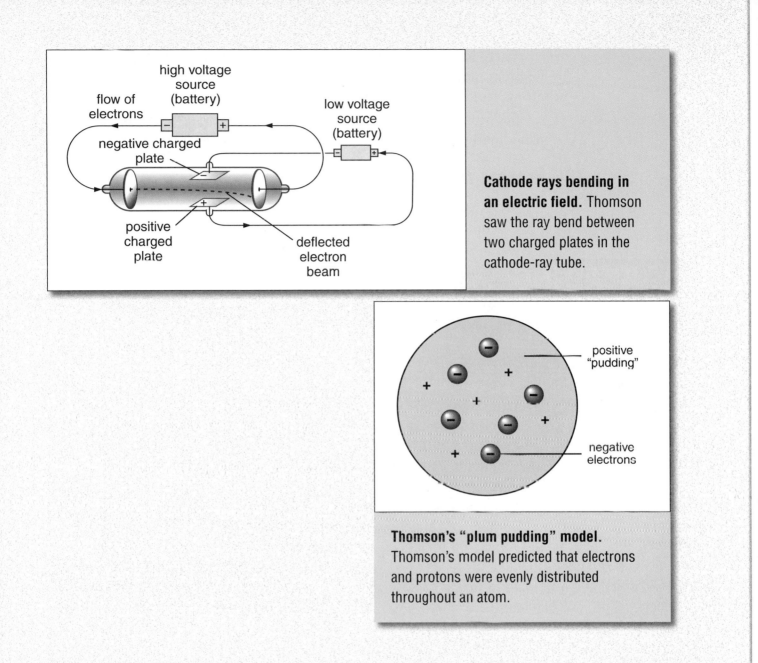

Cathode rays bending in an electric field. Thomson saw the ray bend between two charged plates in the cathode-ray tube.

Thomson's "plum pudding" model. Thomson's model predicted that electrons and protons were evenly distributed throughout an atom.

Part II: The Rutherford Atom: A Mathematical Model

Materials
For each team of three students

1 calculator

1 measuring tape

1 grapefruit or ball used in sports

In Part I, you saw how cloth, beakers, and a marble could help you imagine the structure of atoms. You made a conceptual model. It helped you picture an entire system of particles. That system is called an atom.

There is another way to picture Rutherford's model of the atom. It involves mathematics. Math helps you understand the structure of atoms from a different view.

In Part II, you work individually and with partners to model atoms using math.

Process and Procedure

1. Read the following paragraphs to learn about mathematical models.

READING

Making Math Models

Mathematics helps you picture what you cannot see. Imagine working for $15 per hour. Can you create a mental picture of your earnings after ten hours of work? Of course you can. What does that process look like on paper? Perhaps you thought about how your rate of pay and the time you worked *both* determined your total pay. In your mind, you might have first modeled the problem in sentence form, then translated it to math form. On paper, the process might look like figure 4.6.

You used mathematical models in chapter 2 when thinking about density. Isopropyl alcohol has a density of 0.8 grams per milliliter. How would you model the total mass of isopropyl alcohol that has a volume of 400 milliliters (mL)?

Mathematical models help scientists, businesspeople, and students plan effectively. For example, think about a camping trip. You need 0.5 gallon of drinking water per day. The density of water is 8.2 pounds per gallon. How much mass must you plan on carrying for a 4-day trip? Does your answer affect your plans? If so, how?

Sentence form	My rate of pay	and	the time I work	determine	my total pay.
Math form	$15 \frac{\text{dollars}}{\text{hours}}$	×	10 hours	=	150 dollars

▲ Figure 4.6 **Translation from sentence form to math form.** Translating thoughts in word form to thoughts in math form helps create a mathematical model.

2. Use what you learned about mathematical models to complete 2a–e.
   a. Think of a different situation in your life when a mathematical model helps you plan.
   b. Use a sentence to describe the situation in your notebook.
   c. Translate your sentence into a mathematical model.
   d. Explain your sentence and math forms to a team member.
   e. Listen to your team member's situation.
3. Solve the problems in 3a–e with mathematical models that you and your partners create.

Consider using a table like the one in figure 4.6 to guide your thinking.

   a. Suppose an alpha particle travels at 3.0×10^7 meters per second (m/s). How far does it travel in 4.2×10^{-5} seconds (s)?

Remember from math class that exponents are added when you multiply and subtracted when you divide.

   b. Do you think Rutherford designed his experiment so his alpha particles took 4.2×10^{-5} s to reach the gold foil? Explain your reasoning.
   c. Suppose Rutherford's lab was 10 meters (m) long. How much time would he plan on the alpha particles taking to move from the alpha particle source to the gold foil target?
   d. Suppose the distance between gold nuclei is 50×10^{-9} m and it took 1×10^{-15} s for an alpha particle to pass through the 1-atom-thick foil. How fast did the particle travel?
   e. From what you know about fast-moving particles, is the answer found in Step 3d reasonable? Why or why not?

Scientists check their work against known quantities whenever possible. Use the speed of light, 3.0×10^8 m/s, as a point of comparison for Step 3e.

4. Design a mathematical model of a Rutherford atom and use it to build a *scaled* physical model by using the statements in Steps 4a–e as a guide.

A scale model represents the exact proportions of an atom, only increased to macroscopic size so you can experience the dimensions. Your teacher may recommend building it in your school's parking lot.

   a. Diameters of atoms vary. A hydrogen atom has a diameter of 1.06×10^{-10} m. Written another way, that is 0.000000000106 m across. A typical nucleus has a diameter of 1.6×10^{-15} m. That number can be written 0.0000000000000016 m across.

b. Radius = diameter/2

c. Volume(sphere) = 4/3 π r^3

d. Study figure 4.7 to help you translate your thinking in words to thinking in mathematical terms.

Volume of nucleus	Is to	Volume of atom	As	Volume of grapefruit	Is to	Volume (to model)
$N_{nucleus}$	/	V_{atom}				

e. You can calculate radius if you know the volume.

5. Measure and construct your scale model of the atom, using the materials provided.

Your teacher will tell you whether to build the model inside the classroom or elsewhere.

a. Record in your science notebook all calculations with proper units and labels *before* you measure and construct your scale model.

b. Draw a labeled sketch of your scale model in your science notebook.

6. Respond to 6a–c in your science notebook to help you think about the relative size of the nucleus and atom.

Consult with teammates. If you have any remaining confusion, consult with your teacher.

a. Explain how your mathematical model helped you plan the construction of your scale model.

b. How many nuclei could fit into an atom?

c. If the volume of the nucleus is not large compared with the volume of the atom, what is it about the nucleus that *is* large? How do you know?

Reflect and Connect

Work with your team to answer the following questions, using all of your models of the atom. Write your final answers in your science notebook.

1. Which model helps you best picture a microscopic atom? Why is it most helpful?

2. Using your model, how close, measured in meters, can gold nuclei get to each other?

3. What percentage of the total volume of an atom is space?

Do not forget that percentage is another way of expressing the fraction of space in an atom.

4. Answer the following questions about percentage to help you relate atoms to common situations.
   a. How does the percentage of empty space in an atom compare with the percentage of empty space in your room at home?
   b. How does the percentage of empty space in an atom compare with the percentage of space in a tennis ball (to the outer edge)?
   c. How does the percentage of space in an atom compare with the percentage of space in your mouth?
5. If atoms are mostly space, why doesn't your hand pass through a tabletop when you press on the table?

Noble-ity

EXPLAIN

It is amazing. In chapter 2, you started this unit investigating the physical and chemical properties of a wave toy. From there, you developed an understanding of density, solubility, ionization energy, electronegativity, and bonding. And because of how you just modeled the Rutherford experiment, you understand a lot about the structure of atoms. Now that is science!

But there is more—much more—such as deciding why all of this knowledge is important to you and to others. It is important because knowledge of the material world leads to a better life. Just imagine if *you* designed the medicine that cures AIDS. That medicine would be made of molecules. Those molecules would be composed of atoms bonded together in characteristic ways. There would be an exact formula for the molecule. Manufacturers could then follow your formula in order to use the correct type and number of each element when making the compound.

But how do you come up with the correct formula? How do you *design* a molecule?

This activity, Noble-ity, helps you answer those questions. With the answers, you can apply your understanding of bonding. You can decide whether the molecule you design should be soluble in water, should boil at a high temperature, or should react chemically with other materials. Those characteristic properties will help determine how the compound functions. For example, would you want your AIDS medicine to be soluble in

▼ **Figure 4.8**
Researcher designing molecules.
Researchers design molecules based on what the molecules are supposed to do. How molecules function depends on their physical and chemical properties. How does the organization of the periodic table help researchers design AIDS medicines?

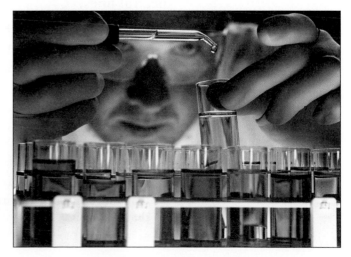

stomach fluid? Should you design your medicine to digest like a piece of bread does?

In this activity, you work individually and in a team to design compounds. Designing correct formulas for compounds depends on bonding. And bonding depends on how electrons behave around nuclei.

In Part I, you learn how electrons behave *close* to the nucleus. You use emission spectra as your primary information source. In Part II, you consider electrons *far* from the nucleus. You use ionization energy as your primary information source. Throughout the activity, keep asking yourself this question: How do I design a molecule with the correct formula and characteristic properties I want? You will soon see that your answer has a lot to do with only one family of elements in the periodic table—the noble gases.

Part I: Back to the Spectra: The Bohr Model

Materials
For each team of three students

colored pencils

Process and Procedure

The way electrons interact depends on their configuration around the nucleus. But Rutherford's model suggested only that electrons are somehow outside the nucleus. His model said nothing about electron configuration.

Why is electron configuration important? Electron configuration is important because it helps predict how atoms bond to form molecules with unique formulas. How did scientists learn about electron configuration? It started with a new model of the atom created by a scientist named Niels Bohr. And his ideas came from analyzing spectral lines.

1. Redraw your line spectra from the element tube for hydrogen. You recorded this spectrum in the Emitting to the Truth activity earlier in this chapter.

   Use colored pencils. Carefully show the position of each of the four lines. Don't forget to show the amount of black space between lines.

2. Review the important features of this spectrum. Focus on differences in energy to answer Steps 2a–d.

   Remember that light is a form of energy. Different colors of light have different amounts of energy. Scientists have determined that blue light has *more* energy than red light.

    a. How do you know that the Rutherford model of atom struc-
ture *did not* explain line spectra?

Your answer helps you review what information Rutherford's experiment did and
did not give you.

    b. How do you know that each line is associated with a *differ-
ent amount of energy*?

The number of lines *does not* correspond to the number of electrons in hydrogen.

    c. What makes you think *rapidly moving electrons*, not rapidly
moving protons, are responsible for spectral lines?

    d. How were differences in the *amount of dark space between
lines* of color important?

  3. Consult with your team regarding answers to Steps 2a–d
and modify your answers based on what you learned from
teammates.

  4. Read Niels Bohr (1885–1962) and think about his model of
the atom.

READING

Niels Bohr (1885-1962)

Niels Bohr was a Danish physicist who became interested in science at an early age. His parents supported his desire to study science. He eventually became a very influential individual in the physical science world and developed the Bohr theory of the atom.

Bohr wanted to conduct research with Joseph John Thomson, the scientist who first discovered electrons. Thomson, however, never showed interest in Bohr's ideas about electrons and had no desire to work with him. So Bohr decided to study the structure of the atom with Ernest Rutherford, the physicist who proposed the existence of the nucleus of an atom in 1911. Rutherford's model of the atom has a positively charged nucleus with negatively charged electrons revolving around it, much like planets revolve around a sun.

Bohr immediately began working on Rutherford's nuclear model of the atom. Both he and Rutherford knew that Rutherford's model was unstable. According to classical physics, the orbiting electrons in Rutherford's model would continuously give off energy and eventually spiral into the nucleus, collapsing the atom. Bohr wanted to improve on Rutherford's model to explain why this did not happen.

Up until this time, scientists believed that the orbit of an electron could be any size. Bohr, however, believed that an electron could move only in an orbit of a specific size. He did not believe that an electron could move halfway into the next orbit, just as a person cannot stand halfway between two rungs of a ladder.

Bohr used spectral line data as evidence that his ideas made sense. When an individual

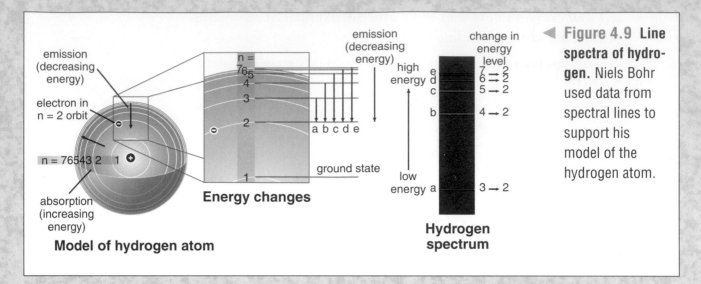

Labels in figure: emission (decreasing energy), electron in n = 2 orbit, n = 76543 2 1, absorption (increasing energy), **Model of hydrogen atom**

n = 76 5 4 3 2 1, **Energy changes**, a b c d e, ground state

emission (decreasing energy), high energy, low energy, change in energy level, e 7→2, d 6→2, c 5→2, b 4→2, a 3→2, **Hydrogen spectrum**

◀ **Figure 4.9 Line spectra of hydrogen.** Niels Bohr used data from spectral lines to support his model of the hydrogen atom.

atom of an element, such as that in a gas, is heated, it gives off light. When viewed through a spectroscope, the light is separated into specific wavelengths. The wavelengths of light emitted by an element, which show up as a pattern of bright lines, make up its line spectrum. This pattern is unique for each element, and it can be used to identify the elements.

Bohr hypothesized that when electrons in an atom absorb energy, they absorb only a specific amount, or **quantum**, of energy, resulting in the electron getting boosted to a higher energy level. When the electron returns to the lower energy level, the quantum of energy is released. The specific quantum of energy released shows up as light and, through a spectroscope, appears as a single line in a bright line spectrum. Each line in a spectrum has a specific wavelength that corresponds to a quantum of energy. The reason every element has a different line spectrum is because each atom has a different number and arrangement

of electrons that can absorb and release different quanta of energy.

As a result of his work looking at the hydrogen line spectrum, Bohr proposed that electrons traveled in a specific path, called an **orbit,** rather than randomly revolving at any distance around the nucleus. An electron, Bohr postulated, has a specific amount of energy to keep it in a given orbit. Electrons in orbits closest to the nucleus are lower in energy; those farther away are higher in energy.

In 1913, Bohr proposed his model of the hydrogen atom, a model similar to the theory of Rutherford's model, but with new details. Bohr still believed that an atom had a positive nucleus, but in his hydrogen model, the electron circled the nucleus in specific orbits, like planets orbiting a sun.

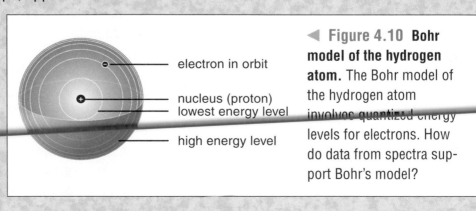

electron in orbit

nucleus (proton) lowest energy level

high energy level

◀ **Figure 4.10 Bohr model of the hydrogen atom.** The Bohr model of the hydrogen atom involves quantized energy levels for electrons. How do data from spectra support Bohr's model?

5. Use your understanding of Bohr's model of the atom to develop responses to 5a–c. Then write your responses in your science notebook.

   a. Describe why Rutherford's model of atoms *did not* explain spectra. Include in your description a labeled sketch with highlight comments and a caption.

   b. Complete the following table in your science notebook. Add more rows as required.

Statement from reading	Evidence from spectra	How I connected first 2 columns
Specific photon released shows up as light . . .	Thin lines of specific colors, not like a rainbow	If photon has specific energy, then the color it makes should be specific, too.
Continue . . .		

   c. Compare your table with the one you constructed after class discussion and modify your table based on what you learned.

6. Examine the chemical symbols in the following expressions. They represent 2 important aspects of the Bohr model. These aspects involve an electron changing from one energy state to another. Use these symbols to answer Steps 6a–e in your science notebook.

$$Sr^{2+} _{\text{ground state}} + energy \rightarrow Sr^{2+} _{\text{excited state}}$$
$$Sr^{2+} _{\text{excited state}} \rightarrow Sr^{2+} _{\text{ground state}} + photon$$

A photon is a way to express the energy of that light.

   a. Which expression involving a strontium ion represents an electron of a strontium ion absorbing energy? How do you know?

▲ Figure 4.11
Evidence and meaning table. Examine the Bohr reading for key statements about his model. Then connect each statement to what you see in spectra.

Topic: emission of photons
Go to: www.scilinks.org
Code: 1Inquiry179

    b. Which expression represents an electron of a strontium ion emitting energy? How do you know?

    c. What particle transports energy away from the excited state of a strontium ion when it falls to the ground state?

An electron with absorbed energy from a flame will be unstable. The electron will shed this excess energy. But the energy is not lost. The excess energy leaves in another form, as a photon of light.

    d. Based on flame tests, what is a reasonable hypothesis about the color of an emitted photon from strontium?

Remember that a hypothesis represents your best thinking about how something works, but your thinking must be linked to evidence.

    e. Did the heat of the flame ionize the strontium ion? How do you know?

Part II: Noble Predictions: Designing Compounds the Easy Way

Materials
For each team of three students

graph paper or grid paper in science notebook

colored pencils

Part I helped you understand how electrons behave when they are relatively *close* to, but not removed from, the nucleus. You saw how electrons moved back and forth between distinct energy levels and never existed between energy levels. The energy levels are unique for every atom. And the difference in energy *between* energy levels is unique for every element on the periodic table.

Energy differences explain unique atomic spectra. What else do energy differences explain? In Part II, you work individually and in a team to study another kind of energy difference. It is one you studied in chapter 3—ionization energy. Do you remember that ionization energy involves removing electrons *far* from the nucleus?

Process and Procedure

    1. Read the following paragraphs to help you generate a focus question for this part of the activity.

READING

Focus on Stability

What is important about understanding the ionization energy of different elements on the periodic table? The important thing is that there are trends in the ionization energies of elements. And those trends help you design molecules.

How? The trends you discover determine which compounds will be stable and which will be unstable. Of course, *stable* compounds are what you want to design. For example, an *unstable* medicine might react before it reaches the target site in your body. In nature, stable compounds are the rule, not the exception. To a large extent, stable compounds make up the materials you touch, see, feel, and taste in your everyday experiences.

How do you learn to design stable compounds? First, you study trends in ionization energies of elements on the periodic table. Those trends are based on how electrons are configured about the nucleus of atoms. Then you use those trends to decide which *family of elements* is stable. Finally, you infer that if you can design compounds with the same electronic configuration as the electronic configuration of this stable family of elements, then it is likely the compound you design will also be stable.

2. Use the information from the reading in Step 1 to generate a question that will focus your investigation in Part II.

3. Review Steps 3a–d to design the layout for a plot of ionization energy versus atomic number for elements 1–20.

Topic: family of elements
Go to: www.scilinks.org
Code: 1Inquiry181

Planning ahead helps you spend less time producing a better graph. Read through each reminder *before* starting your graph.

a. Decide how to scale the axes so your entire graph fits in the upper two-thirds of your graph paper, leaving space for highlight comments and a caption.

Study figure 4.12 and decide as a team the appropriate maximum values for the independent axis (atomic number) and the dependent axis (ionization energy).

b. Discuss the best way to communicate important information about each axis.

c. Inspect the data ahead to anticipate if you should use a best-fit or point-to-point method of showing trends.

d. Label all high points and low points with the corresponding element symbol.

4. Analyze your graph for trends by generating highlight comments and a caption after considering Steps 4a–d.

Remember, highlight comments use the "What I see," "What it means" format. Your caption tells the reader what is important about the graph by combining the highlight comments into sentence format.

a. There are 2 common names given to a vertical column in the periodic table—**family** and **group.** Which family or group of elements has the lowest overall ionization energies? Which has the highest ionization energies?
b. What is the general trend in ionization energies *within* a family of elements?
c. A horizontal row is called a **period.** What is the general trend in ionization energies *across* periods?
d. How can you use colored pencils to emphasize the trends you see?

5. Explain each trend using your model of the atom and completing a double T-table with the following headings: "Statement of Trend," "Elements Involved in Trend," and "Explanation of Trend."

▼ **Figure 4.12**

Ionization energies.

The ionization energies shown represents the amount of energy required to remove the outermost electron completely from an atom.

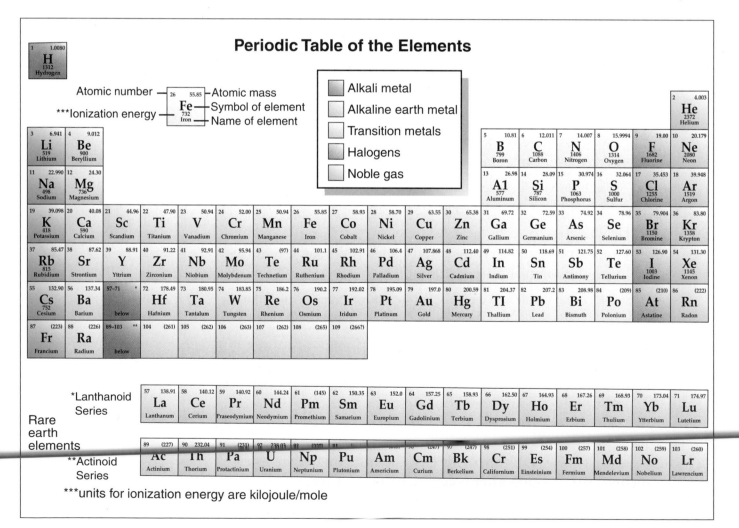

Remember, the larger the atomic number, the more protons in the nucleus, but also the larger the number of electrons. In general, the more electrons outside the nucleus, the larger the atom.

    a. Complete the double T-table on your own.

    b. Check your understanding with your teammates.

    c. Share your T-table in a class discussion and modify your table based on what you learn from others.

6. Divide the questions in Steps 6a–i among team members and answer your assigned questions in your notebook.

Team Member 1

    a. Which family of elements has the lowest ability to attract electrons? Explain from a microscopic viewpoint.

    b. Why are there only a few known compounds involving noble gases, yet thousands of compounds involving other elements?

    c. The way electrons are configured around the nuclei of noble gases is very stable, which is why noble gases have such high ionization energies. When electron configurations in other elements are the same as noble gas electron configurations, those elements are also stable, but not to the same extent. How many electrons must a neutral sodium atom lose in order to have an electron configuration like neon? Answer the same question for magnesium.

Team Member 2

    d. The way electrons are configured around the nuclei of noble gases is very stable, which is why noble gases have such high ionization energies. When electron configurations in other elements are the same as noble gas electron configurations, those elements are also stable, but not to the same extent. How many electrons must a neutral chlorine atom gain in order to have an electron configuration like argon? Answer the same question for oxygen.

    e. Why might some atoms tend to form positive ions and other atoms tend to form negative ions?

    f. How are the most common ions formed for elements 1–20 related to their position on the periodic table?

Team Member 3

    g. Why are stable compounds electrically neutral?

    h. Which electrons are most likely to be involved in bonding: those closest to the nucleus or those farthest away from the nucleus? Use a labeled sketch to show your thinking.

i. What seems to be the number of electrons associated with the outermost electrons of noble gases?

Each period on the periodic table ends with a noble gas on the right side. The total as well as the outermost number of electrons in a noble gas depends on the period in which the noble gas is found.

7. Meet as a team and share your best ideas on each assigned question.
8. Think about the number of outer electrons associated with a stable *ion*. How does that number relate to the number of outer electrons found in all noble gases?

Read the sidebar, Electron Dot Diagrams, to find out more about this number and to learn about a bookkeeping method showing stable ions.

SIDEBAR

Electron Dot Diagrams

After working with the simplified modern model of the atom, you might wonder whether there is an easier way to draw a model of an atom. Actually, there is. Electron dot diagrams are an abbreviated way to highlight the portion of the atom that is involved in chemical bonding: the electrons in the outermost shell. An electron dot diagram consists of the atomic symbol surrounded by dots. The atomic symbol takes the place of the nucleus and the inner energy-level (noble gas configuration) electrons. Each electron in the outer shell is represented by a dot. Take a look at a few examples in this figure.

Notice that a dot is added to each of four sides, before pairing up. This reflects the tendency of the negative charges of the electrons to repel each other.

Electron dot diagrams also can illustrate how atoms combine to make molecules. Some simple examples are illustrated in this figure.

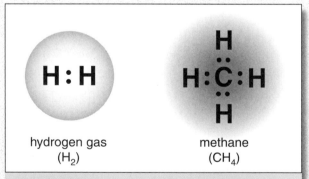

hydrogen gas (H$_2$)

methane (CH$_4$)

Electron dot diagrams for hydrogen gas and methane. Electron dot diagrams can represent molecules, such as hydrogen (H$_2$) and methane (CH$_4$).

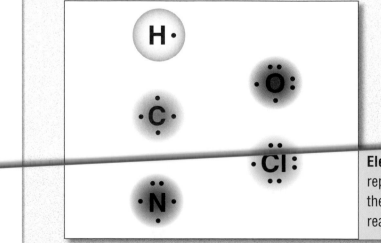

Electron dot diagrams. Electron dot diagrams represent a sort of bookkeeping procedure for the outermost electrons involved in chemical reactions and bonding.

9. Write in your science notebook a rule for designing stable compounds.

Your teacher may use Steps 5–7 as a guide for class discussion. If so, record each answer accurately in your science notebook. Be sure to let your teacher know if you are confused.

10. Write answers to Steps 11–14 in your science notebook and check your answers with teammates. Consult with your teacher if you have any lingering confusion.

11. For the following compounds, determine whether the formula is correct. If it is not correct, modify the formula and explain your correction process.

Determine whether the rule you developed in Step 9 works.

a. $NaCl_2$ d. Li_3F
b. BaF e. Mg_2S
c. KO f. Al_2O_3

12. Where might the ionization energy of Xe be located on your plot from Step 3? What about the ionization energy of Cs? Explain your thinking.
13. What seems to be the more important factor in determining ionization energy *across* a period: atomic size or atomic number (the number of protons in the nucleus)? Explain.
14. What seems to be the more important factor in determining ionization energy *down* a family: atomic size or atomic number? Explain.

Remember that more electrons generally increase the size of the atom.

Reflect and Connect

Write answers to the following questions in your science notebook and check your answers with others.

1. How does the model of a *single* atom help you understand what happens when *multiple* atoms interact to form a compound?
2. How does the graphic organization of the periodic table help you *quickly* predict the correct formulas of compounds?
3. Explain the possible value of predicting correct formulas of compounds.
4. You learned in Part II that stable electronic configurations of atoms involve no more than 8 electrons in the group of electrons involved in bonding. These outermost electrons are called **valence** electrons. Many more electrons may be outside the nucleus, but only valence electrons are involved in bonding. When a set of 8 noble gaslike electrons (2 in the case of the

1st period) exists between the nucleus and the valence electrons, the set is called a filled noble gas core. These cores decrease the attraction between the nucleus and valence electrons. This effect is called shielding.

How might shielding affect the trend of ionization energies in a family of elements?

Molecule Models

Models help you form mental pictures of things that are not easy to see. Good models generate deeper understanding of nature. They do this by giving you a concrete way of testing concepts that you are exploring.

You do not have to be the size of molecules in order to interact with them. All you need are molecular models. The key ingredient is your ability to associate features of the model with particles at the atomic level. As long as you know what each piece of the model represents, you can use it to explore *any* molecular level interactions.

Therefore, the color, shape, length, and material used to make molecular models are not important. Any material will do as long as you understand the connection between the microscopic and macroscopic worlds represented by the model. For example, a ball-and-stick model uses wooden spheres of various colors to represent atoms of unique elements. Often, black is carbon, red is oxygen, and yellow is hydrogen. An equally effective model would be a set of colored paper clips. In either model, you could represent a molecule of methane. The ball-and-stick model uses one black ball and four yellow balls, while the paper clip model uses one "carbon" paper clip and four "hydrogen" paper clips.

Methane at room temperature... or methane on Titan?

All students reach understanding through a variety of perspectives. In the same way, different models represent different perspectives of atoms and molecules. Different perspectives provide tools to use in solving different problems. For any given problem, you use the type of representation best suited to help you solve the problem.

Form of Representation	Example of Representation	When Most Used	
words	Methane	textbook reading	symbolic
chemical formula	CH_4	chemical reactions	
structural formula	H—C—H (with H above and below)	molecular properties	increasing level of abstraction
electron dot	H:C:H (with H above and below, dots around C)	bonding	
ball-and-stick (3 dimensional)		molecular geometry	
particle model		molecular collisions	concrete

various models of methane. What do you think of when you hear the word *methane*? Do you picture one image or several images? Successful problem solvers picture several models and use the best one to solve a problem.

These figures serve as examples. First, study the figure of the boy thinking about methane on the facing page. He has just been asked the question, why is methane a gas at room temperature? The boy has many ways of representing methane in his mind. He selects the ball-and-stick model because it best helps him solve the problem. The ball-and-stick model allows him to see each carbon-hydrogen bond in three-dimensional space. All four carbon-hydrogen bonds exhibit a slight dipole, which might lead him to think that methane is polar. If it were polar, the plus and minus attractions between molecules would make the boiling point high. Then methane would be a liquid at room temperature, like water.

The ball-and-stick model allows you to see symmetry. That is, all four diploes are arranged in space such that their effects mutually cancel each other. The net result is no dipole. With no dipole, methane molecules have very little attraction to one another. Thus, the boiling point is low and methane is a gas at room temperature.

The figure of the girl thinking about sodium represents another question that often comes up in a physical science course. She has just been asked the question, what is the most common ion of sodium and why?

Notice how many ways of representing the sodium ion come to her mind. The chemical symbol Na^{1+} best answers the first part of the question. The second part of the question requires a different model. She probably remembers one or two ways to represent the number of electrons in neutral sodium. Then she remembers that noble gas electronic configurations are very stable. She notices that sodium has one more electron than its nearest noble gas, neon. Therefore, neutral sodium loses one electron to obtain a stable noble gas electronic configuration. Sodium forms a positive one ion.

Models are like tools. They do not do the job for you. However, they can make your work much easier if you have the right tools available and know how to use them for a particular job. Models cannot do your homework, but they can make it easier and more understandable.

Various models of sodium ion. Many problems involve multiple parts. Students who can think of multiple ways to deal with a problem tend to solve more problems correctly. How many models of the sodium ion can you picture?

Sodium ion...

Form of Representation	Example of Representation	When Most Used
words	Sodium ion	textbook reading
chemical symbols	Na^{1+}	chemical equations
Rutherford Model (nuclear atom)	$10e^-$ $11p^+$	charge bookkeeping
electron dot	$[Na]^{1+}$	electronic configuration, bonding
charged particle	+	particle collisions

symbolic

increasing level of abstraction

concrete

All in the Cards

The last activity, Noble-ity, helped you learn how to design thousands of compounds. You based that ability on the location of elements on the periodic table. In other words, the way elements are arranged on the periodic table helps you make important predictions about the molecules you design—such as what their formulas are.

What else does the position of elements on the periodic table tell you? Can the arrangement of elements on the periodic table tell you about something other than ionization energy? For example, can you observe trends in density, phase of matter, solubility, melting point, reactivity, bond type, and spectral patterns as you saw in ionization energy? If so, the periodic table is an amazing resource of information about the material world. And it is organized into trends that make understanding nature easier. All of this information is the power of the most famous graphic organizer in the world—the periodic table.

In All in the Cards, you apply what you know about atoms and molecules to understand the organizing principles of the periodic table. You work individually and in teams. First, you look for trends in the organization of the periodic table. Next, you determine which trends explain the shape of the periodic table most effectively. Finally, you apply what you know about trends to place "unknown" elements on the periodic table.

Part I: Which Organizing Principle Is Best?

Materials
For each team of three students

graph paper

colored pencils

1 set of element cards

You already know ways in which the periodic table is organized. For example, you know that metals such as copper and sodium tend to be on the left side of the stair-stepped line. Nonmetals such as oxygen and fluorine tend to be on the right side. Noble gases are on the extreme right side.

You have used this organization to predict bond types. Elements from the far left and right sides of the periodic table combine to form ionic substances. Their electronegativities are far apart. Elements close to each other on the periodic table generally form covalent bonds. Oxygen and carbon dioxide are examples.

What underlying principle of matter governs the organization of the periodic table? What other ways can you use to organize elements on the periodic table? Which method is best? In Part I, you apply what you already know from previous activities to answer those questions.

Process and Procedure

1. Obtain 1 set of element cards and lay them out before your team.
   a. Organize them according to what you already know from previous activities.
   b. Review the information recorded on each card.

2. Design an investigation to determine which organizing principle best explains the shape of the periodic table. Consider Steps 2a–e while you design.
   a. You already investigated 1 organizing principle. It was based on ionization energy. You plotted ionization energy versus atomic number and looked for patterns. Then you explained those patterns with highlight comments and a caption.
   b. Other properties you could plot are color, phase at room temperature, number of outer electrons, atomic radius, density, melting point, and electronegativity.
   c. You can compare plots most easily when they all have the same scale on the horizontal axis.
   d. Dividing the labor among team members helps you understand the most for the least amount of effort.
   e. Highlight comments and captions are an effective way to summarize important information from a graph.

3. Check your design with your teacher and conduct your investigation.

4. Meet as a team and decide an effective way to share information about each plot.

Use techniques you have learned from previous chapters.

5. Decide as a team which organizing principle best explains how the periodic table is organized and be prepared to share your ideas in a class discussion.

Part I

Record answers to these questions in your science notebook after you have consulted with teammates.

1. What process did you use to notice trends in any of the plots you made?
2. What practical value do trends offer? Give an example from 1 of your graphs.
3. How do models of the atom help you understand trends in the periodic table?

Part II: An Application from History

Materials

For each team of three students

3 copies of Patterns of Elements handout

3 copies of Missing Elements handout

In Part I, you determined that the best organizing principles draw from an atomic view of matter. When you understand atomic structure, you can use that knowledge to organize the periodic table. Once you have accomplished that, you have organized a vast amount of information about the material world.

Why is this important? It is important because the periodic table organizes information in patterns that help you understand the behavior of matter.

That is exactly the lesson history teaches. It is true even in the history of the periodic table. In Part II, you learn how a Russian chemist named Dmitri Mendeleyev organized information in the periodic table. Then he used an organizing principle to make important predictions about the properties of missing elements.

Process and Procedure

1. Read Mendeleyev and the Periodic Table to find out how he organized information in the periodic table.

Mendeleyev and the Periodic Table

By the early 1800s, scientists knew that most materials could be broken down into simpler substances. They had noted that burning wood produced carbon dioxide, water, and ash. Scientists also knew that some materials could not be broken down into other substances. They could heat wood to get charcoal (essentially pure carbon), but they could not break the carbon down any further. Carbon was identified as a chemical element. In 1800, fewer than 30 elements had been isolated. Scientists used new technology, in the form of electrolysis, to make even more discoveries. Electrolysis uses electric current to separate compounds into their elements. By the late 1860s, 63 elements had been isolated. There was a great need to find a way to organize all of the information about the elements.

Who was up for the task? Enter a Russian by the name of Dmitri Ivanovich Mendeleyev. Mendeleyev was born in Siberia in 1834, the youngest of a very large family. His father died at a young age, leaving the family to cope with financial hardships, but his mother saw to it that Mendeleyev attended college in St. Petersburg. He graduated at the top of his class and went on to make significant contributions in a variety of fields.

In 1869, Mendeleyev was a professor at the University of St. Petersburg. He was writing a textbook for a chemistry course he was teaching. Mendeleyev was searching for a way to organize all of the known information about the elements. How did he conduct his search? In his own words, written in his 1905 *Principles of Chemistry* textbook:

▲ **Figure 4.13**
Dimitri Mendeleyev at age 18. Mendeleyev developed the principles used to design the modern periodic table.

I began to look about and write down the elements with their atomic weights and typical properties, analogous elements and like atomic weights on separate cards, and this soon convinced me that the properties of elements are in periodic dependence upon their atomic weights.

Early scientists such as Mendeleyev actually used the term *atomic weight* instead of *atomic mass*. You will learn about differences between those terms later in this program.

What does this mean? Mendeleyev made a card for each element that included information about the element's mass and properties. Then he lined up the elements from lightest to heaviest, according to their atomic masses. Next, he looked for patterns in their characteristic properties.

Although his cards included both physical and chemical properties, he focused on the chemical properties. He noted that many of the properties of the elements repeated themselves in a regular pattern. He found that he could "fold" the line of elements so that the ones with similar characteristics were arranged in groups. He placed hydrogen first and kept the elements in order in a line. He started a new line of elements each time he came across an element with properties similar to those of hydrogen. The result was a table rather than one line. Because physical and chemical properties repeated *periodically* as one moved along the list of elements, the *table* presented them in groups of similar elements. It was called the **periodic table of the elements**.

Mendeleyev's table contained blank spaces. He thought that elements existed to fill the spaces, and he was able to predict the properties of some of those elements that had not yet been discovered. When the elements were discovered later, they fit into his table just where he had predicted. Mendeleyev won international acclaim.

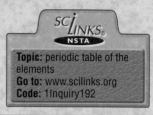

Topic: periodic table of the elements
Go to: www.scilinks.org
Code: 1Inquiry192

2. Determine whether you understand how Mendeleyev used trends in the periodic table by predicting some chemical and physical properties of 2 elements with which you are not familiar.
   a. Obtain 3 copies of the handout, Patterns of Elements, and find the 2 missing elements.

   The Patterns of Elements handout is a reproduction of Mendeleyev's periodic table, including 2 elements yet to be discovered in his time.

   b. Use your team's plots from Part I of this activity to predict properties of the unknown elements and write your predictions on the handout.
   c. Contribute your ideas to a class discussion and adjust your predictions based on what you learn.
3. Obtain 3 copies of the handout, Missing Elements, and evaluate how well your predictions matched the actual information from the modern periodic table.
4. Evaluate how well Mendeleyev's organizing principle worked and record your thoughts in your science notebook.

Reflect and Connect

Work with your group to answer these questions and record your answers in your science notebook.

1. What does the word *periodic* mean in the term *periodic table*?
2. How do the plots from Part I illustrate your definition of *periodic* expressed in Question 1 of this Reflect and Connect?
3. Why would your teacher ask you to focus on the microscopic level when you will never see an atom?
4. Think of graphic organizers other than the periodic table you have used. Spreadsheet programs, calendars, baseball scoreboards, and street maps are possible examples. Explain how the graphic organizer you chose contributes to a better understanding of what you are involved in or helps you produce more effective results.

Testing Pattern

In chapter 4, you have used models of the atom to understand the organizing principles of the periodic table. Those principles led to trends in the vertical and horizontal arrangement of elements. In those arrangements, you observed repeating patterns of physical and chemical properties. And those repeating patterns helped you design stable compounds, ones that could become part of the material world.

But how well do you understand the patterns? Does the world's most famous graphic organizer, the periodic table, make sense to you? Answers to those questions provide you with important feedback. You can analyze the feedback for patterns in your learning. Most of the time that pattern shows steady growth. But occasionally, the pattern shows a misunderstanding—something you didn't quite get the first time. Naturally, you want a chance to learn from feedback and continue learning steadily.

This evaluate activity, Testing Pattern, represents *one* of many ways to get feedback about your learning patterns. You start with a review of the facts, concepts, and skills discussed in this chapter. With your team, you reconfigure what you know into a graphic organizer. This review task gives you feedback on how well you can organize what you know according to principles discussed in the chapter. Finally, you take an individual test. Afterward, you examine your results and look for patterns in your answers. As in all inquiry, the goal is to recognize how feedback can lead to new understanding.

Part I: Structured Review

Materials
For each student

tape

butcher paper

sticky notes

1 copy of Testing Pattern handout

1 copy of Evaluate Scoring Rubric handout

Process and Procedure

In the first part of this activity, work with your team to review the chapter and to prepare for your individual assessment. This involves applying what you learned about the principles of organization associated with the periodic table. Those principles help you understand and remember concepts from this chapter. When you do this, you will perform better on the individual assessment.

1. Meet as a team and review the Evaluate Scoring Rubric handout to see what is expected of you as you complete this activity.
2. Design a *periodic table of the activities* for chapter 4 by considering the following.
    a. Remember, the periodic table is organized according to 2 important graphical features—rows and columns. The intersection of any row and column is an element. The intersections are like cells in a spreadsheet program or days of the week on a calendar.
    b. There are trends in rows (periods) and columns (families). Those trends are based on principles and concepts you have learned in chapter 4.
    c. In your periodic table of the activities, make the family name for each column the name of a key concept in chapter 4. Here are a few examples of key concepts that you could use for column headings: form versus function, model, electron configuration, bonding, and design. Don't forget to think about the *entire* chapter and to add your own concepts.

Another source of ideas is the scoring rubric for this activity.

d. Decide the organizing principle for families. For example, one way to think of the activities you have experienced in this chapter is according to difficulty of understanding. You could place the most difficult activity as the top "element" in a family and all other activities under that concept in decreasing order of difficulty.

e. Decide the organizing principle for periods. For example, the left side of your periodic table could be for activities that are mostly macroscopic. The right side could be for activities that are mostly microscopic.

3. Design the layout of your periodic table of the activities and draw each cell.

Do not forget to label each column with the proper concept and to indicate both the vertical and horizontal organizing principles. You may decide that you need to use butcher paper or to tape several smaller sheets of paper together. You may also find sticky notes to be useful.

4. Carefully review each activity in this chapter and decide into which cell to place it. Then in the proper cell, write a short phrase that reminds you of the activity. Labeled sketches are appropriate, too.

Part II: Positive Feedback

Now it is time to get another kind of feedback on what you know and understand. The feedback is called a test. After the test, you analyze your individual results for patterns in what you understand and what you still find challenging. Then you use the process of scientific inquiry to learn from your mistakes.

1. Read each question carefully and pinpoint exactly what is being asked.

2. Inspect any figures or diagrams for additional information and read through each response before marking your answer.

3. Turn your answers in to your teacher when you are finished.

4. Your teacher will score your test and give you feedback. Part of that feedback will be a discussion of the concepts that are important to each question.

5. Participate in a class discussion of how to demonstrate that you have learned from your mistakes.
6. Carefully read the Learn from Mistakes Protocol before you begin to make corrections.
7. Follow the Learn from Mistakes Protocol for *each* question that you missed and turn in your paper as instructed by your teacher.

Protocol

Learn from Mistakes

School is not just a place to deposit right answers. Sometimes you make mistakes. In fact, most people make mistakes when they try to learn something, especially when the subject is difficult or new. When you learn to identify and explain what is incorrect about a wrong answer, you have a better chance of avoiding that mistake again.

For each of the questions that you missed on the test, perform the following steps. By doing so, you can earn up to 50 percent of the difference between your raw percent score and 100 percent. Before you begin, write your raw percent score at the top of the page along with a list of the numbers you missed.

1. Represent the original question in a different way than it was represented on the test. For example, if the question was mostly words, represent it as a sketch. If it was mostly a sketch, represent it in words. When you use words, paraphrase the question in your own words. Do not copy the question word for word. Label a sketch with all variables, especially the unknown. If the problem mentions any change in condition, show before and after sketches.

2. Identify and explain the mistake you made in the answer you selected. Focus on explaining any conceptual misunderstanding. When you explain what is incorrect, show how the misconception would lead to a contradiction with what you see in nature. Explanations such as "I read the problem wrong" and "I pushed the wrong button on the calculator" will receive no credit.

3. Show the correct solution or answer. When necessary, show all governing equations—first in symbol form, then with number and unit values. Place proper units and labels on answers. Include an explanation of why the answer is reasonable.

CHAPTER 5

Star Material

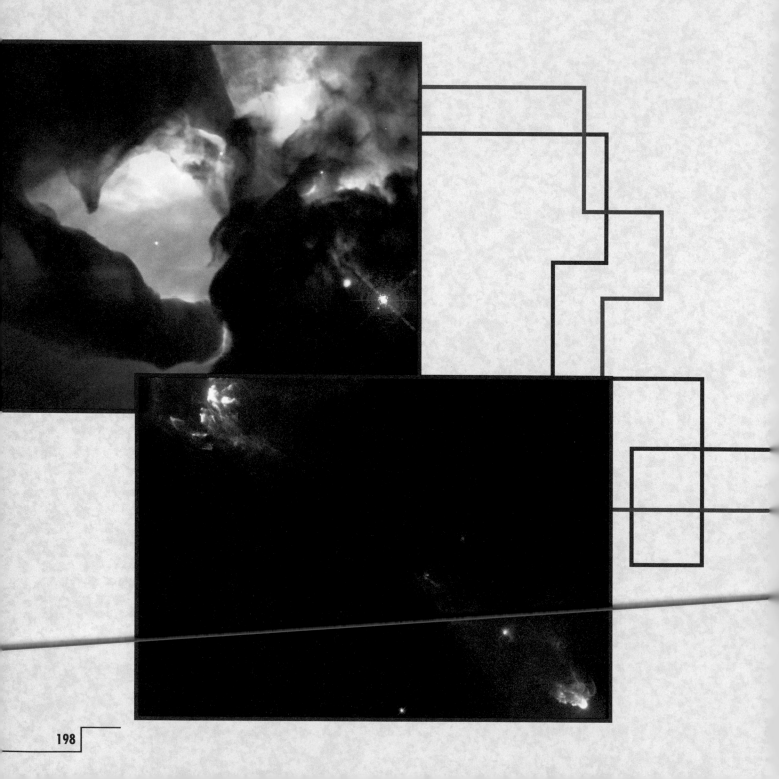

Star
Material

Matter is marvelous. Your curiosity has made you think about this phrase during chapter 2, The Material World; chapter 3, Get a Charge Out of Matter; and chapter 4, Organizing the Elements: The Periodic Table. You started thinking about how marvelous matter is when you first saw the wave toy. Do you remember the surfing penguin? Curiosity led you to much more understanding.

Now you understand how physical and chemical properties make things function properly. You know how characteristic properties depend on the microscopic particles that make up atoms and molecules. You even know how to use the periodic table to organize volumes of information about bonding, solubility, and reactivity.

But the material world doesn't stop on Earth. It travels to the stars. And what you have learned so far goes there with you.

Imagine designing a star rather than a wave toy. What materials would you need? How would you mix those materials together? Is there a recipe for a star?

In chapter 5, Star Material, you will apply what you have learned to an out-of-this-world question: What is the recipe for a star? You use the knowledge you gained in chapters 2–4 to understand something really big. You learn about the physical and chemical properties of the ingredients of a star! Then you can understand how those ingredients determine the way a star functions. Along the journey, you learn *new* knowledge about the material world and connect what you already know to what you learn. Eventually, you extend this knowledge to unit 3, The Earth and Beyond, and learn more about the universe in general.

You will mix together and create a new understanding of the material world. Scientists sometimes call this new understanding a *synthesis* of knowledge. In chapter 5, you synthesize the knowledge ingredients from chapters 2–4 to develop a working understanding of stars.

Goals for the Chapter

By the end of chapter 5, you will be able to answer the following questions:

- Do the amounts of energy produced by chemical and nuclear reactions differ dramatically?
- What are the similarities and differences between chemical and nuclear reactions?
- How do the microscopic particles that make up a star determine its macroscopic properties, which make the star function as it does?
- What role do the physical properties of the materials composing stars play in the nature of stars?
- Are the principles that govern the material world on Earth different from the principles that govern stars?

Fortunately, you will have help answering those questions. Each activity in this chapter gives you another ingredient in the recipe. In the end, you put all of the knowledge together. You see if it makes sense—if it works.

All of the activities in this chapter will help you learn about stars:

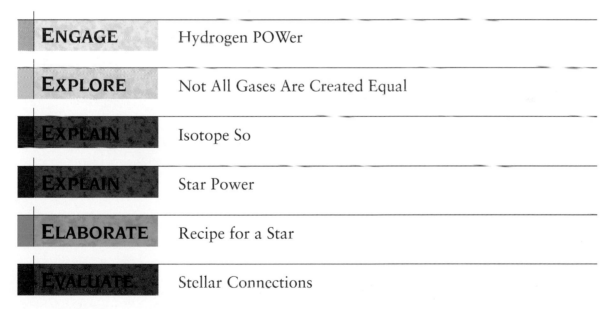

ENGAGE	Hydrogen POWer
EXPLORE	Not All Gases Are Created Equal
EXPLAIN	Isotope So
EXPLAIN	Star Power
ELABORATE	Recipe for a Star
EVALUATE	Stellar Connections

Chapter organizers help you remember what you know and where you are headed. They help you organize your quest to understand the material world. And as with the periodic table, when you are well organized, you need less time to understand more.

Look at the chapter 5 organizer every day. Think about where you are in its organization. Compare what you know now with what you knew a week ago. Think about what you will learn today. Let the chapter organizer help you map your learning and monitor your progress. That way you can look back and see what you have accomplished.

Linking Question

What is one way to
tell if stars produce
new materials?

Hydrogen POWer

Key Idea:

Hydrogen combustion
produces a lot of energy.
Stars produce vastly more.

EXPLORE

*Not All Gases Are
Created Equal*

Key Idea:

Gases with
different densities
form layers.

Star
Material

Linking Question

What part of the
atom is involved in
producing the
energy of stars?

EXPLAIN

Isotope So

Key Idea:

Fusion reactions involve
changing the nucleus to make
new elements.

Stellar Connections

Key Idea:
The laws of nature in one discipline of science are the same in every other discipline of science.

What is different and what is the same about materials and processes in stars and on Earth?

ELABORATE

CHAPTER

5 Major Concepts

▶ **NUCLEAR REACTIONS**
- Energy distinguishes chemical from nuclear reactions.
- Nuclei can fuse together, split apart, or decay.
- Elements exist in versions due to the number of neutrons in the nucleus.

▶ **SCIENCE DISCIPLINES CONNECT**
- Nuclear reactions are integral to the life cycle of a star.
- Nuclear reactions result in changes in characteristic properties of materials.
- Characteristic properties, bonding, and periodic trends would not exist if nuclear reactions did not exist.

Recipe for a Star

Key Idea:
Characteristic properties of materials in stars change over time.

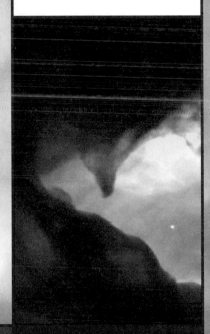

Are there other types of nuclear reactions?

Star Power

Key Idea:
Nuclear reactions also involve fission and radioactive decay.

How are nuclear reactions involved in the life cycle of a star?

Hydrogen POWer

What fuels stars? Is it a chemical reaction like the one in a candle? Or is the source of energy something very different? Will the fuel run out? How can you find the answers to those questions?

▶ **Figure 5.1**
Candles and stars both consume fuel. What fuels these reactions? Are the reactions of the same type? Is it the same reaction?

One way to answer those questions is to apply what you already know about the material world. You know that chemical reactions make products with physical and chemical properties that are different from the reactants. That is why in a burning candle, carbon dioxide and water are so different from paraffin and oxygen.

You also know that reactions follow the law of conservation of matter. This means that combustion breaks the covalent bonds between carbon atoms in paraffin and forms new covalent bonds in molecules of carbon dioxide. No carbon atoms are lost or changed into new elements. The heat energy that is produced results from reactant bonds that are pulled apart and that form new product bonds.

Astronomers have determined that the lightest element in the periodic table fuels the universe. Isn't it odd how the lightest atom can have the biggest impact? Do you remember this element? It is hydrogen.

Did you know that hydrogen is a fuel that combusts in the presence of oxygen? But how can an atom so simple power the Sun? Is hydrogen combustion the same process that occurs in stars? How is hydrogen involved in the recipe for a star?

In this activity, Hydrogen POWer, you work individually and in a team to address those questions. At first, you might generate more questions. That is OK. Scientists commonly do this when learning something new. Eventually, you pick and choose the most important questions. Then you design investigations to answer those questions. Frequently, the important questions are the ones you ask because you notice something unusual, even surprising. That is what you do in this activity. You ask questions about hydrogen POWer.

Materials
For the entire class

safety goggles

Cautions

Always wear your safety goggles when working with chemicals.

Process and Procedure

1. Prepare to learn something new by reviewing what you already know about combustion. Use figure 5.2 to complete Steps 1a–e, using the math symbols $<$, $>$, and $=$.

words	methane (natural gas)	oxygen	carbon dioxide	water
symbols	CH_4	$2O_2$	CO_2	$2H_2O$
particle model sketches				

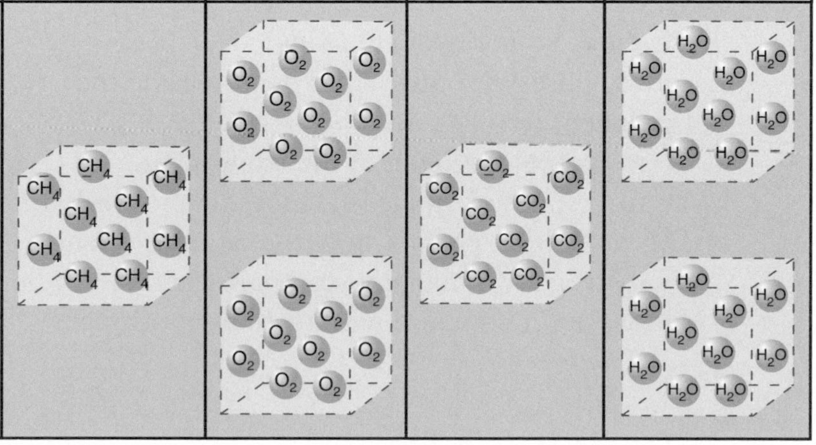

◀ **Figure 5.2**
Methane combustion. You can represent methane combustion several ways. In this figure, the box represents a certain volume of gas. The green spheres represent different gas particles. Notice how gas particles are small compared with the space between molecules. You first learned this in chapter 2.

Don't forget that each green sphere represents an entire molecule and that each molecule has a unique formula. All gases are measured at the same temperature and pressure.

    a. The number of carbon atoms in 1 volume of methane _____ the number of carbon atoms in 1 volume of carbon dioxide.

    b. The number of oxygen atoms in 2 volumes of oxygen gas _____ the number of oxygen atoms in 1 volume of carbon dioxide gas.

    c. The number of oxygen atoms in 2 volumes of oxygen gas _____ the number of oxygen atoms in 2 volumes of water vapor.

    d. The number of oxygen atoms in 2 volumes of oxygen gas _____ the number of oxygen atoms in 1 volume of carbon dioxide gas *plus* 2 volumes of water vapor.

    e. The number of hydrogen atoms in 1 volume of methane _____ the number of hydrogen atoms in 2 volumes of water vapor.

2. Use Step 1 as a guide to represent the combustion of hydrogen to make water. Include sketches.

Remember to apply the law of conservation of matter. This means that the number of atoms of each type of element must be the same in the reactants and products.

3. Predict what you think will happen when your teacher places a burning match under a test tube filled with oxygen gas and hydrogen gas.
    a. Record what you think will happen macroscopically.
    b. Record what you think will happen microscopically.

4. Share your thinking with a classmate.
    a. Read what you wrote to your classmate.
    b. Listen as your classmate reads.

Put on your safety goggles.

5. Carefully observe your teacher demonstrate the combustion of hydrogen.
    a. Draw a labeled sketch of the equipment.
    b. Draw a series of labeled sketches to show what happened.
    c. Discuss with a partner how the amount of energy released by hydrogen combustion compares with a candle burning. How does it compare with methane burning?

6. Read the following paragraphs about hydrogen power in stars. Remember past differences and what you learned from them by completing the table in figure 5.3 in your science notebook.

READING

Surprising Amounts of Energy

Hydrogen combustion produces a powerful reaction. The energy from hydrogen combustion may one day replace the energy that results from burning gasoline in cars. Is hydrogen combustion the same reaction that fuels stars?

Astronomers have discovered that hydrogen is the fuel producing the energy of the Sun and other stars. But the reaction in stars probably produces vastly more energy per hydrogen atom than hydrogen combustion produces. Why do you think that is true? Would the reaction that your teacher demonstrated produce enough energy to power stars?

When 1 gram (g) of hydrogen combusts, it produces the energy equivalent to burning much less than 1/4 teaspoon (tsp) of gasoline in your car. The way hydrogen produces energy in stars is different. How much gasoline do you think

would be equivalent to the energy from 1 g of hydrogen reacting in a star? It turns out to be about 3.3 gallons. That is close to 100,000 times more energy. Think about how much more energy per gram of hydrogen a star produces than ordinary combustion produces. Imagine the gasoline mileage in your car!

Does this result surprise you? If it does, you are thinking like a scientist. You notice striking differences and become curious. You start asking questions. But you have done this before in this program. You investigated several dramatic differences and learned something new about how marvelous matter is. For example, you observed the differences between continuous and line spectra. What questions did those differences prompt? What were the answers?

Big difference I observed	What I learned about marvelous matter
Thin line spectra compared to continuous spectra	Electrons exist in unique energy levels outside the nucleus, not just anywhere.
Complete transfer of electron compared to equal sharing of electrons	
Distance between particles in phases of matter	
Some alpha particles bouncing back from gold foil while most go through	
Ionization energy for noble gases very high	
Mass of proton almost 1,800 times greater than mass of electron	
Metals on one side of periodic table and nonmetals on the other	
Some water solutions conduct electricity and others don't	
Some substances soluble in water, and others not	
Continue on your own	
Energy from hydrogen combustion compared with energy from hydrogen as fuel in stars	

▲ **Figure 5.3**

Differences and what you learned. Think about the differences you observed in chapters 2–4. In the right-hand column, write what you learned about marvelous matter from those differences.

Reflect and Connect

Meet with a classmate and discuss the following questions. Record your answers in your science notebook.

1. From chapter 3, you know how electrons are involved in bonding. Hydrogen combustion breaks and forms bonds. Do you think electrons are involved in combustion the same way they are involved in the reaction that fuels stars? Explain your reasoning.
2. How do surprises play a role in scientific discoveries?
3. What questions do you have about the reaction that powers stars? In your questions, use the concepts you learned in chapters 2–4, such as density, solubility, bonding, energy, phases of matter, ionization, dissociation, spectra, and atomic structure.

Not All Gases Are Created Equal

In the previous activity, you saw hydrogen explode. Was that explosion enough to power a star? Maybe a different type of reaction produces the remarkably larger amounts of energy produced in a star.

Certainly, what atoms do to produce energy in a star is different from everyday chemical reactions such as hydrogen combustion. What else is different in the recipe of a star? Is a star one big blob of similar material? Or are the physical properties of each ingredient different? How could you tell?

Astronomers think stars are made mostly of gas. Could stars be made of just one gas? If so, how could a reaction take place? Wouldn't hydrogen have to change into something with new chemical and physical properties? If this happens, how could scientists find out?

One way scientists could find out whether new materials form is to look for differences in physical properties. For example, you know that the wave toy recipe involved two unique liquids because one liquid floated on top of the other. That is, the liquids had different densities.

In Not All Gases Are Created Equal, you work individually and in teams to explore density differences among gases. Throughout this activity, think about whether stars produce gases of different densities. If star reactions do this, then different gases might form different layers in stars.

Materials
For each team of four students

4 pairs of safety goggles

4 lab aprons

funnel

.75 m rubber tubing

clear plastic tub or aquarium

shallow dish

tongs

soap solution

approximately 10 cm³ of dry ice

various gases

Cautions

Wear safety goggles and a lab apron at all times. Dry ice can freeze skin. Handle it with tongs only. Some gases are combustible. Do not allow open flames in class during this activity. Do not inhale any of these gases.

Process and Procedure

1. Carefully observe how your teacher produces a soap bubble filled with methane and then ignites it.
    a. Generate a labeled sketch of the equipment.

A labeled sketch helps you link what you see to what you write as observations. This helps you remember what you did.

    b. Represent with drawings what happened to the bubble of methane.
    c. Record your thinking regarding differences in density between methane gas and air at the same temperature and pressure.

It is safe to assume that the soap was not involved in combustion.

    d. Record your thinking regarding the amount of energy produced by the combustion of methane compared with the combustion of paraffin.
    e. Compare your thinking in Steps 1c and d with a classmate's and be prepared to discuss any differences as part of a class discussion.
2. Prepare a catch basin for bubbles filled with various gases.
    a. In the bottom of your catch basin, place a piece of dry ice approximately large enough to cover 4 U.S. quarters.

Caution
Do not handle dry ice with bare hands. Always use tongs.

Dry ice is the solid form of the gas you produced in chapter 1, The Process of Scientific Inquiry, by placing antacid tablets in water. Notice that it does not form any liquid. It changes directly from the solid phase to the gas phase. The name of this phase change is *sublimation*.

    b. Sketch the tub and contents in your notebook, using the following labels:
       - CO_2 solid
       - CO_2 gas
       - Cold region
       - Warm region
    c. Draw a phase diagram of carbon dioxide (CO_2) and chart the transition of solid carbon dioxide to gaseous carbon dioxide.

Save time by referring to your chapter 2 materials in your notebook. Remember that pressure in the room remains relatively constant while the temperature of the dry ice increases.

    d. Discuss with your team why carbon dioxide gas remains in the bottom of the tub.

3. Design an experiment to determine the relative densities of different gases supplied by your teacher.

    a. Practice making bubbles until you can consistently make 1 that lasts 30 seconds or more.

You might have to adjust your soap solution to make bubbles last longer.

    b. Record your design and procedure in your science notebook as a series of numbered steps.

    c. Check your thinking with your teacher before proceeding.

4. Perform your experiment and clean up as instructed by your teacher.

5. Meet with your team to analyze your results by answering the following questions in your science notebook.

    a. Suppose *every* bubble you made was exactly the same size. This would mean that the volume, pressure, and temperatures were the same. Which gas would have the largest mass? What evidence would you have to support your answer?

    b. Remember Democritus's particles. Now remember how extremely far apart gas particles are compared with the size of individual atoms or molecules. Assuming that the bubbles have equal volumes, which bubble contains the most gas particles? Explain your reasoning.

    c. If the same number of particles are in each bubble, which molecules are heaviest? What evidence supports your answer?

    d. Find the atomic mass listed for each element on the periodic table in figure 5.4. Do the periodic table and your experiment tell the same story about the mass of atoms and molecules? Give examples from the periodic table *and* your experiment to support your answer.

Periodic Table of the Elements

Key

Atomic number — 26 55.85 — Atomic weight
Fe — Symbol of element
Iron — Name of element

- Alkali metal
- Alkaline earth metal
- Transition metals
- Halogens
- Noble gas

1 1.0080 **H** Hydrogen																	2 4.003 **He** Helium
3 6.941 **Li** Lithium	4 9.012 **Be** Beryllium											5 10.81 **B** Boron	6 12.011 **C** Carbon	7 14.007 **N** Nitrogen	8 15.9994 **O** Oxygen	9 19.00 **F** Fluorine	10 20.179 **Ne** Neon
11 22.990 **Na** Sodium	12 24.30 **Mg** Magnesium											13 26.98 **Al** Aluminum	14 28.09 **Si** Silicon	15 30.974 **P** Phosphorus	16 32.064 **S** Sulfur	17 35.453 **Cl** Chlorine	18 39.948 **Ar** Argon
19 39.098 **K** Potassium	20 40.08 **Ca** Calcium	21 44.96 **Sc** Scandium	22 47.90 **Ti** Titanium	23 50.94 **V** Vanadium	24 52.00 **Cr** Chromium	25 50.94 **Mn** Manganese	26 55.85 **Fe** Iron	27 58.93 **Co** Cobalt	28 58.70 **Ni** Nickel	29 63.55 **Cu** Copper	30 65.38 **Zn** Zinc	31 69.72 **Ga** Gallium	32 72.59 **Ge** Germanium	33 74.92 **As** Arsenic	34 78.96 **Se** Selenium	35 79.904 **Br** Bromine	36 83.80 **Kr** Krypton
37 85.47 **Rb** Rubidium	38 87.62 **Sr** Strontium	39 88.91 **Y** Yttrium	40 91.22 **Zr** Zirconium	41 92.91 **Nb** Niobium	42 95.94 **Mo** Molybdenum	43 (97) **Tc** Technetium	44 101.1 **Ru** Ruthenium	45 102.91 **Rh** Rhodium	46 106.4 **Pd** Palladium	47 107.868 **Ag** Silver	48 112.40 **Cd** Cadmium	49 114.82 **In** Indium	50 118.69 **Sn** Tin	51 121.75 **Sb** Antimony	52 127.60 **Te** Tellurium	53 126.90 **I** Iodine	54 131.30 **Xe** Xenon
55 132.90 **Cs** Cesium	56 137.34 **Ba** Barium	57–71 * **below**	72 178.49 **Hf** Hafnium	73 180.95 **Ta** Tantalum	74 183.85 **W** Tungsten	75 186.2 **Re** Rhenium	76 190.2 **Os** Osmium	77 192.2 **Ir** Iridium	78 195.09 **Pt** Platinum	79 197.0 **Au** Gold	80 200.59 **Hg** Mercury	81 204.37 **Tl** Thallium	82 207.2 **Pb** Lead	83 208.98 **Bi** Bismuth	84 (209) **Po** Polonium	85 (210) **At** Astatine	86 (222) **Rn** Radon
87 (223) **Fr** Francium	88 (226) **Ra** Radium	89–103 ** **below**	104 (261)	105 (262)	106 (263)	107 (262)	108 (265)	109 (266?)									

Rare earth elements

*Lanthanoid Series

57 138.91 **La** Lanthanum	58 140.12 **Ce** Cerium	59 140.92 **Pr** Praseodymium	60 144.24 **Nd** Neodymium	61 (145) **Pm** Promethium	62 150.35 **Sm** Samarium	63 152.0 **Eu** Europium	64 157.25 **Gd** Gadolinium	65 158.93 **Tb** Terbium	66 162.50 **Dy** Dysprosium	67 164.93 **Ho** Holmium	68 167.26 **Er** Erbium	69 168.93 **Tm** Thulium	70 173.04 **Yb** Ytterbium	71 174.97 **Lu** Lutetium

**Actinoid Series

89 (227) **Ac** Actinium	90 232.04 **Th** Thorium	91 (231) **Pa** Protactinium	92 238.03 **U** Uranium	93 (237) **Np** Neptunium	94 (244) **Pu** Plutonium	95 (243) **Am** Americium	96 (247) **Cm** Curium	97 (247) **Bk** Berkelium	98 (251) **Cf** Californium	99 (254) **Es** Einsteinium	100 (257) **Fm** Fermium	101 (258) **Md** Mendelevium	102 (259) **No** Nobelium	103 (260) **Lr** Lawrencium

▲ Figure 5.4

Periodic table. The periodic table is organized in rows of increasing atomic mass. The mass of a molecule is the sum of the masses of the atoms bonded together to make the molecule.

Reflect and Connect

Record answers in your science notebook before consulting with teammates. If your team cannot resolve a question, consult with your teacher.

1. In which activities from chapters 2–4 have you seen differences in densities?
2. What kind of processes can result in different kinds of densities: chemical processes or physical processes? Give examples from previous chapters to support your answer.
3. What makes different gases have different densities when measured at the same temperature and pressure? Answer this question from both the macroscopic and microscopic viewpoints.
4. If processes in a star produce gases of different densities, what would a cross section of a star look like? Sketch a cross section of a star and write a caption to explain your sketch.

Imagine slicing an orange in half and sketching what you see. That's a cross section.

Isotope So

You have just explored one way to determine what kind of reactions might take place in stars. Chemical reactions produce molecules with characteristic properties different from reactant molecules. This occurs in hydrogen combustion when hydrogen gas and oxygen gas chemically react to form water vapor and heat. The product gas has a different density than the reactant gases.

Are stars made of one gas or many gases? If astronomers found layers of gases within stars, that would be an important clue. Different layers would form, much like bubbles filled with different gases floated at different heights in the last activity. But a difference in characteristic properties between reactants and products is not the only clue.

Another important clue is the energy produced by stars. Do you remember that *chemical* reactions consume and produce energy? They do not produce 100,000 times more energy than hydrogen combustion. But the reactions in stars do! Perhaps a different type of reaction fuels the immense energy output of stars.

Astronomers have indeed determined that elements other than hydrogen exist in stars. Helium is one such gas. It would have to be the product of some type of hydrogen reaction. Why?

Look to the periodic table in figure 5.4 for the answer. Hydrogen is the lightest element. Astronomers think it is the starting point for all stars. All other elements are heavier than hydrogen. Somehow hydrogen has to react with itself to make *all* of the other elements.

How does a reaction make new elements? Do chemical reactions make new elements? For example, does hydrogen combustion make new types of atoms? Does any type of reaction you know about change one element into another?

That's what seems to be going on in stars. A type of reaction *different* from chemical reactions seems to take place in stars. Like chemical reactions, this reaction makes materials with different physical and chemical properties. But unlike chemical reactions, this different type of reaction makes *new elements*. Now that's a surprise!

This reaction is what you try to explain in Isotope So. You work individually and in teams to explain this new type of reaction.

SCI LINKS
NSTA
Topic: isotopes of elements
Go to: www.scilinks.org
Code: 1Inquiry213

Materials
For each team of three students

3 copies of Atomic Math handout

Process and Procedure

1. What part of a hydrogen (H) atom do you think is likely to be primarily responsible for reactions in stars? Think about this as you complete Steps 1a–d.

   a. Meet with your team and analyze figure 5.5 for trends.

What happens at microscopic level	What happens at macroscopic level	Energy produced compared to 1 gal of gasoline	Size of particle involved (diameter × 10¹⁰ m)
Forces pull *molecules* further apart or push them closer together.	Phase change	1	10
Forces pull *electrons* away from one nucleus and closer to another.	Chemical reactions (e.g., combustion)	1–10	1
Forces pull *nuclei* apart or push them closer together.	Light production (e.g., stars, nuclear energy)	100,000	.00001

▲ **Figure 5.5**

Comparison of reaction dimensions and energy. Particles are involved in all reactions, but the type, size, charge, and energy vary tremendously.

b. Complete the following statement in your science notebook: As the size of the particles involved _____, the amount of energy produced _____.

c. Suppose forces cause hydrogen atoms to react. How many hydrogen atoms would it take to produce 1 helium (He) atom?

Remember the last activity. You saw gases with different densities. That is because different gas molecules have different masses. Somehow nature makes gases composed of more mass than hydrogen. You find the masses of various elements on the periodic table.

d. Represent your answer to Step 1c with chemical symbols and an arrow between the reactants and the products.

Don't forget energy. It can be included on either the reactant or the product side of the arrow. And don't forget to indicate how many hydrogen atoms you think are involved.

e. Think of H and He as Rutherford atoms. When forces push nuclei so close together that they form a *new* nucleus, the reaction is called a **fusion** reaction. Make a Venn diagram in your science notebook to represent similarities and differences between hydrogen combustion and hydrogen fusion.

2. Show your Venn diagram to team members and modify your diagram based on your conversations.

3. Use the periodic table to complete the following 2 relationship statements with <, >, or =. Write the completed statements in your science notebook.

   a. The number of protons in 4 H nuclei _____ the number of protons in 1 He nucleus.

Remember, the atomic number tells you how many protons are in the nucleus of any element. The number of protons in a nucleus makes one element different from another.

   b. The total mass of 4 H nuclei (rounded) _____ the mass of 1 He nucleus (rounded).

Remember, electrons have negligible mass compared with protons.

4. Discuss with your partners a surprise you may notice and be prepared to compare your ideas with classmates' in a class discussion.

5. Complete the highlight comments and a caption in figure 5.6 to offer a possible explanation for your surprise in Step 4.

The large circles with + signs represent protons. Think of the mass of one proton as one unit of *atomic mass*. By this thinking, a hydrogen atom has one unit of atomic mass and a helium nucleus has four units of atomic mass.

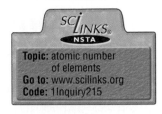

SCI LINKS®
NSTA

Topic: atomic number of elements
Go to: www.scilinks.org
Code: 1Inquiry215

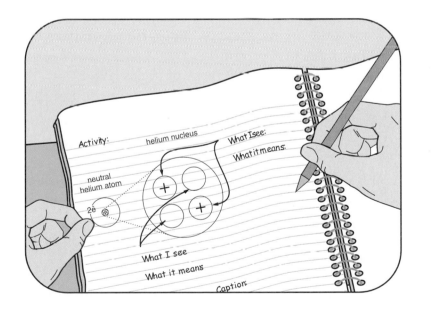

◀ **Figure 5.6**
Helium nucleus. A helium nucleus has two protons. It also has two other particles with no charge. What is the name of these uncharged (or electrically neutral) particles with approximately the same mass as a proton?

6. Read the following clues to solve the mystery of 4 H atoms changing into 1 He atom.

Neutrons: Something Different

The mass of a helium nucleus is very close to 4 times greater than the mass of a hydrogen atom. The helium nucleus has only 2 protons in it. The charge on the helium nucleus is 2+. There are 2 electrons in neutral helium. There must be more mass than 2 protons in the helium nucleus for it to be roughly equivalent to 4 hydrogen atoms. The extra mass is not due to charged particles.

Scientists have determined that in the extremely high-energy environment of the interior of stars, an electron and a proton can combine to form a *neutron* by the following reaction: $e^- + p^+ \rightarrow n + energy$.

7. Based on what you just read about neutrons, answer Steps 7a–d in your science notebook.
   a. What particle is probably responsible for the additional mass in the helium nucleus being greater than the mass of 2 protons? How many of those particles are in the helium nucleus shown in figure 5.6?
   b. What is the atomic mass of that particle compared with the atomic mass of 1 proton?
   c. What electric charge do these particles have?
   d. Besides mass, what might be another function of these particles?

Think about the requirements to hold two positively charged protons close together in the same nucleus. To learn more about the history of the neutron, read the sidebar, James Chadwick (1891–1974). To learn more about the nucleus, read the sidebar, Other Nuclear Particles.

James Chadwick (1891–1974)

James Chadwick was a young Englishman who planned to study math when he grew up. While enrolling in college, however, he accidentally got into a line for physics majors and was too shy to change lines. Thus, he began his career as a physicist and became one of the founders of atomic physics.

In 1920, many scientists were investigating the atom. Chadwick was influenced by many of the well-known scientists of his day: Ernest Rutherford, who proposed that the nucleus was made of positively charged particles called protons; Joseph John Thomson, who discovered the electron; and Niels Bohr, who suggested a structure for the atom. At the time, most scientists agreed that the number of protons in the nucleus did not account for its mass. Chadwick worked with Rutherford. Together they suspected that the extra mass came from an uncharged particle in the nucleus.

It was not until 1932 that Chadwick learned of the research of Irène Joliot-Curie, Marie Curie's daughter, and her husband, Frédéric. Scientists knew that radiation from charged particles could be stopped by beryllium foil and would not be detected by a Geiger counter (which counts charged particles). Irène and Frédéric Joliot-Curie discovered something interesting when they placed paraffin wax between the beryllium foil and the Geiger counter. Radiation, which in earlier experiments seemed to be stopped by the beryllium foil, hit the paraffin, knocking protons loose. The protons were detected by the Geiger counter. It seemed to Chadwick that uncharged particles were passing through the beryllium and striking the paraffin wax.

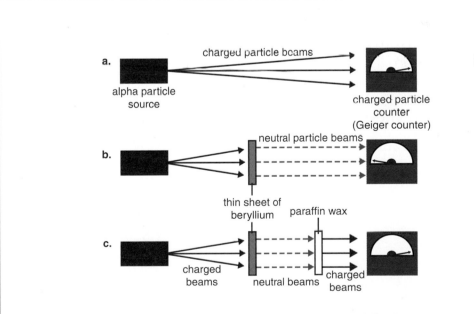

Experimental diagram for Chadwick's experiments. (a) When not disrupted, the charged particles can be detected with a Geiger counter. (b) Beryllium foil seems to stop the charged particles from reaching the counter. (c) When paraffin wax is placed between the foil and the counter, charged particles are knocked loose by a stream of neutral particles.

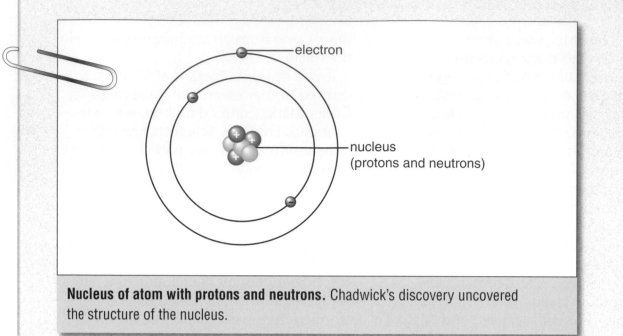

electron

nucleus
(protons and neutrons)

Nucleus of atom with protons and neutrons. Chadwick's discovery uncovered the structure of the nucleus.

Chadwick repeated the experiment with a new goal: to look for the uncharged particles. He determined the velocity of the protons coming from the paraffin. Using this information, he calculated the mass of the neutral particles that dislodged the protons. Chadwick determined that the mass of one neutral particle was approximately equal to the mass of one proton.

Chadwick called the neutral particle a **neutron** and published his idea in a paper in 1932. Scientists realized that the mass of atoms now could be explained by the addition of neutrons in the nucleus. **Isotopes**, which are atoms of the same element that have a different mass, made sense in light of the neutron: some atoms of the same element have greater or fewer neutrons.

Chadwick's discovery of the neutron earned him the Nobel Prize in 1935. His knowledge of the composition of the nucleus also made him one of the first British scientists to be involved in the development of an atomic bomb.

Other Nuclear Particles

For many years, scientists believed that atoms were the smallest particles to make up matter. Then, during the last century, they discovered ways that atoms behaved that indicated that they were made up of even smaller particles. You already know about the subatomic particles called protons, neutrons, and electrons. Is it possible that there are other, even smaller, subatomic particles?

During the last several decades, scientists have been working to answer that question. In fact, physicists have discovered about 200 particles that make up the building blocks of the universe. Two of the fundamental particles are **quarks** and **leptons**.

In 1964, Murray Gell-Mann and George Zweig proposed the existence of quarks. Gell-Mann named these particles quarks after a nonsense word used by James Joyce in his 1939 novel *Finnegans Wake*. There are six kinds of quarks, but physicists have grouped them into pairs. They have odd names: top/bottom, charm/strange, and up/down.

Quarks are never found alone. Instead, they are found in combination with other quarks in larger particles of matter. Groups of quarks are called hadrons.

There are two kinds of hadrons: baryons and mesons. Baryons consist of three quarks, and mesons consist of two quarks. The most common baryons are protons and neutrons. A proton is made up of two up (u) quarks and one down (d) quark, expressed as *udd*. A neutron is made up of one up quark and two down quarks, expressed as *udd*.

There are six leptons; three have a charge, and three do not. The best-known charged lepton is the electron. The other two charged leptons are the muon and the tau. The remaining leptons are three types of neutrinos. Each neutrino corresponds to one of the charged leptons.

Physicists learn more about particles by developing new and more powerful particle accelerators and detectors. Many of these newest particles were discovered in the 1960s and 1970s, but the top quark was not discovered until 1995. Physicists continue to experiment, trying to discover whether there are other subatomic particles—and it is possible that there are. After all, not long ago scientists thought protons, neutrons, and electrons were the smallest particles to make up matter!

8. Read the following paragraphs to help you answer the questions in Step 9.

Isotope Symbols

Reactions that result in changed nuclei are called **nuclear** reactions. These reactions are different from chemical reactions because they produce new elements, which were not part of the reactants. Both reactant and product elements in nuclear reactions come in versions. These versions are called isotopes.

Isotopes are versions of elements with exactly the same number of protons, but a different number of neutrons in the nucleus. The chemical properties of isotopes are the same. Why? Remember that chemical reactions involve electrons. The number of electrons equals the number of protons for a neutral atom. The number of protons does not differ from one isotope to another. So the number of electrons remains the same for all of the atomically neutral isotopes, and the chemical interactions do not change.

But isotopes differ in mass. To show the differences in mass, chemists use symbols. Figure 5.7 shows an example.

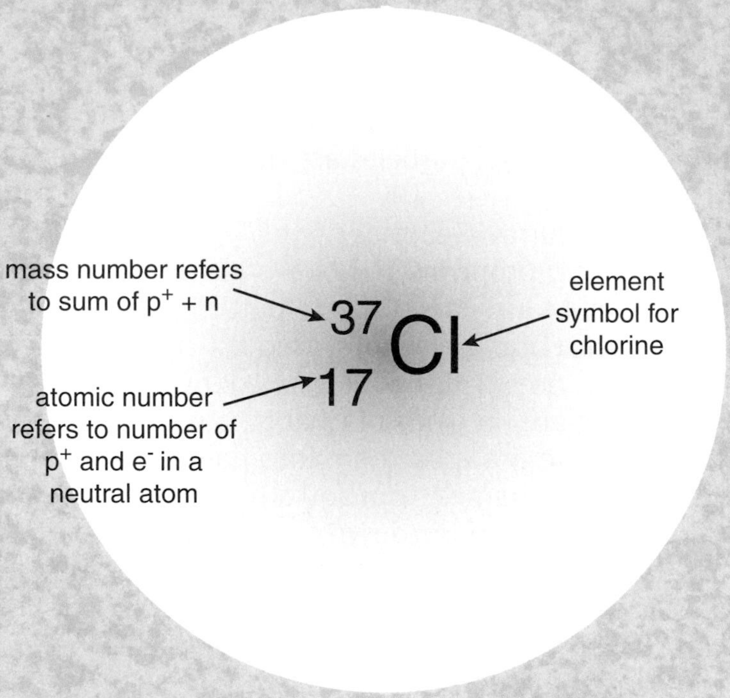

mass number refers to sum of $p^+ + n$ → ^{37}Cl ← element symbol for chlorine

atomic number refers to number of p^+ and e^- in a neutral atom → $_{17}$

▲ **Figure 5.7 Chlorine-37; the element symbol for chlorine is Cl.** The superscript 37 represents the atomic mass, or the sum of protons and neutrons. The subscript represents the atomic number, or the number of protons (and electrons) in a neutral atom.

9. Look at the atomic mass reported for chlorine in figure 5.4 to help you answer Steps 9a–c. Notice that many elements in the periodic table exist in several isotopic forms. For example, there are 2 primary isotopes of chlorine.

   a. Why are there numbers to the right of the decimal point in most atomic masses on the periodic table?

b. Does the 2nd isotope of chlorine have more or fewer neutrons in its nucleus than chlorine-37? How do you know?

The number 37 refers to the mass number.

c. Suppose you had 10 g of the ionic solid sodium chloride. Would there be more atoms of chlorine-35 or chlorine-37 in this crystal? Explain your reasoning, using the atomic mass reported on the periodic table.

10. To become familiar with isotopes other than chlorine-35 and chlorine-37, obtain 1 Atomic Math handout per team member.

a. Complete the handout on your own. Then check your answers with team members.

b. If your team cannot produce the same answers, consult with your teacher.

Reflect and Connect

Record your responses in your science notebook and check your thinking with classmates. Discuss any lingering confusion with your teacher.

1. Some scientists call neutrons nuclear glue. What do you think this means?

2. What evidence leads you to think that reactions in stars are very different from reactions like hydrogen combustion?

3. When forces are large enough to push nuclei together, a fusion reaction results. Huge amounts of energy are produced, enough to power stars. What kind of reactions result when forces split nuclei apart? Is the energy produced more, less, or about the same as in fusion reactions? Explain your reasoning.

Review figure 5.5 from Step 1 to get a sense of the amount of energy involved in putting nuclei together.

Star Power

EXPLAIN

You have just learned about one of the most powerful reactions in the universe—fusion. It happens when tremendous forces put nuclei of lighter elements together to make heavier, new elements. Just imagine. All of the elements on the periodic table heavier than hydrogen are made by stars. Even the elements found in the ingredients for the wave toy began with smaller atomic masses. In fact, fusion reactions in stars create so many different nuclei that there are versions of elements, called isotopes.

But are fusion reactions the only type of nuclear reaction? What happens when forces *pull apart* nuclei instead of putting them together? Do these reactions take place in stars? Do they take place on Earth? Why would you want to know?

To understand *any* recipe, you should know as much as possible about the characteristic properties of the ingredients. When you do, you will understand why the final product works. That's true for wave toys, and it's true for stars. If something goes wrong with the recipe, understanding each ingredient helps you find an answer. And finding answers to problems helps scientists become more successful.

In Star Power, you work individually and in a team to understand other kinds of nuclear reactions. You use what you know about atomic structure to explain those reactions. Along the way, you learn about radioactive decay.

Materials

Process and Procedure

1. Form a learning team of 3 students and move to a section of the room that allows the group to discuss quietly without disturbing other teams.
2. Read through each step in this procedure to prepare yourself to lead a discussion in your team about 1 of 3 important types of nuclear reactions. Then come back to this step (Step 2) and accomplish each task.
    a. Select 1 of the 3 readings, Fusion, Radioactive Decay, or Fission. You will become the team discussion leader for your selected aspect of nuclear reactions.

   Each team member should select a different reading.

    b. Read your selection and complete a T-table with the headings "What I Understood" and "What I'm Unsure About."

   You do *not* have to become an expert on the material or teach it to your team. Instead, you will lead a discussion expressing what you do and do not understand about the reading.

3. Record in your science notebook your best thinking on the questions at the end of your selected reading. Be prepared to discuss your solutions with teammates.
4. Meet with your team again and lead your discussion by accomplishing Steps 4a–e.
    a. Read to the team your comments from the "What I Understood" column of your T-table.

Use figures from your reading as visual aids when you explain what you understand.

    b. Repeat Step 4a with the "What I'm Unsure About" column of your T-table.

    c. Show your science notebook to teammates and use it to explain how you solved each problem at the end of the reading.

    d. Make corrections and additions to your solutions as needed based on what you learn from teammates.

    e. Record important information from the 2 remaining discussions.

READING

Fusion

Fusion reactions fuel stars. In a way, they fuel every reaction on Earth, too. That is because the carbon in hydrocarbon fuels such as methane, coal, and gasoline comes from stars. Certainly, much of the carbon in those fuels originated in plants and animals millions of years ago. But all of that carbon came from fusion reactions that took place even earlier. And the most common location for fusion reactions is the incredibly hot centers of stars. In fact, the centers of stars can be 10 million degrees centigrade (C)! Compare that temperature with the average temperature of Earth's surface, 18°C, or a candle flame, 400°C.

To understand how stars create carbon-based fuels, you might want to know which nuclei fuse to make carbon. First, remember how hydrogen fuses to make helium, as shown in figure 5.8.

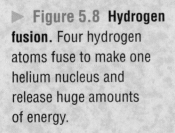

▶ **Figure 5.8 Hydrogen fusion.** Four hydrogen atoms fuse to make one helium nucleus and release huge amounts of energy.

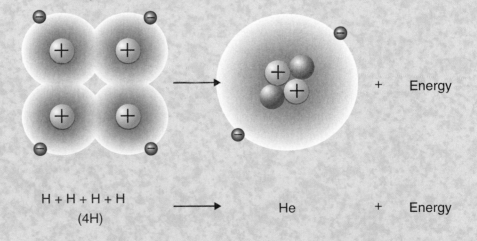

H + H + H + H   ⟶   He   +   Energy
(4H)

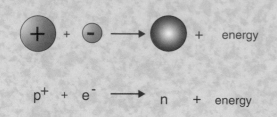

$$p^+ + e^- \longrightarrow n + energy$$

▲ **Figure 5.9 Production of a neutron.**
A neutron forms when an electron and a proton combine.

Remember that part of this process involves 2 protons and 2 electrons forming 2 neutrons, as shown in figure 5.9.

In a star, hydrogen fuses to make helium. Then helium can fuse to make carbon. Inspect the periodic table and figure 5.10 to decide how many helium nuclei combine to make one carbon atom.

This fusion reaction also produces huge amounts of energy compared with the amounts from chemical reactions like combustion. How? The energy results from an unusual event in nature. Some tiny fraction of mass converts to energy. For example, 454 g (1 pound [lb]) of hydrogen fuses to make only 451 g of helium. There is a loss of 3 g, or about 1 percent. That 1 percent is responsible for most of the energy from the Sun.

The vast energy produced by the Sun results from the force required to hold protons together in the nucleus. This force is called the **strong nuclear force**. It is much stronger than the force between electrons and protons, which is called the **electrostatic force**.

How do scientists know that the electrostatic force is much weaker than the strong nuclear force? They know because forces are closely related to energy. For particles the size of atoms, the stronger the force, the greater the energy involved. Chemical reactions like combustion involve far less energy than fusion reactions do. That is because electrostatic forces are much smaller than strong nuclear forces.

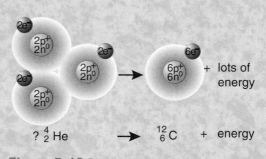

$$? \, {}^{4}_{2}\text{He} \longrightarrow {}^{12}_{6}\text{C} + energy$$

▲ **Figure 5.10 Production of carbon.** Helium fuses to make carbon. How many helium nuclei make one carbon nucleus?

1. Carbon is an element essential for life. From previous courses, what are some of the other elements essential for life?

2. Use symbols in a reaction to show how carbon and helium could fuse to make oxygen.

3. Write a reaction to show what element results when oxygen and helium fuse.

4. If energy is an equivalent form of matter, does fusion represent a violation of the law of conservation of matter?

5. Why does the temperature in the centers of stars have to be extremely high for fusion to occur?

READING

Radioactive Decay

Fusion is not the only way nature alters a nucleus. Some nuclei break apart on their own in a process called **radioactive decay**. You already know about one type of radioactive decay product. It is the alpha particle. Remember how important the alpha particle was to Rutherford's model of the atom.

An alpha particle is another word for a helium nucleus. You can see this by inspecting the radioactive decay process shown in figure 5.11.

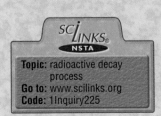

Topic: radioactive decay process
Go to: www.scilinks.org
Code: 1Inquiry225

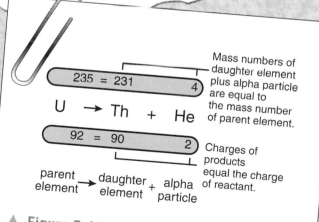

▲ Figure 5.11 **Alpha decay of uranium.** A uranium nucleus spontaneously breaks apart into unequal-sized particles. The product element decays further until, finally, a stable isotope of lead is formed.

Notice how the mass numbers compare between reactants and products. Both sides are equal because of conservation of mass. Also, notice how charge compares between reactant and product. Both sides are equal because charge is conserved. Remember, the atomic number shows the number of protons and identifies an element on the periodic table.

There are other radioactive decay particles. Two common ones besides the alpha particle are the beta particle and the gamma particle. Figure 5.12 shows a summary of properties of these radioactive decay products.

▼ **Figure 5.12 Properties of three types of decay products.** Each decay particle has unique properties.

Decay particle	Charge	Mass relative to 1 proton	Symbols	Ability to penetrate material
alpha (α)	2+	4	Helium nuclei, $^4_2He^{2+}$	Short range, stopped by a piece of paper
beta (β)	1-	$\frac{1}{1,837}$	Electron, $^0_{-1}e$	Intermediate range, stopped by a few centimeters of water
gamma (γ)	0	0	High-energy radiation shorter in wavelength than X-rays	Long range, stopped by a few centimeters of lead

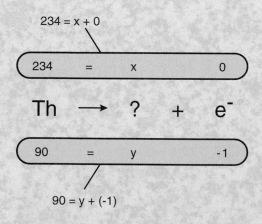

▲ **Figure 5.13 Beta decay of thorium.** You can predict the product element by comparing mass numbers and charges.

You can predict the new isotope produced from a radioactive decay process. The mass number of the reactant isotope must be equal to the sum of the mass numbers of the decay particle and the product isotope. Similarly, the charge of the reactant isotope must balance with the charge of the decay particle added to the charge of the product isotope. Figure 5.13 illustrates this point.

Though the reactants and products of radioactive decay reactions can be predicted, the time at which an *individual* radioactive decay reaction occurs cannot be predicted. All radioactive decay processes are random. But scientists can determine the rate of decay of a large sample. For example, one of the radioactive waste products of a nuclear power plant is iodine-131. A 100 g sample requires eight days to decay to 50 g of iodine-131. After another eight days, only 25 g of iodine-131 remain.

Can you guess how much iodine-131 remains after the next eight days? Yes, the answer is 12.5 g. The eventual product of decay is the noble gas xenon.

Figure 5.14 shows a graphic way to think of the rate of decay. You will notice how half of the original amount decays each eight days. This eight-day period for iodine-131 is called its **half-life.** Naturally, isotopes with a shorter half-life produce decay products at a faster rate.

Half-life is a characteristic property of an isotope. Half-life varies from 4.5 billion years for uranium-238 to fractions of a second for some heavier-than-uranium elements, such as einsteinium, created by scientists in advanced research facilities.

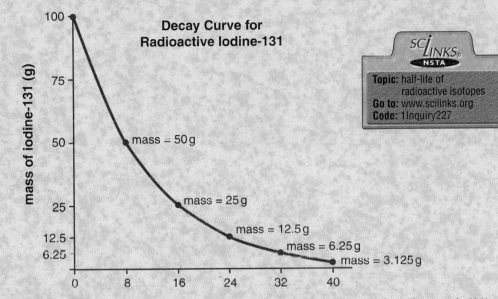

Topic: half-life of radioactive isotopes
Go to: www.scilinks.org
Code: 1Inquiry227

▲ **Figure 5.14 Half-life graph.** Every eight days, the amount of iodine-131 decreases by one-half the original amount.

Stop & THINK

1. How is radioactive decay different from nuclear fusion?
2. How is radioactive decay similar to nuclear fusion?
3. Write a properly balanced radioactive decay reaction showing how Pa-234 decays to U-234.
4. Determine the product element when Th-230 decays by alpha emission.

   Refer to figure 5.12 for a reminder of how alpha particles are products associated with alpha emission.

5. How can a radioactive decay process cause the atomic number to increase?

Fission

Fusion involves putting together nuclei. **Fission** involves taking apart nuclei. Fission is different from other nuclear reactions such as radioactive decay and fusion, even though all involve the nucleus changing. In fission reactions, nuclei split into approximately equal parts.

Nuclear power plants use fission reactions to produce energy. Study this nuclear reaction.

$$\underset{92}{235}U + \underset{0}{1}n \rightarrow \underset{56}{141}Ba + \underset{36}{92}Kr + 3\underset{0}{1}n + \text{energy}$$

Look for features of fission that are similar to fusion. Look for features of fission that are different from fusion.

Notice how the mass numbers compare between reactant and product. The sum of the mass numbers of the products equals the sum of the mass numbers of the reactants. The same kind of equality is true for charge. The isotopes produced by fission have masses that are close in size to each other.

Like fusion reactions, fission reactions produce energy in amounts vastly greater than chemical reactions. Figure 5.15 helps you understand this difference. Notice the energy requirement for holding together nuclei. Reactions such as solvation, ionization, phase change energy, and combustion rarely exceed a few hundred joules for similar amounts of reactants.

Joule is a standard unit of energy equivalent to the amount of heat required to increase the temperature of 1 g of water 1°C.

Fission reactions tend to proceed in one of two ways. In an uncontrolled fission reaction, high-energy neutrons hit unfissioned nuclei that then split apart. These split-apart nuclei are produced along with more neutrons. These neutrons hit unfissioned nuclei, causing an ever-increasing number of fission reactions. Such an explosive increase in the rate of reaction is called a **chain reaction**. If there is enough fissionable material to sustain the chain

Topic: fission reactions
Go to: www.scilinks.org
Code: 1Inquiry228

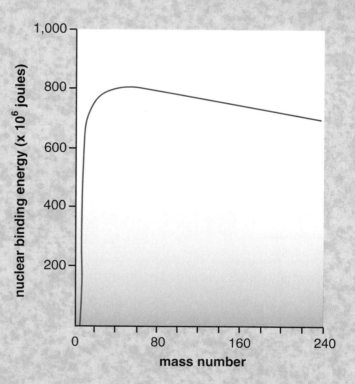

▲ **Figure 5.15 Energy needed to hold different nuclei together.** The amount of energy needed to hold nuclear particles together is immense compared with other reactions you have studied.

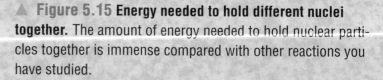

reaction, a mighty explosion takes place. The minimum amount of material required to produce an atomic explosion is called the **critical mass**. The critical mass of fissionable material for some atomic bombs is only 45 lb.

A controlled fission reaction does not explode. Engineers control the number of fission neutrons carefully. No chain reaction starts because materials such as water surround the fissionable material and absorb many of the extra neutrons. Nuclear energy power plants use controlled fission reactions to produce heat that boils water, which turns turbines to produce electricity.

Several of the products of fission reactions are radioactive isotopes with very long half-lives. These materials are difficult to dispose of safely. One option includes burying radioactive wastes underground. Yet fission reactions can produce vast amounts of electricity. As you might expect, engaging debate continues regarding the use of nuclear power.

Topic: nuclear chain reaction
Go to: www.scilinks.org
Code: 1Inquiry229

1. How is fission like fusion?

2. How is fission different from fusion?

3. Uranium-236 is an unstable isotope formed when uranium-235 is struck by a neutron. Uranium-236 then undergoes fission and can produce a number of products. Suppose it produces strontium-90 and 3 neutrons. What is the other product?

4. Are the nuclear reactions in stars due to chain reactions? Explain your reasoning.

5. Thorium-234 has a half-life of 24 days. How many grams of thorium-234 would remain from 100 g after 72 days? Show your problem-solving technique.

Recipe for a Star

ELABORATE

Now you are ready. You have the required knowledge of the ingredients needed to make a star. All you need is the recipe.

You know how nuclear reactions make different elements and versions of elements called isotopes. Elements have different chemical and physical properties. Two ways you can observe these differences are by looking for layers of gases and looking for differences in spectra.

In Recipe for a Star, you work in a team to apply what you know. You use what you know about nuclear reactions and characteristic properties to understand the recipe for a star. But the recipe in this activity goes beyond listing ingredients and telling when to mix those ingredients. It explains the interaction among particles involved in making a star. Those interactions depend on the same principles of nature you have learned throughout this program.

Materials

For each team of three students

colored pencils

glue

scissors

colored construction paper

Process and Procedure

1. Form a team of 3 and read through each step in this procedure before you read Recipe for a Star.

This activity depends on your ability to be creative and to apply knowledge from the reading. The task becomes much easier when you know what to look for in the reading. Reviewing the steps ahead of time helps you know what to look for and how to organize your thoughts.

2. Read the following paragraph to understand the creative product of this activity.

Your team will design and construct a box for a cereal, a cake mix, or another food product. The box will communicate how characteristic properties and nuclear reactions apply to the recipe of a star. The appearance of the box will mimic what you see on food product boxes such as snack crackers, cookies, and energy bars. But the product inside, catchy banners, contests, additional recipes, logos, company name, and celebrity endorsement will communicate what you know about star formation.

3. Review the *individual* student responsibilities in figure 5.16. Divide the responsibilities so that each team member has 1 responsibility from column A and 1 responsibility from column B.

▼ **Figure 5.16 Table of responsibilities.** Each team member selects one responsibility from each column.

Column A Portion of the box	Column B Knowledge area
Front	Concept words—Student will check the entire box to make sure the following science words are used and convey the correct scientific meaning in a proper context: gravity, density, matter, element, mass, gas, fusion, radioactive decay, atom, nucleus, temperature, energy, layer.
Back	Reactions—Student will show important nuclear reactions, explaining where they happen in the recipe and why they are important. Reactions must show how fusion, fission, and radioactive decay are different from one another.
Sides and top	Process and sequence—Student will convey why each step is important and how it depends on characteristic properties of matter.

4. Review the *team* responsibilities in the following paragraph. The team as a group has 3 primary responsibilities:
   - *Designing and constructing the box.* The team will work cooperatively to generate a creative design and to construct a final product. The first design decision will be your product name. For example, you might choose Sugar Frosted Nebulas as a cereal name to show what you know about making a star.
   - *Including charts and graphs.* The team will determine ways to include charts, tables, graphs, and sketches that convey the members's understanding of important concepts. The team must generate at least 1 graph of density versus distance from the core of a star.
   - *Incorporating quantities.* The team will include as many numerical values as possible. More credit will be awarded for showing calculated values and focusing numbers discovered from outside sources such as the library or Internet.
5. Read Recipe for a Star, thinking about what will go on the box your team will soon create.

Recipe for a Star

Several factors are important for star formation. All of these factors depend on the way materials interact. That is what you have studied in this unit, Matter Is Marvelous.

First, gravity pulls a cloud of hydrogen gas together. Second, density increases within the cloud. The center of the cloud gets extremely hot. After a great deal of time, sometimes millions of years, the star finally "turns on." What does that mean? What has to happen for a star to "turn on"? In this reading, you will follow a recipe that turns hot, dense matter into a star.

Do you realize that virtually every element on Earth was once part of a star? Processes in stars formed the carbon in animals and plants, iron in your blood, nickel in your pocket, and oxygen you breathe. To understand how stars make these elements and how these elements got to Earth, you need to understand what makes a star.

Imagine that there is a recipe for making stars. The recipe starts the same way for all stars. However, the end of the recipe varies because stars have a variety of masses. Look at the recipes for stars of different masses in figure 5.17.

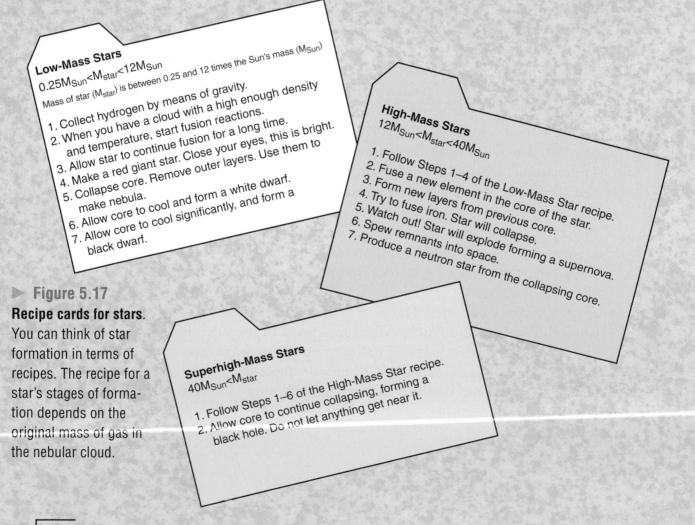

Low-Mass Stars
$0.25M_{Sun} < M_{star} < 12M_{Sun}$
Mass of star (M_{star}) is between 0.25 and 12 times the Sun's mass (M_{Sun})

1. Collect hydrogen by means of gravity.
2. When you have a cloud with a high enough density and temperature, start fusion reactions.
3. Allow star to continue fusion for a long time.
4. Make a red giant star. Close your eyes, this is bright.
5. Collapse core. Remove outer layers. Use them to make nebula.
6. Allow core to cool and form a white dwarf.
7. Allow core to cool significantly, and form a black dwarf.

High-Mass Stars
$12M_{Sun} < M_{star} < 40M_{Sun}$

1. Follow Steps 1–4 of the Low-Mass Star recipe.
2. Fuse a new element in the core of the star.
3. Form new layers from previous core.
4. Try to fuse iron. Star will collapse.
5. Watch out! Star will explode forming a supernova.
6. Spew remnants into space.
7. Produce a neutron star from the collapsing core.

Superhigh-Mass Stars
$40M_{Sun} < M_{star}$

1. Follow Steps 1–6 of the High-Mass Star recipe.
2. Allow core to continue collapsing, forming a black hole. Do not let anything get near it.

▶ **Figure 5.17**

Recipe cards for stars. You can think of star formation in terms of recipes. The recipe for a star's stages of formation depends on the original mass of gas in the nebular cloud.

The general categories are low-mass stars, such as the Sun, with a mass of M_{Sun}, and high-mass stars a lot more massive than the Sun. As you will see, you can predict what elements a star can produce by noting the starting mass of the star.

So making a star looks simple, doesn't it? In fact, recipe cards are easy to follow if you know what each step means. For example, you might have tried to follow a recipe for making a cake, only to get to a step that did not make sense, such as "fold in the egg whites." Coming across this step in a cake recipe, you might wonder how you "fold in" egg whites.

As you read these recipes for stars, you might have trouble following them without getting some explanation of each step. Make note of these questions in your science notebook and read on to learn more.

Recipe for a Low-Mass Star

Step 1: Collect hydrogen and dust.

A star starts out as a huge cloud of hydrogen gas. Gravity pulls the cloud together. The cloud begins to spin. This spinning cloud is called a protostar. Compared with actual stars, protostars are very bright, but their atmospheres are still relatively cool (3,000 Kelvin [K]).

Step 2: Start fusion reactions.

The protostar continues to contract. High energy strips nuclei of their electrons. Hydrogen nuclei collide constantly. As gravity continues to pull the nuclei inward, the cloud becomes denser. Hydrogen nuclei collide more frequently. The collapse causes the temperature and pressure in the protostar to rise. When the temperature gets high enough, hydrogen nuclei have enough energy to break through the electron repulsion of other hydrogen nuclei. Nuclear reactions then take place. Hydrogen nuclei begin to fuse. The name of this process is nuclear fusion.

When nuclear fusion occurs, the star "turns on." Hydrogen fusion results in the formation of a heavier element, helium. Vast amounts of nuclear energy are released, increasing the temperature of the star and giving off light.

Step 3: Continue fusion.

The energy of nuclear fusion causes the star to shine as the radiation moves outside of the core (see figure 5.18). The Sun is currently at this stage.

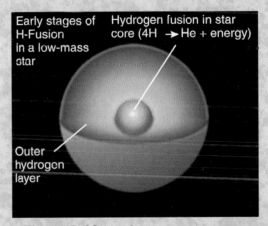

▲ **Figure 5.18 Burning star.** In the early stages of hydrogen fusion in a low-mass star, the core is surrounded by a thick outer layer of nonburning (nonfusing) hydrogen gas, which shines.

Step 4: Make a red giant.

Eventually, the amount of hydrogen decreases, which decreases the amount of hydrogen fusion. The star stops producing energy to shine. Without the outward pressure created by nuclear fusion, gravity causes the star to collapse. This initial collapse causes the core to get even more dense. Particles in the core collide more frequently and with greater energy. The core gets hotter.

The higher temperature causes the outer layer to expand and cool. Now the star has a dense, hot core with an expanded outer layer. The star is called a red giant because it is brightest in the red portion of the spectrum. Because the star's diameter is larger, it is much brighter than it was as a normal star.

Red giants may vary in size depending on their mass. An example of a red giant is the star called Aldebaran, in the constellation Taurus. As described in the next step, this type of star can make carbon.

Step 5: Collapse core. Make nebula.

The core of a red giant is full of helium. This core continues to collapse. The core becomes hot and dense enough for helium fusion. When this happens, helium nuclei fuse to form carbon nuclei.

The periodic table shows that carbon is heavier than helium or hydrogen. As a result, gravity pulls carbon to the star's core. Without their electrons, helium and hydrogen gradually concentrate in surrounding outer layers because

they are less dense than carbon. The core of the star is nonfusing carbon, surrounded by a shell of mostly helium, then another shell of mostly hydrogen (see figure 5.19). The helium fusion in the core continues until helium is all used up in making carbon.

Most of the red giants's mass remains concentrated in the dense carbon core. These red giants are not hot enough to start carbon fusion. This means that carbon does not change to heavier elements. Red giants, therefore, are the main source of carbon for life in the universe. In fact, most of the carbon in your body was produced in red giants that shone long before Earth was formed.

Time passes. The red giant's layers expand. These outer layers keep expanding. Eventually, these layers escape the surface of the star. They are literally blown into space. The matter from these layers becomes a nebula. A nebula is a cloud of gas and dust that floats around a former star. Light from the star allows astronomers to see the nebula. Figure 5.20 shows one such nebula.

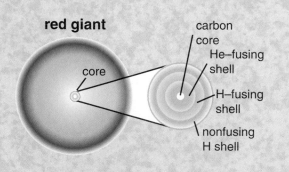

▲ **Figure 5.19 Red giant.** This figure shows a four-layered star. It is large and luminous, making it a red giant. The core consists of carbon surrounded by helium and then hydrogen shells undergoing fusion. These shells are then surrounded by hydrogen gas in a thick outer layer that is not undergoing fusion.

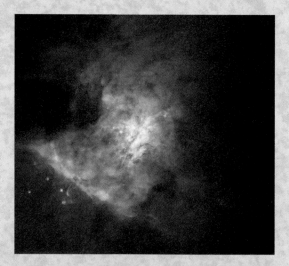

▲ **Figure 5.20 Helix Nebula.** The Helix Nebula is a cloud of dust and gas left over from the red giant stage. It is one of the closest and largest planetary nebula. The nebula is about 450 light-years (ly) from the Sun in the direction of the constellation Aquarius.

Step 6: Allow core to cool to a white dwarf.

You might predict that the carbon atoms will fuse. This does not happen. There is not enough energy in a low-mass star to fuse carbon. The low energy makes it impossible for carbon to fuse. Much of the star's mass is blown away in the nebula; the remaining core becomes a white dwarf. It is called a white dwarf because it is still very hot (white hot), but also small (dwarf) and not very luminous. White dwarfs are dim and hot stars.

Step 7: Let core get cold and become a black dwarf.

Eventually, white dwarfs cool completely. They become cold black dwarfs. The life of a low-mass star is over!

Recipe for a High-Mass Star

To review, the recipe for a low-mass star begins with a protostar that becomes a low-mass star, usually less than eight times the mass of the Sun. Then in a series of steps, the star changes into a red giant, a nebula, a white dwarf, and finally a black dwarf.

But not all stars begin with a low mass. Some stars begin fusion with much more hydrogen in the initial cloud. How do you make a high-mass star? To find out, follow these easy recipe directions.

Step 1: Follow Steps 1–4 of low-mass star recipe.

To make a high-mass star, follow the recipe for a low-mass star through Step 4. Then switch to the recipe card for high-mass stars and begin with Step 2, which follows.

Step 2: Use nuclear fusion to make carbon in core.

The core of a high-mass star collapses rapidly through the force of gravity. It becomes dense and hot enough to make three helium nuclei fuse. This results in one carbon nucleus. Carbon then can fuse with itself and lighter nuclei to make heavier elements.

This is where things really get exciting! For example, how can a star manufacture elements with an atomic mass greater than carbon? The star has to fuse carbon with hydrogen to form nitrogen. You probably know that nitrogen is a vital element for life. If carbon fuses with helium, it forms another vital element for life, oxygen. The core region of the star now consists of a mixture of carbon, nitrogen, oxygen, helium, and hydrogen. All of those elements are undergoing nuclear fusion and beginning to separate into distinctive layers.

Step 3: Form new layers as more fusion reactions begin.

The number of fusion reactions increase, making more and more nitrogen, carbon, and oxygen. These reactions produce heavier and heavier elements from the periodic table. Gravity draws these elements toward the core of the star. Lighter elements move outward to form a layer. The heaviest elements in the core then undergo more nuclear fusion, making heavier and heavier elements. Heavier elements displace lighter elements, forcing them outward from the core. The star has a layered appearance, something like the concentric layers of an onion.

Fusion reactions continue in the core of a high-mass star. Each new layer results from the fusion deep in the core. The star continues to produce layers corresponding to heavier elements such as oxygen, neon, magnesium, silicon, and sulfur. As you will see, this sequence of reactions slows down when the core of the star consists of greater and greater amounts of iron. Iron is not able to begin fusion because the star

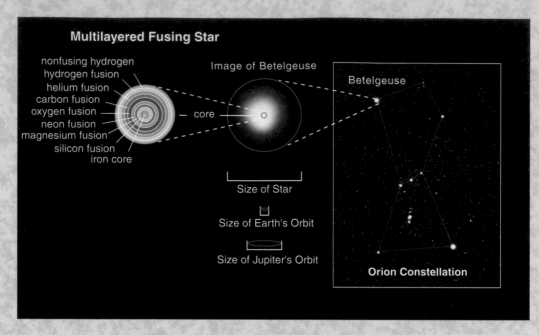

▲ **Figure 5.21 Multilayered fusing star**. The diagram shows the core of a high-mass star in the supergiant stage. The center of the core consists of iron (a nonfusion core). Layers surrounding the core are undergoing nuclear fusion reactions and consist of shells of Si, Mg, Ne, O, C, He, and H. The nine-layered core would be surrounded by a thick, non-fusing hydrogen gas shell. These layers mix some at boundaries between layers.

does not produce enough energy to make iron nuclei fuse. The iron then forms a nonfusing core. Astronomers say that this part of a star's life is the supergiant stage (see figure 5.21). An example of a red supergiant is Betelgeuse. Figure 5.21 shows Betelgeuse at Orion's left shoulder.

> What is the pattern you see in the layers of elements when you locate the elements in the periodic table?

Step 4: Try to fuse iron nuclei. The star will collapse.

Fusion continues until elements with atomic numbers 1–26 form. On the periodic table, those are all of the elements up to iron. When the star reaches this stage, things get even more exciting because, until now, fusion reactions produced heat. In contrast, the fusing nuclei of iron absorb heat.

The iron core of the star absorbs energy from the layer above it. The outward force to expand the star decreases. Gravity pulls the material inward from outer layers. The star collapses on itself extremely rapidly, and the core temperature and pressure increase tremendously. Soon the temperature becomes so hot that nuclei fall apart into protons and neutrons. The core becomes a soup of protons, neutrons, and electrons.

Step 5: Explodes to a massive-star supernova. (Stand back and wear your safety goggles!)

Still, the collapse continues. Eventually, it squashes protons and electrons together, causing them to become neutrons. The star is now a core made of neutrons surrounded by collapsing outer layers. The star "bounces" against its own neutron core, and all of the layers explode into space, leaving the core behind.

This explosion is known as a massive-star supernova. The explosion is so powerful that it can briefly outshine an entire galaxy. It is the most violent and spectacular explosion in the universe. While the core explosion occurs in about one second, the massive-star supernova may continue to shine for weeks or months. Massive-star supernovae are incredibly important because a flurry of fusion reactions before and during the explosions creates all elements in the natural environment with atomic masses greater than iron.

Look at the periodic table. How many elements have you heard of with atomic masses greater than iron? These less familiar elements are rare because they form only during a massive-star supernova explosion.

Step 6: Scatter remains of massive-star supernova event.

Take everything from the supernova explosion and scatter it in space. This will form a blurry-looking nebula around the exploded core of the star. This matter may eventually become the building material for the other bodies in space, such as planets like Earth, and your very own body!

Step 7: Collapse core to a neutron star.

All that remains of the core after a massive-star supernova event is a very hot, small, and dense core of neutrons. This is called a neutron star. A neutron star is so dense that 1 tsp of it would weigh 100 million tons on Earth!

Extra recipe steps for extra high-mass stars: Make a black hole.

If the remaining mass at the core is great enough, the core of a neutron star can collapse even further. After blowing away much of the star during the massive-star supernova, the remaining mass of the neutron star collapses to a black hole. These bizarre objects are areas in space that pull in everything around them—even light! Because they do not emit light, black holes are invisible.

If black holes are invisible, what makes astronomers think they exist? Astronomers know black holes exist because they can watch the behavior of stars and other material orbiting around black holes. People also have observed stars, matter, and even light being pulled into regions of space that could be black holes. In fact, it is a good thing that the solar system is 28,000 ly from the center of the Milky Way galaxy—strong evidence indicates that the center of our Milky Way contains a black hole!

6. Meet with your team and review the individual and team responsibilities.
7. Make a list in your science notebook of the tasks each team member will accomplish and have your teacher approve the list.
8. Design each side of the box and place a sketch of your design in your science notebook.

Include sketches of all sides of the box from each team member. This gives you a lasting record of your work that you can use for future study.

9. Construct your box based on your design sketches and turn it in to your teacher as instructed.

To learn more about objects and reactions in space, read the sidebar, Crazy Ideas? Incredible Evidence!

Crazy Ideas? Incredible Evidence!

The matter that existed in the early universe was primarily hydrogen and helium. This matter formed immense clouds of gas pulled together by gravitational attraction. The clouds did not collapse by their own gravity for long periods of time, however, because they slowly rotated. As they rotated, the outward force of rotation balanced the inward pull of gravity.

Sometimes an external force disrupted the balance between the force of rotation and the pull of gravity. Perhaps another cloud of gas moved through or close by, or perhaps a star was formed or died nearby. When the balance was upset, the cloud began to collapse under its own gravity. As it collapsed, the density and temperature inside the cloud began to rise. As the cloud became smaller, its rotation rate increased (just as a figure skater's spin rate increases when he or she brings the arms in toward the body). The cloud began to bulge outward in the middle, forming a disk around its equator. The slower, cooler matter at the edges of the bulge moved toward the

poles in response to the magnetic field that the spinning cloud generated.

As more matter moved toward the center of the collapsing, spinning cloud, the temperature continued to increase. If the core of the cloud reached a temperature of 10^7 K and a density of about 105 kilograms per meter cubed, a star was born. Hydrogen nuclei fused to become helium nuclei. Hydrogen nuclei can be thought of as a "fuel" that keeps the star burning brightly.

How do astronomers explain this process of early star formation? They use their knowledge of gravity, matter, magnetic fields, and the forces involved with spinning. In addition, they also look to the nighttime sky for real evidence to test the validity of their explanations.

Some astronomers think that the magnetic field of a star's core takes cool material from the disk (the bulge) and pulls it in toward the poles of the core. The scientists believe that as this material nears the poles, it is superheated by the core and is squirted out into space in two great jets, one above each pole of the core. This has the important consequence of keeping the collapsing cloud from flattening too much from its rotation.

Scientists can test their theories in different ways. For example, physicists and astronomers can do laboratory experiments (simulations) that mimic the processes just described that take place during formation of the cores of stars. When they do these experiments in the lab, they find that some of the colder matter is ejected as a jet stream by the *hot* center of the spinning gas cloud. If the models are correct, astronomers logically predict that they should be able to look at stars that are forming and see the same pattern of behavior of matter—jet streams squirting from the center of young stars.

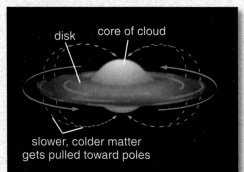

disk   core of cloud

slower, colder matter gets pulled toward poles

Spinning gas cloud. This diagram shows a spinning cloud of gas. Matter moves from the bulge at the equator (disk) to the poles. Gathering more and more matter near the core of the cloud increases the temperature at the center.

When astronomers look closely at star-forming regions, they do see clouds of gas that clearly show this pattern. They see small-scale shock regions caused by jets of gas propelled outward from the center of the cloud. They call this a Herbig-Haro object. The existence of Herbig-Haro objects is evidence that confirms part of astronomers's explanation of star formation.

Herbig-Haro object. A Herbig-Haro object shows the ejection of matter from a star-forming cloud of gas (the cloud of gas is hidden in the center of the picture). The small-scale shock regions caused by jets of gas propelled outward from the center of the cloud are seen as the bright areas on the right and left sides of the photograph.

Reflect and Connect

Answer these questions with your team. Record your responses in your science notebook.

1. On Earth, carbon is essential to life. Where did Earth get its carbon? Write a complete explanation in your science notebook.

2. Nuclear fusion in the core of a star forms elements of higher mass. It usually releases energy. Newly formed heavy elements gravitate to the core while the lighter elements form overlying layers. The process starts with hydrogen, and stars have a lot of hydrogen as fuel.

Complete the equations in figure 5.22 using the periodic table. The equations represent the fusion reactions between nuclei that occur in layered regions inside a massive star. The first two equations are done for you as examples.

▶ **Figure 5.22**
Various fusion reactions. Think what might result from each fusion reaction.

$$4\,{}_{1}^{1}\text{H} \longrightarrow {}_{2}^{4}\text{He} + \text{energy}$$
$$3\,{}_{2}^{4}\text{He} \longrightarrow {}_{6}^{12}\text{C (carbon)} + \text{energy}$$
$${}_{6}^{12}\text{C} + {}_{2}^{4}\text{He} \longrightarrow ?$$
$${}_{8}^{16}\text{O} + {}_{2}^{4}\text{He} \longrightarrow ?$$
$${}_{10}^{20}\text{Ne} + {}_{2}^{4}\text{He} \longrightarrow ?$$
$${}_{8}^{16}\text{O} + {}_{8}^{16}\text{O} \longrightarrow ?$$
$${}_{6}^{12}\text{C} + {}_{8}^{16}\text{O} \longrightarrow ?$$

In massive stars, a significant amount of iron is produced by fusion reactions. All of that iron is not simply produced by a sequence of helium fusion, however, as it is for some of the reactions in figure 5.22. The key nuclear fusion reaction is silicon + silicon to make nickel (Si + Si → Ni). After this, the nickel undergoes radioactive decay to change to cobalt (Co). The cobalt then decays to iron (Fe). The decay of nickel to iron takes about two years. The total sequence is shown by the following:

$$\text{Si} + \text{Si} \to \text{Ni} \qquad \text{nuclear fusion}$$

$$\text{Ni} \to \text{Co} \to \text{Fe} \qquad \text{two radioactive decays}$$

3. Draw a model of a star that has experienced the fusion reactions you filled out in figure 5.22. Show the various layers that would exist (like a cross section through the layers of an onion). This star is on its way to becoming a massive-star supernova. Label the layers with the type of reaction that produced them.

4. Describe why scientists believe that black holes exist even though they cannot see them.

Stellar Connections

You have seen recipes for different kinds of stars. In each case, different ingredients make the star function in a way that astronomers can observe. Whether white dwarf or red giant, stars with different behaviors have different elements.

Those elements have different chemical and physical properties. Do you remember the underlying reason for differences in chemical and physical properties? Yes, it is the microscopic particle called the atom *and* the way atoms interact.

Stars are part of the material world. Wave toys are, too. What connects them? From the surfing penguin to a supernova, microscopic form leads to macroscopic function. That is, laws of nature govern the tiny particles that make up all matter. When those particles interact, marvelous things happen. New materials are made. Those materials have characteristic properties. Scientists use what they know about characteristic properties to understand nature and to make useful products. It's an age-old recipe for success.

In Stellar Connections, you work individually and in teams to connect what you know from chapters 2–4 to what you just learned about stars. When you are done, you will better understand the unifying principles of the material world, whether they apply to a simple wave toy or to stars.

Materials
For each team of three students

3 Scoring Rubric handouts

Process and Procedure

You will be making connections between activities from chapters 2–4 and star recipes. That is, you will look for similarities between activities, skills, or observations you have already experienced and features of star recipes you have just investigated. Throughout this activity, you will think about what these connections tell you about the material world.

1. Meet as a team of 3 and discuss what the scoring rubric tells you about different levels of performance on this activity.

Chapter	Activity, skill, or observation to connect	Concept to connect	Information from star recipe	How connected (in words)	How connected (with sketches)
2	Density column	Differences in density can cause layers.	Stars have layers.	Density differences make density column function based on the same principle as layers in stars.	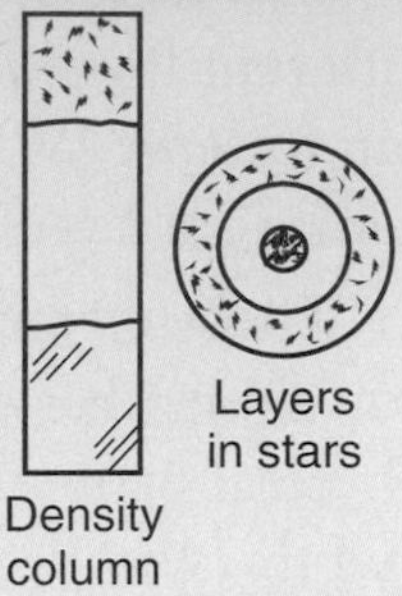 Density column / Layers in stars
	Continue . . .				

▲ **Figure 5.23**

Connections chart.
Complete this chart for each activity, concept, or skill in chapters 2–4. Four to six entries per chapter is a reasonable goal.

2. Study the example connections chart in figure 5.23 and discuss with team members the type of information that may be most appropriate under each column.

Place this chart sideways in your science notebook (landscape format) to give yourself more space to write and sketch.

3. Assign 1 chapter to each team member and complete the connections chart for your assigned chapter.

4. Think about connections, which might incorporate the following concepts in your chart:

- Chemical properties
- Physical properties
- Density
- Solubility
- Solvation
- Dissociation
- Ionization energy
- Conductivity
- Bonding

- Phases of matter
- Particle model
- Periodic trends
- Predicting formulas
- Noble gas electron configuration
- Spectra
- Atomic structure
- Nuclear reactions

5. Lead a discussion with team members about connections in your chapter.
    a. Show your connections chart to team members.
    b. Use your connections chart as a visual aid when you discuss each row.
    c. Listen to input from team members.
    d. Modify and improve your chart based on what you learn from team members.
6. Record important connections discussed by other team members.

UNIT 2

The Machinery of Life

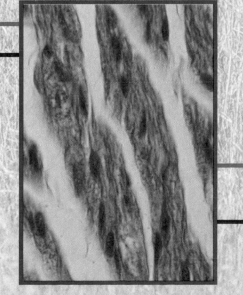

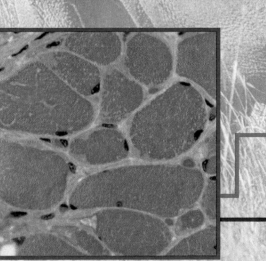

The Machinery of Life

What do you notice about the images in the opening art? You are looking at different levels of organization in organisms. Life is organized from atoms and molecules into cells. Sometimes an entire organism is a single cell, but organisms such as humans are complex systems of millions of cells working together in tissues and organs. How do cells and organisms perform the work they do? This is an important question that biologists, scientists who study living things, try to answer. Learning about cells and body systems provides useful explanations for how living organisms function. In The Machinery of Life unit, you learn some important ideas that scientists use to understand life.

Goals for the Unit

In the Machinery of Life unit, you learn about the substances that make up living things and that all living things share the same structures for their basic functions. You discover how living things collect energy from the environment, use it to survive, and how energy drives their activities. You find out how living things respond to stimuli and to their environments. Finally, this unit helps you develop an understanding of how animals move by learning about both biological and physical systems.

As you learn about living things, you also refine your ability to do science and you develop a better understanding of scientific inquiry. You

- design investigations to answer questions about the natural world;

- use math, models, and technology to gather data;

- develop explanations using evidence; and

- understand that technology helps scientists gather data about the living world.

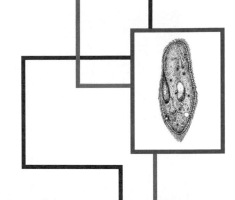

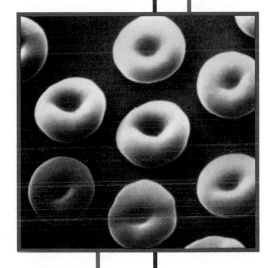

CHAPTER 6

Cells: The Building Blocks of Life

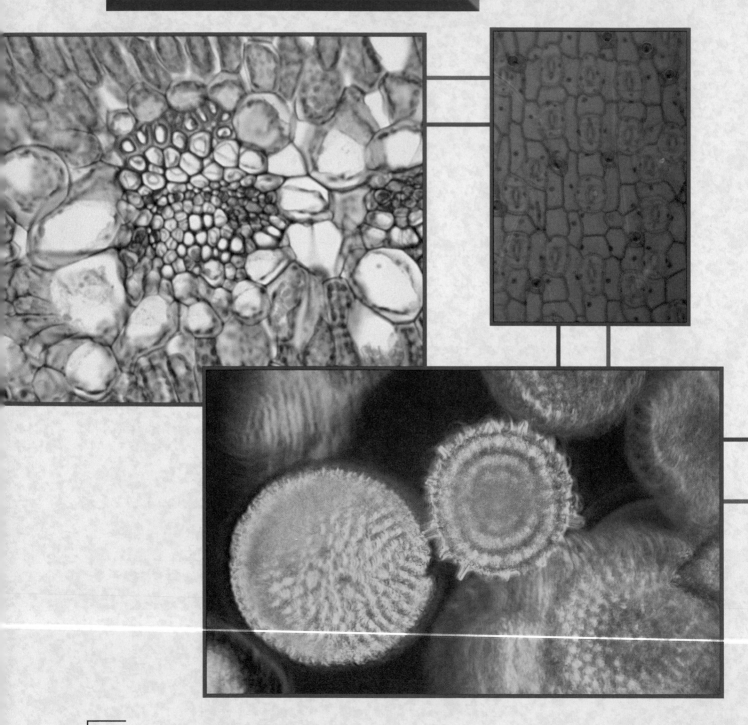

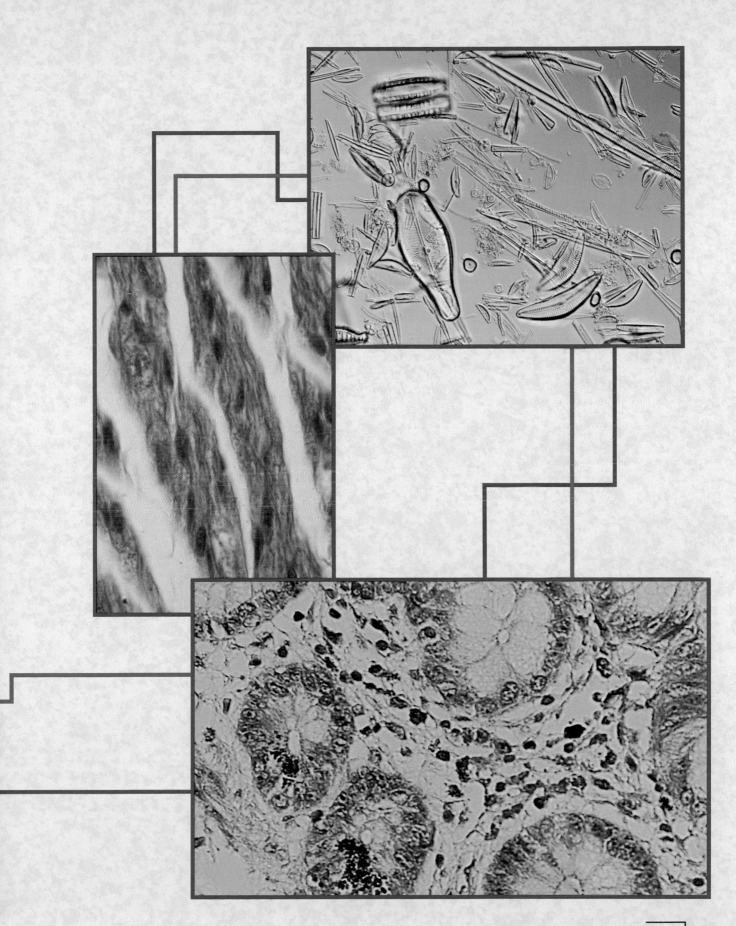

Cells: The Building Blocks of Life

All living things are made of cells. Notice the cells in the opening pictures. Some of these cells are an entire organism, while others are just one of many cells in an organism. Living things look very different on the outside, but you will learn in chapter 6, Cells: The Building Blocks of Life, that cells are fundamentally similar on the inside. All living things share the same machinery for their basic functions.

Just as a car has many parts, a cell has many structures. These structures are made of a specific group of molecules. Like the parts of a car, structures in a cell contribute to the cell's function. How are cells organized to perform the work that they do? You learn the answer to this question as you investigate cells in this chapter.

Goals for the Chapter

In chapter 6, you learn about the characteristics that are universal to the cells of all living things, such as the following:

- Molecules form a variety of specialized structures in cells.
- Specialized structures in cells carry out cell functions.

The two important cell functions you learn about are these:

- Cells selectively take in some substances from their environment, while rejecting or releasing others.
- Cells divide through a regulated process.

You will be better able to answer these questions by participating in the following activities:

ENGAGE	What Do You Know about Your Cells?
EXPLORE	What Is a Cell?
EXPLAIN	Molecules into Structures
EXPLAIN	Movement through Membranes
EXPLAIN	Cell Division
ELABORATE	Using Technology to See Inside Cells
EVALUATE	A Celly Adventure

What Do You Know about Your Cells?

Key Idea:
Cells are found in
living organisms.

What do cells look like?

EXPLORE

What Is a Cell?

Key Idea: Plants, animals,
and bacteria are all
composed of one or
more cells.

Linking Question

What are cells made of and what
makes some cells look different
from others?

EXPLAIN

Molecules into Structures

Key Ideas:

• All the molecules that make up
cells contain carbon.

• All cells contain structures that
carry out basic cell functions.

• Multicellular organisms have
specialized cells that perform
specialized functions.

Cells: The Building Blocks of Life

Linking Question

How do molecules enter cells
and exit cells?

EXPLAIN

Movement through Membranes

Key Ideas:

• Membranes are selectively permeable.

• Molecules move into and out of cells through diffusion,
osmosis, and active transport.

Linking Question

Is there a limit to the size
of cells?

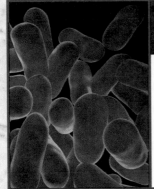
A Celly Adventure

Key Idea:

All cells are composed of the same molecules and structures and share many of the same functions.

How can I use what I have learned to demonstrate my understanding of the molecules, structures, and functions in cells?

ELABORATE

CHAPTER

6 Major Concepts

▶ **Cells**
- **Cells are the fundamental unit of life.**
- **Cells are composed of organic molecules.**
- **Cells have membranes that control what enters and leaves the cell.**
- **Cells divide through a regulated process.**

▶ **Math and Technology in Science**
- **Measurement is important for making accurate comparisons.**
- **Technology, such as microscopes, improves the gathering of data.**

Using Technology to See Inside Cells

Key Idea:

Advances in technology help scientists learn more about the organelles and molecules that make up cells.

Cell Division

Key Ideas:
- Growth of multicellular organisms occurs through cell division.
- The cells of multicellular organisms differentiate to form specialized cells.

How do scienctists learn about cells?

What Do You Know about Your Cells?

What do you know about cells? You may have heard that organisms are made of cells. The word *cell* implies a small compartment or room, like a room in a monastery or prison, or a small unit of organization. But where are cells found, and how large is a cell? To share your ideas about cells, begin by answering the following questions with a partner.

Materials

Process and Procedure

Discuss each question with your partner. Write your answers in your science notebook. Be prepared to share your answers in a class discussion.

1. Where might you find a cell?
2. Are cells alive? Why or why not?
3. What do you think cells are made of?
4. Draw a sketch of what you think a cell looks like. Do this as best you can at this point.
5. Do you think it is possible to see a cell? Why or why not?
6. How large do you think a cell is? Compare the size of a cell to something you are familiar with, such as the head of a pin or a strand of hair.
7. Think of a question that you have about the cells in your body. Write this question in your notebook. Write any ideas or thoughts you have about a possible answer.
8. Consider the items in the following list. Copy the items into a table with the following headings: "Single Cell," "Many Cells," "Not a Cell." Place the items in the appropriate column. You may create a fourth column titled "Not Sure" if you are not familiar with one or more of the items.
   - Chicken egg
   - Red disk-shaped structures in blood
   - Water in tree bark
   - Tree bark
   - Amoeba
   - Bacterium (plural is bacteria)
   - Human egg
   - Virus
   - Chlorophyll
   - Sperm
   - Chloroplast

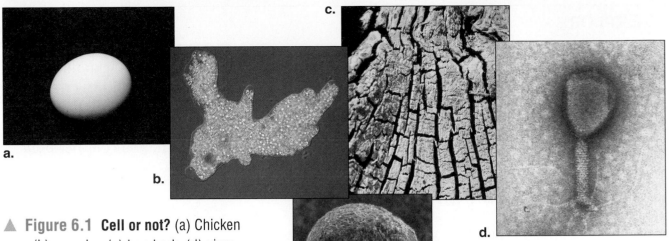

▲ Figure 6.1 **Cell or not?** (a) Chicken egg, (b) amoeba, (c) tree bark, (d) virus, (e) human egg; the photos do not reflect the size difference of the items. Which of these is a single cell, many cells, or not made of cells?

9. Share your ideas and thoughts about Questions 1–8 in a class discussion. Take notes on ideas that emerge from the discussion.

Reflect and Connect

Answer the following questions individually, recording your ideas in your science notebook.

1. Did other teams think it was possible to see a cell? Why or why not?

2. In Step 7, what types of questions did your classmates write about their cells? Which question interested you? Why?

Some questions might be related to the appearance of a cell, such as what the shape of a cell is. Other questions might be related to the function of a cell, such as whether cells breathe.

3. In the Matter Is Marvelous unit, you learned that atoms are the building blocks of cell matter, yet cells are the building blocks of life. Complete the following tasks to show what you know about atoms and cells.
   a. Write what you know about atoms.
   b. Write what you know about cells. You can use information that you learned from the class discussion. For example, what do you know about the appearance or function of cells?
   c. Draw labeled sketches to show how you think atoms and cells might be related. Your drawing should indicate the relative size of atoms and cells.

What Is a Cell?

Scientists are able to explore cells with a variety of technological tools. These tools let scientists see an entire cell, as well as details inside cells as small as atoms. In Part I of the What Is a Cell? activity, you study cells in your classroom. You see amazing cell *structures* and *features* with a simple microscope. Then in Part II, you consider *how many* cells are needed to make up an organism.

Part I: Let's Check Out Some Cells

Materials
For each team of two students

1 microscope	access to methylene blue stain
glass slides	access to a protozoan-inhibiting agent
coverslips	1 transparent ruler in millimeters
1 dropper	
1 forceps	1 calculator
flat toothpicks	1 copy of Explore Cells handout
samples provided by your teacher	

Cautions

Be careful not to get methylene blue stain on your clothes. Wash hands after preparing samples. Follow your teacher's instructions for handling coverslips and glass slides.

Process and Procedure

1. Before starting this activity, you should become familiar with the proper use of a compound microscope. Follow your teacher's instructions for going to a microscope station with a partner. Listen for special instructions from your teacher about proper use and handling of a microscope.
2. Check that you have the materials you need to observe cells with a microscope and your science notebook to record your observations and ideas.
3. The cells you observe in this activity might be smaller than you think. Read the Field-of-View Protocol with your partner to learn how you can determine the size of the cells you view through a microscope.

4. Follow the protocol to determine the width of the field of view for each of the lenses on your microscope. Record the eyepiece magnification, objective lens magnification, and values for the field of view in a table similar to figure 6.2.

Eyepiece magnification (a)	Objective lens magnification (b)	Total magnification (a × b)	Field of view width (diameter, mm)	Field of view width (diameter, µm)	Field of view radius (mm)	Field of view radius (µm)

▲ **Figure 6.2 Magnification and field of view.** You will use the values you record in this table to estimate the size of cells that you view.

Protocol

Field-of-View

The characteristics of objects change as the measuring device changes—the scale changes, and the object looks different. You experience this when you look at maps with different scales (as shown in the images).

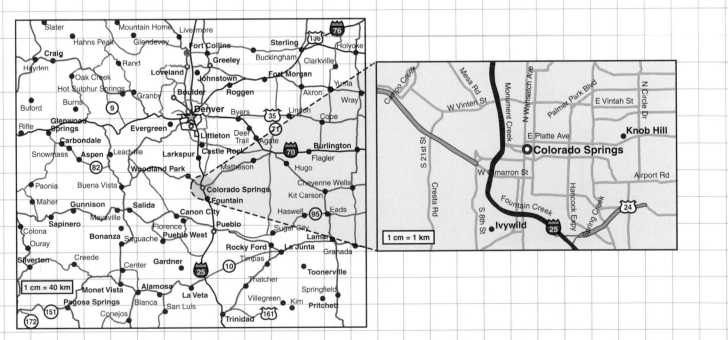

Scaling. The area of a map you can see is different for maps with different scales. The scale for the field of view of your microscope will differ depending on the magnification of the lens you use.

A map of your state may have a scale of 1 cm = 40 km. Your community appears as a dot on the map. On a map with a scale of 1 cm = 1 km, you may see a few of the major streets in your community. This protocol shows you how to create a scale for the field of view of your microscope.

The field of view is the circular area that is visible when you look through a microscope. You create a scale by determining the size of the field of view for each magnification on your microscope. Then you can determine the actual size of a microscopic object by comparing it with the size of the field of view. Follow these steps to measure, or calibrate, the field of view for the various lenses of your microscope.

1. Determine the magnification ($\times$) of the microscope at its lowest power. To do this, multiply the magnification of the eyepiece (a) by the magnification of the objective lens (b). Begin with the lowest-magnification lens. Write the total magnification in the 1st row of the table.

For example:

eyepiece magnification (a) = 10$\times$ objective lens magnification (b) = 4$\times$

total magnification = $a \times b$ = 10 $\times$ 4 = 40$\times$ magnification

Use the compound microscope figure to help you locate the eyepiece and objective lenses on your microscope.

The microscope you are using is called a compound microscope. This is because there are 2 lenses magnifying the specimen at the same time: the eyepiece and the objective lens. So to determine the magnification, you must multiply (compound) the magnification of the 2 lenses.

2. Determine the field-of-view width. This is the width from one side to the other (see the field-of-view figure). Using Steps a–c as a guide, write the width in the first row of your table.

a. Place a ruler marked in millimeters (mm) beneath the lowest-power lens.

b. Carefully move the ruler until you can see the marked edge.

c. Count the number of divisions that you see in the field of view. The marks will appear wide. The distance from the center of one mark to the center of the next mark is 1 mm.

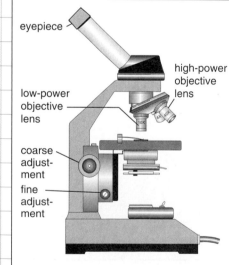

eyepiece

high-power objective lens

low-power objective lens

coarse adjustment

fine adjustment

Compound microscope. If the magnification of the eyepiece is not visible, ask your teacher for help. Most microscopes have three or four objective lenses.

3. Calculate the field-of-view diameter for the next most powerful objective lens, which might be the 10× objective lens. Use the following equations:

$$\frac{\text{magnification of high-power lens}}{\text{magnification of low-power lens}} = A$$

$$\frac{\text{diameter of low-power field of view}}{A} = \text{diameter of high-power field of view}$$

For example:

Total magnification of low-power lens = 40×

Total magnification of high-power lens = 100×

$$\frac{100×}{40×} = 2.5 = A$$

Field-of-view diameter of low-power lens = 4.5 mm

Then $\frac{4.5 \text{ mm}}{2.5}$ = 1.8 mm = field of view diameter of the 10× objective lens

4. Calculate the field-of-view width for the next most powerful objective, which might be the 40× objective lens. Using the same equation from

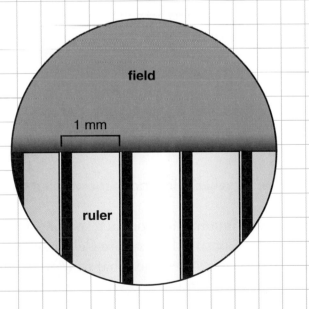

Field of view. The field of view is the circular area that is visible when you look through a microscope. You can determine the diameter of the field of view by using a ruler. In this image, the diameter is 4.5 mm. If your microscope has a micrometer built into the eyepiece, you do not need to use a ruler. A micrometer is visible when you look through the eyepiece, and it is used to measure items that you view.

Step 3, use the total magnification for the next most powerful objective lens.

For example:

Total magnification of low-power lens = 40×

Total magnification of high-power lens = 400×

$$\frac{400\times}{40\times} = 10 = A$$

Field-of-view width of low-power lens = 4.5 mm

Then $\frac{4.5 \text{ mm}}{10}$ = 0.45 mm = field of view of the 40× objective lens

Scientists convert measurements smaller than 1 mm to micrometers (µm; 1 mm = 1,000 µm). To convert mm to µm, do the following:

$$0.45 \text{ mm} \times \frac{1,000 \text{ µm}}{1 \text{ mm}} = 450 \text{ µm}$$

5. If your microscope has a 4th lens, move to the next most powerful objective lens. This usually is the highest magnification (such as 100×). Use the same equation and give your answer in µm.

Following the previous examples, the field of view would be 180 µm.

6. When estimating the size of structures, sometimes you can compare them with 1/2 of the field of view. For each of the 4 lenses you've measured, divide the diameter of the field of view by 2 for the radius. Write each value in the last column of the table.

5. Follow your teacher's directions for obtaining cell samples to observe.

6. Prepare a wet mount slide for each sample. Then complete these 4 steps. Consult the Explore Cells handout for guidelines on how to prepare slides and what to look for in the samples.
   a. Move the slide around and view a selection of the cells in the sample.
   b. Make a sketch in your science notebook of the cell or cells. Make notes on the similarities and differences that you observe in different cells.
   c. Label the sketch with the name of the sample and with a scale bar (in millimeters).
   d. Next to your sketch, write the typical size of the cells in the sample (in mm or µm). The size is the distance across

(diameter) if the cell is approximately round. If the cell is significantly longer than wide, you can average the length and width. Note this on your sketch.

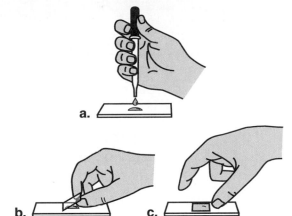

◄ **Figure 6.3**
Preparing a wet mount. Place sample in the middle of the slide. (a) Place one drop of water on the sample. (b) Hold a coverslip at a 45-degree angle to the slide and (c) slowly lower the coverslip.

Remember, for the tissues that you mount, small and thin are best. At times, you may not be able to see the cells on the slide until you view them with the microscope. Your teacher may post a list of tips for viewing your class's cells. When you see a cell that you wish to view more closely, make subtle changes in focus to help you see features in the cell.

Consult your teacher before using a 100× objective lens. This lens requires special handling and care.

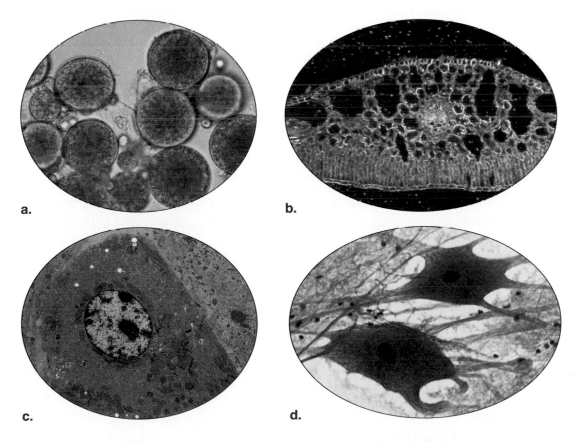

▲ **Figure 6.4 Various cell types.** (a) Alga cells, (b) cross section of a plant, (c) mouse liver cells, (d) human nerve cells. What similarities and differences can you see among the groups of cells in these photos? How do these cells compare with the cells you are observing?

Stop & THINK

Part I

After looking at a selection of cells, complete the following questions with your partner. Record your answers in your science notebook.

1. Biologists often say that the average cell is about 10–20 µm in diameter. Write answers to these questions about the cells that you saw.

   a. What was the average size of all of the cells that you observed?

   Remember, when calculating an average, all of the units should be the same before you add them.

   b. How does the average cell size in your samples compare with estimates by biologists of about 10–20 µm for all cells?

2. Consider the variety of cells that you observed. What did you observe that suggests how they might be similar and how they might be different? You can answer the question using labeled sketches, a table, or a short paragraph.

3. For green plant leaves that grow in the sunlight, what is a main feature that you noted in the leaf cells? How does this compare with cells in the bulb of an onion?

Part II: True or False: An Onion Has about 1 Billion Cells

In Part I, you looked at a variety of types of cells. You observed features in those cells and the sizes of the cells. How many cells do you think are needed to make an entire plant or animal? How would you estimate this number?

To help you visualize how to calculate the number of cells in an organism, imagine a gym filled with 1 m³ boxes. How would you estimate the number of boxes in the gym? You would determine the volume of the gym and then calculate how many 1 m³ boxes it would take to fill that volume. In Part II, you work with a partner to estimate the number of cells in an onion, using the same process.

Materials
For each team of two students

1 microscope

1 forceps

access to an onion cut in half

1 ruler in millimeters

1 calculator

onion notes from Part I

Cautions

Your teacher will cut the onion in half. After handling the onion, do not touch your eyes or nose and immediately wash your hands.

Process and Procedure

1. Get together with your partner. Obtain the materials needed for this investigation from your teacher.
2. Estimate the volume of your onion. To do this, follow these steps.
   a. Measure the radius of your onion in millimeters. The radius (r) is $\frac{1}{2}$ of the average diameter, or width, of your onion half.

Your teacher will cut the onion in half.

   b. Calculate the volume of your whole onion in cubic millimeters, using the following formula:

$$\text{volume} = \frac{4}{3} \times \pi \times r^3$$

   Show your work.

   If you have time, you may wish to take apart the onion to explore how the cell sizes vary in different parts of the onion. How does the size of cells on the onion's exterior compare with the size on the interior? Record all of your observations in your science notebook.

3. Estimate the volume of an onion cell using cells from the skin layer and the onion's interior. Make slides and estimate the sizes of the cells. Show your calculations in your science notebook.
   a. First, estimate the area of your onion cells in millimeters. This is the length (mm) multiplied by width (mm) of a cell (area = length $\times$ width, with units of mm^2).
   b. Estimate the thickness in millimeters of a given layer of onion cells. Be creative in how you do this. Explain your method and result in your science notebook.
   c. Estimate the volume of an onion cell. (The units are cubic millimeters, or mm^3.) To do this, multiply your estimate of the thickness of onion cells (Step 3b) by the area of onion cells (Step 3a). Record your estimate in your notebook. Using units of mm, the volume of an onion cell is as follows:

$$\text{volume} = \text{length} \times \text{width} \times \text{thickness}$$

4. Estimate the number of cells in an onion. To do this, divide your estimate of the volume of an onion in mm³ (Step 2) by your estimate of the volume of an onion cell in mm³ (Step 3).

Reflect and Connect

Complete this activity by answering these questions in your science notebook.

1. Decide whether this statement is true or false: An onion has about 1 billion cells. Explain your reasoning.

   Make sure you give your estimate for the number of cells in an onion and consider the estimates of others in your class.

2. What sources of uncertainty did you encounter when estimating the number of cells in an onion? Write each one in your notebook and indicate whether it had a big or small impact on your answer.

3. Select the cell that you found most interesting to observe.
   a. Write a brief, descriptive paragraph about your observations of that cell. Describe how you prepared your sample and what it looked like.

   Later you will compare this paragraph with a paragraph written by a scientist in 1665.

   b. Do you think you have any cells in your body that are like that cell? Explain why or why not.
   c. Record in your notebook the typical diameter (in µm) of your selected cell. If you arranged a bunch of these cells end to end, how many cells would fit across the outer layers of skin on the tip of your finger? The outer layer of skin on your fingertip is about 1.5 mm thick. Show your work.

   If your favorite cell is from the *Anabaena* sample and the average diameter is about 4 µm in width, here is how you would cancel the units:

   $$(1.5 \text{ mm}) \times \left(\frac{1{,}000 \text{ µm}}{1 \text{ mm}} \right) \times \left(\frac{1 \text{ cell}}{4 \text{ µm}} \right) = 375 \text{ cells}$$

Molecules into Structures

You investigated cell size in the previous activity and saw that cells are about 10–20 µm wide (or about 15×10^{-6} meters [m]). Compare this width with the width of a carbon atom. Carbon is an essential element for all organisms. A carbon atom is about 0.15 nanometers (nm) wide (0.15×10^{-9} m, or 15×10^{-11} m). Dividing cell size by

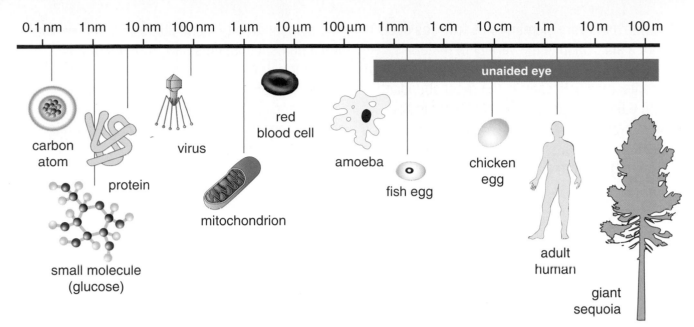

| 0.1 nm | 1 nm | 10 nm | 100 nm | 1 μm | 10 μm | 100 μm | 1 mm | 1 cm | 10 cm | 1 m | 10 m | 100 m |

carbon atom

protein

small molecule
(glucose)

virus

mitochondrion

red
blood cell

amoeba

fish egg

unaided eye

chicken
egg

adult
human

giant
sequoia

carbon atom size, cells are typically about 100,000 times larger than carbon atoms (15×10^{-6} m / 15×10^{-11} m = 1×10^{-5}). The size difference between a carbon atom and a cell, such as a red blood cell or bacterium, is shown in figure 6.5. Note that molecules are larger than atoms but much smaller than cells. Cells are the smallest unit that is alive. This is why cells are considered the building blocks of life.

What is the relationship between carbon atoms and cells? What were some of the features in cells that you saw in the previous activity? What are the similarities and differences between different kinds of cells? To answer those questions, with a partner, read the following sections. Before you begin, review the tasks and questions in Stop and Think to guide your reading.

▲ **Figure 6.5 Graph of the size of objects from atoms, molecules, and cells to organisms.** Most cells are too small to be seen with the unaided eye. Carbon and hydrogen atoms are less than a nanometer wide. Note that the scale is in factors of 10. Each measurement (for example, 1 m and 10 cm) is one-tenth the size of the measurement to the right.

READING

What Are We Made Of?

What is the meaning of the expression *cells are the building blocks of life*? You learned in the Matter Is Marvelous unit that all matter is made of minute particles called atoms. Indeed, parts of cells consist of many, many atoms. A system or an order is needed for those atoms to be joined in a meaningful way. The system combines atoms to make molecules. From there, molecules are combined to build all of the parts of cells.

Atoms combine chemically in many ways to form the millions of compounds that give Earth its variety of materials. Recall from chapter 5, Star

Material, that every element on Earth was once part of a star. Despite the variety of materials, living organisms are made of a limited number of elements, of which water is the most abundant. Figure 6.6 shows the elements present in the human body. About 97 percent of the compounds present in organisms consist of only six elements: oxygen (O), carbon (C), hydrogen (H), nitrogen (N), phosphorus (P), and sulfur (S). The remaining 3 percent contain small amounts of other elements. Some 20 other elements also are essential, but occur in smaller amounts. For example, calcium and potassium are necessary to make bones and teeth. This composition is very different from the nonliving environment (see figure 6.6).

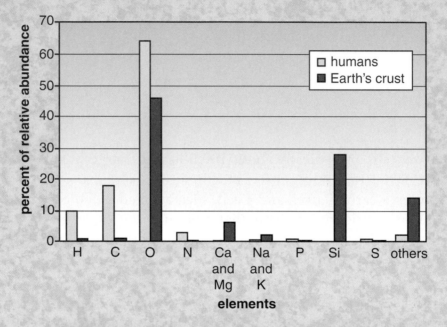

▲ **Figure 6.6 Abundance of elements in humans and the nonliving environment.** About 97 percent of the human body consists of only six elements: oxygen, carbon, hydrogen, nitrogen, phosphorus, and sulfur. The large proportions of hydrogen and oxygen reflect the fact that living organisms consist mostly of water. The dry matter in organisms consists mostly of compounds of carbon with other elements, especially hydrogen, oxygen, and nitrogen. What differences do you notice between the abundance of elements in humans and the nonliving environment?

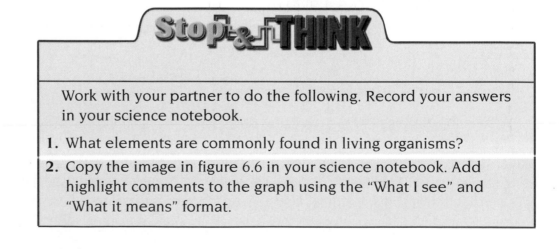

Stop & THINK

Work with your partner to do the following. Record your answers in your science notebook.

1. What elements are commonly found in living organisms?

2. Copy the image in figure 6.6 in your science notebook. Add highlight comments to the graph using the "What I see" and "What it means" format.

Carbon Atoms Are Essential for Life

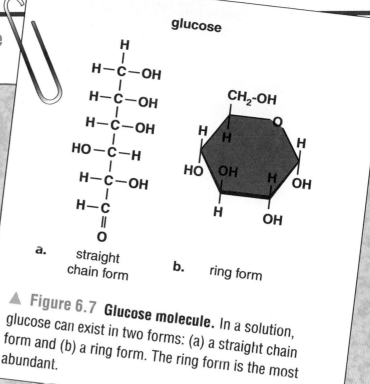

Figure 6.7 Glucose molecule. In a solution, glucose can exist in two forms: (a) a straight chain form and (b) a ring form. The ring form is the most abundant.

a. straight chain form

b. ring form

All organisms are composed almost entirely of six elements, but none of your friends looks like oxygen, carbon, or hydrogen. So how do atoms link together to form cells? The answer lies in the unique ability of carbon atoms to bond with one another and with other elements to form large molecules. A carbon atom can form covalent bonds with four other atoms. The covalent bonds between carbon atoms are very stable and allow carbon atoms to form chains and rings. When molecules are built with chains or rings of carbon atoms, they are said to be **carbon-based molecules**, or **organic molecules.**

Four basic types of these carbon-based, or organic, molecules are found in all living organisms. They are **carbohydrates, lipids, proteins,** and **nucleic acids.** Indeed, carbon atoms are the basis for each of these organic molecules and, as such, are essential for life. When molecules from these groups link together into long chains, they form **macromolecules.** Not all molecules found in cells fall into these groups. However, most of the mass of cells is composed of these four groups or the macromolecules they form. These molecules perform specific functions. The unique chemical properties of each group make them suited to different roles in cells.

Carbohydrates are organic molecules built mostly from chains of carbon with hydrogen and oxygen. Glucose is an example of one of the simplest carbohydrates formed from six carbon atoms, or a 6-carbon molecule (see figure 6.7). Glucose is the primary *energy source* for cells.

You may recognize its chemical formula, $C_6H_{12}O_6$. Sucrose is a 12-carbon sugar ($C_{12}H_{22}O_{11}$) that breaks down into glucose and fructose. You know sucrose as table sugar.

Simple carbohydrates, such as glucose, can be joined into much larger molecules. When they do this, they make complex carbohydrates. Examples of complex carbohydrates are starch and cellulose, commonly formed by plants. Starch is a molecule in plants that stores energy. It is also an important food source for animals and humans. Animals store carbohydrates in the form of glycogen, which is also called animal starch.

Carbohydrates do more than produce and store energy. They also provide support in cells. For example, cellulose is a structural molecule found in the rigid walls surrounding plant and alga cells (see figure 6.8). It is an important part of wood, giving wood its strength and rigidity. The cotton fibers used in clothes also are made of cellulose. The molecules in cellulose are

▲ **Figure 6.8 Cellulose fibers.** Overlapping layers of these fibers and other materials make the cell wall rigid.

linked together in a different way than the molecules in starch. As a result, humans cannot digest cellulose and they cannot use paper or other sources of wood as food. Another common structural carbohydrate is chitin, which forms the exoskeletons of insects.

Lipids, also called fats, are organic molecules that have two primary functions. Lipids provide long-term storage of energy and carbon. Lipids are also used in the construction of cell membranes. Lipids, like carbohydrates, are composed of carbon, hydrogen, and oxygen, but not in a fixed ratio. Lipids provide concentrated

energy storage that can produce more than twice as much usable energy as glucose. Fatty acids also form phospholipids. Together with proteins, phospholipids form cellular membranes, which form the boundary around cells. You learn more about the importance of lipids in a later activity.

Fatty acids are a type of lipid that make up the fats in your diets. The lipids, or fats, in meat are different from the oils in vegetables because the fatty acids are different (see figure 6.9). In saturated fatty acids, single bonds join the carbon atoms. One way to remember this is that the carbon atoms are saturated with hydrogens. In unsaturated fatty acids, double bonds join some of the carbon atoms. Polyunsaturated fats contain two or more double bonds.

Unsaturated fats (fats containing unsaturated fatty acids) tend to be oily liquids at room temperature. Olive oil, corn oil, and sunflower oil consist mostly of unsaturated fats. Polyunsaturated fats are also liquids at room temperature and are divided into groups. Two of these groups are the omega-6 and omega-3 fatty acids. They are often called essential fatty acids because humans cannot produce them in the body and they must be obtained in the diet. Omega-6 fatty acids are found in corn, sunflower, and soybean oil. Omega-3 fatty acids are less common and are found in salmon oil, walnuts, and flaxseeds. Saturated fats tend to be solids at room temperature. Butter and lard consist mostly of saturated fats. Trans-fatty acids, also known as trans fats, are a type of fat formed when liquid oils are made into solid fats like shortening or margarine. Trans fat is made when hydrogen is added to vegetable oil through a process called hydrogenation. Food manufacturers use hydrogenation to increase the shelf life of oils. Trans fats are found in fried foods, crackers, and snack foods.

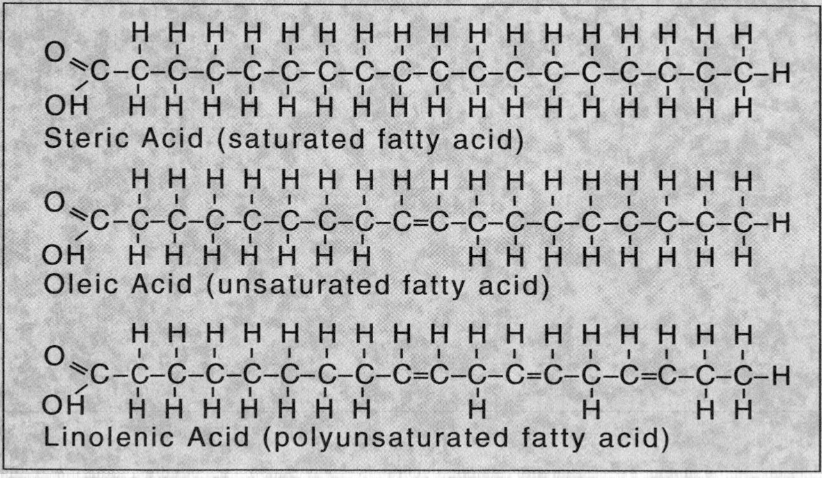

Steric Acid (saturated fatty acid)

Oleic Acid (unsaturated fatty acid)

Linolenic Acid (polyunsaturated fatty acid)

▲ **Figure 6.9 Fatty acids.** The chemical formula for each type of fatty acid is unique. How does the saturated fatty acid differ from the unsaturated and polyunsaturated fatty acid? Notice the double bonds.

3. Glucose is a carbohydrate used in many cell functions. Two main forms of glucose are shown in figure 6.7.

   a. From your teacher, get materials to use in representing the correct number of atoms and bonds. Then construct a model of the ring form of glucose. Clearly indicate the different atoms in the model.

   b. Draw a sketch in your science notebook of your glucose molecule.

   c. Clearly label the elements of glucose in your drawing and write its chemical formula.

4. Animals usually store energy reserves as lipids. Plants usually store energy as starches. What is the advantage of animals storing energy as lipids?

READING

Proteins and Amino Acids

Proteins are a diverse group of organic molecules composed of amino acids. Amino acids contain carbon, hydrogen, oxygen, and nitrogen. Two amino acids also include sulfur atoms. Figure 6.10 shows the general structural formula of an amino acid.

Proteins are macromolecules constructed from a unique sequence of amino acids. The shape a protein adopts and the function it performs is determined by the order of the tens or thousands of amino acids in a protein chain. Twenty different amino acids are commonly found in proteins. The same 20 amino acids are found in proteins, whether they are in bacteria, plants, or animals. Humans can produce nine of the 20 amino acids (see figure 6.11). The other

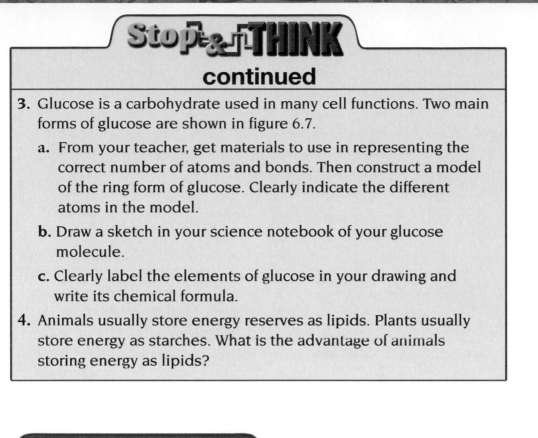

▲ **Figure 6.10 Structure of amino acids.** Most amino acids have a central carbon atom bonded to a hydrogen atom, an amino group, an acid group, and an *R* group. The *R* group is any of 20 arrangements of carbon, hydrogen, oxygen, nitrogen, and sulfur atoms, giving a unique structure to each amino acid.

11 amino acids are called essential because they must be obtained in the diet. Otherwise, the body breaks down proteins in muscle tissue to provide the body with the amino acids it needs to make proteins necessary to sustain life. The essential amino acids vary from one animal species to another. However, plants can make all of the amino acids they need.

If a friend tells you that he or she needs to eat some protein, you may think of foods such as red meat, fish, soybeans, cheese, or nuts. However, proteins are more diverse than the proteins found in those foods. Your body consists of over 100,000 different proteins. Protein in your diet can come from plant or animal protein. Most animal proteins are called *complete* because they contain all of the essential amino acids (see figure 6.11). Vegetable sources of protein often are low in or are missing essential amino acids. For example, wheat is low in lysine. However, by combining different vegetable sources, you can get all of the essential amino acids that you need. Digestion breaks down proteins into amino acids. The amino acids enter the bloodstream. Then cells use these amino acids to build different proteins in your body. You'll see that each protein plays a vital role in your body's cells. Proteins are much more than meat, cheese, and nuts.

Every living cell contains from several hundred to several thousand different proteins. Proteins are structural components of cells. Proteins are used to make key parts of structures in cells and combine with lipids to make membranes, such as the cell membrane. They are also messengers and receivers of messages (receptors) between cells. They play an important role in defending against disease. Skin, hair, muscles, and parts of the skeleton are made of protein. The most important role of proteins, however, is as enzymes, specialized molecules that assist the many reactions occurring in cells.

Nucleic acids are the fourth type of organic molecules. They carry the instructions for

Essential amino acids	Nonessential amino acids
Histidine	Alanine
Isoleucine	Arginine
Leucine	Asparagine
Lysine	Aspartic acid
Methionine	Cysteine
Phenylalanine	Glutamic acid
Threonine	Glutamine
Tryptophan	Glycine
Valine	Proline
	Serine
	Tyrosine

▲ Figure 6.11 **Essential and nonessential amino acids.** Humans can produce 11 of the 20 amino acids. These 11 are the nonessential acids. The other nine amino acids must be obtained in the diet and are called essential. Do you think you are getting all of the amino acids that you need to make proteins in your body?

cell processes. Nucleic acids are made of nucleotides, which consist of three parts— a 5-carbon sugar, a nitrogen base, and a phosphate group (see figure 6.12). Figure 6.13 shows a chain of nucleotides connected to form a nucleic acid molecule. These chains store and transmit hereditary information in cells. Nucleic acids are unique because the sugar and phosphate groups link together to form a backbone (see figure 6.13). The exposed edges on the opposite side of the strand make it possible for the chain to pair with other nucleic acid chains. There are two main types of nucleic acids— deoxyribonucleic acid (DNA) and ribonucleic acid (RNA). You will learn more about them next year.

The organic molecules—carbohydrates, lipids, proteins, and nucleic acids—serve many vital functions in cells. You will learn more about these throughout this unit. In the following sections, you learn about some of the most basic structures in cells and their functions. In fact, you already observed some in the previous activity.

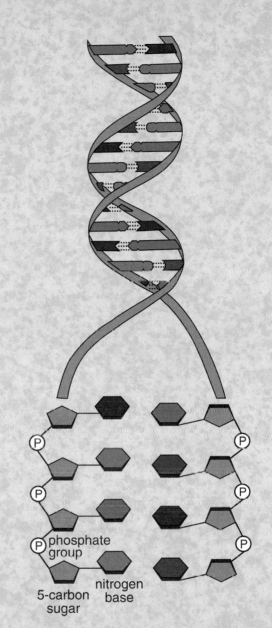

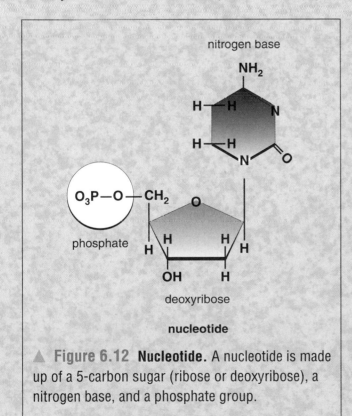

▲ **Figure 6.12 Nucleotide.** A nucleotide is made up of a 5-carbon sugar (ribose or deoxyribose), a nitrogen base, and a phosphate group.

▲ **Figure 6.13 Model of a nucleic acid.** Nucleotides are connected in a chain. The sugar and phosphate groups link together and form a backbone, shown here as a ribbon in the top part of the figure. Hydrogen bonds pair the nitrogen bases of the two chains together.

Topic: organic molecules
Go to: www.sclinks.org
Code: 1Inquiry271

continued

5. What are the functions of organic molecules in cells? Report your answer in a T-table with the headings "Organic Molecule" and "Function in Cell." You may have to record organic molecules in the table multiple times because some molecules have multiple functions.

6. Describe how it is possible for so many different proteins to exist.

7. Many foods are soluble in water so that you can digest them. Many parts of your body are not soluble in water. Yet both food and body parts are made from carbohydrates, lipids, proteins, and nucleic acids. How can this be?

READING

A Closer Look at Cells

Now you know about the organic molecules from which living cells are made. You learned that organic molecules are arranged in organized patterns to make carbohydrates, lipids, proteins, and nucleic acids. Those organic molecules make up the membranes and other structures found in cells. But what are some of the common features of cells? What is the relationship between cells and organisms?

All living organisms are made of cells. In some cases, such as *Paramecium* and *Blepharisma,* the entire organism is a single cell. Organisms such as these are usually less than 0.5 mm in size and are called **single-celled,** or **unicellular,** organisms. Examples that you've probably heard of include bacteria, yeast, and algae. Other organisms are **multicellular** and may be composed of trillions of cells. Examples include animals, plants, and fungi.

Because cells are found in all organisms, scientists consider them to be the basic units of life. (To learn how scientists developed the idea that cells are the basic units of life, read the sidebar, The Development of Cell Theory.)

All cells can be separated into two groups—prokaryotes and eukaryotes (see figure 6.14). Cells of prokaryotes do not have a membrane enclosing the genetic material of the cell. In eukaryotes, the genetic material of the cell is enclosed in a nucleus. Besides a nucleus, eukaryotes have other membrane-enclosed structures, or organelles, that prokaryotes lack. Prokaryotes include organisms such as bacteria. They are generally single-celled organisms. Eukaryotes can be single-celled and multicellular organisms. Examples of eukaryotes include plants, animals, and fungi.

▶ **Figure 6.14 A prokaryotic cell (top) and a eukaryotic cell (bottom).** The prokaryotic cell is relatively simple, with a cell wall, cell membrane, and interior. Note the greater structural complexity of the eukaryotic cell (an amoeba). What differences can you see?

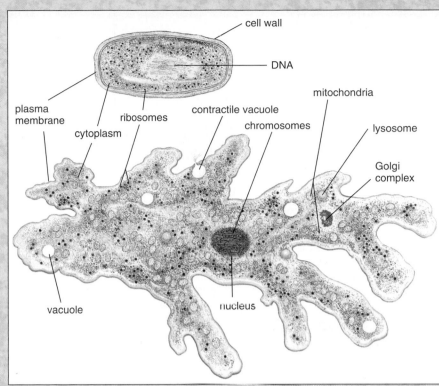

cell wall

DNA

mitochondria

plasma membrane

contractile vacuole

lysosome

cytoplasm

ribosomes

chromosomes

Golgi complex

vacuole

nucleus

Prokaryotes do not have a barrier that encloses the genetic material of the cell. Rather, all material of the cell resides together within one cell membrane, the outer boundary of the cell. Most prokaryotes are very small, averaging 1–10 μm long (see figure 6.15). Ancient rocks on Earth show that prokaryotes were the first life on Earth, beginning about 3.5 billion years ago. You will learn more about these ancient prokaryotes in chapter 13 of The Earth and Beyond unit.

▶ **Figure 6.15 Prokaryotic cells.** Many bacteria are visible in this scanning electron micrograph of human skin and a hair follicle. Prokaryotes are very small, averaging 1–10 μm long. Up to 35,000 could fit side by side on the point of a pin.

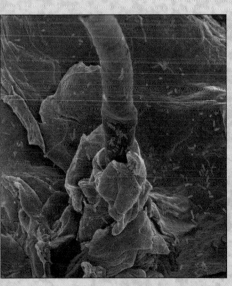

Stop & THINK
continued

8. Make a list of the samples you viewed in the What Is a Cell? activity. Next to each item, write whether it is a prokaryote or eukaryote and a single-celled or multicellular organism.

Eukaryotes

Cells of eukaryotes have a more complex structure than cells of prokaryotes. The eukaryotic cell is a highly organized system divided into distinct compartments by membranes. Those compartments are called **organelles.** The presence of many compartments within a cell allows many different internal environments. Those environments provide the conditions that are required for specialized functions. Almost all eukaryotic cells have the same basic set of organelles, or compartments.

Cells are fundamental to all life-forms. A key feature of cells in multicellular organisms such as plants and animals is their compartmentalization into smaller functional parts called organelles. Illustrated on these pages are generalized animal and plant cells with enlargements of their major organelles. (The colors are artificial.)

generalized animal cell

cell membrane: semifluid cell boundary that controls passage of materials into and out of cell; made of two lipid layers with proteins on surface and embedded within the layers

nucleus: large organelle that is the control center of cell; enclosed by double membrane with pores (the nuclear membrane); contains most of cell's genetic information in DNA; contains one or more nucleoli, where some RNA is made

cytoskeleton: network of protein filaments that provides internal organization, cell shape, and the capacity for movement

lysosomes: small organelles containing enzymes that carry out intracellular digestion

centrioles: pair of tubular structures that play a role in cell division in protist and animal cells

The most noticeable organelle in eukaryotic cells is usually the **nucleus.** You may have noticed a nucleus as a dark spot on your stained slides of animal or plant cells, such as cells from inside your cheek. The nucleus contains genetic information in the form of DNA. Remember that DNA is composed of nucleic acids. Because genetic information controls the basic functions of the cell, the nucleus is considered the control center of the cell.

A **plasma membrane** encloses the entire contents of eukaryotic cells as well as prokaryotic

▼ **Figure 6.16 Animal and plant cells.** Generalized animal (left) and plant (right) cells are shown with enlargements of the major organelles so that you can compare similar structures. What structures do you see that are found only in this plant cell? Do you see structures that are found only in animal cells?

cell wall: outer boundary of plant cells that provides rigidity; formed of cellulose fibers

Organelles allow for a division of labor that enables a cell to carry on thousands of chemical reactions continuously and simultaneously. Although many of these reactions are not compatible, they can proceed without difficulty because they are separated from each other in the organelles.

generalized plant cell

mitochondria: small organelles that are the site of energy-releasing reactions in all cells; enclosed by double membrane with inner membrane much folded

endoplasmic reticulum: tubular or flattened membrane system that compartmentalizes the cytoplasm and plays a role in the synthesis of proteins

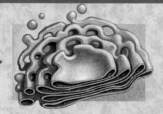

Golgi apparatus: system of flattened sacs that modifies, sorts, and packages macromolecules for secretion or for delivery to other organelles

cytoplasm: semifluid material surrounding organelles; site of many cellular reactions

chloroplasts: small organelles in plant cells that are the site of all reactions of photosynthesis; enclosed by double membrane; third, inner membrane forms layered structures

vacuole: large organelle in plant cells that stores nutrients and waste products; may occupy more than 50 percent of volume in plant cells; some animal cells also have small vacuoles.

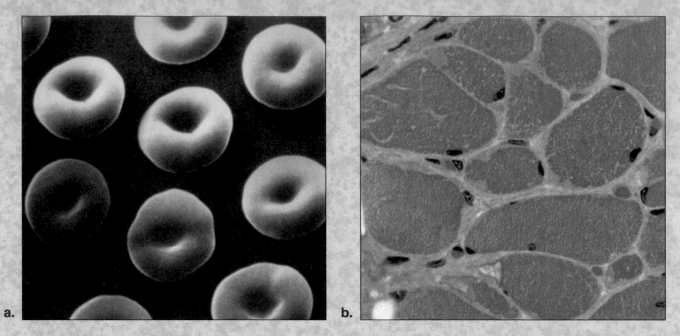

a.

b.

▲ **Figure 6.17 Specialized animal cells.** (a) A red blood cell is about 6–7 μm in diameter. Red blood cells play a vital role in bringing oxygen to all tissues of the body. (b) Muscle cells contract only when they are stimulated by a nerve impulse or hormone (chemical messenger).

cells (see figure 6.14). In plant and fungal cells, the plasma membrane also is surrounded by a rigid structure called the cell wall. The wall is composed of cellulose and other complex carbohydrates (see figure 6.14). This enables the wall to support and protect the cell.

Within the plasma membrane, but outside the nucleus, is the cytoplasm. The cytoplasm is a gelatin-like material that effectively fills the cell and surrounds all of the organelles. Many chemical reactions occur in the cytoplasm. The cytoplasm consists of networks of protein strands, tubes, and filaments that provide some strength for the cell. These proteins of the cytoplasm allow materials to be transported in and out of the cell and between organelles within the cell. This protein network is called the cytoskeleton. The cytoskeleton gives the cell its distinct shape and its capacity for movement.

In addition to the nucleus, the main types of organelles present in all eukaryotic cells are the endoplasmic reticulum (ER), Golgi apparatus, and mitochondria. Scattered throughout the cyto-

plasm of both eukaryotes and prokaryotes are many small bodies called ribosomes, which manufacture proteins. Both plant and some animal cells contain vacuoles. Two other types of organelles common in animal cells are lysosomes and centrioles. Organelles found in plant cells but not animal cells include chloroplasts. Study figure 6.16 to learn more about these organelles.

SCiLINKS®
NSTA

Topic: organelle
Go to: www.scilinks.org
Code: 1Inquiry276

In general, each organelle performs the same set of functions in all cell types. However, organelles vary in abundance, and the properties of organelles may differ from cell type to cell type. Those differences allow different cell types to perform specialized functions.

Many different types of cells exist in multicellular organisms. All cells must carry on the basic activities of life, but each type of cell often takes on a special job as well. For example, specialized cells called red blood cells transport oxygen (see figure 6.17a). A nerve cell is efficient in conducting electric signals, enabling an organism to respond to its internal and external environments. A muscle cell is specialized to contract (see figure 6.17b). In plants, mesophyll cells are specialized for photosynthesis and guard cells are specialized to regulate water loss (see figure 6.18).

In multicellular organisms, a group of cells with the same specialization usually works together to perform a particular function. Groups of specialized cells form tissues, organs, and systems. For example, muscle cells are part of the muscular-skeletal system. You learn about body systems in the final chapter of this unit.

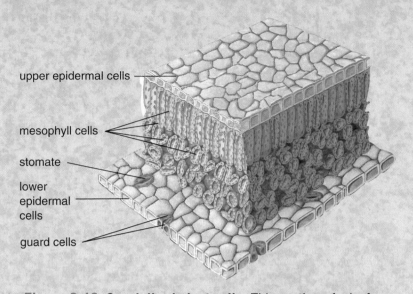

upper epidermal cells

mesophyll cells

stomate

lower epidermal cells

guard cells

▲ **Figure 6.18 Specialized plant cells.** This portion of a leaf shows some of the cells that make up plant tissue. Covering the upper and lower surfaces of the leaf is a layer of transparent epidermal cells. Mesophyll cells have numerous chloroplasts. Photosynthesis occurs in these cells. Guard cells regulate water in plants by opening and closing stomates—openings in a plant leaf.

Reflect and Connect

Work with your partner to do the following. Record your answers in your science notebook.

1. Explain why it is important for all cells to have a cell membrane. Why might it be beneficial?
2. Make a Venn diagram to illustrate the similarities and differences between the following.
   a. Prokaryotes and eukaryotes
   b. Plants and animals
3. Describe in your own words why carbon atoms are essential to life.
4. What differences are likely to exist between single-celled organisms and the cells of a multicellular organism?
5. Build a concept map using the following words: *atoms, carbohydrates, cells, elements, lipids, nucleic acids, organic molecules,* and *organism.*

The Development of Cell Theory

Much of the biological progress that occurred in the seventeenth century depended on the development of glass lenses. By 1650, the art of grinding and polishing pieces of glass into lenses had developed so that it became possible to build good microscopes.

In the 1660s, an Englishman named Robert Hooke devised a compound microscope and illumination system to examine small objects. When Hooke examined the cork layer of bark from an oak tree, he observed rows of compartments. The compartments reminded him of the small cells in which monks lived in medieval monasteries. For that reason, he called the compartments cells. Around the same time, Anton van Leeuwenhoek was grinding his own lenses and making observations of microorganisms. He discovered an amazing, invisible world. For 50 years, he described and made careful drawings of bacteria and detailed structures in small insects—even sperm cells from humans, dogs, frogs, and insects.

Scientists gradually began to realize that cells were the fundamental units of living organisms. In 1838, two German biologists, Matthias Schleiden, a plant biologist (botanist), and Theodor Schwann, an animal biologist (zoologist), proposed the cell theory. According to the cell theory, all organisms consist of cells and cell products and one can understand how living creatures are built and how they function if cells can be understood. Until the development of the cell theory, the emphasis had been on the cell walls. In looking at animal cells, however, Schwann and others had been unable to find the boxlike cells seen in plants. Schwann interpreted his observations in a new way, emphasizing what was inside the "box," rather than the box itself. Further studies showed that certain structures were common to plant and animal cells as well as to microorganisms. Once the contents of cells began to be studied, ideas about the origins of organisms began to change.

For hundreds of years, people thought that organisms could come from nonliving matter, an idea known as spontaneous generation. Several different studies disproved the idea. In 1855, Rudolf Virchow, a physician and biologist, proposed that all cells produce more cells through time, but his idea was not accepted by everyone. In 1864, Louis Pasteur, a French scientist working with yeast cells, demonstrated that microorganisms could not arise from completely nonliving matter. By the 1880s, the work of French and German scientists showed how cells divided and produced more cells—that organisms, therefore, came from existing organisms and that their cells arose from existing cells.

Today the cell theory is summarized in two main ideas: (1) Cells are the units of structure and function in living organisms, and (2) all new cells come from cells that already exist. New technologies have made possible extremely detailed studies of cell structure and function. Although there are conflicting ideas about how cells first came to be, the cell theory is still one of the major unifying themes of biology.

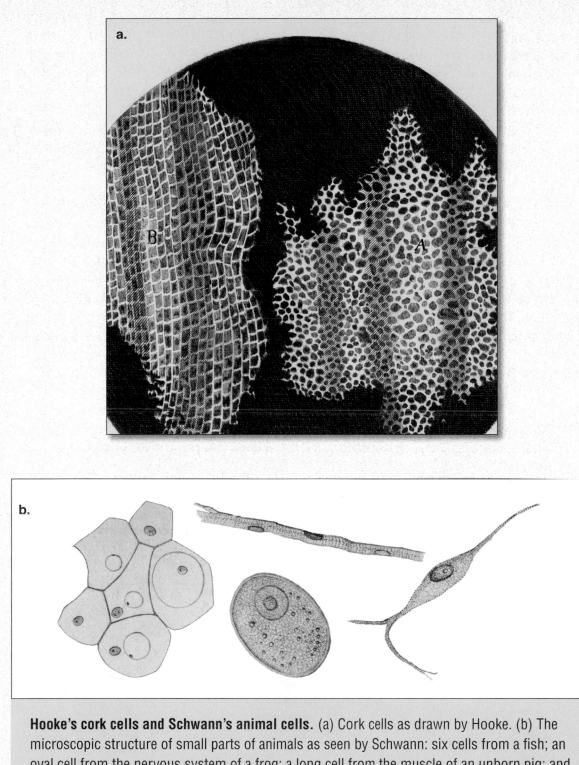

Hooke's cork cells and Schwann's animal cells. (a) Cork cells as drawn by Hooke. (b) The microscopic structure of small parts of animals as seen by Schwann: six cells from a fish; an oval cell from the nervous system of a frog; a long cell from the muscle of an unborn pig; and a spindle-shaped cell, also from an unborn pig.

The Origin of Eukaryotes

The most unique feature of eukaryotic cells is the presence of membrane-enclosed organelles such as nuclei, mitochondria, and chloroplasts. Where did they come from?

One hypothesis is that mitochondria and chloroplasts originated as free-living prokaryotes. This hypothesis was developed by Lynn Margulis. Margulis proposed that eukaryotes originated from a symbiotic relationship between a large prokaryote and a small prokaryote. Symbiosis is a relationship in which different species of organisms live together. The large prokaryotic cells absorbed the smaller ones (or alternatively, small parasitic cells bored into larger cells). Instead of being digested, the smaller cells survived, protected inside the larger (host) cells.

Photosynthesis and aerobic (requiring oxygen) respiration in the small cells produced sugars and energy that may have benefited the host cells. This relationship may have allowed all of the partners to survive in higher numbers than those cells that lacked such relationships. Eventually, the internal partners, or endosymbionts, lost the ability to live independently. An endosymbiont is an organism that lives inside its symbiotic partner (the host). Aerobic purple bacteria were the likely ancestors of mitochondria. Photosynthetic bacteria—cyanobacteria—were the likely ancestors of chloroplasts.

A large body of evidence supports Margulis's endosymbiont hypothesis that mitochondria and chloroplasts were once free-living prokaryotes. For example, both organelles have their own genetic material (DNA) and ribosomes (organelles that manufacture proteins). Their genetic material and ribosomes are similar to those of bacteria, which are prokaryotes. Both mitochondria and chloroplasts also have double membranes. The outer membranes of these organelles may have originated as vacuoles that surrounded the organelles when their host cells first took them in.

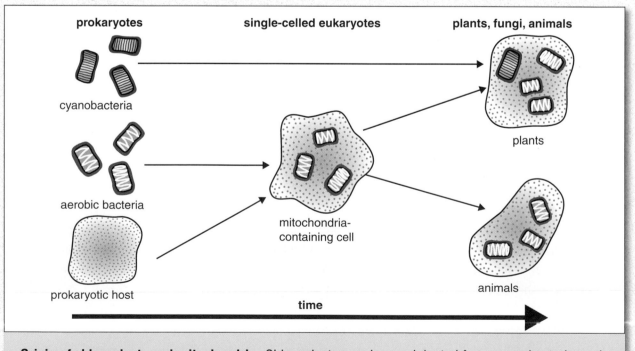

Origin of chloroplasts and mitochondria. Chloroplasts may have originated from cyanobacteria, and mitochondria may have originated from aerobic bacteria.

Movement through Membranes

In the last activity, you learned how organic molecules are used to construct the organelles of cells. The molecules and organelles do all of the work necessary to keep the cell functioning and to keep an organism like you alive. To do that work, cells need many types of fuel and supplies. Waste products must exit the cell as well. This is true for single-celled organisms as well as multicellular organisms. But how do fuel and supplies in the form of molecules enter and exit cells?

You work with a partner to begin to answer this question. In Part I, you observe how plant cells respond to changes in their environment. In Part II, you build a model of a cell and design an experiment to test your ideas about the movement of molecules.

Part I: Changing Environments

Materials
For each team of two students

1 dropping pipet

1 microscope

1 glass slide

1 coverslip

1 dropper

5% salt (NaCl) solution

distilled water

1 thin layer of red onion or small leaf of *Anacharis*

1 forceps

paper towels

Process and Procedure

Cell membranes create a barrier between a cell's internal and external environment. Work with a partner to investigate how changes in the external environment affect a cell.

1. Prepare a wet mount slide of red onion or *Anacharis*.
2. Focus the microscope to locate a few cells in the sample. Make sure you can see several pink (or green) cells.

Take turns observing the cells.

3. Make a sketch in your science notebook of the cells. Your sketch should be big enough so that you can draw the cell wall, cell membrane, and chloroplasts, if present.
4. Place a small piece of paper towel at one edge of the coverslip.
5. Test the effects of changing the external environment of the cells you are viewing. To do this, place several drops of 5 percent salt solution against the edge of the coverslip on the

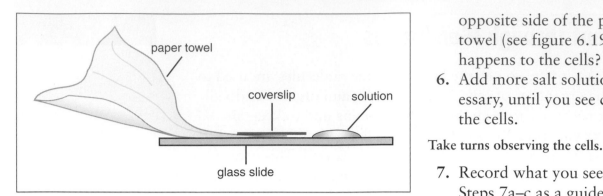

▲ **Figure 6.19**
Adding solution.
Carefully hold a small piece of paper towel on one side while you drop solution on the other side.

opposite side of the paper towel (see figure 6.19). What happens to the cells?

6. Add more salt solution, if necessary, until you see changes in the cells.

Take turns observing the cells.

7. Record what you see using Steps 7a–c as a guide.
   a. In your science notebook, make a sketch of the cells.
   b. Use highlight comments to indicate how the cell changed with the addition of the salt solution. For example, did the size of the cell change? Did the inside of the cell change?
   c. Use arrows and highlight comments to indicate the movement of water.

Use the "What I see" and "What it means" format to make comments on your sketches.

8. Dilute the salt solution on the slide by adding distilled water. Use the same technique that you used to add the salt solution. Add more distilled water if necessary until you see changes in the cells. What happens to the cells?

9. Repeat Step 7, recording how the cell changed with the addition of distilled water.

10. Special terms are used to describe the similarities and differences between the contents of the external environment and the internal environment of a cell. Read Relative Concentrations of Substances to learn what these terms are.

READING

Relative Concentrations of Substances

Remember that a solution is a mixture of 2 or more substances. The dissolved substance in a solution is a solute, and the substance that the solute is dissolved in is the solvent. In living systems, liquid water is frequently the solvent. An **isotonic** (*iso* means "equal") solution provides an environment in which the concentration of solutes outside the cell equals the concentration of solutes inside. A **hypertonic** (*hyper* means "over") solution is one in which the concentration of solutes outside a cell is greater than the concentration inside. A **hypotonic** (*hypo* means "under") solution is one in which the concentration of solutes outside the cell is less than the concentration inside.

11. The area around the sketches of your cells represents the solution. Label this area on your sketches as isotonic, hypertonic, or hypotonic.

Part I

Discuss the following questions with your partner and be prepared to share your ideas with the class. Record your ideas in your science notebook, adding new information that you learn from the class discussion.

1. What questions do you have after observing the changes in the cells?

2. Based on your observations, what evidence do you have that molecules move into and out of cells? Did the size or shape of anything in the cells change? You can give your evidence in written form or use labeled sketches to illustrate your evidence.

3. Propose an explanation for what might have happened in the cells as you changed the external environment. What do you think was moving into and out of the cells?

Part II: Modeling Membranes in Cells

Do you think a membrane allows molecules to pass through it? You will make a model of a cell and design an experiment to find out.

Materials
For each team of two students

2 pairs of safety goggles	concentrated glucose solution
2 lab aprons	distilled water
2 250-mL beakers	1 dropping bottle of Lugol's iodine solution
2 20-cm pieces of dialysis tubing	
	glucose test strips
1 scale	2 10-cm pieces of string
starch suspension	paper towels

Cautions

Lugol's iodine solution is a poison when ingested. It is a strong irritant that can stain clothing. Avoid skin and eye contact; do not ingest. If contact occurs, flush the affected area with water for 15 minutes. Rinse mouth with water. Call the teacher immediately. Wear safety goggles and a lab apron when working with cell models. Wash hands after handling cell models.

Process and Procedure

1. Read Steps 1–5 with a partner and review the protocol for making a cell model.
2. Your cell model must use *dialysis tubing,* a *glucose solution,* and a *starch suspension.* Read Parts of a Cell Model to learn more about those items and how their structure might influence your investigation.

Protocol

Making a Cell Model

1. Rinse all lab equipment with water. Handle the internal and external solutions for your model carefully to reduce the chance of contamination.
2. Obtain a section of dialysis tubing. Tie one end of the tubing securely so that nothing can leak out of the knot.
3. Decide which solution and how much of it you will add to each cell model. Consult with your teacher to make sure you won't overfill your model.
4. Measure and record the amount of solution you decided to use in the previous step.
5. After carefully pouring the internal solution into your cell, tie the open end securely to prevent any leaking.
6. Rinse the outside of your cell model to be certain there is no internal solution present to contaminate the external environment.
7. Blot the cell model dry with a paper towel.

Parts of a Cell Model

Dialysis tubing is a synthetic membrane made of a thin, cellophane-like material. Microscopic pores in dialysis tubing allow molecules *smaller than a certain size* to pass through the membrane. *Glucose* is a simple sugar that dissolves readily in water. *Starch* is a complex molecule that forms a suspension in water. A suspension is a mixture in which fine particles (in this case, starch molecules) are suspended in a fluid. Representations of water, glucose, and starch molecules are shown in figure 6.20. Starch is composed of many glucose units as represented by $(\ )_n$.

For a cell model to work, the membrane must be the only barrier between the internal and the external environment.

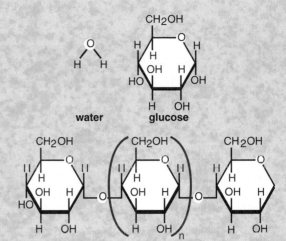

▲ Figure 6.20 **Water, glucose, and starch.** Representations of the molecules you will use in this investigation are shown here.

3. How do you think the size and the concentration of molecules affect the movement of molecules through a cell membrane? Consider what you already know about water molecules, glucose, and starch molecules. Then predict which of those molecules will pass through the membrane (dialysis tubing) of your cell model.

4. You can investigate what molecules move through your cell model by placing it in another solution. With your partner, discuss how you might design an investigation to test your prediction.
   a. How can you conduct a controlled experiment?
   b. What will serve as evidence of movement in or out of the cell model?
   c. Record your procedure.
      This investigation will take place over 2 days. Your design must be safe, and it must use dialysis tubing, starch suspension, glucose solution, and appropriate indicators. Your teacher has provided 2 indicators. *Glucose test strips* indicate the presence of glucose in a solution by changing color. (Your teacher will give you information you need to interpret the color change.) *Lugol's iodine solution* is an indicator that changes color in the presence of starch. Use 1 drop of Lugol's iodine solution for every 1 milliliter (mL) of starch suspension; a blue-black color indicates the presence of starch.

Figure 6.21 Cell model investigation table. Use a table similar to this one to record the plan and predictions for your investigation.

Remember to identify the variables in your experiment and plan to test only one variable at a time. Make sure your design will test your prediction from Step 3.

5. In your science notebook, make a data table similar to figure 6.21. Use your data table to record your predictions. Make sure you rinse and dry your cell model and record the initial mass.

Cell model	Contents of internal environment	Contents of external environment	Predicted change	Explanation for prediction
A				
B				

Caution Put on your safety goggles and lab apron.

6. Have your teacher check and approve your design.
7. Set up and conduct your investigation. Record your observations and results in your data table.

Make observations of your cell models and record all observations and results in your data table.

8. Wash your hands thoroughly before leaving the laboratory.
9. During the next class session, observe your cell model again. Record your final observations and results in your data table. Rinse and dry your cell model before recording its final mass.
10. Wash your hands thoroughly.
11. Participate in a class discussion of the results from the investigations. Based on your results and what you learn from the class discussion, record in your science notebook an answer to the following question: What molecules do you think passed through the cell model? What is your evidence?

Part II

Work with your partner to answer the following questions. Record your answers in your science notebook.

1. What does dialysis tubing represent in your model?
2. Imagine that you measured the mass of your cell model after another 5 days passed.
   a. Do you think the mass of the cell model would continue to change? Why or why not?

b. In Step 11, you provided evidence that molecules passed through your cell model. If the mass of your cell model remains the same after 5 days, do you think molecules will continue to pass through your cell model? Explain your answer.

3. How are the results from your investigation similar to what you observed in red onion cells in Part I? Did 1 of the cell models expand or shrink?

4. Why do you think some molecules passed through the cell membrane of your model and others did not? Remember that dialysis tubing allows only molecules smaller than a certain size to pass through it.

Part III: How Cells Exchange Molecules

Using a cell model, you learned that some molecules move through a cell membrane and others do not. Why those molecules moved is still a mystery. In this part of the activity, you work alone and with a partner to develop a molecular explanation for why those molecules moved.

Materials

Process and Procedure

1. Read Diffusion and Osmosis with a partner to learn how molecules move. Before you begin, review the tasks in Steps 2 and 3 to guide your reading.

2. Complete Steps 2a–c in your science notebook to connect what you saw in red onion (or *Anacharis*) cells and your cell model to how molecules move.

    a. When salt solution was added to the outside environment of red onion cells, the concentration of water molecules was _____ in the solution than in the cells.

    b. Molecules move from a region of _____ concentration to a region of _____ concentration.

    c. A cell model that contains a 10 percent sugar solution is placed in a beaker with a 40 percent sugar solution. Water molecules will _____ from the _____ into the _____.

3. Sketch what was happening *microscopically* in your cell model. Label the molecules and use arrows to show movement. Figure 6.23 provides 1 example of how to represent diffusion microscopically.

Someone in the next room opens the oven and takes out a pan of hot brownies. Almost immediately, your mouth starts to water as you smell the chocolate. How did the odor get to your nose? Molecules from the chocolate were released by heat and traveled through the air. Receptors on cells in your nose detected the chocolate molecules. This is an example of molecular movement called **diffusion**. Diffusion is the random movement of molecules from an area of higher concentration to an area of lower concentration.

a.   b.   c.

▲ **Figure 6.22 Diffusion.** (a) A drop of dye is placed in a glass of water. (b) The dye molecules begin to spread out from the drop, where they are highly concentrated, to areas where they are less concentrated. (c) In time, the dye molecules become evenly distributed throughout the glass of water.

How does this movement happen? All molecules are in constant motion; they move and collide. In the Matter Is Marvelous unit, you used this phenomenon to explain why a

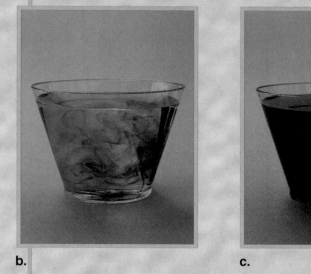

time 0   time 1   time 2

◄ **Figure 6.23 Microscopic illustration of diffusion.** Although molecules move in every direction, the overall direction of movement is outward to areas of lower concentration. The colored circles represent molecules of dye.

balloon remained inflated. The movement of each molecule is random, but in general, molecules move from an area of higher concentration toward an area of lower concentration. Figures 6.22 and 6.23 illustrate this point *macroscopically* and *microscopically*. The result is that a substance moves from higher to lower concentration when it is not held backby something.

The concentrations of molecules at various points between the high and low areas form a gradient, which is known as the **concentration gradient.** If you made a graph of the concentration versus the distance from a given spot, the graph would resemble figure 6.24. Notice that the shape of the graph resembles a ramp. Going up the ramp requires energy; coming down is much easier. Because molecules diffuse from regions of higher concentration to regions of lower concentration, they are described as moving down their concentration gradient.

▷ **Figure 6.24 Concentration gradient.** The graphs represent a concentration gradient, a difference in concentration across a distance. (a) Molecules easily diffuse down a concentration gradient. (b) Moving against a concentration gradient requires energy. Diffusion in liquids effectively moves substances only short distances.

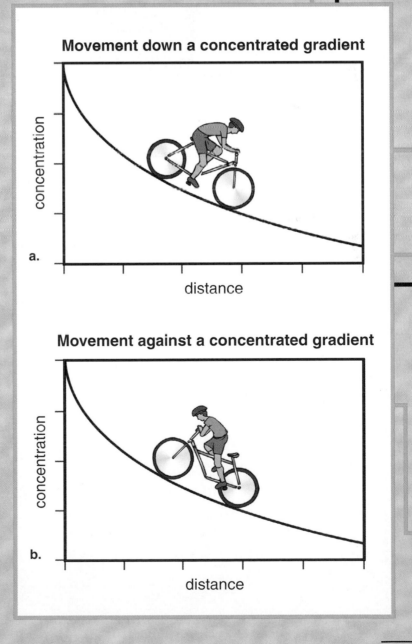

Movement down a concentrated gradient

concentration

a.

distance

Movement against a concentrated gradient

concentration

b.

distance

This explains why the oxygen inside your lungs diffuses into the blood vessels, and not the other way around. Because more oxygen molecules are in the air in the alveoli (air sacs in the lungs) than are dissolved in the blood, more of them move toward the blood than away from the blood (see figure 6.25).

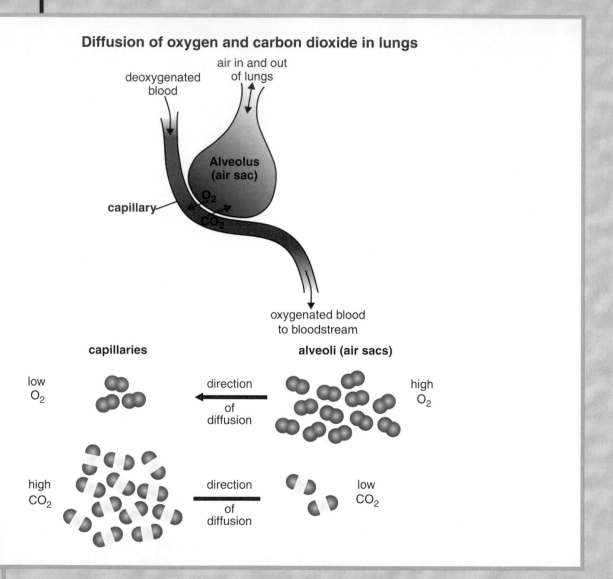

Diffusion of oxygen and carbon dioxide in lungs

▲ **Figure 6.25** **Diffusion of oxygen and carbon dioxide in the lungs.**
The concentration of oxygen is much higher in the air sacs than in the blood in the adjacent capillaries. Therefore, oxygen diffuses from the air sacs *into* the blood in the capillaries. Why does the carbon dioxide diffuse in the opposite direction?

Many substances move in and out of cells by diffusion alone. Once a substance has passed into a cell through the cell membrane, it can continue to diffuse throughout the cytoplasm down its concentration gradient. Thus, diffusion aids in the even distribution of materials within a cell (see figure 6.26).

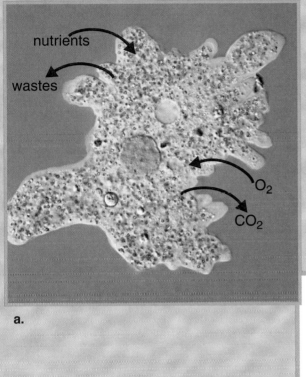

a.

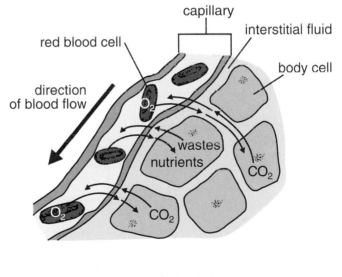

b.

▲ Figure 6.26 **Exchange in single-celled and multicellular organisms.** (a) Amoebas are microscopic, single-celled organisms that do not have circulatory systems. Because amoebas are so small, diffusion can accomplish the effective exchange of substances between the amoeba and its environment. (b) In humans and other mammals, diffusion transports substances across small distances between blood and interstitial (between cells) fluid. Diffusion also transports substances between interstitial fluid and cells.

Water moves in and out of cells and diffuses down its concentration gradient in the same manner as other substances. Diffusion of water across membranes is so important that biologists call it **osmosis**. When an animal cell is placed in pure water, the concentration of water is higher outside the cell than inside. Water moves in, and the cell swells dangerously, possibly breaking open. When an animal cell isplaced in a concentrated solution of a substance such as glucose, water moves out and the cell shrinks. Figure 6.27 illustrates how plant and animals cells respond to differences in concentration. Cells of plants, fungi, and bacteria are surrounded by a rigid cell wall as well as a cell membrane. The cell wall protects the cells from too much swelling.

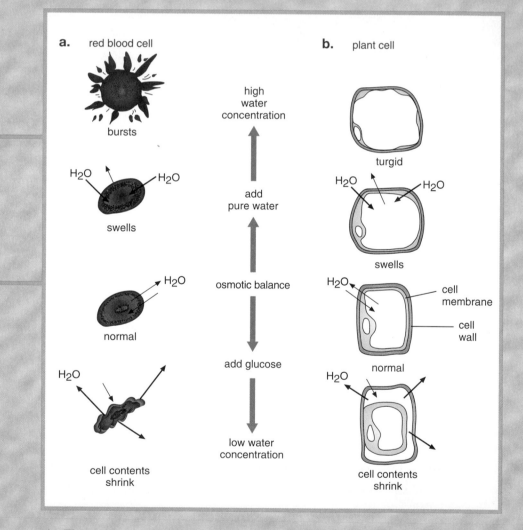

▲ **Figure 6.27 Osmosis.** Effects of the environment on (a) an animal cell and (b) a plant cell in different water solutions. When a cell is in osmotic balance, it is in a solution that has the same concentration of dissolved material as is found inside the cell. An animal cell can survive only small variations from this concentration. What conditions make an animal cell shrink or burst?

4. Recall from the Molecules into Structures activity that membranes are composed of lipids and proteins. Lipids and proteins form phospholipids. Two layers of phospholipids, or the phospholipid bilayer, form a cellular membrane. Study figure 6.28, which shows the molecular structure of a cell membrane.

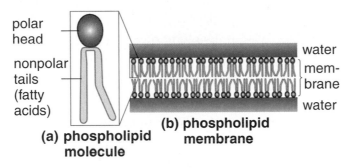

▲ **Figure 6.28 Phospholipid structure of membranes.** (a) A phospholipid molecule is composed of a polar group and a lipid tail composed of two fatty acids. When phospholipids form (b) membranes, the polar heads face water on the membrane surface and the tails face the interior of the membrane.

5. Using what you learned about substances in the Matter Is Marvelous unit, are lipids (fats and oils) polar or nonpolar? Connect what you know about polar and nonpolar molecules to phospholipids as a way of explaining what happens because the heads face out toward the water and the tails face each other. Record your answer in your science notebook using sketches, a table, or a paragraph.

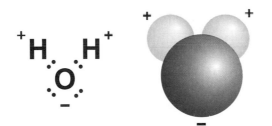

▲ **Figure 6.29 Water molecule showing polarity.** Why is water polar?

6. Read Transport of Molecules to learn how substances pass through membranes using processes *other* than diffusion.

Transport of Molecules

Cell membranes are only **selectively permeable;** only certain molecules can diffuse freely through them. For example, small molecules such as oxygen, carbon dioxide, and water can diffuse easily through membranes. Simple diffusion of those molecules is called passive transport. Passive transport does not require energy. Osmosis is an example of passive transport.

Larger molecules (for example, glucose and amino acids) and ions with a charge cannot diffuse through membranes. Those molecules can pass through only with the help of special proteins, called transport proteins. Transport proteins move substances down their concentration gradient either into or out of the cell. For example, special proteins in the membranes of red blood cells permit the diffusion of glucose from the blood into the red blood cells. This is called facilitated diffusion, which is another type of passive transport.

In active transport, cells use energy to move substances against their concentration gradients. For example, the soil around a plant may contain low amounts of elements necessary for the plant's growth, such as nitrogen, phosphorus, potassium, and calcium. Ordinary diffusion would not provide the plant with enough of those elements. By means of active transport, however, the plant's root cells accumulate the elements in relatively high amounts.

Another example of active transport is the transport of sodium ions (Na^+) out of animal cells and potassium ions (K^+) into animal cells. As a result, animal cells have a concentration of potassium ions 20 times greater inside the cell than outside and a concentration of sodium ions 10 times greater outside the cell than inside. This causes a net charge across the membrane, with the interior of the cell being negatively charged with respect to the exterior of the cell (see figure 6.30). Later you learn why this difference in charge is important.

Topic: active transport
Go to: www.scilinks.org
Code: 1Inquiry294

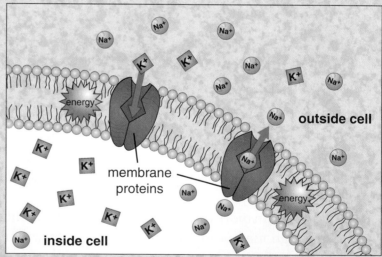

▲ **Figure 6.30 Active transport of sodium and potassium in animal cells.** Membrane proteins transport potassium ions (K^+) into the cell. Transport of sodium ions (Na^+) also occurs through membrane proteins, but in the opposite direction. Active transport requires energy.

Reflect and Connect

Discuss the questions below with your partner and write answers in your science notebook.

1. Sketch or describe what happens to ions and molecules when they are in balance inside and outside the cell. Clearly label the sketches.

2. Membranes regulate the movement of molecules into and out of cells. To show what you know about how membranes regulate movement, fill out a T-table with the headings "Ions or Molecules" and "How They Move through Membranes."

3. Why is it a bad idea to drink seawater if you are stranded on a boat on the ocean? What do you think would happen to your cells?

Water Balance

Why is osmosis important for living organisms? Osmosis helps maintain water balance in organisms. For example, how can you explain a wilting plant or a limp stick of celery? A plant wilts when too little water is present in its cells. When you soak celery, carrot sticks, or lettuce in water, they become crisp. In the same way, when a plant is well watered, it remains erect. When plant cells have adequate supplies of water, the water exerts pressure, known as turgor pressure, against the cell walls. You hear the release of turgor pressure when you bite into a crisp celery stick. Turgor pressure supports the stems and leaves of plants. If more water is lost from a plant's cells than is replaced, the stems and leaves are no longer held upright and the plant wilts. Osmosis is the primary way that water enters plants from their surrounding environment.

Osmosis also helps explain the water balance mechanisms in aquatic organisms. Sea cucumbers and other marine invertebrates maintain water and salt balance because their internal fluids have a salt concentration similar to seawater. Some marine species, such as salmon, live in both freshwater and seawater and must have other methods of maintaining water balance. The body fluids of salmon have a salt concentration between that of freshwater and seawater. In seawater, salmon counter water loss through osmosis and by excreting salt through their gills. The opposite occurs in freshwater. Salmon excrete excess water in dilute urine and absorb the salts they need through specialized cells in the gills.

Water balance in plants. Plants without an adequate supply of water wilt because there isn't enough turgor pressure to keep the stems and leaves upright. Notice the change in the wilted plant two hours after it was watered.

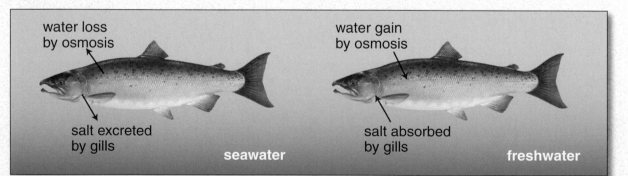

water loss by osmosis

salt excreted by gills

seawater

water gain by osmosis

salt absorbed by gills

freshwater

Water balance in salmon. Salmon must counter the effects of osmosis by using different mechanisms in freshwater and seawater. In seawater, salmon counteract water loss by drinking seawater and excreting excess salts. In freshwater, salmon excrete excess water and absorb salt through their gills to maintain a normal water balance.

Cell Division

Diffusion supplies cells with needed materials and helps remove waste products. However, it takes a long time for substances to diffuse great distances. What might this indicate about the size of cells? Usually, when a cell reaches a certain size, it begins a series of changes that permit it to divide into two cells. In this way, cells maintain an optimal size. In the Cell Division activity, you work with a partner to model this process.

Materials

Process and Procedure

1. Work with a partner and read Cells Divided to learn why cells divide.

READING

Cells Divided

Nearly all organisms grow during their lifetimes. In multicellular organisms, growth occurs primarily through an increase in the *number* of cells, not through an increase in the *size* of cells. Why? The processes of cellular transport—diffusion and osmosis—place upper limits on how large cells can become. If a cell is to function well, it cannot be too large. These physical limitations have influenced development in a way that favors more cells rather than larger cells.

Cells reproduce by making copies of themselves. A prokaryotic cell replicates its genetic material (DNA) and then divides in two (see figure 6.31). Because the time required to replicate DNA may be quite short, prokaryotes such as

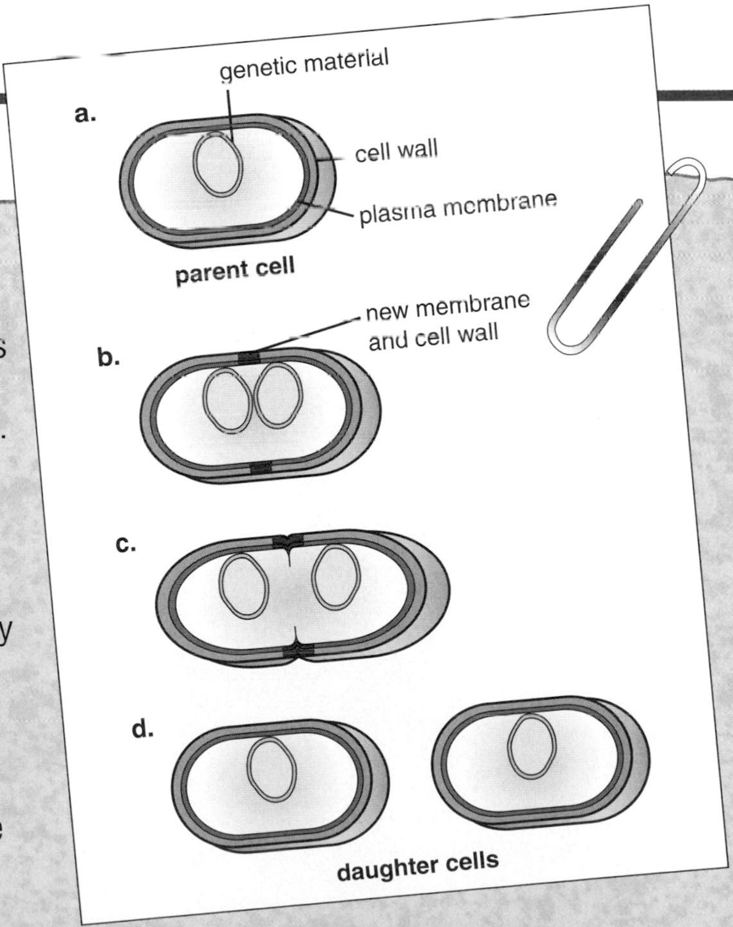

▶ Figure 6.31 **Prokaryotic cell division.** (a) The circular genetic material in prokaryotes is attached to the plasma membrane. (b) After the genetic material has replicated, each has a separate attachment to the membrane. (c) A new membrane and cell wall form midway along the length of the cell. (d) Cell division is complete when the parent cell has divided into two new daughter cells.

Escherichia coli (*E. coli*) bacteria can reproduce in 30 minutes. Eukaryotic cells also reproduce by dividing in two. However, eukaryotic cell division is part of a more complex series of stages called the **cell cycle.** In single-celled organisms such as yeast and amoeba, cell division produces a complete, new organism. Plants and animals, on the other hand, are multicellular organisms that develop from a single fertilized egg cell. The egg cell goes through a complex sequence of cell divisions that ultimately results in many types of cells that make up the organism's tissues and organs.

Cell division is needed for the growth of plants and animals. Plants have specialized regions at the tips of their roots and stems. Repeated cell division in these regions produces the new cells that develop into the mature tissues of growing roots, stems, and leaves. During animal development, cell division produces many different types of cells that form the nerves, skin, and other organs.

Cell division also replaces cells that wear out or are damaged during the life of an organism. For example, cells in your skin are constantly dividing to replace those on the surface that have died or have been scraped off. Cell division is also necessary to form a new layer of skin at the site of an injury, such as a cut.

The cell cycle, which results in cell division, is remarkably similar in all eukaryotes. Some parts of the cycle vary from organism to organism and may vary at different times in one organism's life. However, for all organisms, the cell cycle results in a single cell producing two daughter cells with identical genetic information. All cells in an organism—with the exception of sperm and egg and red blood cells, which do not have nuclei—contain the same genetic information. (You will learn why sperm and egg cells are different when you study genetics next year.) The length of time it takes for different types of cells to complete the cell cycle varies. Some cells divide every 2 hours; others divide every 24 hours. Some cells even stop in one stage and do not divide.

The cell cycle starts when a new cell is formed and continues until the cell has divided into two new cells (see figure 6.32). Each new cell then begins the cell cycle again. New cells usually contain the same structures as their parent cells. That means the genetic material, the organelles in the cytoplasm, and the cell membrane must be duplicated before a cell divides to form two new cells. If these structures are not duplicated, the offspring cells are incomplete and unable to survive.

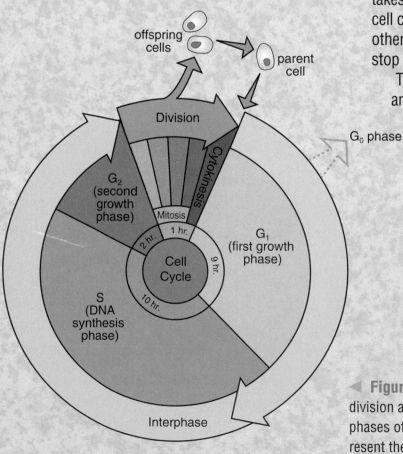

Figure 6.32 Cell cycle. The cell cycle consists of cell division and interphase. Most of a cell's life is spent in the phases of interphase. The times given for each phase represent the approximate times for a liver cell grown in a lab.

Most of a cell's life is spent in interphase (see figure 6.32). During this phase, a cell grows and performs its intended functions. The cell's genetic material (DNA) is organized into structures called chromosomes, which are duplicated during interphase, through a process called DNA synthesis. (You will learn about this process in Level 2.) Exact copying ensures that each new daughter cell will receive a complete copy of the parent cell's genetic information. Once the genetic information has been copied, the cell enters the M phase. Mitosis occurs during the M phase. Some cells, such as nerve and muscle cells, stop dividing once their development is complete and enter G_0 phase. Those cells never leave the first stage of interphase (G_1).

Mitosis is the precise distribution of DNA to daughter cells. Figures 6.33 and 6.34 illustrate the process. Mitosis results in the precise distribution of genetic material from parent cell to offspring cells. Recall that during interphase, DNA (chromosomes) is duplicated. During the four phases of mitosis, the duplicated chromosomes condense, line up, and separate into two newly formed offspring cells. Other parts of the cell also are distributed between these offspring cells during cell division. The result of mitosis and cell division is two cells where there used to be only one, each containing a copy of the same genetic information and the same types of subcellular compartments that were contained in the parent cell.

A few differences occur in mitosis between animals and plants. Animal cells contain centrioles that move to opposite ends of the cell during mitosis. Centrioles play an important role in mitosis in animal cells, but are not found in plant cells. Another difference occurs at the end of mitosis when the cytoplasm divides (cytokinesis). In plant cells, a cell plate begins to form across the middle of the cell, dividing the cell in two. This is the developing cell wall. No cell plate forms in animal cells. Instead, the cell constricts across the middle as the cells divide.

Although all cells of multicellular organisms contain the same genetic information, the cells of those organisms are specialized. As discussed earlier, multicellular organisms develop from the division of a single cell. Throughout their lifetimes, humans may form about 200 different types of cells. Each type has a specialized function. Cells become specialized through a process called differentiation. **Differentiation** is the process by which new cells specialize and become different in appearance and function from their parent cells.

If your cells have the same genetic information, how can they become different in appearance and function? How does one cell become a muscle cell, another a red blood cell, and still another a nerve cell? Your cells change and become specialized according to a genetically determined plan. Differentiation occurs as a result of a combination of signals that cause different cells to activate different portions of their genetic information. Thus, differences in how cells look and behave reflect differences in how they *use* the genetic information they have.

As cells become specialized, they take on specific shapes and cell cycles may become more distinctive. For example, different types of cells may require different amounts of time to complete a cell cycle. Some cells divide about every 8 hours. Others divide only once every several months. In adult animals, certain types of cells, such as muscle and nerve cells, almost never divide. In plants, cell division occurs only to specialized cells in the tips of stems, branches, and roots and in bark.

Go to: www.scilinks.org
Topic: cell division
Code: 1Inquiry299a
Topic: mitosis
Code: 1Inquiry299b
Go to: differentiation
Code: 1Inquiry299c

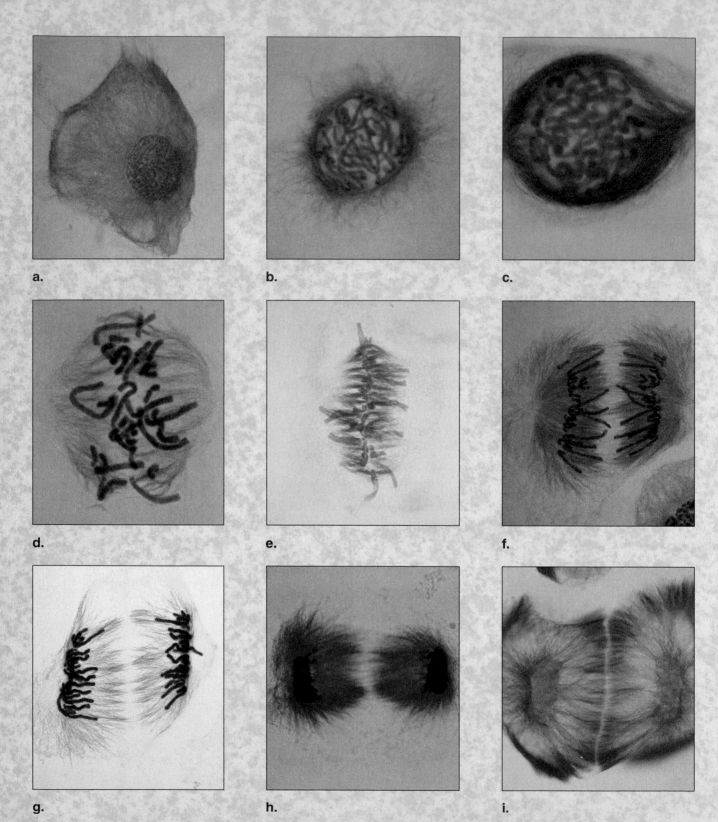

▲ **Figure 6.33** **Stages of mitosis in the blood lily, *Scadoxus*.** (a) interphase, (b) prophase, (c) late prophase, (d) early metaphase, (e) metaphase, (f) early anaphase, (g) late anaphase, (h) early telophase, (i) late telophase showing formation of the cell plate. Can you find these stages in the illustrations of mitosis shown in figure 6.34?

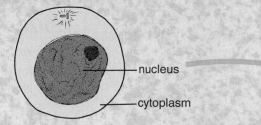

— nucleus

— cytoplasm

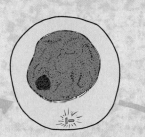

a. During **interphase**, which is a long and active phase of the cell cycle, materials required for the next cell division are synthesized. For example, DNA and chromosomes are duplicated in the nucleus and cell structures such as mitochondria are made in the cytoplasm. The cell grows.

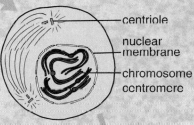

— centriole
— nuclear membrane
— chromosome
— centromere

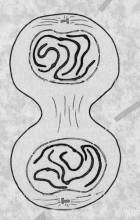

f. During **telophase** the chromosomes approach the opposite ends of the cell and group together. A new nuclear membrane is synthesized around the chromosomes. The cytoplasm begins to divide and a new cell membrane forms. (In plant cells, a new cell wall is laid down between the two new cells.) The new cells enter interphase.

b. As **prophase** begins, the long thin chromosomes coil and become shorter and thicker. Each chromosome now appears as a doubled structure joined at a centromere. The centrioles, which were duplicated during interphase, begin to move to opposite ends of the cell. (In plant cells there are no centrioles, but the events of mitosis otherwise occur as described here.)

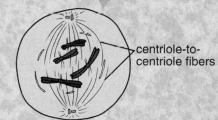

— centriole-to-centriole fibers

e. The doubled chromosomes separate during **anaphase**. The new chromosomes are pushed and pulled to opposite ends of the cell by the cytoplasmic fibers.

c. Later in prophase, the nuclear envelope breaks down. The chromosomes contract to their shortest lengths. Cytoplasmic fibers stretch from centriole to centriole and from each doubled chromosome to both centrioles.

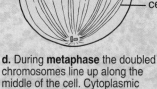

— centromere-to-centriole fibers

d. During **metaphase** the doubled chromosomes line up along the middle of the cell. Cytoplasmic fibers now are attached to each doubled chromosome at the centromere.

▲ **Figure 6.34 Stages of mitosis.** Mitosis leads to the production of two nuclei in one cell, followed by the division of the cell into two identical cells.

2. Explain how growth occurs in a multicellular organism. Record your answer in your science notebook using sketches or a paragraph.
3. Study the illustrations in figure 6.35, which represent a section of DNA from a cell before cell division and the resulting daughter cells.
   a. How does the genetic information in the cells compare?
   b. Why do you think it might be important for all cells to contain the same genetic information?

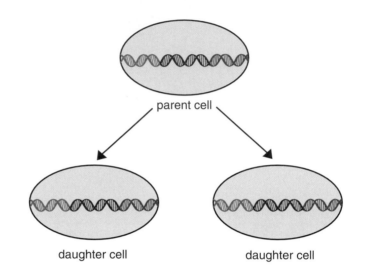

parent cell

daughter cell   daughter cell

▲ Figure 6.35 **Genetic information in parent and daughter cells.** The sections of genetic material that are the same color represent the same genes. Genes are units of hereditary information. What do you notice about the genetic information in the cells?

Reflect and Connect

Work with a partner to complete the following tasks and questions. Record your answers in your science notebook.

1. Draw a series of sketches to illustrate important stages of the cell cycle and mitosis. Your drawings should
   - Include a starting cell with the genetic material represented as 2 pairs of chromosomes (see figure 6.36)
   - Include a nucleus with the appropriate number of chromosomes in each of the cells
   - Indicate when in your flowchart or sketches the genetic material is duplicated (DNA synthesis)
   - Show the cells formed as a result of mitosis

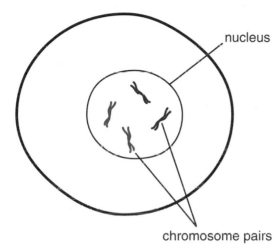

▲ **Figure 6.36 Model of a cell.** Use this image as a basis for your sketches.

2. Why is it important that the DNA (chromosomes) duplicates before mitosis?
3. Describe why cell division is an important process for all organisms.

Controlling Growth

In the cells of most tissues, controlling growth means controlling the occurrence and rate of mitosis. Two major levels of control regulate mitosis. The first level, called internal control, involves substances inside the cell. These critical substances regulate the timing of the specific phases of the cell cycle. That regulation is necessary. Without regulation, a cell could enter mitosis before it replicated its genetic material. If that happened, there would not be a full set of genetic material (chromosomes) in each offspring cell. Both offspring cells would die as a result.

A second level of control involves environmental factors. These external signals trigger internal events in the cell that initiate or suppress the events of the cell cycle. The actions of hormones represent one form of external growth control. Hormones are chemical messages produced by one set of cells that exert their effects on other cells, often in distant locations of the body. For example, growth hormone coordinates the proportional growth of the body. As its name suggests, growth hormone stimulates cells to divide. An excess of growth hormone before puberty results in gigantism. Likewise, a lack of growth hormone produces dwarfism. Although growth hormone's most obvious effects are seen in the long bones of the limbs, it affects growth all over the body.

Another example of external control is contact inhibition, which causes cells to stop dividing. Contact inhibition occurs when cells reach a certain population density or degree of crowding. This happens even though nutrients may be plentiful in the environment. Contact inhibition prevents overcrowding of cells within a particular organ or area of the body. Sometimes this inhibition must be relaxed to allow healing. When your skin is cut, the cells at the edge of the wound begin to divide and slowly cover the bare spot. Once the open wound is repaired, however, these cells detect the degree of crowding that exists and stop dividing.

Contact inhibition is an important example of growth control, and problems arise when this control is lost. Cells that no longer experience contact inhibition continue to divide, piling up on top of each other. A cell that has mistakes in the genetic material that controls contact inhibition may divide without regard to external signals and eventually form a cancerous tumor. A tumor is a mass of cells that are growing in an uncontrolled manner. Cancer represents an error in which the normal controls over cell division are altered and are no longer effective.

Cell growth.
(a) Cells experiencing normal growth control stop dividing when they make contact with other cells.
(b) Cells that have lost this regulation will continue to divide, piling up on one another.

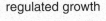

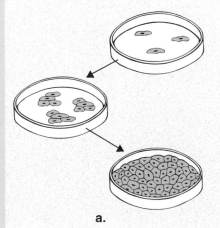

a.   b.

Using Technology to See Inside Cells

Technology has many important roles in society and, of course, in your life. Technology gives you access to the Internet. It transmits television signals to your house and enables lasers to read CDs and DVDs. Technology also provides new insights into the world of science. Inventing, and then using, new technologies lets you deepen and enhance your views of the world and the universe.

Sometimes what is seen with new technology can be a surprise. This has certainly been true as the Hubble Space Telescope has peered to the edge of the visible universe. In the same manner, Robert Hooke got a real surprise in about 1665 when he used a microscope to look at microscopic pores and holes in tree cork. He called those holes cells.

How has technology provided a better understanding of cells and the organic molecules that make up cells? Follow the procedure to learn about some of the key technologies that let scientists study cells at molecular and atomic levels.

Materials

Process and Procedure

1. Make a T-table with the headings "Example of Technology" and "How It Helps Us Understand Cells." Fill out this table as you complete the reading.
2. Read Technologies of the Past and Present to learn about some of the technologies that have contributed to an understanding of cells and organic molecules.
3. Compare your sketch and paragraph from the What Is a Cell? activity with Hooke's sketch and paragraph in figure 6.38. For example, did Hooke see the same details that you were able to see through your microscope?

Technologies of the Past and Present

Cells are small, and their structures are difficult to see. It is even more difficult to see their organelles and their molecular composition. Scientists rely on technology to learn what they can about cells. Many of the major advances in cell biology have resulted from the introduction of new techniques and technologies.

Robert Hooke used a simple microscope to view cells in the mid-1600s (see figure 6.37). Figure 6.38 shows one of his first descriptions and sketches. His method was to place a thinly sliced sample (cork) on a dark background and to view it through a lens system. Light for imaging reflected off the sample. Hooke saw compartments in the cork and named them cells. After Hooke published his observations, other scientists discovered that living parts of plants were also made up of cells (see the sidebar, The Development of Cell Theory).

The light microscope was an important advance in microscope technology. Light shines

> Obſerv. XVIII. *Of the* Schematiſme *or* Texture *of Cork, and of the Cells and Pores of ſome other ſuch frothy Bodies.*
>
> I Took a good clear piece of Cork, and with a Pen-knife ſharpen'd as keen as a Razor, I cut a piece of it off, and thereby left the ſurface of it exceeding ſmooth, then examining it very diligently with a *Microſcope*, me thought I could perceive it to appear a little porous; but I could not ſo plainly diſtinguiſh them, as to be ſure that they were pores, much leſs what Figure they were of: But judging from the lightneſs and yielding quality of the Cork, that certainly the texture could not be ſo curious, but that poſſibly, if I could uſe ſome further diligence, I might find it to be diſcernable with a *Microſcope*, I with the ſame ſharp Pen-knife, cut off from the former ſmooth ſurface an exceeding thin piece of it, and placing it on a black objeĉt Plate, becauſe it was it ſelf a white body, and caſting the light on it with a deep *plano-convex Glaſs*, I could exceeding plainly perceive it to be all perforated and porous, much like a Honey-comb, but that the pores of it were not regular; yet it was not unlike a Honey-comb in theſe particulars.

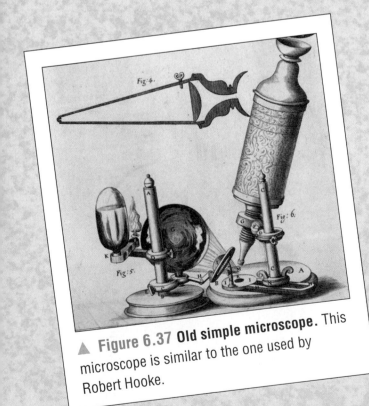

▲ **Figure 6.37 Old simple microscope.** This microscope is similar to the one used by Robert Hooke.

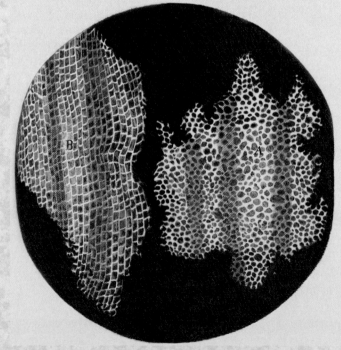

▲ **Figure 6.38 Hooke's cork cells.** Hooke's observations were published in 1665. You might notice that the text looks a little different; for example, the letter *s* looks like the letter *f*. This is characteristic of the printing style during that time.

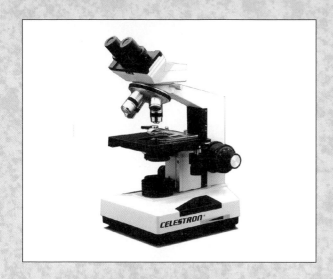

▲ **Figure 6.39 Light microscope.** Scientists continue to use light microscopes in research today.

from beneath the sample, through the sample, and into a series of lenses before entering the eye. This is probably what you have in your classroom! Light microscopes are still an essential tool used by scientists today. The microscopes can distinguish objects as small as 200 nm, including the organelles in cells. Unlike some newer techniques, light microscopy is nondestructive and allows scientists to watch movements in living cells.

Many cells are almost transparent when viewed through a light microscope. In the late 1800s, scientists discovered that textile dyes could be used to dye biological tissues. Today scientists use a variety of dyes and stains to make cells more visible. When you viewed cells, you may have used methylene blue to see certain features of cells better. One dye, called eosin, is very effective in staining the proteins of the cytoplasm pink. This enhances the features outside a cell nucleus. In contrast, a dye called hematoxylin stains the cell nucleus blue. Scientists continue to develop new dyes that selectively stain specific proteins and other macromolecules in cells.

In the 1980s, scientists began using electronic imaging systems with light microscopes (see figure 6.39). Sensitive video cameras capture images, which a computer processes before the viewer sees the image. Image processing enhances the images and makes it easier to see fine details.

Electron microscopes were first developed in the 1930s and continue to be used today. Rather than using light, electron microscopes work by focusing a thin beam of electrons on the sample. A detector records interactions of the electron beam with the sample. This is analogous to your eye, which serves as the detector when using light microscopes. Figure 6.40 shows images of specimens taken by electron microscopes. The

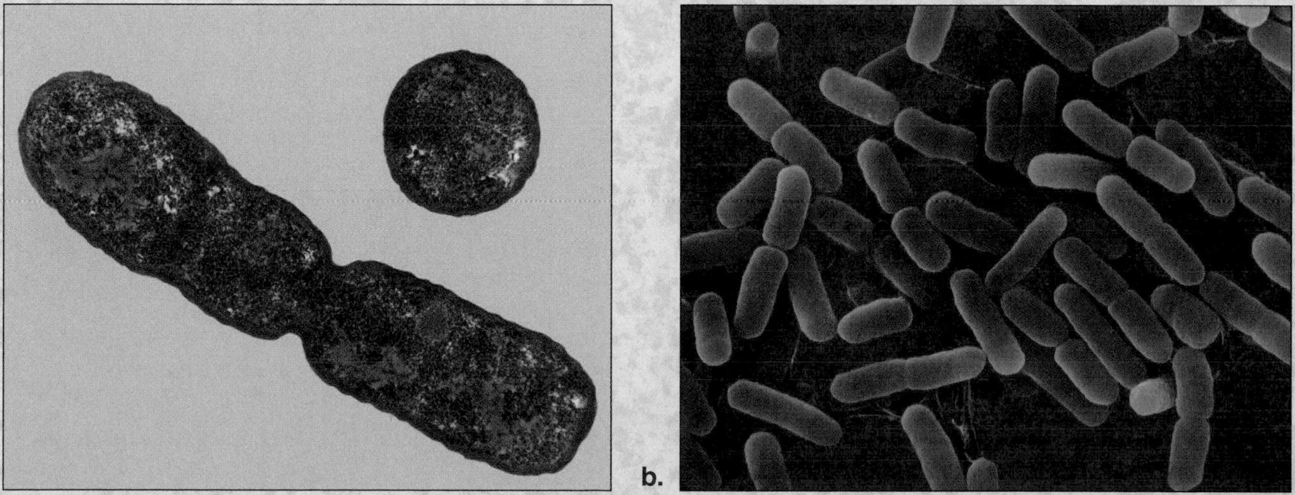

a.

b.

▲ **Figure 6.40 (a) Transmission electron microscope (TEM) image and (b) scanning electron microscope (SEM) image of *Escherichia coli* (*E. coli*).** Some forms of *E. coli* bacteria can cause cramps and diarrhea.

resolution of an electron microscope is 1,000 times better than that of a light microscope. Resolution is the ability of a microscope to form detailed images.

Although the design and physical appearance of electron microscopes have changed over the years, the essential characteristics remain the same. All electron microscopes require a high vacuum in which to form an electron beam and high voltage to control this beam. Unfortunately, the vacuum prevents viewing live samples. There are two primary kinds of electron microscopes. The transmission electron microscope (TEM) enables scientists to see the detailed structure of membranes and organelles. The scanning electron microscope (SEM) allows scientists to see the three-dimensional structure of the surface of a specimen.

A new kind of microscope called the scanning probe microscope (SPM) has the same resolution as an electron microscope. However, samples can be viewed with less preparation and in air or liquid rather than in a vacuum. SPMs use a microscopic needlelike probe (3–50 nm at the tip) that is scanned back and forth across a surface. A three-dimensional image is constructed from the recorded

▶ **Figure 6.41 Protein molecules.** Scientists obtained this image of protein molecules using a scanning probe microscope (SPM).

interactions between the probe and the atoms in the sample. The SPM can magnify an object up to 10,000,000 times. Under ideal conditions, scientists use the SPM to look at individual atoms, such as the atoms in protein molecules (see figure 6.41).

X-ray crystallography is also used to study the structures of protein molecules. The instrument uses X-ray beams (high-energy radiation) rather than electron beams or visible light. The X-ray beam is directed from its source through a protein crystal (see figure 6.42). The array of atoms in the crystal separate and scatter X-rays,

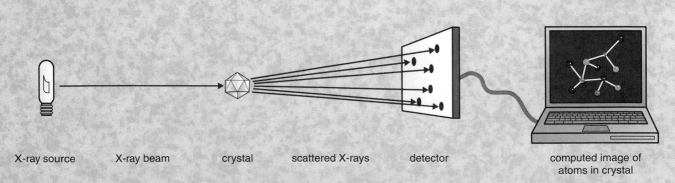

X-ray source   X-ray beam   crystal   scattered X-rays   detector   computed image of atoms in crystal

▲ **Figure 6.42 Steps in X-ray crystallography.** The scattering of X-rays from a beam directed at a crystal are recorded by a detector. The positions of the peaks on the detector reflect the arrangement of atoms in the molecule. This can be displayed on a computer screen.

which are then recorded by a detector. The positions of peaks on the detector reflect the arrangement of atoms in the molecule. Using these data, a computer can calculate the position of atoms and display an image of a molecule on a computer screen (see figure 6.43).

The technologies used for studying cells depend on the size of the feature of interest (entire cell, organelles, or molecule). The range extends from tissues and cells down to organelles, then molecules, all the way down to atoms. The instruments used to view these cell features have different ranges of resolution. The resolution indicates the size range in which the resolution is most useful. Figure 6.44 matches the resolution of technologies for studying cells with the size of organisms, cells, and cell parts.

▲ **Figure 6.43 Three-dimensional structure of a protein.** The structure as shown is determined by X-ray crystallography.

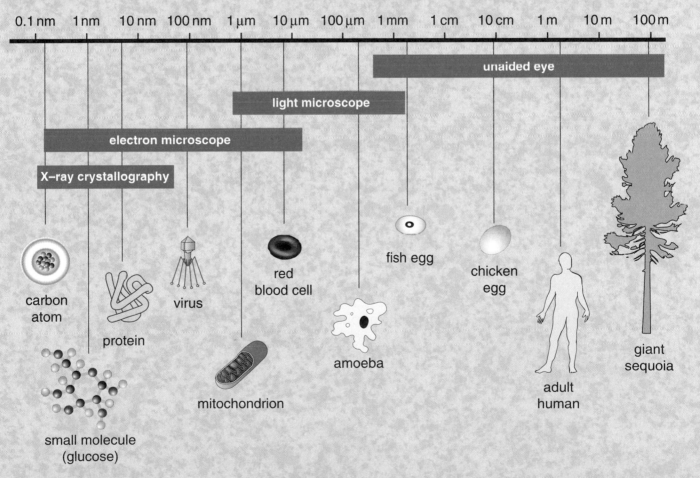

▲ **Figure 6.44 Ranges of resolution for technologies used to study cells.** How would you decide whether to use an electron microscope or X-ray crystallography to study a virus?

Reflect and Connect

Work with your partner to answer the questions below in your science notebook. Be prepared to share your ideas in a class discussion.

1. How has the light microscope helped scientists learn more about cells?
2. Explain why a single type of technology cannot provide information about all levels of an organism (from molecules to a whole organism).
3. Name another form of technology that scientists use. Explain how it helps scientists understand more about the world.

EVALUATE

A Celly Adventure

In this chapter, you began to study cells, the building blocks of life. You learned that cells are made of organic molecules, and you learned some basic functions of cells. You observed examples of the simplest kinds of cells on Earth (prokaryotes), as well as more complex cells with nuclei (eukaryotes). You even estimated the number of cells in an onion and in you. How might you share some of this information with others?

In the Celly Adventure activity, you make up a short story or an adventure in which the main character is a type of cell. The goal is to use the story or adventure to share information about that type of cell and about other cells or organisms. Be creative. At the same time, use accurate science to show how that cell represents a building block of life and describe some of the structures and functions of the cell. The procedures will help you.

Materials
For each student

resources for research about cells: where they are found and what they do

materials and supplies for writing a short story or an adventure

1 copy of Scoring Rubric for a Celly Adventure handout

Process and Procedure

There are many types of cells, but from your work in this chapter, which do you find most interesting or most unusual? Is it a simple bacterium or a cell in the leaf of a tree? Perhaps it is a specialized cell making up a vital organ in an animal?

1. Do some brainstorming. Think of all of the cell types that you have studied so far.

   a. Write in your science notebook 3–4 cell types that are most interesting to you. Next to the cell name, write why it is interesting to you.

   b. Select 1 of the cell types to be the main character of your short story. Record where that cell type is normally found and what its function is. This should help you identify the environment in which the cell is typically found.

   Look at the figures throughout the chapter to find examples of different cells, such as bacteria, muscle cells, and guard cells in plants. Read the captions to learn the functions of those cells.

   c. Name your "main character" cell and begin thinking of an adventure that the cell might experience. The adventure should be related in some creative way to a function of the cell. What other types of cells, organs, or organisms might your cell encounter during the celly adventure?

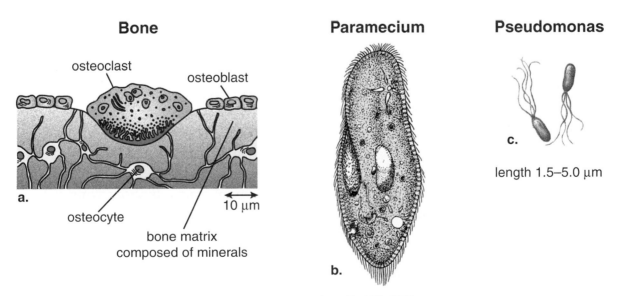

Bone

osteoclast
osteoblast
osteocyte
bone matrix composed of minerals
a.
10 μm

Paramecium

b.
length 100–300 μm

Pseudomonas

c.
length 1.5–5.0 μm

▲ **Figure 6.45 Examples of cells.** (a) Bone cells such as osteoblasts, which form new bone, and osteoclasts, which help shape bones, are important to the human body. (b) Paramecia are common single-celled organisms found in ponds. (c) Pseudomonas is a type of bacteria found in soil that is important for decomposition. What kind of cell will be the main character in your story?

For example, is it brick-red Burly Barbara Blood Cell circulating oxygen to the body's tissues? Or is it Betraying Bob Bacterium, whose offspring have colonized meat that was not stored or prepared properly at a restaurant? You get the idea.

It is fine to have the main character leave its normal setting in the adventure. However, make it clear to the reader what the normal setting is, what function the cell has in that setting, and what organelles would be expected in the cell.

2. Remember, your story should be fun, but it must show your understanding of science. Write in your notebook answers to these items to help you remember a few key points.
   a. What kind of cell is your main character? Where is it found in nature or in an organism?
   b. What size is your cell?
   c. What molecules make up your cell?
   d. What are at least 2–3 organelles in your cell? Refer to diagrams earlier in the chapter as needed.
   e. How do materials move in and out of your cell's membrane?
   f. How does your cell divide?
   g. What does your cell typically do (apart from its adventure)? What sort of function does it have?
3. Write 1–2 sentences about how your cell and other cells in the story will demonstrate that cells are the building blocks of life.
4. Write 1–2 ideas for an adventure that your cell can experience.
5. Hand in the ideas you wrote down in Steps 2–4 to your teacher.
6. Review the handout, Scoring Rubric for a Celly Adventure. This rubric tells you what the main categories and expectations for your story are and how your teacher will evaluate your work. Refer to this rubric as you develop your celly adventure.
7. You may want to do additional research about your cell character. Use resources from the library, the Internet, or your teacher. You must cite each resource in a reference list at the end of your story. Also, add new information that you gather to your responses in Step 2.

8. Now it is time to write the adventure.
   - Write the adventure of your cell—the narrative. It should be at least 2 pages long.
   - Using your creativity, draw 2 or 3 figures that show your main character in action. You can draw these pictures by hand or use a computer.
   - Create a title for your story and list your name as the author.
   - Include a reference list.

CHAPTER 7

Cells Are Busy Places

Cells Are Busy Places

In chapter 6, Cells: The Building Blocks of Life, you learned that all living things are made of the same organic molecules. You also learned that all living things share the same structures and that these structures have certain functions. Look at the organisms in the opening art. In addition to matter in the form of organic molecules, what else do living things need? You know from your own experience that you need energy in order to function. All living things, including single-celled organisms and plants, need energy to function. Where do the molecules and energy that you and all living things need come from? You will learn the answer to this question by gaining an understanding of two life-sustaining processes that occur in cells—photosynthesis and cellular respiration.

Goals for the Chapter

By the end of this chapter, you will be able to answer the following questions:

- How do some cells use light energy to make energy-rich molecules?
- Where do cells get the energy they need to function?
- Where do cells get the matter they need to function?
- How does photosynthesis connect the Sun to the energy needs of living organisms?

You will be better able to answer those questions by participating in the following activities.

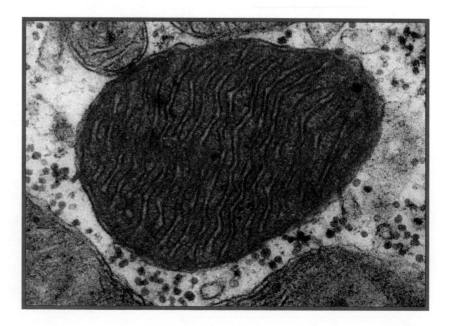

What's Going On Inside a Cell?

Key Idea:

Plants and animals require energy and matter to function.

EXPLORE

Cellular Activities in Plants

Key Ideas:

- Plants exchange gases with the atmosphere.
- Plant leaves can contain varying amounts of starch.

Linking Question

How do plants meet their energy needs?

EXPLAIN

Cells Are Busy Places

Converting Sunlight into Sugar

Key Ideas:

- Plants use light energy, carbon dioxide, and water to make sugars.
- Sugars produced during photosynthesis are used for maintenance and growth.

Linking Question

How do plant and animal cells get the energy they need to function?

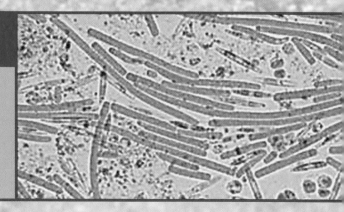

Tracing a Carbon Atom and Energy

Key Idea:
Photosynthesis and cellular respiration explain where most organisms get the matter and energy they need to survive.

How can I use what I have learned to diagram how organisms get their matter and energy?

ELABORATE

Sun Worship

Key Ideas:
- Photosynthesis connects the sun to the energy needs of all organisms, including animals.
- Biosynthesis and breakdown reactions provide the energy and matter needed by organisms.

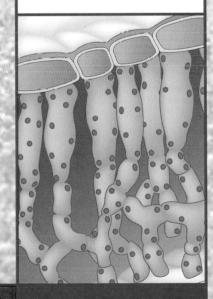

CHAPTER

7 Major Concepts

▶ **Cellular Processes**
- **Photosynthesis occurs in chloroplasts and converts light energy into chemical energy.**
- **Cellular respiration provides the energy for cells to function.**

▶ **Matter and Energy in Living Systems**
- **The sun provides the energy for almost all living systems on Earth.**

▶ **Scientific Communication**
- **Writing and diagramming are required for effective communication.**

EXPLAIN

Powering Cellular Activities

Key Ideas:
- Cellular respiration occurs in the cells of all living things.
- Cellular respiration converts glucose into ATP, the form of energy used by cells.

Why are photosynthesis and cellular respiration important for all organisms to meet their energy needs?

What's Going On Inside a Cell?

Now that you know quite a bit about the structure of a cell—the basic unit of life—it is amazing to consider all of the important functions that this tiny structure performs. In What's Going On Inside a Cell?, you and your classmates share what you already know about some of these important functions. Throughout the rest of the chapter, you continue to add to your foundation of knowledge about the many remarkable functions of the cell.

Materials

several potted geranium plants

Process and Procedure

1. Study the photograph of the plant in figure 7.1. This is a photograph of a young geranium plant. Also, study the mature geranium plants in your classroom. Consider the following questions and be prepared to share your ideas with your classmates.

   a. Based on your experience from the activity, True or False: An Onion Has about 1 Billion Cells, in chapter 6, answer these questions: How many cells would you estimate are in the plant in the photograph? How many cells would you estimate are in 1 of the geranium plants in your classroom?

   b. What do you think happens at the cellular level to allow a geranium to grow from the size of the plant in this photograph to the size of the plants in your classroom or for a cottonwood tree to grow from a seedling to a towering 21-meter tree? Use labeled sketches or a short paragraph to provide your answer.

   Think about the physical changes and the processes that must occur for a plant to get bigger.

   c. Where does the energy come from to support this type of growth?

   d. Where does the matter come from to support the associated increase in mass?

   e. Where does the energy and matter come from to support your own growth and increase in mass?

2. Participate in a class discussion of the questions above. Record in your science notebook some of the best ideas you hear.

▲ **Figure 7.1 A young geranium plant.** How many cells do you think make up one of the new leaves on this plant?

Reflect and Connect

Record 3 additional questions that you have about the details involved in acquiring energy and matter for growth for either plants or animals. During the course of the chapter, look for opportunities to develop answers to your questions.

Cellular Activities in Plants

What are some of the functions of plant cells? In Cellular Activities in Plants, you investigate two processes that occur in plant cells. These processes are vital for plant cells as well as for plants as a whole to function. In this activity, you work in teams and with your class to learn about these functions by observing the products produced by plants. In Part I, you conduct an investigation to learn how light influences the gases exchanged by an aquatic plant—*Anacharis*. In Part II, you investigate how light influences the starch concentration in leaves.

Part I: Gas Exchange in *Anacharis*

Materials
For each team of three students

2 250-mL flasks

1 250-mL beaker

1 100-mL graduated cylinder

1 10-mL graduated cylinder

1 dissolved oxygen probe

1 pH probe

1 temperature probe

1 ruler

water at room temperature

distilled water

bromothymol blue

1 bunch of *Anacharis* (4–6 sprigs)

1 drinking straw with hole punched in it

1 lamp with 100-watt spotlight or fluorescent bulb

aluminum foil

Cautions

Bromothymol blue may be harmful if swallowed and may cause irritation to the skin and eyes. Wash the area with water only if you get any on your skin. Notify your teacher if you accidentally ingest any or get some in your eyes.

Process and Procedure

All organisms continually take in substances and give off different substances. Those substances are the result of cellular activities. For example, when you exhale, you release carbon dioxide into the air. In this activity, you investigate some of the substances given off by an aquatic plant—*Anacharis*.

1. With your team, read Measuring Dissolved Gases to learn about the model system you will investigate.

READING

Measuring Dissolved Gases

Aquatic plants such as *Anacharis,* shown in figure 7.2, exchange gases with the environment just as land plants do. Gases such as carbon dioxide (CO_2) and oxygen (O_2) dissolve in water. When carbon dioxide dissolves in water, it combines with some water molecules (H_2O) to become carbonic acid (H_2CO_3). You can indirectly measure CO_2 concentration in an aquatic environment by measuring the pH (pH is a measure of how acidic or basic a solution is). When carbonic acid is added to water, the pH decreases. You can measure oxygen dissolved in water using a dissolved oxygen probe. Light affects the amount of gas, CO_2 or O_2, that Anacharis exchanges with its environment.

▲ Figure 7.2 **Anacharis.** *Anacharis, commonly called elodea, is found in ponds, lakes, and streams throughout North America. It is sold in pet stores as an aquarium plant. What gas do you think is present in the gas bubbles?*

In this activity, you investigate how light influences the gases exchanged by *Anacharis*.

2. Read through the protocol, Measuring Gas Exchange, with your team to learn how to measure the gases exchanged by *Anacharis*. Be prepared to participate in a class discussion in the next step.

Protocol

Measuring Gas Exchange

1. Set up your probe ware according to your teacher's instructions.
   a. Calibrate the pH probe to a pH 4-11 range.
   b. Calibrate the dissolved oxygen probe.
   c. Choose appropriate settings to monitor the 3 probes (pH, oxygen, and temperature), save your data, and graph your results.

   Consult your teacher for help selecting the settings.

2. Put 125 milliliters (mL) of distilled water in a flask.

3. Put a straw in the flask and blow gently through the straw into the water for 3 minutes. What are you adding to the water?

   Blow into the end of the straw with the additional small hole in it. This helps prevent you from sucking any liquid into your mouth. Discard the straw after use.

4. Add 2.5 mL of bromothymol blue to the water in the flask that you have been blowing into and swirl the flask to mix.

5. In a 2nd flask, add 2.5 mL of bromothymol blue and 125 mL of distilled water.

6. Use a pH probe to test the pH of the water in both flasks.

7. Place 4-6 sprigs of *Anacharis*, cut end up, into a 250-mL beaker.

8. Fill the beaker 3/4 full with the mixture from the second flask (the flask you did not blow into).

9. Place the pH probe, the oxygen probe, and the temperature probe in the beaker.

10. Position the beaker in front of a light source, as shown in the figure.

11. Take pH, oxygen, and temperature readings for at least 30 minutes.

12. Remove the probes and rinse them with distilled water.

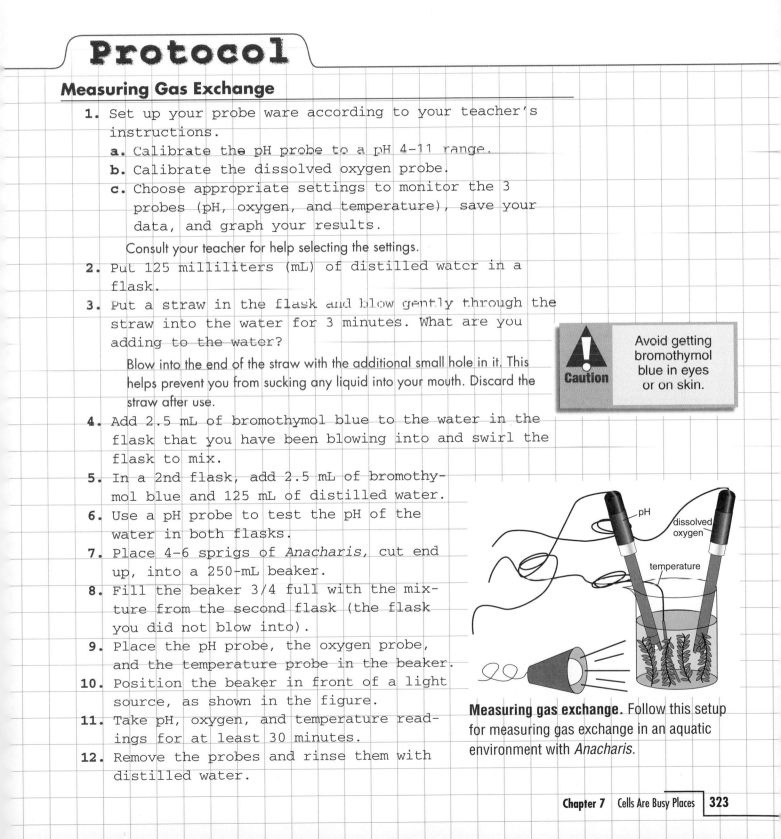

Caution Avoid getting bromothymol blue in eyes or on skin.

Measuring gas exchange. Follow this setup for measuring gas exchange in an aquatic environment with *Anacharis*.

3. Discuss the following questions with your team. Record in your science notebook all important ideas that you hear.
   a. How could you investigate how light influences the gases exchanged by *Anacharis*? How could some teams design their investigations one way and other teams design their investigations another way to accomplish this?
   b. How might monitoring temperature as well as pH and oxygen be important?

Remember that a control is an important part of an investigation.

4. Record in your science notebook the design and procedure that your team will use and have your teacher approve it.
5. Predict how the following will change during your investigation. Record your predictions in your science notebook.
   a. Color of the bromothymol blue solution
   b. pH level
   c. Dissolved oxygen level
   d. Temperature
6. Create a data table to record your observations, such as bubbling and color changes, and the times of your observations.

Refer to your design and procedure to help you decide what your data table needs to include. Remember that a data table should look like a grid with headings for each column and labels for each row. To make sure you include all of the rows and columns that you need, have your teacher check your data table.

7. Gather the materials that you need and conduct your investigation. Record your observations in your science notebook.
8. When you have finished collecting and recording data, rinse the probes and clean and return the other equipment. Then wash your hands thoroughly with soap and water.
9. Generate 3 separate line graphs showing pH, oxygen, and temperature (on the *y*-axis) against time (on the *x*-axis).

Title your graphs to indicate the design of your investigation. An example is "pH of Water When *Anacharis* Is Placed 10 Centimeters from Light." Then add "What I see" and "What it means" highlight comments and a caption to each of your graphs.

10. Compare your results with your predictions in Step 5. Discuss your results with your team and be prepared to share your results with the class.
11. Participate in a class discussion about the results of the different teams and the effect of light on gas exchange in *Anacharis*.
    a. Present your team's results, including your graphs, to the class.
    b. How did oxygen, pH, and temperature change in the different investigations?

12. Your teacher has a test tube containing *Anacharis* and bromothymol blue solution that has been in the dark for at least 24 hours. The solution in it was blue initially. Predict the pH and color of the solution now.

13. Study the test tube that your teacher will show you.
    a. What color is the solution? What pH does your teacher obtain from the solution?
    b. Which teams observed similar changes in their solutions? Explain why they observed similar changes.

Part I

Complete the following questions on your own. Record your answers in your science notebook.

1. You saw that water that you had blown into turned green or yellow when you added bromothymol blue solution. You observed the same change (from blue to green or yellow) in the test tube displayed by your teacher in Step 13. Do you think the process in your body that caused the color change is the same process in the *Anacharis*? Why or why not?

2. How did light affect the oxygen levels in the solutions? Why do you think the oxygen levels changed?

Part II: Stored Starch

Recall from chapter 6 that plants store energy as starch. How do the leaves of plants placed in the light or in a dark room differ in their starch content? Complete Part II to find out.

Materials
For each team of three students

3 pairs of safety goggles   Lugol's iodine solution

3 lab aprons   1 leaf partially covered with black paper

1 petri dish

Cautions

Lugol's iodine solution is a poison if ingested. It is a strong irritant and can stain clothing. Avoid skin or eye contact; do not ingest. If contact occurs, flush affected area with water for 15 minutes. Rinse mouth with water, Call your teacher immediately.

Process and Procedure

1. Discuss with your team why you would use Lugol's iodine solution in this investigation. Remember that you used this solution in the previous chapter when you made cell models.

If you have not done so already, read the introduction to Part II to learn what this investigation is about.

2. Remove the leaf your team partially covered in chapter 6 and place it in a petri dish.
3. Predict how the leaf will stain with the Lugol's iodine solution. Will some parts have more starch than others? Record your prediction in your science notebook, using sketches as indicated.
   a. Draw 1 sketch of how your leaf looks now. Indicate where your leaf was covered with black paper.
   b. Draw a 2nd sketch indicating where on your leaf there will be more or less starch.
4. Before testing your leaf for starch, you must remove chlorophyll (a green pigment in plant cells) from the leaf. Your teacher will remove the chlorophyll by placing the leaf in a beaker of boiling 95 percent alcohol until the leaf is white. Take your leaf to your teacher to have the chlorophyll removed.
5. Watch as your teacher heats the alcohol and leaf.
   a. Record your observations in your science notebook.
   b. Discuss with your team why you think it is important to remove the chlorophyll from the leaf before testing for starch.
6. Once the chlorophyll has been removed, place your leaf back in a petri dish. Then test for starch.
   a. Cover the leaf with Lugol's iodine solution for a few minutes.
   b. Rinse the leaf with tap water.
   c. Observe which parts of the leaf stain a dark color.
7. In your science notebook, draw a labeled sketch of your leaf. Indicate where there is more or less starch.

Let the Lugol's iodine solution absorb for a few minutes before you make your sketch.

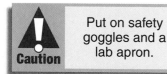
Caution Put on safety goggles and a lab apron.

Reflect and Connect

Work with your team to answer the following questions. Record your answers in your science notebook.

1. Why do you think light was important in terms of which parts of the leaf contained starch?
2. Why do you think starch might be an important organic molecule in plants? Recall what you learned about starch in chapter 6.

3. All cellular activities require a source of energy and matter. Share your current ideas about the cellular activities you investigated in this activity.
    a. What is the source of energy for the *Anacharis* and the potted plants?
    b. What is the source of matter or molecules for the starch you observed in the plant leaf?
4. Do you think the following statements are true or false? Explain your answers.
    a. Light provides energy for plants in the same way that food provides energy for animals.
    b. Plants carry out *respiration* all day long.
    c. Animals cannot survive without plants in their environment.

Converting Sunlight into Sugar

EXPLAIN

You have been investigating processes that occur in plant cells. To grow, plants need only light, water, air, and a few essential elements that are available in the soil. Unlike animals, plants are able to make their own food in the form of sugars. The process of making those sugars is called *photosynthesis*. Work with a partner to read the following sections and to learn more about this cellular process. Begin by reading Energy because energy is an important part of photosynthesis.

READING

Energy

Living things need energy. **Energy** is the capacity to do work. Energy comes in a variety of forms, including chemical, light, electrical, and mechanical. Organisms store energy in the organic molecules from which the organisms are made. Such energy is known as chemical energy. Food and gasoline are examples of chemical energy. You learned about light energy in the Matter Is Marvelous unit when you studied spectra. You will learn about examples of electrical (nerve impulses) and mechanical (muscle movement) energy in the next two chapters.

An important property of energy is that it can be transferred from one form to another. For example, a car engine converts the chemical energy stored in gasoline into the mechanical energy that powers the car (see figure 7.3). Energy transfer is important for living things. For example, you get your energy from food, which is converted into mechanical energy when you

◀ **Figure 7.3 Energy conversion.** Molecules in gasoline store energy. Combustion converts it into mechanical energy in a car. What other energy conversions can you think of?

SCILINKS
NSTA

Topic: photosynthesis
Go to: www.scilinks.org
Code: 1Inquiry328

do activities such as hiking in the mountains or lifting a book. Plants also must convert energy. Plants don't eat food as you do, so where does the energy that a plant needs come from?

Capturing the Energy in Sunlight

Photosynthesis is the series of reactions by which plants, algae, and some bacteria use light energy from the Sun to make food. This reading focuses on photosynthesis in plants. Read the sidebar, Photosynthesis Isn't Just for Plants, to learn about photosynthesis in other organisms.

You might be surprised to know that light is the only source of energy for plants. No organism can use light energy directly from the Sun

as a source of food energy. Plants must first convert *light energy* into *chemical energy*.

Photosynthesis uses only certain wavelengths of visible light. Recall from the Matter Is Marvelous unit that visible light consists of a spectrum of colors, each with a different wavelength and energy content, as shown in figure 7.4. When light strikes an object, it may be transmitted, absorbed, or reflected. In photosynthetic cells, several different pigments absorb certain wavelengths of light and reflect or transmit all others.

In plants, most light is absorbed by a green pigment called chlorophyll. Plants appear green because chlorophyll reflects rather than absorbs

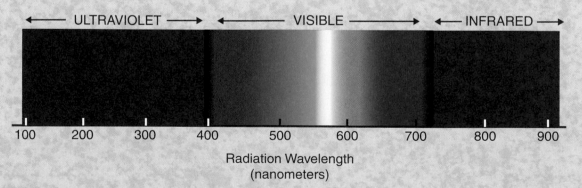

▲ **Figure 7.4 Light spectrum.** The Sun is the source of different types of radiant energy, including ultraviolet light, visible light that can be detected by the human eye, and warming infrared light. Photosynthesis uses only visible light.

green light. In addition to chlorophyll, plants contain other pigments, such as those visible in the plant shown in figure 7.5. Some of these accessory pigments work with chlorophyll to absorb additional wavelengths of light. Plants contain two form of chlorophyll, *a* and *b*, which absorb light in the violet-blue and orange-red range. Plants can use only the energy from absorbed wavelengths. In the wavelengths that are strongly absorbed, the rate of photosynthesis is high.

▶ **Figure 7.5 Coleus plant.** Why do you think it might be useful for plants to have pigments other than green chlorophyll?

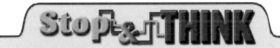

Work with your partner to answer the following questions. Record your answers in your science notebook.

1. The chemical energy in gasoline is converted into mechanical energy to make a car move. Give another example of energy being converted from one form to another.

2. Where do plants get their energy?

3. Explain why the following statement is incorrect: Plants get their food from the soil.

4. Imagine the discovery of a new desert plant that has a unique pigment in its leaves called azurephyll. This pigment strongly absorbs all sunlight from green light (500 nanometers [nm]) to red light (700 nm). If you observed this plant in the desert, what color would the leaves appear to be? Why?

   Look at figure 7.4 to see all of the colors in the visible light spectrum.

MAKING CARBON COMPOUNDS

Topic: chloroplast
Go to: www.scilinks.org
Code: 1Inquiry330

You have learned about the source of energy for plants, but how is it converted into chemical energy? Plants also need carbon compounds to make their own food or chemical energy. Where does the carbon come from? To answer those questions, you need to know more about the process of photosynthesis. Three major events occur in plant cells during photosynthesis: (1) absorption of light energy, (2) conversion of light energy into chemical energy, and (3) storage of chemical energy in sugars. Those three events occur in two distinct but interdependent sets of reactions.

Light-Dependent Reactions

The first phase of photosynthesis, called the light-dependent reactions, requires the presence of sunlight. The light-dependent reactions begin when sunlight hits a chlorophyll molecule in a chloroplast (see figure 7.6e). Light causes electrons in chlorophyll to become excited and to move to a higher energy level. This starts a series of reactions that converts light energy into adenosine triphosphate, or ATP, a form of chemical energy. ATP

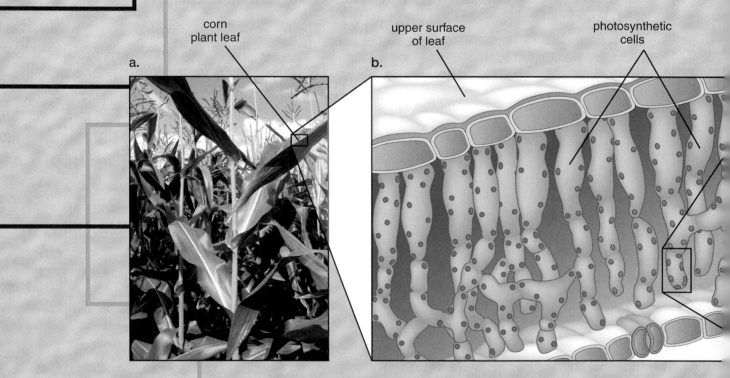

corn plant leaf

upper surface of leaf

photosynthetic cells

a.

b.

▲ **Figure 7.6 Overview of photosynthesis.** Plants such as (a) corn have photosynthetic cells in (b) their leaves. Within the photosynthetic cells are (c and d) numerous chloroplasts where photosynthesis reactions occur. (e) In the light-dependent reactions, absorption of light energy by chlorophyll is an important source of energy used in cells. You can learn more about ATP in the FYI—Energy Currency of Cells.

This phase of photosynthesis cannot occur without water. Plants absorb water through their roots. **Enzymes,** which are special proteins that speed up or **catalyze** reactions, remove electrons from water (H_2O) and split it into oxygen (O_2) and hydrogen ions (H^+). Oxygen gas (O_2) is given off as a by-product. During the Cellular Activities in Plants activity, you observed this by-product when you saw that the dissolved oxygen levels were higher for *Anacharis* in the light.

Light-Independent Reactions

The second phase of photosynthesis does not directly require light. That is, the second phase does not require sunlight for the reactions to occur, but it does require ATP produced during the light-dependent reactions. Therefore, the second phase is called the light-independent reactions. Although the light-independent reactions do not directly require light, the reactions occur in the light because they occur simultaneously with the light-dependent

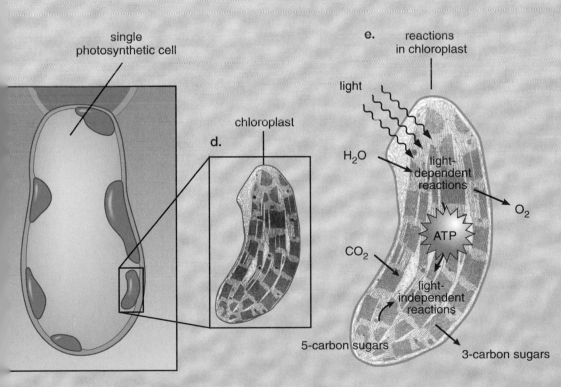

single photosynthetic cell

chloroplast

d.

e. reactions in chloroplast

light

H_2O

light-dependent reactions

O_2

ATP

CO_2

light-independent reactions

5-carbon sugars

3-carbon sugars

starts a series of chemical reactions that result in the production of ATP and release oxygen from water. In the light-independent reactions, a series of reactions uses carbon atoms from carbon dioxide to build sugars. ATP provides the energy for these reactions.

reactions. The light-independent reactions often are referred to as the Calvin cycle, named after a scientist who made important discoveries about the reactions.

In the light-independent reactions, carbon molecules combine to produce sugars, a form of chemical energy (see figure 7.6e). The source of the carbon molecules is atmospheric carbon dioxide. Carbon dioxide is added to an existing 5-carbon sugar, creating two 3-carbon sugars. This process is called carbon fixation because the reactions incorporate, or *fix*, carbon into an organic molecule. The light-independent reaction fixes one molecule of CO_2 into a sugar while at the same time replacing the 5-carbon sugar needed for the next round of the cycle. The ATP produced in light-dependent reactions provides the energy for those reactions.

The following equation summarizes the overall reactions of photosynthesis:

$$\text{light} + 3\ CO_2 + 3\ H_2O \xrightarrow{\text{enzymes}} C_3H_6O_3 + 3\ O_2$$

energy   carbon dioxide   water   3-carbon sugar   oxygen

The 3-carbon sugars produced during photosynthesis supply energy and carbon skeletons for the entire plant. Carbon skeletons describe the chains of carbon atoms found in organic molecules (see figure 7.7). As shown in figure 7.8, several things can happen to the 3-carbon sugars produced through photosynthesis. Much of the sugar is converted into sucrose, starch, or cellulose. Leaf cells

▼ **Figure 7.7**
Carbon skeleton. All organic molecules contain a carbon skeleton made of carbon atoms bonded together.

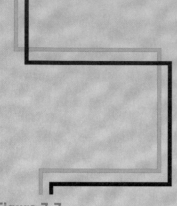

chain

branching chain

rings

▷ **Figure 7.8 Fate of 3-carbon sugars in plants.** Plants use the sugars produced in photosynthesis to supply energy and carbon skeletons for biosynthesis and other energy-requiring processes.

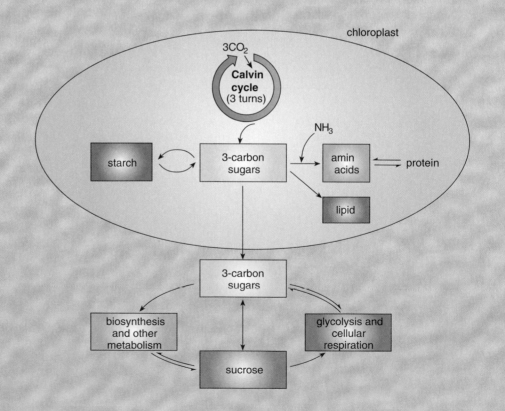

can consume sucrose or export it through veins to supply the rest of the plant with energy and carbon skeletons. Some of the sugars are converted to starch, which accumulates in the chloroplasts during daylight. When photosynthesis shuts down at night, the chloroplasts break down the starch to supply the plant with energy. The carbon skeletons in sucrose and starch can, in turn, be used to form lipids, proteins, and other molecules that plants need for maintenance and growth.

Energy Currency of Cells

Energy stored in sugars and glycogen cannot be used directly by cells. To make the energy stored in these molecules useful, the energy must be converted to a different chemical form. The direct source of energy for most cellular activities is ATP. A good analogy for ATP is money. While it is good to have a lot of $100 bills, breaking them down into $10 bills makes them easier to use. In the same way, long-term storage molecules are like large bills and ATP is the small change in the energy world.

Study the figure. ATP stores energy in its structure. This energy came ultimately from the sun and is stored in food. Small amounts of energy are required to initiate the reaction. In cells, this energy comes from interactions between molecules in the presence of catalysts called enzymes. As the reaction progresses, one phosphate group is removed from the ATP and energy is released. This energy is available for cellular work. Notice the conversion of ADP to ATP in the illustrations of photosynthesis.

The energy released when ATP is converted to ADP is used in energy-requiring reactions in cells. Many of the important tasks in the cell involve several reactions that require energy. Thus, each cell in your body requires large amounts of ATP each day just to perform its most basic activities. Building one protein molecule for a muscle, for example, can require hundreds of ATP molecules. You learn more about how ATP is used in Powering Cellular Activities.

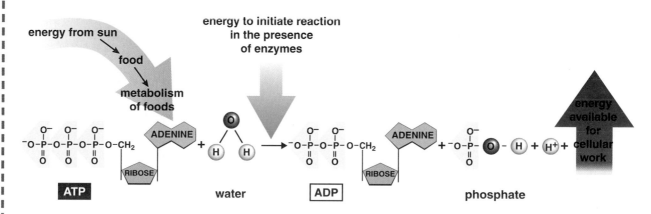

ATP and ADP. Each ATP molecule is composed of adenine, ribose, and three identical groups of phosphorus and oxygen atoms called phosphates. ATP contains more energy than ADP. ATP stores this additional energy until the energy is released by a chemical reaction that removes one phosphate group. The energy that is released when this phosphate group is removed is used for cellular work.

Reflect and Connect

Team up with a partner and discuss the following questions. Be ready to present your answers in a class discussion. Record your answers in your science notebook, adding additional information, if necessary, after the class discussion.

1. Complete the following tasks about photosynthesis.
   a. Where in a plant cell does photosynthesis occur?
   b. List 3 or more ways that plants use the 3-carbon sugars produced during photosynthesis.
   c. Describe why you think the carbon skeletons supplied by the 3-carbon sugars might be important for organisms that eat plants.
2. What is the source of the mass increase in plants during their growth? Where does the matter come from that plants use to build their structures?
3. How do plants benefit from the Sun's energy?
4. Explain why some parts of the leaves in the previous activity contained more starch than other parts.
5. Create a concept map of the process of photosynthesis using the following words and any other words you would like to add. Remember to use verbs to connect the concepts to show relationships. Arrange the concept map so that the most universal concept is at the top.
   - Light energy
   - Photosynthesis
   - Chemical energy
   - Chloroplast
   - Water
   - Carbon dioxide
   - Oxygen

Photosynthesis Isn't Just for Plants

Like plants, most algae contain chlorophyll and other pigments and carry out photosynthesis. They may be single-celled or multicellular, or they may form colonies. Algae can be found just about anywhere you find tiny droplets of water: in the air, on tree trunks and branches, in the bottoms of streams, on soil particles, and on rocks at the seashore. Algae are found in diverse environments that include fresh-water habitats, the ocean, desert sands, and hot springs. In aquatic environments, algae are the dominant photosynthetic organism. There are many different groups of algae. Although all algae are photosynthetic, not all of them appear green. Examples of algae include green algae, red algae, brown algae, diatoms, and dinoflagellates.

Sea lettuce. Sea lettuce is a type of multi-cellular algae found on rocky shores.

The major seaweeds of the world are multicellular red and brown algae. The brown algae inhabit rocky shores in cooler regions. Kelps, for example, form extensive offshore beds. Brown algae appear brown because they contain gold and brown pigments as well as chlorophyll. Most seaweed in warm oceans is red algae. They generally grow attached to rocks or other algae. Because red algae absorb blue light, which penetrates farther into the ocean water than other wavelengths of light, they can grow at greater depths than any other algae.

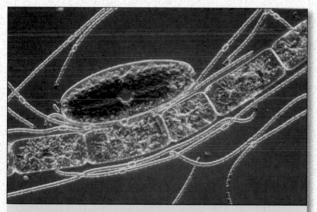

Mixed algae. Microscopic algae are found in diverse environments.

Green algae are the most widely studied and the most similar to plants. You can find them in your aquarium at home or on the shady side of trees. Many green algae are single-celled and microscopic, but they may be so abundant that they color the water of ponds and lakes green or form huge floating mats. Some marine species of green algae form large, multicellular seaweeds, such as sea lettuce (*Ulva*).

Kelp. Kelp forests provide shelter and protection for many marine organisms.

Diatoms are abundant in both freshwaters and marine waters. They are the primary photosynthetic organism in oceans. Diatoms have glasslike cell walls made of silica. They are some of the most intricately patterned creatures on Earth. Electron microscope studies have shown that the patterns on their cell walls are created by pores that connect the inside of the cell with the outside environment. As shown in the photograph, the silica cell walls of diatoms remain intact for many years after the organism has died. Great masses of shells that have slowly accumulated over many years are now mined as diatomaceous earth. That material is used in many ways—for example, as a filter (for swimming pools), as an abrasive in silver polish, and as a brightener for the paint used to mark highways.

Dinoflagellates are found primarily in marine waters. About half of the dinoflagellates are photosynthetic. In mid- to late summer, a surplus of nutrients can cause blooms of photosynthetic dinoflagellates. When dinoflagellates occur in large numbers, the water may appear golden or red, producing a *red tide*. When this happens, marine species may suffer because some species of dinoflagellates produce a neurotoxin, a poison that damages the nervous system. Humans are sometimes affected by red tides after eating fish or shellfish containing neurotoxins.

Some bacteria are photosynthetic. However, most photosynthetic bacteria do not produce oxygen as a by-product of photosynthesis. Some examples are purple bacteria, green sulfur bacteria, green nonsulfur bacteria, and heliobacteria. Cyanobacteria are the only group of bacteria that produces oxygen through photosynthesis.

Purple bacteria are widespread, especially in anaerobic (without oxygen) environments such as sewage treatment ponds. Green sulfur bacteria are found in the anaerobic zone at the bottoms of lakes. Green nonsulfur bacteria are often found in microbial mats with cyanobacteria. Heliobacteria live in soil environments. Cyanobacteria are hardy and are found in almost every environment where light is available. They live in freshwater, marine, and terrestrial environments. They also live in extreme environments such as hot springs and rocks found in Antarctica as well as scorching deserts.

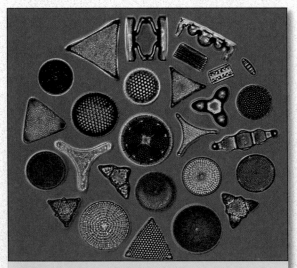

Diatoms. Each species of diatom has a characteristic shape. Notice the striking geometric patterns.

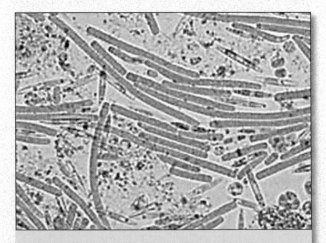

Purple bacteria. Most species of purple bacteria are anaerobic. Unlike cyanobacteria, purple bacteria do not produce oxygen as a by-product of photosynthesis.

Powering Cellular Activities

In Converting Sunlight into Sugar, you learned how plants convert light energy into food. In Powering Cellular Activities, you learn how organisms (plants and animals) convert food energy into energy that cells use easily. This occurs through a process called cellular respiration. In Part I, you work in a team to design an investigation. With your class, you test the effects of different variables on cellular respiration in yeast cells. Then in Part II, you read about cellular respiration and learn why it is important for all organisms.

Part I: Respiration Is a Gas!

Materials

For each team of two students

1 250-mL beaker

1 scale

1 500-mL plastic bottle, empty

water at room temperature

sugar

baker's yeast

1 25- or 30-cm round balloon

tape

sewing tape measure or string and ruler

1 marker

1 calculator

1 large test tube

wooden splint

something to light the splint

Cautions

Be careful around an open flame. Make sure that you have water available to put out the flame and that you tie back long hair.

Process and Procedure

During cellular respiration, yeast produces a gas. You will collect the gas in a balloon and see how much your balloon has expanded by the next class period. Follow the steps to learn what affects the amount of gas produced by yeast.

1. Read through Steps 2–9 to get an idea of the expectations for this activity before beginning your work.
2. Read the following paragraph to learn about the setup you will use in your investigation.

   Yeast needs only sugar, oxygen, and water to survive and reproduce. Yeast placed in a plastic bottle with sugar and water carries out basic processes such as cellular respiration. You can collect a gas produced during cellular respiration by placing a balloon over the opening of the bottle.

3. Discuss the following questions with your partner and write answers in your science notebook.
   a. What do you think are the main variables in this investigation?
   b. All teams must fill their bottles with 200 mL of water. Why do you think it is important for all teams to use the same size bottles and the same amount of water?
   c. How might the amount of yeast affect the amount of gas that you gather in the balloon?
   d. How might the amount of sugar affect the amount of gas that you gather in the balloon?

4. Participate in a class discussion of the questions in Step 3 and decide as a class what would be an appropriate control (or controls) for this investigation.

5. With your teammate, design an investigation to test the effects of different variables on the amount of gas produced. Use the answers to the questions in Step 3 to help with your design. Record your design in your science notebook.

6. Have your design approved by your teacher.

7. Predict the results of your investigation with your teammate. For example, predict what volume of gas you will collect, how the variables will affect the volume, and how the experimental bottles will differ from the control bottles. Record in your science notebook your prediction and your justification for your prediction.

8. Create a data table in which to record your results. Include columns to record the amount of each variable and the amount of the product. Record this information in your science notebook.

Make sure you use the appropriate units.

9. Begin your investigation by doing the following:
   a. Blow up the balloon twice to a very large size in order to reduce the tension as the gas "blows up the balloon" again.
   b. Label your team's bottle with the amount of water, yeast, and sugar you will use.
   c. Add 200 mL of water and the amount of yeast and sugar you decided on. Then carefully swirl the bottle to mix.
   d. Firmly attach the balloon using tape.
   e. Record the time in your science notebook.

10. Observe what is happening to your setup and to other setups in your classroom. Note changes occurring in the bottles as well as in the balloons. Record your observations at regular intervals, such as every 5 minutes, in your science notebook.

11. The balloon may begin to inflate right away. Measure the volume of gas that accumulates. Follow these steps to estimate the volume of gas in the balloon.

   a. Use a sewing tape measure or a string and a ruler to determine the circumference (C) of the balloon at its widest point. This is the length around the balloon.

   b. Circumference is related to the radius by $C = 2\pi r$. Use this equation to estimate the radius of the balloon.

   c. Volume is related to radius by $V = (4/3)\ \pi r^3$. Use this equation to estimate the volume of gas in the balloon.

Show your work for those calculations and record the volumes in your data table.

12. Let your setup sit overnight.

13. During the next class period, measure the circumference of your balloon and estimate the volume of gas in the balloon. Use Step 11 as a guide for your calculations. Record your results in your data table.

14. Do you know what gas filled the balloon? Do the following tasks to find out.

   a. Trap the gas in the balloon as you carefully take off the tape and slide the balloon off the bottle.

One of you should hold the balloon while the other person removes the tape and slides the balloon off the bottle.

   b. Slowly release the gas into a large test tube.

   c. Immediately place a flaming wooden splint in the test tube.

   d. What happened? What do you think the gas is? Record your observations and ideas in your science notebook.

Flammable!

15. Participate in a class discussion about the results of the investigations. Which teams had the most and the least balloon expansion? How did their volumes relate to the amount of yeast or the amount of sugar that they used?

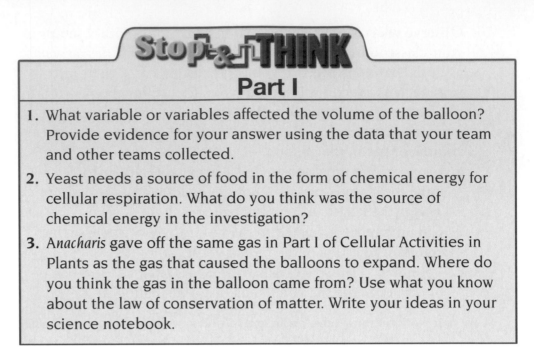

Part I

1. What variable or variables affected the volume of the balloon? Provide evidence for your answer using the data that your team and other teams collected.

2. Yeast needs a source of food in the form of chemical energy for cellular respiration. What do you think was the source of chemical energy in the investigation?

3. *Anacharis* gave off the same gas in Part I of Cellular Activities in Plants as the gas that caused the balloons to expand. Where do you think the gas in the balloon came from? Use what you know about the law of conservation of matter. Write your ideas in your science notebook.

Part II: Cellular Respiration

You may know that yeast is added to dough when bread is made. The dough is allowed to sit a while, and it expands and rises. The texture becomes fluffier, and the dough becomes filled with holes and pores, like in a sponge. But how does this relate to cellular respiration? Read How Cells Convert Food into Energy with a partner to find out.

READING

How Cells Convert Food into Energy

Topic: cellular respiration
Go to: www.scilinks.org
Code: 1Inquiry340

You may be familiar with respiration, or breathing, but cellular respiration is different. Unlike breathing, which occurs only in animals, **cellular respiration** occurs in the cells of all living organisms. In fact, cellular respiration is essential for all life to survive. You might be surprised that it occurs in plants as well as animals. It is the process that all cells use to break down fuels— primarily glucose—to yield the energy required for cells to function.

Without this energy, most processes critical to life would stop.

Cellular respiration can occur with or without the presence of oxygen. This chapter emphasizes cellular respiration with oxygen, also called **aerobic respiration.** In the presence of oxygen, cellular respiration takes place in cells and has three main stages—glycolysis, the Krebs cycle, and the electron transport system. Each stage, shown in figure 7.9, involves a series of chemical reactions catalyzed by nzymes. The result of those reaction sequences is to produce ATP molecules for use in the cell, which gives the cell energy.

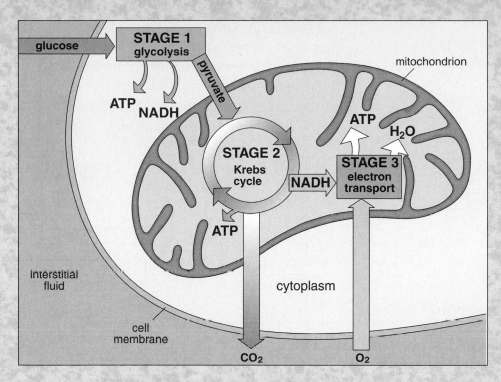

Figure 7.9 **Major stages and molecules involved in cellular respiration.** The molecules involved in cellular respiration are glucose, ATP, oxygen, carbon dioxide, and water. Do you see any similarities with the molecules that are involved in photosynthesis?

Cellular respiration begins with glycolysis. Glycolysis is a series of reactions that break down 6-carbon glucose into two molecules of 3-carbon pyruvate (see figure 7.10). In plants, sucrose or starch is broken down into glucose before entering glycolysis. During those reactions, a small amount of ATP and molecules of NADH (nicotinamide adenine dinucleotide with a hydrogen atom) are produced. NADH is a hydrogen and an energy carrier. Most of the energy in the glucose is transferred to pyruvate molecules at this point. The fate of pyruvate depends on whether oxygen is present.

If oxygen is present, the Krebs cycle completes the breakdown of glucose to carbon dioxide (CO_2) (see figure 7.11). The Krebs cycle begins as pyruvate is transported into the mitochondria. In a series of reactions, enzymes release carbon dioxide from pyruvate and more molecules of NADH and ATP are produced. Because glycolysis produced two molecules of pyruvate, two passes through the Krebs cycle are required to break down the original glucose molecule completely. Carbon dioxide is released from the cell as gas. The release of carbon dioxide by yeast cells

SCiLINKS
NSTA

Go to: www.scilinks.org
Topic: glycolysis
Code: 1Inquiry341a
Topic: Krebs cycle
Code: 1Inquiry341b
Topic: electron transport
Code: 1Inquiry 341c

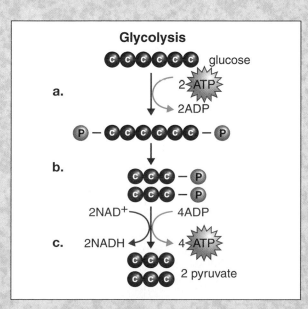

Figure 7.10 **Glycolysis.** In glycolysis, glucose is broken down into two molecules of pyruvate. Energy from ATP (a) is needed to begin the glycolysis reactions. Two ATP molecules each transfer a phosphate to glucose. Then the glucose molecule is broken down into two molecules that contain three carbons each (b). During later steps (c), carbon atoms are rearranged to form pyruvate and ATP and NADH are produced.

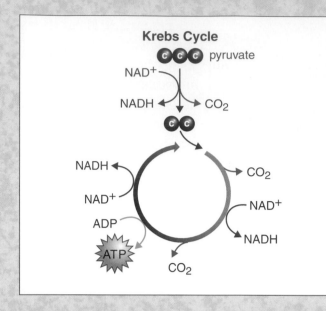

Krebs Cycle

◀ **Figure 7.11 Krebs cycle.** In preparation for the Krebs cycle, each pyruvate molecule produced by glycolysis is converted into a two-carbon molecule. Many enzyme-catalyzed reactions occur that release two molecules of carbon dioxide and ATP. In addition, several NADH molecules are produced.

caused the balloon in Part I to expand, and it causes bread dough to rise.

The electron transport system uses the NADH molecules formed during the previous stages. NADH molecules carry hydrogen atoms. The electron transport system consists of a series of electron carrier molecules that are embedded in the inner membrane of a mitochondrion (see figure 7.12). The hydrogen

atoms carried by NADH are separated into electrons and protons. The electrons are passed to the chain of electron carrier molecules. As the electrons move from one carrier to the next, they release energy. Some of the protons are pumped across the membrane of the mitochondrion, creating a concentration gradient. This proton concentration gradient drives the production of ATP as protons diffuse back into the

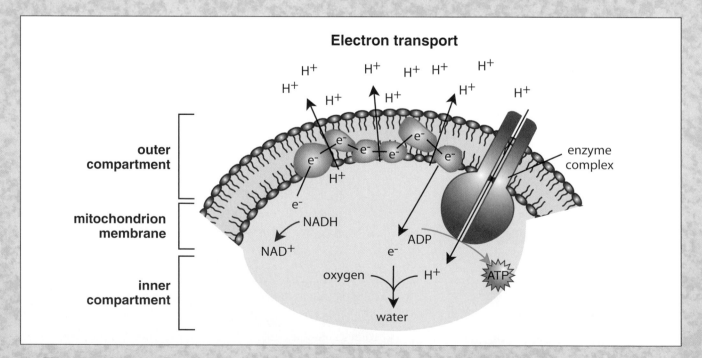

Electron transport

▲ **Figure 7.12 Electron transport.** As electrons pass from one carrier to the next, hydrogen ions (H⁺) are pumped into the outer compartment. The resulting proton gradient drives the production of ATP.

mitochondrion. As the protons diffuse in, they pass through an enzyme complex that synthesizes ATP. This is how most ATP is generated. At the end of the electron transport chain, the electrons and protons join with oxygen to form water. The requirement of oxygen at this point in the electron transport system explains why humans—as well as other animals, plants, fungi, protists, and many prokaryotes—require oxygen for their survival.

In summary, cellular respiration is a series of reactions that release energy as glucose and other molecules are broken down into carbon dioxide and water. The overall reaction is summarized in the following equation:

$$\underset{\text{glucose}}{C_6H_{12}O_6} + \underset{\text{oxygen}}{6\ O_2} \xrightarrow{\text{enzymes}} \underset{\text{carbon dioxide}}{6\ CO_2} + \underset{\text{water}}{6\ H_2O} + \underset{\text{energy}}{ATP}$$

As in aerobic respiration, glycolysis is the first stage of **anaerobic respiration**—cellular respiration that does not require oxygen. Glucose is broken down into pyruvate, and a small amount of ATP is produced. However, no more ATP is produced beyond glycolysis. Pyruvate is converted to other molecules, as shown in figure 7.13. This process is also known as fermentation. Fermentation by bacteria and yeast is important in the production of yogurt, vinegar, and wine.

As shown in figure 7.13, the energy yield of anaerobic respiration is considerably less than that of aerobic respiration. The small energy yield from anaerobic respiration is enough for single-celled organisms. In fact, anaerobic respiration is the only form of cellular respiration for some bacteria and organisms that live in anaerobic environments. Anaerobic respiration helps some cells through times when oxygen levels are low. For example, anaerobic respiration occurs temporarily in animal and bacteria cells when insufficient oxygen is present. This happens in your own muscle cells during strenuous exercise. To learn more about this experience, read the sidebar, Respiration during Exercise. Overall, anaerobic respiration does not produce enough energy for the needs of large, multicellular organisms.

SCI LINKS
NSTA
Topic: anaerobic respiration
Go to: www.scilinks.org
Code: 1Inquiry343

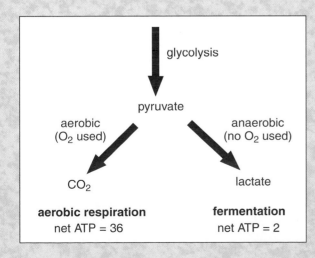

glycolysis

pyruvate

aerobic (O₂ used)

anaerobic (no O₂ used)

CO₂

lactate

aerobic respiration
net ATP = 36

fermentation
net ATP = 2

◀ **Figure 7.13 Oxygen and the fate of pyruvate.** The oxygen concentration in a cell can affect the fate of pyruvate. When oxygen is present, pyruvate undergoes anaerobic respiration and enters the Krebs cycle. When oxygen is low or absent, pyruvate undergoes anaerobic respiration or fermentation. Fermentation forms lactic acid, ethyl alcohol, acetic acid, and other compounds. Anaerobic respiration occurs in some cells even when oxygen concentrations are high enough for aerobic respiration to occur.

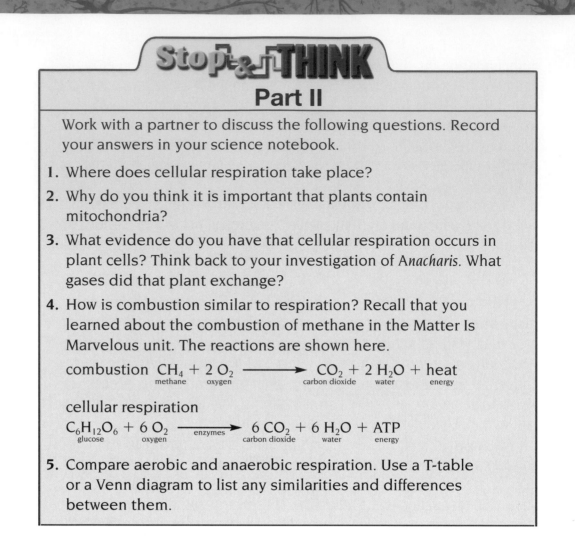

Stop & THINK

Part II

Work with a partner to discuss the following questions. Record your answers in your science notebook.

1. Where does cellular respiration take place?

2. Why do you think it is important that plants contain mitochondria?

3. What evidence do you have that cellular respiration occurs in plant cells? Think back to your investigation of *Anacharis*. What gases did that plant exchange?

4. How is combustion similar to respiration? Recall that you learned about the combustion of methane in the Matter Is Marvelous unit. The reactions are shown here.

combustion $\underset{\text{methane}}{CH_4} + \underset{\text{oxygen}}{2\ O_2} \longrightarrow \underset{\text{carbon dioxide}}{CO_2} + \underset{\text{water}}{2\ H_2O} + \underset{\text{energy}}{\text{heat}}$

cellular respiration

$\underset{\text{glucose}}{C_6H_{12}O_6} + \underset{\text{oxygen}}{6\ O_2} \xrightarrow{\text{enzymes}} \underset{\text{carbon dioxide}}{6\ CO_2} + \underset{\text{water}}{6\ H_2O} + \underset{\text{energy}}{\text{ATP}}$

5. Compare aerobic and anaerobic respiration. Use a T-table or a Venn diagram to list any similarities and differences between them.

READING

ATP: The Fuel of Cells

The cells of all living organisms, including plants, use ATP as fuel to complete basic cell functions. Therefore, cellular respiration takes place constantly in these organisms to provide the ATP they need. ATP supplies the energy for a cell to do its work. For example, ATP provides the energy used to actively transport ions and molecules across cell membranes, to trigger muscle contraction, and to send nerve impulses. ATP also provides the energy for biosynthesis reactions in cells. Biosynthesis reactions form larger, more complex molecules from small, less-complex molecules. Examples include the formation of starch from glucose in plants and the building of proteins from amino acids in plants and animals. Biosynthesis in cells enables organisms to grow and maintain their structure.

Because ATP is required for many types of reactions in cells, it is often referred to as the energy currency of cells. The energy stored in food can be compared to investments such as stocks, whereas the energy stored in ATP is like cash in that it is readily available for use in cellular work.

SCiLINKS
NSTA

Topic: ATP
Go to: www.scilinks.org
Code: 1Inquiry344

Reflect and Connect

Work with a partner and discuss the following questions. Record your answers in your science notebook.

1. What functions are ATP molecules needed for?
2. What role does glucose play in cellular respiration?
3. Create a concept map of the process of cellular respiration using the following words and any other words you would like to add. Remember to use verbs to connect the concepts to show relationships. Arrange the concept map so that the most universal concept is at the top.
   - Cellular respiration
   - Water
   - Carbon dioxide
   - ATP
   - Oxygen
   - Biosynthesis reactions
   - Glucose
4. Why is cellular respiration important for all living things, including plants?
5. What do you think the relationship is between photosynthesis and cellular respiration? Keep in mind how the reactants, products, and energy in these processes might be related. The generalized equations are shown here.

photosynthesis

$$\underset{\text{energy}}{\text{light}} + 3\,\underset{\text{carbon dioxide}}{CO_2} + 3\,\underset{\text{water}}{H_2O} \xrightarrow{\text{enzymes}} \underset{\text{3-carbon sugar}}{C_3H_6O_3} + 3\,\underset{\text{oxygen}}{O_2}$$

cellular respiration

$$\underset{\text{glucose}}{C_6H_{12}O_6} + 6\,\underset{\text{oxygen}}{O_2} \xrightarrow{\text{enzymes}} 6\,\underset{\text{carbon dioxide}}{CO_2} + 6\,\underset{\text{water}}{H_2O} + \underset{\text{energy}}{ATP}$$

Respiration during Exercise

SIDEBAR

Even when you are sitting on the couch, your cells need a steady supply of ATP from respiration. Glucose travels through your bloodstream to your cells, where respiration takes place to power your cellular activities. But what happens when you exercise? Cells respond by increasing the rate of cellular respiration. Of course, an increased rate of cellular respiration means an increased use of both glucose and oxygen and an increased production of carbon dioxide.

When carbon dioxide levels in your blood start to rise, your breathing rate increases. Rapid breathing rids the body of excess carbon dioxide and delivers oxygen to the bloodstream more quickly. If you exercise at a moderate pace, your heart and lungs supply enough oxygen to your muscles to meet the demand of cellular respiration. But people may exercise so hard that muscle cells require more oxygen than the blood can deliver. Oxygen-starved muscle cells switch from

Aerobic exercise. Tennis is one form of aerobic exercise. Aerobic exercise is a form of exercise that increases the body's need for oxygen.

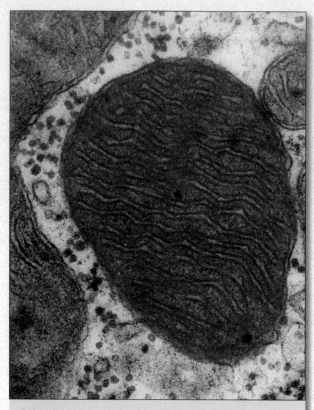

Mitochondrion. Some cells have between only 10 and 20 mitochondria. Others, such as muscle cells, have thousands.

aerobic respiration to anaerobic respiration. Rapid breathing eventually restores oxygen supplies to muscle.

Anaerobic respiration also allows us to produce the energy we need for rapid bursts of energy. During anaerobic respiration in muscle cells, fermentation of glucose produces lactic acid. Many people believe that lactic acid causes the burning sensation you feel in your muscles when exercising. Scientists now know that lactic acid helps regulate conditions that are necessary for muscles to contract. Lactic acid is produced in larger quantities during anaerobic respiration and splits into lactate and hydrogen ions. The bloodstream carries lactate out of the muscles and back to the liver, where it is slowly converted back to glucose. The buildup of hydrogen ions causes the burn you feel *during* intense exercise. Hydrogen ions build up in muscle during aerobic as well as anaerobic exercise. Soreness of muscles after exercise is usually due to slight tears in muscles.

The greater efficiency of aerobic respiration explains why aerobic conditioning is advantageous to a person. Aerobic respiration produces 19 times more ATP than anaerobic respiration. During aerobic conditioning, muscle cells produce more mitochondria. This provides the potential for greater release of energy (ATP) during heavy use of muscles. People who exercise infrequently have fewer mitochondria. In addition, aerobic conditioning improves blood circulation to the muscles, and better circulation provides a greater supply of oxygen to those busy mitochondria. As a result of those two changes, a conditioned person's muscle cells can convert a greater proportion of the energy in glucose into usable cellular energy than can an unconditioned person's.

Sun Worship

You have learned that plants use light energy and carbon dioxide to make their own food through the process of photosynthesis. You also have learned that through the process of cellular respiration, all organisms convert glucose into ATP, which is needed to carry out their life functions. In Sun Worship, you work with a partner to learn how those two processes are connected and you see how energy and matter flows through living systems.

Materials

Process and Procedure

1. Read We Can't Live without Them with a partner to learn more about energy flow among living systems. As you read, think about how different organisms obtain the energy and carbon molecules they need to survive and grow.

READING

We Can't Live without Them

All living things grow, move, and reproduce. Those and other types of biological activity require a source of energy. Plants, like all other organisms, must expend energy to stay alive and grow. As you learned in Powering Cellular Activities, plants obtain this energy by breaking down some of the 3-carbon sugar molecules they made through the process of photosynthesis. Plants break down glucose using the same process that animals and fungi use: cellular respiration.

Recall that cellular respiration produces ATP molecules. Plants use some of the ATP molecules they make to power the energy-requiring biochemical reactions that sustain life. They use other ATP molecules to power chemical reactions that create more body tissue, such as new leaves. Where did the energy to power those chemical reactions originally come from? It came from the Sun.

Plants differ from other organisms because they make their own food. Organisms that produce their own food are called producers. Animals cannot make their own food because they do not carry out photosynthesis. Organisms that cannot produce their own food are called consumers. How do those organisms obtain the energy they need to stay alive and grow? They eat other organisms!

Herbivores, for example, are animals that eat plants (see figure 7.14). The tissues of plants are made up of energy-rich molecules such as sugars, fats, and proteins. When an herbivore needs energy to survive and grow, it eats plants and, through digestion and the process of cellular respiration,

▲ **Figure 7.14 Herbivores.** (a) You probably recognize cattle as herbivores. (b) Krill, shrimplike invertebrates, are also herbivores. Krill eat microscopic plants called phytoplankton that live in the ocean. Can you think of other herbivores?

breaks down the molecules that make up the plant. This releases chemical energy that is stored in the bonds of the food molecules in plants and produces ATP. Herbivores then use the energy stored in ATP to stay alive; to move around by contracting their muscles; and to build new body tissue, such as muscle. Where did this energy originally come from? It came from the Sun.

Now consider carnivores and omnivores. A carnivore is an animal that eats other animals. An omnivore is an animal that eats both plants and animals. The tissues of animals are made up of energy-rich molecules such as sugars, fats, and proteins. When carnivores and sometimes omnivores need energy to survive and grow, they eat another animal and break down the animal's molecules through the process of cellular respiration. This releases chemical energy that is stored in the bonds of the food molecules and produces ATP. Carnivores and omnivores then use the energy stored in ATP to stay alive; to move around by contracting their muscles; and to build new body tissues, such as muscle. Where did this energy originally come from? We will let you can figure out the answer.

Herbivores, carnivores, and omnivores are examples of heterotrophs. Heterotrophs obtain energy from other organisms, either living or dead. Animals, fungi, and bacteria are

heterotrophs. Other organisms obtain energy and nutrients from nonliving sources such as the Sun, minerals, and the air. Those organisms are autotrophs. Autotrophs include plants, certain bacteria, and other organisms that capture energy from the Sun or from chemicals. The relationship between autotrophs and heterotrophs is shown in figure 7.15. Autotrophs, such as plants, directly (for herbivores) and indirectly (for carnivores) supply the energy and organic molecules needed for the maintenance and growth of all heterotrophs.

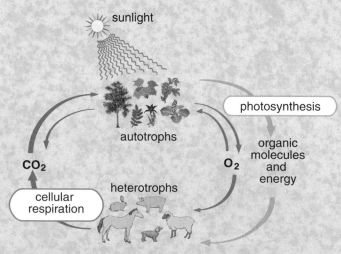

▲ **Figure 7.15 Relationship between autotrophs and heterotrophs.** Energy and organic molecules pass from autotrophs to heterotrophs. Oxygen and carbon dioxide cycle repeatedly between them.

2. Complete the following question and task. Record your ideas and sketches in your science notebook.
   a. Why do you think plants are called producers?
   b. How does photosynthesis connect sunlight to the energy needs of plants and animals? Answer using a paragraph or a labeled diagram.

Use figure 7.15 as a guide.

3. Study the calorimeter set up by your teacher. Then read the following paragraph to learn about it.

   A calorimeter is an instrument that measure calories-the amount of energy in foods. A calorie is a unit of measure for energy. It is the amount of heat energy required to raise the temperature of 1 gram (1 mL) of water 1° Celsius (C). The unitof measure for food energy is the kilocalorie (kcal). However, on food labels, it is written as Calories, with a capital C. Kilocalorie is the unit for energy in biology; however, joule (J) is used as the unit for energy in chemistry and physics.

4. Watch as your teacher burns a peanut and other food items in the calorimeter. Answer the following questions in your science notebook.
   a. What do burning foods give off?
   b. How is burning the food similar to what happens during cellular respiration?
   c. Why do you think burning different foods produces different results?

5. Scientists have conducted extensive investigations to determine the amount of kilocalories in different organisms and to determine the amount of kilocalories used and given off by organisms. How much energy, in kilocalories, do you think is transferred from one organism to another? Study the energy budget for a living system shown in figure 7.16 to find out.

6. Answer the following questions about the energy budget.
   a. What do you notice about the amount of energy transferred from one organism to another?
   b. Can you think of another example where an energy budget might be used? Describe how this energy budget might look. For example, what energy is used and given off by a household?

7. More than energy is transferred from one organism to another. Organisms also need matter in the form of organic molecules. Read Biosynthesis and Breakdown to learn how animals get the molecules they need from food.

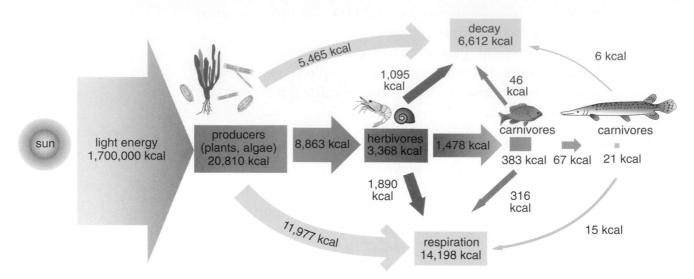

▲ **Figure 7.16 Energy budget of Silver Springs, Florida.** Energy budgets show the flow of energy among organisms in an environment. Notice the amount of energy taken in by a group of organisms and given off by a group of organisms.

READING

Biosynthesis and Breakdown

Living systems are continuously breaking down and building up molecules. Energy links the reactions responsible for both processes (see figure 7.17). For example, when you eat potatoes, your body breaks down the potato starch into glucose molecules. The glucose molecules then can be broken down through cellular respiration.

All of the chemical activities and changes that take place in a cell or an organism are collectively known as its **metabolism.** All chemical reactions in cells are of two types: (1) synthesis and (2) breakdown or decomposition reactions. As shown in figure 7.18, these reactions either build larger, more complex molecules or break down larger molecules into smaller molecules. For example, biosynthesis reactions build proteins from amino acids and, in turn, build tissues, such as muscle and blood, from the

proteins. Generally, breakdown reactions, such as cellular respiration, release energy and biosynthesis reactions, such as photosynthesis, require energy. That energy is provided by food that is made by the plants themselves or that is consumed by animals.

Energy is not the only thing provided by food. In addition to energy, producers and consumers need organic molecules for making sugars, amino acids, and other compounds necessary for life. Food supplies energy as well as organic molecules. Without organic molecules, cells would not have the raw materials needed to repair structures or make new cells.

In the Converting Sunlight into Sugar activity, you learned that plants make their organic molecules from the 3-carbon sugars that are produced through photosynthesis. The food animals ingest, however, is not immediately useful to

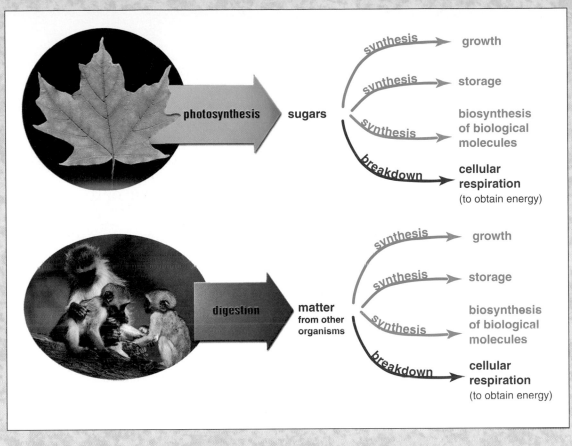

▲ **Figure 7.17 Synthesis and breakdown.** Both plants and the organisms that consume plants use the sugars made during photosynthesis. These sugars are used in biosynthesis and breakdown processes that are necessary for life. Is photosynthesis a biosynthesis or breakdown process? What about digestion?

their bodies. So how do animals get the organic molecules they need from food?

Animals break down food into organic molecules through digestion. Digestion involves the breakdown of large molecules to smaller, simpler molecules. Enzymes that help accomplish the breakdown of food are present in the mouth, stomach, and small intestines. Remember that enzymes catalyze, or speed up, molecular reactions. Final digestion occurs in the small intestine. There, complex food molecules are broken down into their simple components. For example, the sandwich you eat for lunch contains carbohydrates, proteins, and fats that are broken down into sugars, amino acids, glycerol, and fatty acids through digestion. Those organic molecules are small enough to pass through the

small intestine cell membranes and into the bloodstream.

Once in the bloodstream, the organic molecules end up in cells, where they can be converted into intermediate compounds (see figure 7.19). For example, fats can be broken down into glycerol, a 3-carbon molecule, and fatty acids, which are long chains of carbon and hydrogen. Glycerol can be converted into one of the 3-carbon intermediates of glycolysis. The 3-carbon intermediates can enter cellular respiration. Fatty acids can be converted into molecules that enter the Krebs cycle, as shown in figure 7.19. Similarly, proteins can be broken down to amino acids. After the nitrogen-containing group has been removed from the amino acid, the remaining carbon skeleton can be broken down

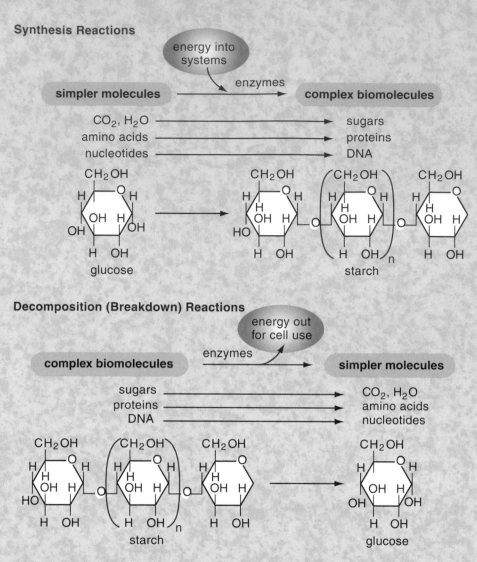

Synthesis Reactions

energy into systems

simpler molecules $\xrightarrow{\text{enzymes}}$ complex biomolecules

CO_2, H_2O $\longrightarrow$ sugars
amino acids $\longrightarrow$ proteins
nucleotides $\longrightarrow$ DNA

glucose $\longrightarrow$ starch

Decomposition (Breakdown) Reactions

energy out for cell use

complex biomolecules $\xrightarrow{\text{enzymes}}$ simpler molecules

sugars $\longrightarrow$ CO_2, H_2O
proteins $\longrightarrow$ amino acids
DNA $\longrightarrow$ nucleotides

starch $\longrightarrow$ glucose

▲ **Figure 7.18 Biosynthesis and decomposition.** The breakdown of glucose from glycogen (animal starch) is an example of decomposition.

into intermediates. The intermediate compounds also can enter glycolysis and the Krebs cycle, as shown in figure 7.19.

Intermediate compounds can be used in biosynthesis reactions as well (see figure 7.19). Organisms require organic molecules for maintenance and growth. For example, each of the many chemical reactions that take place in an organism requires enzymes. Enzymes are synthesized from amino acids. Cell membranes require lipids, and these, too, must be synthesized. Whether a protein, carbohydrate, or fat, each organic molecule must be synthesized from the matter the organism takes in.

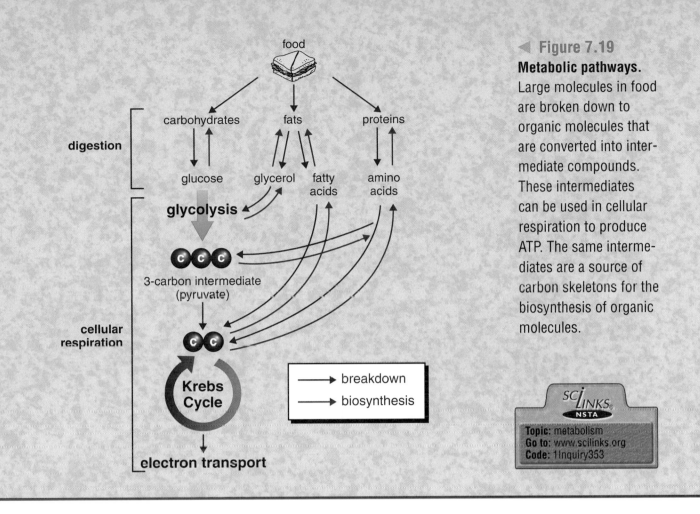

◀ **Figure 7.19**
Metabolic pathways.
Large molecules in food are broken down to organic molecules that are converted into intermediate compounds. These intermediates can be used in cellular respiration to produce ATP. The same intermediates are a source of carbon skeletons for the biosynthesis of organic molecules.

Topic: metabolism
Go to: www.scilinks.org
Code: 1Inquiry353

Reflect and Connect

Team up with a partner and discuss the following tasks and questions. Record your answers in your science notebook.

1. Complete the following tasks to show your understanding of the biosynthesis and breakdown processes.
   a. Use a T-table to list examples of the biosynthesis and breakdown processes. List at least 3 examples of each.
   b. Describe in a few sentences why biosynthesis and breakdown processes are important for all organisms.
2. Figure 7.20 provides an overview of the sources of organic molecules and energy for plants. It also shows the processes by which the molecules and energy are converted from one form to another.
   a. Sketch a similar diagram for an herbivore. Include organic molecules, energy, and biosynthesis and breakdown processes such as digestion and cellular respiration.
   b. Write a caption for your diagram. Your caption should be 1 or more sentences long and briefly describe important parts of your diagram.

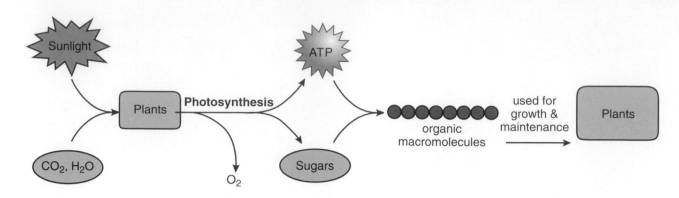

▲ **Figure 7.20 Energy and molecule conversion in plants.** Plants use energy from sunlight and molecules from carbon dioxide and water to produce ATP and sugars. Sugars are converted into organic molecules using ATP for energy. Those organic molecules are used for growth and maintenance of the plant.

3. Why can food be considered a fuel?
4. Is it possible for animals to survive without plants? Why or why not?

Tracing a Carbon Atom and Energy

Biologists can investigate the steps in metabolic processes (biosynthesis and breakdown) by feeding extremely small (or trace) amounts of radioactively labeled matter to laboratory organisms. This labeled matter undergoes changes in molecular structure during chemical reactions within the organisms that consumed it, but the label remains detectable. The labeled matter continues to be traceable through transfers between the organisms. As those changes and transfers occur, the scientists can collect samples and trace the course of events by following the radioactivity.

In Tracing a Carbon Atom and Energy, you work on your own to trace the path of an imaginary radioactively labeled *carbon atom* through the various molecules in which it is organized. The atom begins its journey as part of a carbon dioxide molecule and ends up as part of a muscle protein in a human arm. Your task is to use the knowledge that you gained in this chapter to draw a diagram of what happens to the atom during its journey. Then you explain the source of energy for those events.

Materials
For each student

materials needed to complete the project, such as poster board and markers

1 copy of Tracing a Carbon Atom Scoring Rubric handout

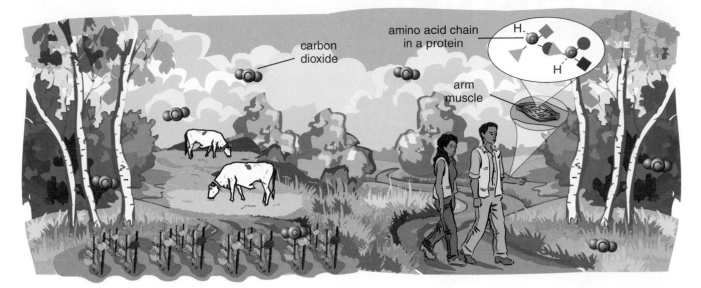

carbon
dioxide

amino acid chain
in a protein

H

H

arm
muscle

▲ **Figure 7.21 You
will trace the path of
an imaginary radioac-
tively labeled *carbon
atom*.** The atom begins
its journey as part of an
atmospheric carbon
dioxide molecule
(shown here) and ends
up as part of a muscle
protein in a human
arm.

Process and Procedure

1. Construct a diagram or another visual aid to show a plausible set of events that could explain how a labeled carbon atom in a molecule of atmospheric carbon dioxide ends up in a human muscle protein.

   More than 1 scenario is possible, but you must show a sequence that actually occurs in nature, and you must be able to justify and explain the sequence that you choose.

2. Consult the Tracing a Carbon Atom Scoring Rubric handout to learn what you need to do to best show your understanding.

3. Label your diagram so that it explains the sequence of events that you have illustrated. Clearly state the following:
   - The type of metabolic process in each step (breakdown or biosynthesis)
   - The energy source for each step
   - The matter source for each step
   - The names of and details describing the metabolic processes that occur in the sequence

Recall that biosynthesis reactions form larger, more complex molecules from smaller, less complex molecules. Some examples of biosynthesis are the formation of starch from glucose and the building of proteins from amino acids.

4. Participate in a class discussion of the questions your teacher raises.

5. After participating in the discussion, add any appropriate changes to steps in your diagram.

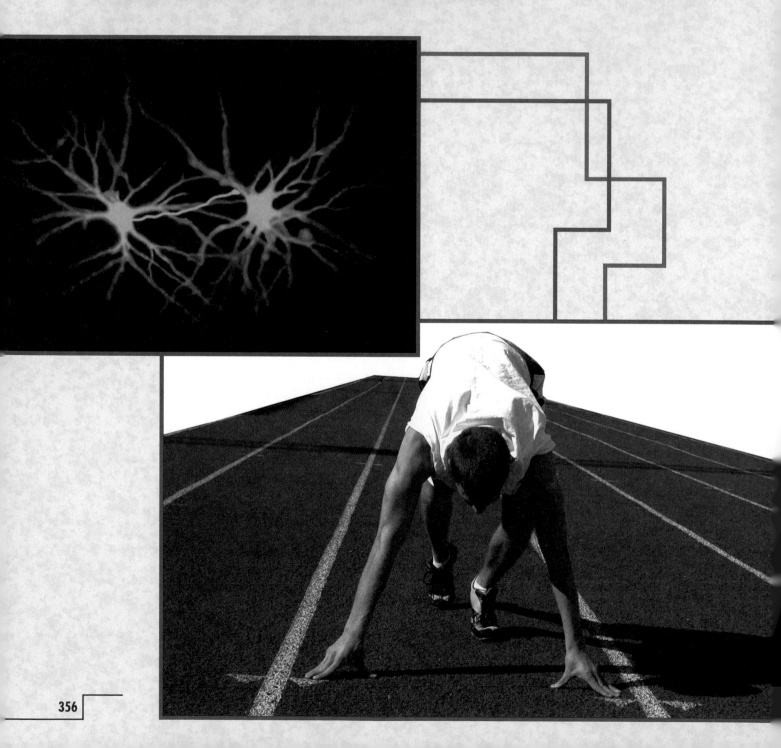

CHAPTER 8

The Nature and Networks of Behavior

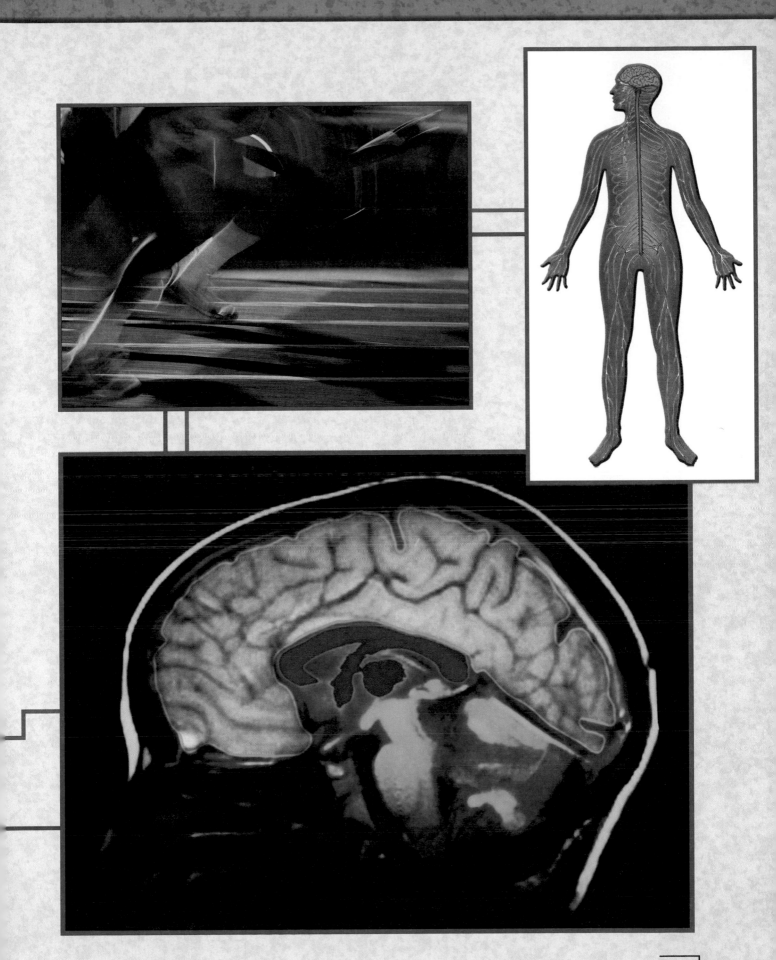

The Nature and Networks of Behavior

You learned in chapter 7, Cells Are Busy Places, that cells and organisms need matter and energy to function. What are some of those functions, and why are they so important? All living organisms are *doing* something continuously. They respond to changes in their external and internal environments. These collective responses and activities are called **behavior**. Chapter 8, The Nature and Networks of Behavior, focuses mostly on how organisms respond to changes in their external environment. Behavior includes all of the actions of animals and plants—actions that help organisms carry out their life activities—actions that help organisms survive, develop, and reproduce. Although we often think of animal behavior, behavior also includes the responses of plants to light, contact, and other triggers.

Study the opening art. How do you think cells and a behavior such as running are related? Often, what someone seems to do so easily actually requires an amazingly complex set of biological actions. Think of what happens when a runner hears the starting gun. First, his eardrums convert the sound into signals and send them to his brain. His brain then processes the signals, makes decisions, stores information, and begins a complex pattern of actions that allows him to begin running down the track. Networks of precisely connected cells regulate those actions. His nervous system's ability to sense and interpret information efficiently and to activate his muscles quickly is a critical factor in determining whether he wins the race. In this chapter, you learn how specialized cells in the nervous system produce behavioral responses such as movement.

Goals for the Chapter

In chapter 8, you investigate the way organisms behave. By the end of this chapter, you will be able to answer the following questions:

- What counts as behavior?
- What kinds of behaviors do organisms exhibit?
- In what ways do those behaviors benefit organisms?
- What types of things influence or determine the behavior of organisms?
- How do the specialized cells of the nervous system allow behavior to occur?

You will be better able to answer those questions by participating in the following activities:

ENGAGE	Been There, Done That
EXPLORE	A School of Guppies
EXPLAIN	The Biological Basis of Behavior
EXPLAIN	Neuron Networks
ELABORATE	Trapping Flies
EVALUATE	What Do You Know?

Linking Question

What behaviors do
animals display?

ENGAGE

Been There, Done That

Key Idea:
Humans have different
behavioral tendencies.

EXPLORE

A School of Guppies

Key Idea:
Animals display
a variety of behaviors that
benefit them in nature.

Linking Question

What influences and
shapes behavior?

EXPLAIN

*The Biological Basis
of Behavior*

Key Ideas:
• Animals display both innate
and learned behaviors that
are influenced by genes and
the environment.
• Behavior promotes individual
survival and reproduction.

The Nature and Networks of Behavior

Linking Question

How does behavior occur?

What Do You Know?

Key Ideas:

• Observational investigations help explain certain animal behaviors.

• Neurons transmit signals to initiate behavioral responses.

How can I use what I have learned to investigate animal behavior and answer questions about behavior and nervous systems?

ELABORATE

Trapping Flies

Key Idea:

Plants respond to stimuli.

CHAPTER

8 | Major Concepts

► BEHAVIOR

• **Behaviors help animals survive in their environments.**

• **Multicellular animals have nervous systems that generate behavior.**

• **Organisms have behavioral responses to internal and external stimuli.**

► DESIGNING INVESTIGATIONS

• **Establishing a procedure to answer a question guides an investigation.**

EXPLAIN

Linking Question

Neuron Networks

Key Ideas:

• Animals detect environmental stimuli through their sense organs.

• Nervous systems are composed of neurons and produce behavior in animals.

Do plants behave?

Been There, Done That

▲ **Figure 8.1**
Parasailing. Would you enjoy becoming a human kite? Parasailing has become a popular water sport in many vacation spots. A para-sail is a parachute attached to a car or boat. Parasailors wear a harness that is clipped to the parachute, and they soar hundreds of feet in the air.

Would you go parasailing? Would you eat something if you didn't know what it was? Those are examples of novelty-seeking behaviors. Novelty seeking is the tendency for a person to seek out and enjoy new and sometimes risky experiences. Novelty seeking is one of the most studied human behaviors. Like other traits, the degree of novelty seeking in the human population varies. High novelty seekers are often more impulsive and like new challenges, while low novelty seekers prefer routines and tend to be more cautious.

Human behavior is studied through observations, self-reporting, and physiological measures such as brain activity. In Been There, Done That, you and a partner report on your own novelty-seeking behaviors by filling out a novelty-seeking survey.

Materials

For each team of two students

2 copies of Novelty-Seeking Survey handout

Process and Procedure

1. How interested are you in trying things you have never done before just for the sake of doing something new or different? Do you think you are more or less likely than your classmates to try something different? To find out, do the following tasks.
   a. Obtain the Novelty-Seeking Survey handout from your teacher.
   b. Begin the survey, keeping track of the number of items on the survey to which you respond yes.
      • Do not write on the survey itself. Keep track of your tally in your science notebook.
      • Complete the task quickly and without talking to other students.
   c. Total your yes responses.
2. Work with a partner to complete the following:
   a. Discuss what you think your total score means.
   b. Predict what the distribution of scores for the entire class might look like. Will scores be evenly distributed, be at one extreme or the other, or be somewhere in the middle?

3. Follow your teacher's instructions to construct a histogram of the scores for your class.

Histograms graphically represent the frequency of a set of numbers.

4. Participate in a class discussion of how you might explain the distribution of scores.
   a. As you study the histogram, discuss what you see and what it means.
   b. Does your class histogram look like a bell-shaped curve? An example is shown in figure 8.2.
   c. What do you know about bell-shaped curves?
   d. Why do you think some individuals are more likely than others to participate in novelty-seeking behaviors?

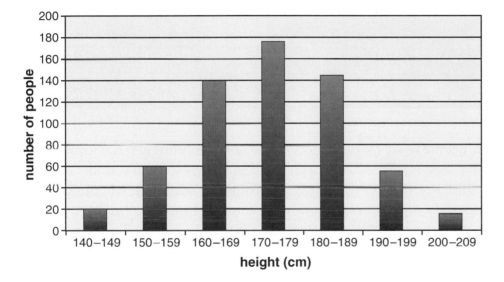

◀ **Figure 8.2**

Example of a bell-shaped curve histogram. Why do you think most of the data fall in the middle of the histogram?

Reflect and Connect

Discuss the following questions with your partner. Record the answers in your science notebook.

1. How do you think novelty-seeking behaviors affect your life? How might those behaviors affect society?
2. Do you think novelty-seeking behaviors are influenced by your genes, by experiences you had growing up, or by both your genes and your experiences? Explain your answer.

Genes are units of hereditary information.

3. Do you think your total score would be different if you took the survey when you were 45 years old? Explain why or why not.
4. Psychologists, sociologists, anthropologists, and behavioral biologists study human behavior. Why do you think it is important to study human behaviors such as novelty seeking? Why might it be important to study behavior in other organisms?

A School of Guppies

Guppies are common aquarium fish. Male guppies are smaller and more brightly colored than females. Why do you think this is?

In Been There, Done That, you explored a human behavioral trait—novelty seeking. Studying novelty seeking helps scientists understand how humans interact with their environment. Humans, of course, are not the only organisms that communicate with others and interact with their environment. Different species of animals display a wide variety of behaviors.

In A School of Guppies, you learn about the behaviors of one animal by investigating guppies (*Poecilia reticulata*). Guppies exhibit a wide variety of behaviors and are easy to care for. They have been used extensively in behavioral research. In this activity, you work in a team and make observations of guppies.

Materials

For each team of four students

1 small aquarium with 1 guppy	1 small container (optional)
1 net	1 felt-tip marker
1 watch or timer	artificial plants (optional)

Cautions

When removing fish from an aquarium, use a net. If you must handle fish, wet your hands thoroughly. Touching fish with dry hands will scrape away mucus and increase the risk of infection.

Process and Procedure

1. As your teacher directs, visit 1 of the aquariums with your team of 4.

2. Quietly observe the guppy in your aquarium. To avoid influencing the behavior of the guppy, do not tap on the aquarium or create other distractions. In your science notebook, make notes of the guppy's behavior.

Notice whether the guppy stays in a particular part of the aquarium. Does the guppy seem to have a routine swimming pattern?

3. The more you know about an organism, the more detailed your observations of that organism can be. Scientists often read the research of other scientists before they begin making observations. Read the following information about guppies to learn more about the organism you are observing. As you read, you might want to stop and make additional observations.

READING

Guppies

Wild populations of guppies are found in tropical streams in northeastern South America and Trinidad, an island off the coast of Venezuela (see figure 8.4). Females have silver-brown coloration. Males are smaller and more brightly colored. They are omnivores, eating fine algae, insect larvae, and small crustaceans. They also eat their own young. Guppies are members of a group of fish called the live-bearers. Rather than lay eggs, females bear live young in broods of one to 25.

Guppies also are common aquarium fish. Many colorful strains of guppies, called fancy guppies, are sold in pet stores. Breeders have selectively bred guppies to produce males with a variety of fin colors and elaborate tail shapes. Females from all strains are almost identical. You might also find feeder guppies in a pet store. Feeder guppies are more closely related to wild guppies and are less colorful than fancy guppies.

▲ **Figure 8.4 Wild guppies live in shallow mountain streams in northeastern South America and Trinidad.** In the 1970s, evolutionary biologist John Endler began studying Trinidad's wild guppies. He found wide variation among the guppies living in different parts of the same streams.

Sleeping and resting
- head straight
- head tucked

Movement
- swimming
- walking
- flying

Care of body
- bathing
- shaking
- running bill through feathers

Social behavior
- approach and quacking
- head bobbing

Feeding
- head submerged
- feet up, almost entire body submerged

▲ **Figure 8.5**

Mallard duck ethogram. You might have seen mallard ducks in a local pond or lake. Domesticated ducks that have white feathers often are found in city parks and exhibit similar behaviors. Have you observed a duck exhibiting any of the behaviors listed?

4. Now that you have observed guppies and have read about them, you can construct an ethogram of guppy behavior. An **ethogram** is a tool scientists use when making observations of animal behavior that helps them organize their observations in a useful way. Essentially, an ethogram is a list of the behaviors an animal exhibits. The list is grouped according to specific categories. Study figure 8.5, which provides an example of an ethogram you might create after observing a mallard duck.

5. Creating an ethogram will help you describe the behavior of your guppy. To create an ethogram, do the following tasks:

a. Divide your team into 2 pairs. In each pair, one of you will be the observer and describe what you see. The other will be the recorder and write down what the observer says.

b. Make observations of the guppy in your aquarium for 2 minutes. At the 1-minute mark, exchange roles so the observer becomes the recorder and the recorder becomes the observer. Each pair can sit on opposite sides of the aquarium.

c. Combine the behaviors your team has recorded into 1 list.

6. The ethogram you have created provides a range of behaviors exhibited by guppies. To learn about a behavior that interests scientists who study guppy populations, read the following paragraph.

One of the behaviors that scientists have studied in wild guppies is schooling behavior. When fish form and swim in groups, which are called schools, they are exhibiting schooling behavior. Some wild guppies exhibit schooling behavior; others do not.

7. Do you think domesticated guppies exhibit schooling behavior? How could you design a simple investigation to find out? Work with your team to do the following tasks:

a. Agree on how you will define *schooling* for your investigation. That is, what behaviors will count as schooling?

You will recall from previous science classes that criteria used to define a targeted action or behavior during an investigation is referred to as an *operational definition*. Why is an operational definition important?

    b. Develop a procedure for your investigation.

- How long will you make observations?
- How many guppies will you observe?
- How will you collect data on the schooling behavior?
- Will you use an ethogram?

    c. Record the procedure in your science notebook.

    d. Have the procedure approved by your teacher before beginning your investigation.

8. Conduct your investigation.

9. Participate in a class discussion of the results of your investigation. Note how the other teams conducted their investigations and the type of data they collected.

10. Work with your team to respond to the following tasks and record your answers in your science notebook.

    a. Describe the design of your investigation.

    b. Compare the data that your team collected with the data from other teams.

    c. Do you think some of the investigations were designed better than others? Why or why not?

    d. What can you infer from the data that the teams collected?

    e. How would you design an investigation if you had more guppies and more time?

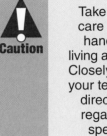

Caution Take extra care when handling living animals. Closely follow your teacher's directions regarding special handling.

Reflect and Connect

Work with a partner to record in your science notebook the answers to the following questions:

1. Do you think the guppies that you observed exhibited schooling behavior? Why or why not?

2. How might schooling behavior be beneficial for wild guppies?

3. Scientists also investigate novelty-seeking behaviors in non-human animals. Animals exhibit novel behaviors when they explore or investigate something new or strange in their environment. In what ways might novelty behaviors be a risk or a benefit to guppy survival?

4. Do you think schooling displayed by guppies is an inherited behavior or a behavior they learn? Explain your answer.

5. What other behaviors of guppies might be important to their survival? How might you design an investigation to study those behaviors?

The Biological Basis of Behavior

While you were investigating guppies and considering aspects of their behavior, more questions about behavior began to come up. What counts as behavior? Where do the behaviors come from? What purpose do certain behaviors serve? In The Biological Basis of Behavior, you will begin to develop better answers for questions such as those.

Behavior refers to the way an organism acts. Animals, for example, display a wide variety of behaviors toward the living and nonliving things around them. Some of those behaviors look simple; others look complex. Scientists who study animal behavior in nature ask 3 main questions: (1) What behaviors do animals display? (2) Why do different species display different behaviors? (3) What physiological mechanisms cause these behaviors to occur? In The Biological Basis of Behavior, you focus on Questions 1 and 2. During the next two class periods, you work with a partner to identify the types of behaviors several species display and learn some of the reasons why different species behave differently. In the next activity, Neuron Networks, you learn about Question 3—the physiological basis for behavior.

▶ **Figure 8.6**

Animals display a wide variety of behaviors. What behaviors do they have in common? What behaviors are unique?

Part I: Animal Behavior

Materials

Process and Procedure

1. In Been There, Done That, you were asked to consider whether novelty-seeking behaviors were influenced by genes, by your experiences, or by both. Read Behavior: Learned or Innate? with a partner to learn more about what scientists currently understand about behavior.

READING

Behavior: Learned or Innate?

Scientists have observed that animals display an enormous range of behaviors. Snakes flick out their tongues; spiders spin intricate webs of silk; honeybees remove diseased larvae from the hive; monkeys wash their food in water before eating it; certain birds perform mating dances; and humans drive around in cars. How did those behaviors come about?

Scientists talk about two major categories of behavior: innate behavior and learned behavior. Scientists have discovered that all behaviors fall somewhere along a continuum from those that are primarily innate to those that are primarily learned.

Innate behavior is a behavior, the capacity for which an organism is born with. Innate behavior does not depend on an organism's experience. Some innate behaviors, such as sucking or crying, occur as soon as an organism is hatched or born. Others appear later in life. The familiar term *instinct* refers to innate behaviors. In general, an **instinct** is a response to a specific stimulus that does not require learning or practice. Feeding behaviors of young animals

are typical instincts. Environmental influences may trigger an instinct, but they do not explain it. In many cases, it is difficult to determine whether experience has influenced a behavior that appears to be instinctive. Some examples of innate behaviors are shown in figure 8.7.

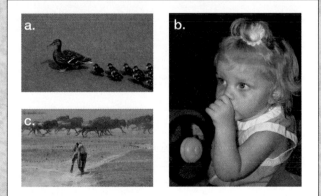

▲ **Figure 8.7 Innate behaviors.** (a) Many species of birds, such as these mallard ducks, will follow the first moving thing they see. (b) Human babies and other baby animals begin the sucking response as soon as they are born. (c) Fleeing from danger is a behavior observed in many animals—and in humans.

Some innate behaviors do not change despite different settings. For example, dogs that have spent their entire lives indoors will attempt to bury a bone by scratching the carpet as if they were digging. Captive raccoons go through the motions of dunking and washing their food in water even when water is not available. These innate patterns of behavior are characteristic of a given species.

Learned behaviors, on the other hand, consist of all of the responses an organism develops as a direct result of specific experiences. An individual's capacity for learning has an innate component, but what is actually learned depends on the setting and the context. Learned behaviors, then, are those that are acquired during an individual's lifetime through experience. Most animals have the capacity to learn to behave in new ways. Learned behaviors range from simple behaviors such as tying a shoe to complex behaviors used to cook a meal or learn algebra. Other examples include dogs learning to sit on command and parrots learning to imitate the human voice.

One famous example of learned behavior occurs in some macaque monkeys, as shown in figure 8.8. In the early 1950s, on an island off Japan, scientists had begun feeding macaque monkeys potatoes to get closer to the monkeys and to make observations. In 1953, a scientist saw a young female macaque monkey wash a sweet potato in a stream before eating it. Within a few months, the monkey's playmates and mother were also seen washing their potatoes. Within 5 years, more than 3/4 of the individuals in the population were washing their potatoes before eating them. Within 10 years, almost all of the monkeys in the population were washing their potatoes. They are still doing it today. The macaques apparently prefer eating clean potatoes to dirty ones and learn the behavior from each other.

▲ **Figure 8.8 Macaque washing a potato.** Potato washing is a learned behavior in some populations of macaque monkeys.

2. Take a few minutes to study the behaviors pictured in figure 8.9. Then draw a line in your science notebook. Label the left end of the line "Innate" and the right end of the line "Learned." Place each behavior pictured at a particular point along the continuum to designate to what extent you think each behavior is innate or learned. Be prepared to explain your reasoning.

3. Read Thinking Biologically about Behavior to learn about a range of behaviors and their importance.

▲ Figure 8.9
Behavioral examples. To what extent is each behavior innate or learned?

Thinking Biologically about Behavior

Animals display an amazing variety of behaviors. Read FYI—Categories of Behavior to learn more about common animal behaviors. For example, animals eat, drink, defecate, mate, groom, move, play, hide, sleep, and fight; some even use tools. Scientists carefully observe and describe behaviors, investigate the significance of behaviors, and study their physiological basis.

A behavior has a biological significance if it promotes individual survival and reproduction. Most major patterns of behavior that animals display promote survival and reproduction in some way. Those behaviors help animals adapt to their environments and allow them to survive as conditions change. For different animals in different habitats, the behaviors, of course, may be quite different. Organisms in desert habitats need to exhibit behaviors that allow them to survive during the hot summers. Organisms in alpine habitats need to exhibit behaviors that allow them to survive during the cold winters. To learn how animals respond to their environments, read the How Do Organisms Adjust to Environmental Changes? sidebar.

4. Complete Steps 4a–d to examine investigations of animal behavior. The investigations provide insight into the biological significance, or advantage, of a specific behavior in a bird, an insect, and a lizard.

   a. Divide into teams of 3 as directed by your teacher.

   b. Select an investigation from Investigating the Significance of Behavior. Each team member should select a different investigation.

   c. Answer the question that follows, which relates to the investigation you just read. Record your answer in your science notebook.

   What does this investigation reveal about the biological significance of

   • eggshell removal in black-headed gulls?

   • power dive behavior in moths?

   • behavioral fevers in desert iguanas?

   d. Describe the investigation to your teammates and explain the biological significance of the behavior you read about. That is, explain how this behavior might help the organism survive and reproduce.

READING

Investigating the Significance of Behavior

▲ Figure 8.10 **Black-headed gull.** Black-headed gulls remove broken eggshells from their nests. What is the significance of this behavior?

Investigation 1: Eggshell Removal in Black-Headed Gulls

Black-headed gulls nest along the sandy beaches of northern Europe. In a mass of grass and straw on the ground, the female lays light-brown eggs with dark speckles. Both parents take turns sitting on the nest to keep the eggs warm. When a chick hatches, the parent on duty picks up the broken eggshell in its beak and dumps the shell far from the nest. The inside of the shell is shiny white.

A scientist investigated the significance of this behavior by conducting the following experiment: The scientist placed broken eggshells at various distances from gull nests to see what would happen. He discovered that nests with broken eggshells nearby were three times more likely to lose eggs to predators than nests without eggshells nearby.

Investigation 2: Power Dives in Moths

Bats feed on flying insects such as moths, using echolocation to locate the insects. A bat emits high-pitched sounds that bounce off flying insects and return to the bat as echoes. The bat uses the echoes to pinpoint the location of the insect and to capture it in flight. Scientists noticed that some individuals of a moth species reacted to the sounds of a nearby bat by doing a power dive, but others did not. In a power dive, moths fly around erratically and unpredictably (see figure 8.11).

▲ **Figure 8.11 Moth power dive.** Moths display a power dive when a bat is near.

The scientists investigated the biological significance of power dive behavior by observing 402 encounters between bats and moths. The scientists recorded whether a moth went into a power dive when a bat approached and whether the bat ate the moth. They discovered that moths displaying power dives in the presence of a bat had a 40 percent higher survival rate than moths that did not.

Investigation 3: Behavioral Fevers in Lizards

Lizards are **ectothermic** animals. They regulate their body temperatures by moving between hot and cool places in the environment. Mammals and birds are **endothermic**. They regulate their body temperatures through internal physical processes.

Scientists observed that healthy desert iguanas maintained an average body temperature of 38° Celsius (C). Diseased iguanas kept their body temperature around 42°C (see figure 8.12). Scientists inferred that the increase in temperature was not due to the disease because sick iguanas kept at 38°C did not develop a fever. Scientists wondered

▲ **Figure 8.12 Desert iguana.** Diseased desert iguanas maintain a warmer body temperature.

whether sick iguanas were maintaining a warmer body temperature by staying in warm places longer than they did when they were well.

Scientists conducted an experiment to investigate the possible biological significance of this type of behavior in lizards. In the experiment, they infected two groups of healthy lizards with disease-producing bacteria. They kept one group at the temperature lizards maintain when they are healthy (38°C). They kept the other group at the temperature lizards maintain when they are sick (42°C). The graph in figure 8.13 shows the survival rates of the two groups over a week.

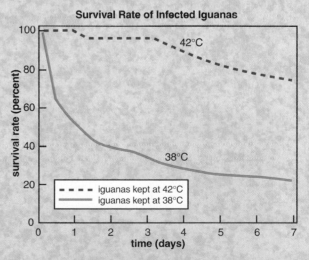

▲ **Figure 8.13 Survival rates at different temperatures.** This graph shows the different survival rates of sick lizards kept at different temperatures.

Part I

1. What are some general statements you can make about how behaviors, such as those described in the investigations you just read, contribute to the survival of an individual and a population?

2. What are some behaviors of humans that contribute to the ability to survive in climates with a range of temperatures? In your response, include examples that address very cold conditions as well as examples that address very hot conditions. How are the behaviors similar to and different from the behaviors of other organisms you just read about?

FYI

Categories of Behavior

Animals display a wide variety of behaviors. Plants and bacteria behave, too, although their range of behaviors is more limited than that of animals. Biologists classify behavior into different categories based primarily on the result of the behavior. This FYI describes some of those categories, particularly for species in the animal kingdom.

Body maintenance involves movements that keep the body clean of dirt and parasites. Sometimes animals groom themselves, and sometimes they are groomed by others. Grooming often involves the use of fingers and mouths. Sometimes

it involves the use of tools, such as when chimpanzees use pieces of wood to remove food from the teeth of fellow chimps.

Exploration involves movements that help an animal become familiar with its environment. Through exploratory behavior, animals obtain information about the location of food, mates, shelter, water, and other important features of the environment.

Ingestion involves taking in food, liquids, and oxygen. There are five basic ways that animals ingest food: carnivory (eating other animals),

Chimpanzees grooming. Grooming is one example of a body maintenance behavior.

Lions eating. Lions are carnivores—they eat other animals.

herbivory (eating plants), omnivory (eating animals and plants), filtration (filtering water that contains food particles), and parasitism (living in or on another organism and obtaining nourishment by consuming the organism's tissues).

Locomotion involves movement from place to place in an environment. Organisms move by beating cilia (short, hairlike appendages on a cell) or flagella (long appendages on a cell), changing body shape, wriggling the body, expelling water, or moving limbs. These ostriches (*Struthio camelus*) are flightless birds that run on their hind limbs to get about.

Ostriches running. Ostriches can run up to 70 kilometers per hour. They also use their powerful legs to defend themselves.

Play involves behaviors that do not appear to be directly related to survival. However, biologists consider play to be adaptive because it provides animals with exercise and an opportunity to develop and practice body movements and social skills. Play behavior is common in young mammals such as these Eurasian lynx (*Lynx lynx*).

Eurasian lynx kittens. Scientists think that play behaviors in young animals may help them develop hunting skills and other skills that are important for their survival.

Predator avoidance involves behaviors that protect an animal against predators. Animals avoid predators by actively resisting, hiding from predators, escaping, and displaying warning coloration.

Reproductive behavior involves the production of offspring. Reproduction often involves a variety of behaviors having to do with courtship, mating, and care of the young. These Colorado potato beetles (*Leptinotarsa decemlineata*) are mating.

Colorado potato beetles. All living things reproduce. Reproduction is necessary to maintain populations of species, such as these potato beetles.

Sheltering behavior results in animals being protected from the physical environment and from other animals. Some animals, such as lizards, find shelter simply by slipping into a rock crevice. Other animals create shelter by modifying the environment, such as when beavers construct a lodge out of branches and mud.

Sleep is a prolonged period of inactivity and decreased responsiveness that occurs at regular intervals. Animals typically sleep in certain locations and in certain postures. A wide variety of animals sleep, including mammals, birds, reptiles, amphibians, insects, and fish.

Thermoregulation involves regulating body temperature. Ectotherms—so-called cold-blooded animals such as reptiles and insects—regulate their body temperature through their behavior. For example, desert lizards regulate their body temperature by moving in and out of sunny areas. Endotherm—so-called warm-blooded animals such as mammals and birds—regulate their body temperature primarily through internal physical processes. Behavior often plays a secondary role. For example, when many mammals (including humans) become chilled, they curl up, which

Dog panting. What other behaviors help animals regulate their body temperature?

conserves heat. When they become overheated, they stretch out their limbs, which dissipates heat. Dogs dissipate heat by panting.

Tool use involves animals manipulating objects in a way that enhances or extends some aspect of their behavior. For example, some birds use cactus spines or twigs to dislodge insects from inaccessible areas. Chimpanzees use sticks to remove ter-

mites from holes and crumple leaves to use as sponges to soak up water for drinking. Humans's use of tools, of course, is extensive.

Rhythmic behavior includes behaviors that occur regularly in a cycle. For example, the behaviors of many animals are organized around a daily cycle. Nocturnal species such as bats are active at night, but not during the day. Diurnal species such as parrots are active during the day, but not at night.

Social behavior involves animals interacting with one another and frequently involves displays of aggression, cooperation, and competition. In some species such as the orangutan, individuals lead relatively solitary lives and interact socially only when they encounter each other in the forest. In other species such as honeybees, individuals live in complex and tightly integrated societies. Through body movements that look like dances, honeybees communicate to other honeybees in the hive the direction and distance to food sources.

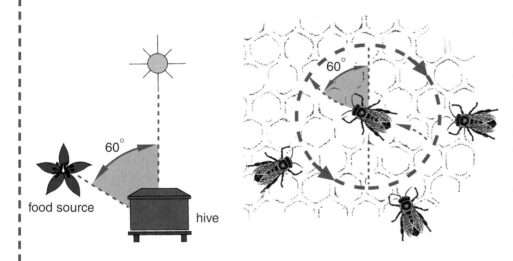

Honeybee communication. Honeybees use the position of the Sun as a compass. Inside the hive, a honeybee indicates the distance and direction of a food source by performing a dance for other honeybees.

How Do Organisms Adjust to Environmental Changes?

Environments vary across the globe. Even within a single environment conditions may vary drastically. The surface temperature of a sand dune in Death Valley, for example, may climb to over 58°C (136° Fahrenheit [F]) in the day and drop to below 0°C (32°F) at night. Individual organisms well adapted to this range of temperatures can respond to such drastic changes in the environment through changes in their behavior, physiology, and appearance or form.

The quickest response of many animals to an unfavorable change in the environment is to move to a new location— sometimes just a few feet away! Rainbow trout, for example, can sense the heat and lower oxygen levels of the upper zone in a lake and move to deeper water that is cooler and that has more oxygen. Other animals are able to modify their immediate environment by cooperative social behavior. Honeybees, for example, cool the inside of their hives on hot days by collectively beating their wings. By doing so, the bees are able to keep the hive at a set temperature, within one or two degrees.

In general, physiological responses change more slowly than behavioral reactions. If you moved from Galveston, Texas, which is at sea level, to Santa Fe, New Mexico, which is about 2,135 m (7,045 ft) above sea level, one physiological response would be an increase in your red blood cell count. This reaction would take several weeks to develop. Some physiological responses are faster, such as the contraction of blood vessels close to the skin surface when you go outside on a cold day. This contraction helps reduce heat loss.

Many small- to medium-sized animals in northern regions tolerate low temperature and food scarcity by entering a state of prolonged dormancy, called hiberna-tion (see photograph). True hibernators, such as ground squirrels, jumping mice, and marmots, prepare for hibernation by building up large amounts of body fat. Entering into hibernation is a gradual process. After a series of "test drops," during which the body temperature decreases a few degrees and then returns to normal, the animals cool to within a degree or two of the surrounding air temperature. Metabolism decreases to a fraction of normal. Some mammals, such as bears, raccoons, badgers, and opossums, enter a state of prolonged sleep in winter with little or no decrease in body temperature. This is not considered true hibernation.

Organisms may react to some change in the environment with growth responses that change their form or internal anatomy.

Golden mantle ground squirrels, Spermophilus lateralis, are true hibernators. They spend up to eight months in hibernation.

One example is the arrowleaf plant, which can grow on land or in water. The leaves of submerged plants are flexible and lack a waxy surface. This allows the leaves to absorb nutrients from the surrounding water. Arrowleaf plants that live on land, however, have extensive root systems and more rigid leaves covered with a thick surface that retards water loss. In general, plants are more capable than animals of showing this range of response to environmental change.

Part II: What Influences Behavior?

Materials

Process and Procedure

1. Now that you have a better understanding about behavior as a continuum from innate to learned, read Nature or Nurture to better understand how genes and the environment contribute to the expression of behavior.

READING

Nature or Nurture

Scientists no longer talk about behavior as the result of *either* genes or the environment because *both* genes and the environment influence the development and expression of behaviors to varying degrees. When scientists talk about the environment as an influence on behavior, they include in this discussion conditions such as habitat, climate, and temperature, but also all the experiences animals have, including what they have learned. You might have heard this idea referred to as *nature* (genetics) and *nurture* (learning and environment). Study figure 8.14 to begin to look at this idea the way scientists do. Consider ways this important idea might be demonstrated in the guppies you just observed and in yourself as you go about your daily activities.

▲ **Figure 8.14 Genes and the environment.** Both genes and the environment influence the development and expression of behavior.

Scientists have discovered the genetic basis for a wide variety of behaviors in animals. Although several genes influence most behaviors, some behaviors are influenced by only one gene. For example, some strains of fruit flies tend to search widely for food and some strains stay close to home. A single gene controls this behavior. Flies that search widely for food have a different gene (or a different form of the gene) than the flies that search close to home. The genes produce different enzymes that affect the flies's nervous systems, which control this behavior. In humans, the ability to taste certain chemicals is controlled by a single gene. Breeding experiments with crickets have revealed that the hybrid offspring of parents from different species have a chirp pattern that is intermediate between the parents.

Those examples show the strong influence that genes can have on certain behaviors. Other behaviors, however, tend to be more strongly affected by environmental influences such as life experiences, learning, and habitat. For

Topic: behavior
Go to: www.scilinks.org
Code: 1Inquiry378

example, chimpanzees have a great capacity for learning, but the learning potential and the behaviors learned are affected by environmental factors such as social experience, nutrition, and disease.

Species vary in the degree to which genes and environment influence their behavior. Figure 8.15 shows the influence of genes and environment on behaviors in different groups of animals. In which groups is the genetic influence stronger? In which groups is the environmental influence (that is, life experiences and learning) stronger?

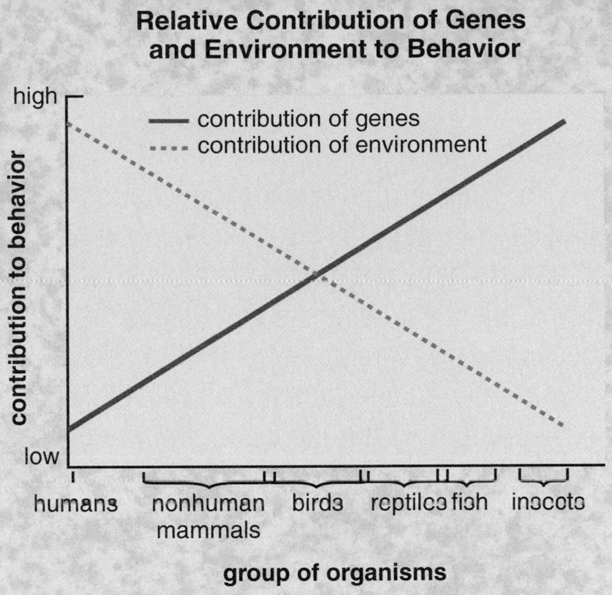

▶ **Figure 8.15 Genes and the environment graph.** Animals vary in the degree to which genes and the environment influence their behavior.

Relative Contribution of Genes and Environment to Behavior

— contribution of genes
---- contribution of environment

contribution to behavior: high / low

group of organisms: humans, nonhuman mammals, birds, reptiles fish, insects

2. With your partner, study figure 8.15 and consider the following question: What probably has the largest influence on schooling behavior in fish—genes or the environment?

3. Humans and mammals tend to exhibit behavior that is influenced more by the environment than the behavior of other species. Answer the following questions about behavior in humans.
   a. How do you think behaviors resulting from life experiences may help humans adapt to certain changes in their environment? Consider, as an example, how humans might deal with a change in the types of food available during summer and winter.
   b. Give 2 examples of how you think people's culture may affect the behavior of humans. For example, do you dress the same way as someone from China or Iceland?

4. In Been There, Done That, you recorded the novelty-seeking scores for students in your class. Recall that novelty-seeking behaviors are the tendency for people to be interested in and to seek out new and sometimes risky experiences.
   To what extent do you think genes influence the differences in novelty-seeking behaviors among people? Do you think genes play a big role, a moderate role, or no role in explaining those differences among people? Select a specific example of a novelty-seeking behavior, record your ideas in your science notebook, and explain your reasoning.

5. Read Twin Studies to learn how genes and the environment contribute to novelty-seeking behaviors.

Twin Studies

To discover the relative contribution of genes and environment to novelty-seeking behaviors, scientists have compared identical and fraternal twins. Identical twins are genetically the same because they develop in the mother from the same fertilized egg that splits apart early in development. Fraternal twins, on the other hand, develop from two different fertilized eggs, so they share only 50 percent of their genes.

Scientists have compared the novelty-seeking scores of identical twins who have been raised in different families with the scores of fraternal twins who have been raised in different families. Through studies such as these, scientists have been able to determine whether genes or the environment contribute more to individual differences in novelty-seeking behaviors. Before you examine novelty-seeking behavior, you will examine the trait of height in twins.

If identical twins raised apart are more similar in height than fraternal twins raised apart, then it is likely that genes influence height more strongly than the environment. Since twins from both pairs were raised apart, environmental factors seem to be less of a factor. Therefore, the remaining difference between identical and fraternal twins is presumed to be genetic. If

▲ Figure 8.16 **Identical twins.** Would you expect identical or fraternal twins to be more similar in height?

identical twins were not more similar in height than fraternal twins, then environmental factors would be considered more of a factor in determining height. What does figure 8.16 suggest about whether height is determined by genes or the environment?

Studies show that height between identical twins is more similar than height between fraternal twins who are raised apart. This suggests that height differences are more strongly influenced by genes than by the environment. In fact, 80–90 percent of height differences among people is due to genetic variation.

Although scientists debate the extent to which human behaviors are genetically based, twin studies show that at least some complex human behaviors are influenced by genes as well as the environment. People's ability to learn language, for example, appears to be influenced by specific genes that direct the development of parts of the nervous system specialized for learning language. A baby's environment, specifically the language the baby hears from his or her parents, however, determines what language he or she will learn. This type of flexibility in certain behaviors, such as language, is a characteristic of humans.

▲ Figure 8.17 **Language.** Both genes and the environment influence a person's ability to learn language.

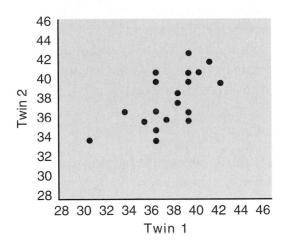

a. Identical twins

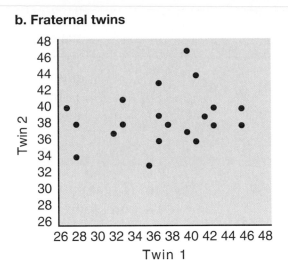

b. Fraternal twins

6. Study the graphs in figure 8.18. The graph in figure 8.18a shows the association between the novelty-seeking scores of identical twins who were raised apart. The graph in figure 8.18b shows the association between the novelty-seeking scores of fraternal twins who were raised apart.

   Most of the methods in behavioral genetic research estimate genetic and environmental effects using statistics. **Correlation** is a statistic that indicates how closely two measurements are related. Points that are clustered along the lines on the graphs indicate a correlation. When points are more randomly scattered, there is less or no correlation.

7. Discuss with your partner the following questions about the graphs shown in figure 8.18. Record your best ideas in your science notebook.

   a. Compare the novelty-seeking graphs for identical and fraternal twins. What similarities do you see? What differences do you see?

   b. What does this tell you about the relative influence of genes and the environment on differences in novelty-seeking behaviors among humans? Explain your reasoning.

   c. If the correlation for a trait is perfect between identical twins raised apart, then all of the data points will fall on a straight line and the correlation value will be 1. This means that a trait is influenced entirely by genes. If the points are widely scattered and no correlation exists, then a trait is influenced entirely by the environment. If a correlation exists but the points are slightly scattered, then the correlation will be less than 1. This means that a trait is influenced both by genes and the environment. The degree of correlation tells how much genes influence a trait.

▲ **Figure 8.18**
Twins scatter plots.
Comparisons of the novelty-seeking scores between pairs of (a) identical twins and (b) fraternal twins raised apart.

Look at the correlation of novelty-seeking scores for identical twins raised apart. Write "What I see" and "What it means" highlight comments for both graphs. Provide general answers to the following questions: To what extent do genes influence novelty-seeking behaviors? To what extent does the environment influence novelty-seeking behaviors?

Reflect and Connect

Organize into teams of 3 and discuss the following questions. Record your answers in your science notebook.

1. Explain why you think scientists study the behaviors of identical and fraternal twins to discover how genes and the environment influence behavior.
2. Animal behavior must be flexible (adjust to change) to help animals survive in different conditions. Which do you think has more of an effect on the flexibility of an animal's behavior— genes or the environment (life experiences)? Explain your answer.
3. Draw an organizer like the one shown in figure 8.19. Fill out the organizer for innate behavior.

► **Figure 8.19**
Understanding words. Completing an organizer like this for a word you just learned is one strategy to help you better understand the word.

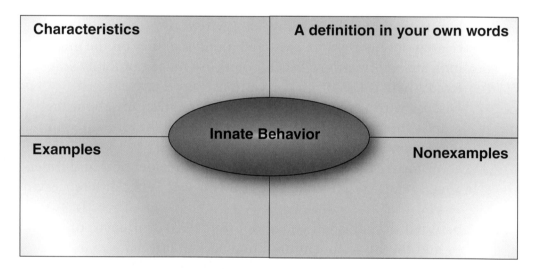

Characteristics	A definition in your own words
Examples	**Nonexamples**

Innate Behavior

4. Animals often live in unpredictable environments. In order to survive, their behavior must be flexible enough to deal with change. For example, in hunting and gathering societies, humans live in areas where the availability of prey can change in unpredictable ways. How do you think the behavioral flexibility of humans allows them to survive in those areas? Give 2 examples.

Neuron Networks

By now, you have a better idea about the range of behaviors some animals display and the way those behaviors contribute to their survival. But what physiological mechanisms are going on inside animals that allow the behaviors to occur?

Animals, including humans, sense the environment in various ways and respond by displaying certain behaviors. How do you think animals sense the environment? Do you think all animals sense the environment in the same ways? What factors in the environment do you think animals respond to? What do you think causes behavioral responses?

To begin answering those questions in more detail, you and a partner investigate the behavior of termites in Neuron Networks. This activity sets the stage for learning more about the physiological basis of behavior.

Part I: Animal Sense Organs

Materials
For each team of two students

1 magnifying glass

1–2 living worker or soldier termites (genus *Reticulitermes*)

2 sheets of white photocopy paper

1 bag of termite investigation materials

Cautions

Termites are easy to injure because they are small and soft. Remember, termites are living creatures, so handle them with care and treat them humanely.

Process and Procedure

Multicellular animals have organs that are specialized for sensing different environmental factors (or stimuli), such as light, sounds, objects, smells, and tastes. Those organs help the animals identify changes that occur in their environment. In Part I, you investigate how termites respond to a certain change in their environment.

1. To investigate termite behavior in response to change in the animal's environment, organize into teams of 2.
2. Obtain 2 sheets of white photocopy paper, a bag of termite investigation materials, and 2 termites from your teacher.

▼ **Figure 8.20**
Redirecting a termite's movement. To move the termite without harming it, block the termite's path without touching it.

Your teacher will give you the termites on a small card. Termites are soft-bodied insects and must not be pinched. As shown in figure 8.20, use a paintbrush or cotton swab to block or redirect the termites as you take them back to your desk. *Do not* try to pick up your termites with your fingers or push them around with the paintbrush.

3. Gently place the termites on a sheet of white paper. Observe the behavior of the termites for 1 minute. Record your observations in your science notebook.

4. Now investigate how termites respond to a specific change in the environment by doing the following tasks:

    a. Set the termites aside on the card your teacher gave you.

    b. Use your colored pens to draw some lines and shapes on the sheet of white paper.

    c. Place the termites back on the paper with your drawings.

    d. Observe the termites's behavior. Record your observations in your science notebook.

5. What questions come to mind as you watch the termites? Work with your partner to select 1 question about the termites's behavior that you think you might be able to answer with an investigation. Record your question in your science notebook.

6. Predict the answer to your question and provide an explanation. Record both in your science notebook.

7. Discuss with your partner how you will make observations and conduct a brief investigation to test your question. You can use the 2nd sheet of paper to draw more lines and shapes.

8. Conduct your investigation and record all observations in your science notebook. Pay attention to the amount of time your teacher gives you to conduct your investigation.

9. Use the information and observations that you gathered to develop a possible explanation for the termite behavior that you observed and to develop an answer to your question.

Recall from chapter 1, The Process of Scientific Inquiry, that explanations must be based on evidence.

10. Be prepared to share with the class the question that you tested, the results of your investigation, and your explanation.

11. Participate in a class discussion about the termite investigation. In your science notebook, summarize the class's results of the termite investigations.

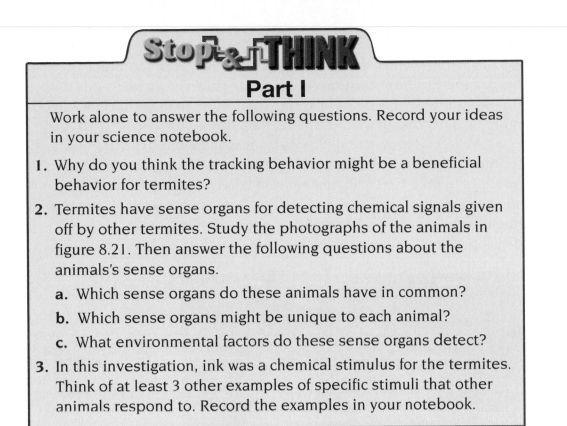

Stop & THINK

Part I

Work alone to answer the following questions. Record your ideas in your science notebook.

1. Why do you think the tracking behavior might be a beneficial behavior for termites?

2. Termites have sense organs for detecting chemical signals given off by other termites. Study the photographs of the animals in figure 8.21. Then answer the following questions about the animals's sense organs.

   a. Which sense organs do these animals have in common?

   b. Which sense organs might be unique to each animal?

   c. What environmental factors do these sense organs detect?

3. In this investigation, ink was a chemical stimulus for the termites. Think of at least 3 other examples of specific stimuli that other animals respond to. Record the examples in your notebook.

◀ **Figure 8.21**
Diverse animals. What sense organs does each animal have?

Part II: The Nervous System Controls Behavior in Animals

Behaviors such as the one you just investigated in termites are fascinating to study. Results of one study lead to more questions for further study. At this point in your exploration, you are likely asking more detailed questions about what the purpose of specific behaviors is, as well as what is actually going on inside animals, such as the termites, when they display certain behaviors. What is going on at the level of the cell? How can you connect what you have learned in chapter 6, Cells: The Building Blocks of Life, and chapter 7 to what might be going on here? In this part of the activity, you begin to develop more detailed answers.

▶ **Figure 8.22**

Neurons in the brain. Neurons are specialized cells that make up the nervous system. This image shows neurons in the brain. How do these cells differ from the cells you observed in chapter 6?

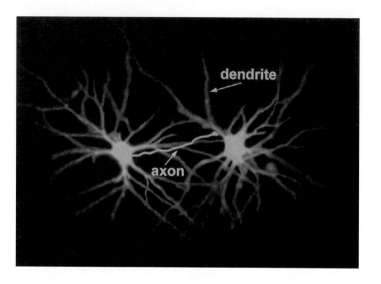

Materials

Process and Procedure

1. Read Having the Nerve to Respond to learn about what cells are responsible for behavior and how changes in electric charges generate nerve impulses.

   a. Look ahead to the questions in Step 2 to guide your reading.

   b. As you read, begin sketching details of the nervous system. Add to or redraw your diagram as you continue to read and learn more details.

   c. Include in your diagram notes that are relevant to this discussion, identifying what you already know about cells.

   d. Record your questions along with your sketches and see how many of your questions you have answered by the end of the reading.

Having the Nerve to Respond

Nervous systems have two basic functions in multicellular animals—to control responses to the external environment and to coordinate the functions of internal organs. A change in the environment that causes an organism to respond is called a **stimulus.** A stimulus can be either internal or external. The nervous system interprets stimuli and coordinates other organ systems to respond to the stimuli. However, there is great diversity in how nervous systems are organized. As shown in figure 8.23, hydra have a nerve net—the simplest type of nervous system. Unlike the hydra, simple worms such as planarians have a small brain and information travels along two nerve cords. Grasshoppers and other insects have a brain, a nerve cord that runs the length of the body, and better-developed sense organs to coordinate more complex behaviors. For example, the social behavior of bees, wasps, and ants is often elaborate.

For most animals other than the simplest invertebrates (animals without backbones), the

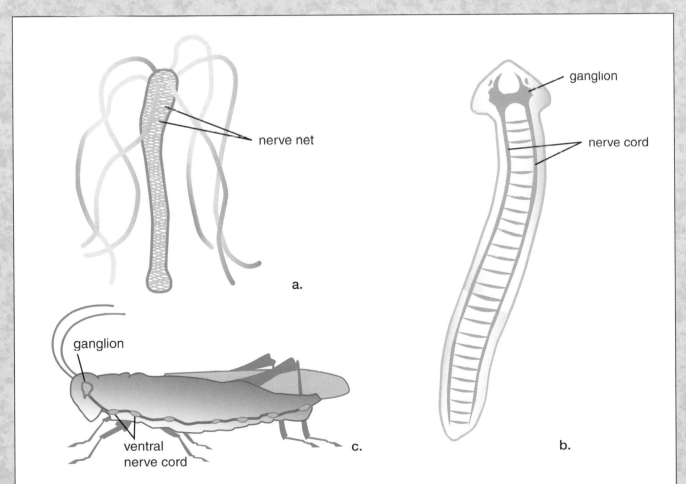

▲ **Figure 8.23 Nervous system structure.** (a) Hydra have a nerve net made up of simple interconnected neurons. (b) A planarian has a nervous system with two nerve cords, many neurons, and a small brain. (c) Insects have a nervous system with a brain, many neurons, and more advanced sense organs.

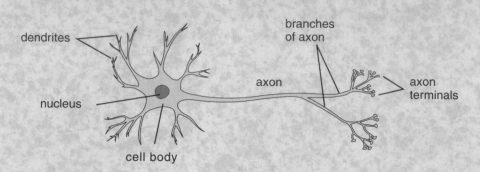

▶ **Figure 8.24 Neurons.** Neurons are cells that are specialized for receiving stimuli and for transmitting the information to other cells. In which direction does the signal travel?

nervous system is made up of specialized cells called **neurons**. As shown in figure 8.24, a neuron usually consists of three main parts—the cell body, dendrites, and the axon. The cell body of the neuron contains a nucleus, cytoplasm, and other organelles such as mitochondria. The **dendrites** receive signals from the external environment and from other neurons. Dendrites are usually short and fibrous, and neurons usually have many of them. The **axon** sends signals to other neurons or to other cells, such as muscle or gland cells. Most neurons (but not all) have only one axon, although the axon may have many branches at its end. Some axons in humans can be over 1 meter in length. How is a neuron different from other body cells you learned about in chapter 6?

A neuron cannot function by itself to regulate the body's functioning. Neurons can relay information

only when they are connected with other neurons (see figure 8.25). Imagine that someone steps on your big toe. Neurons form an elaborate network that enables a signal received by a neuron in your big toe to be processed by neurons in your brain. Then neurons in your brain send the signal to muscles to allow you to say "ouch" and to pick up your foot. Neurons connect with each other in a specific way that is related to how they work. If an axon is the part of the neuron that can send a signal and a dendrite is the part that can receive a signal, how can two neurons go together? Study the diagram in figure 8.25. The endings on the axon of one neuron are close to the endings of the dendrite of the next neuron. The combination of an axon ending, the dendrite ending, and the space between them is called the **synapse** (see figure 8.26).

The nervous system of animals, including humans, is more complex than figure 8.25 indicates. Dendrites on one neuron may receive signals from many different neurons through

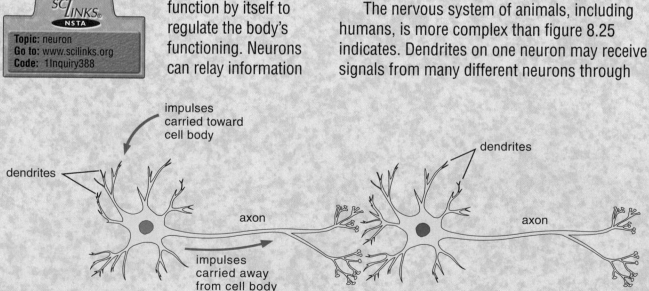

▲ **Figure 8.25 Neurons are connected to other neurons.** Neurons transmit information to other neurons. Information passes from the axon of one neuron to the dendrite of another neuron.

many different synapses. Different endings on an axon can send signals to several different neurons. One cubic centimeter of human brain tissue contains about 50 million neurons, each of which can form synapses with thousands of other neurons. That's a lot of signals passing around the brain!

As you have learned, neurons are arranged in a specific way with respect to their dendrites and axons. You also have learned that dendrites receive signals and axons pass them on. Based on those two pieces of information, what can you say about how neurons pass information? Knowing those facts should lead you to understand that neurons pass signals in only one direction. What other questions do you have about how neurons relay information? What are the signals that are passed along a neuron? What does it mean that a neuron relays information?

Topic: stimuli
Go to: www.scilinks.org
Code: 1Inquiry389

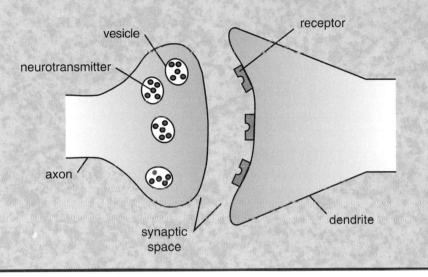

◀ **Figure 8.26 Synapse.** The synapse is the site where chemical signals pass between neurons. Vesicles are saclike structures that store and release chemical messengers.

2. Answer the following questions using what you learned from the reading. Record your answers in your science notebook.
   a. What are the specialized cells that allow an animal to respond to a stimulus?
   b. How are these specialized cells similar to and different from the cells you learned about in chapter 6?
   c. In what direction do nerve impulses travel? Include these words in your answer: *axon, dendrite,* and *cell body.*
3. Now that you understand more about neurons, read Sending and Receiving to learn how neurons pass signals to one another.
   a. As you read, develop a visual organizer, such as a concept map, to help you organize and make sense of what you are reading and learning.
   b. Include the relevant information that you already know from previous chapters.
   c. Add to or redraw your diagram of the nervous system as you continue to read and learn more details.
   d. As you read, keep track of questions that arise and see which questions are answered by the end of the reading.

The passing of a signal along one neuron and between neurons is called **neurotransmission**. Neurotransmission includes two main components: the passing of an electrical signal through one neuron and the passing of a chemical signal between two neurons. Both the electrical and chemical processes are necessary for a signal to pass between neurons. How does each process work? What is the relationship between the electrical and chemical processes?

Consider how a neuron passes an electrical signal that begins at its dendrite, moves through the cell body, and then moves along the axon. Before looking at how a signal in a neuron starts or is passed, think about the situation in a resting neuron—a neuron that is not transmitting an impulse. As figure 8.27 shows, the inside of a resting neuron has a negative charge compared with the outside environment because the neuron has fewer positively charged ions inside the cell than outside. As with other types of cells, the concentration of potassium ions (K^+) is higher inside the neuron and the concentration of sodium ions (Na^+) is higher outside the neuron. How does this compare with what you learned in chapter 6?

In neurons, the negative charge results from the unequal distribution mainly of sodium ions (Na^+); potassium ions (K^+); chloride ions (Cl^-); and other large, negatively charged organic molecules such as proteins and amino acids. The inside of the neuron is kept in an electrically negative state through a combination of diffusion and active transport (see figure 8.28). Potassium ions tend to diffuse out of the cell. Sodium ions can diffuse in, but they do so at a lower rate than potassium ions diffusing out. Remember, diffusion carries the ions from where they are at higher concentration to where they are at a lower concentration. Other large, negatively charged molecules cannot cross the membrane. Active transport uses energy to pump Na^+ ions back out and K^+ ions back inside the neuron. Where do neurons get the energy for all of those activities? Review Powering Cellular Activities in chapter 7 to help refresh your memory.

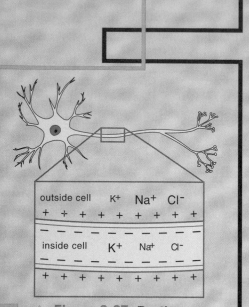

▲ **Figure 8.27 Resting neuron.** In resting neurons, the inside of the cell has a negative charge. Sodium ions (Na^+) are more concentrated outside the cell, and potassium ions (K^+) are more concentrated inside the cell.

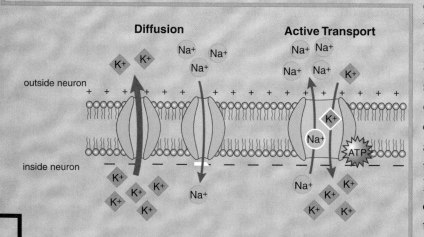

▲ **Figure 8.28 Diffusion and active transport of sodium and potassium ions.** Potassium ions tend to diffuse out of the cell at a faster rate than sodium ions diffuse into the cell. Active transport uses energy released from ATP to pump sodium ions (Na^+) out of the cell and potassium ions (K^+) into the cell.

The difference in charge across the cell membrane creates an electrical potential across the membrane. An **electrical potential** is a form of potential energy, and it is measured as voltage. The potential is tiny in resting neurons, only 70 millivolts (seventy thousandths of a volt). When this potential is present, scientists say that the neuron is polarized. Compare the electrical potential of a neuron to a small red LED light that produces 2.2 volts, like the one on the conductivity meters you used in chapter 3, Get a Charge Out of Matter.

The electrical signal that is passed along a neuron is called a **nerve impulse**. The impulse is a tiny electrical current produced by the movement of ions across the neuron's membrane. When a neuron is stimulated, a small section of the neuron's membrane changes its **permeability** and the distribution of ions changes across the neuron membrane. The stimulation causes sodium channels in the neuron's membrane to open, and sodium rushes in through the sodium ion channels (see figure 8.30b). The inside of the neuron becomes positive in its electrical charge. This temporary change in the neuron's electric potential to a positive state compared to the neuron's outside environment is called **depolarization**. Then the sodium channels close and the potassium channels open (see figure 8.30c). Potassium ions now rush

out of the cell through their channels, helping to restore the original negative charge inside the cell. To fully restore the electrical potential, the sodium and potassium concentration gradients are restored through active transport (see figure 8.30d). The change in electrical potential to the resting condition in which the inside of the neuron is more negative than the outside environment is called **repolarization**.

Scientists call the rapid depolarization and repolarization in the neuron an **action potential**. When an action potential occurs in one part of the membrane, it stimulates an action potential in the adjacent portion of the membrane, and so on. It is similar to a row of dominoes falling. Once initiated, the action potential continues along the length of the neuron. Interestingly, although the changes in ion distribution across the membrane occur quickly—within a fraction of a second—they are not instantaneous. A part of the neuron that has just depolarized cannot depolarize again until the balance of ions is back to the resting state. Because an area of the neuron membrane that has just transmitted an action potential cannot immediately depolarize again, the action potential can move only in one direction.

▶ **Figure 8.29** **Action potential.** This graph shows the voltage difference across a neuron membrane when a neuron is stimulated. (1) Notice that the voltage of a resting neuron is −70 millivolts. The minus sign indicates that the inside of the cell is negative in charge compared to the outside of the cell. (2) The voltage is positive when the cell is *depolarized* because the inside of the cell is positive in charge compared to the outside of the cell. (3) During *repolarization*, the voltage returns to the resting state (1).

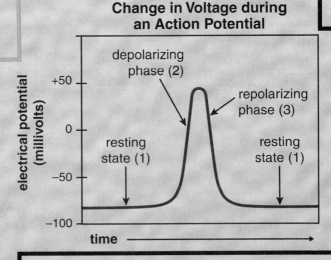

Change in Voltage during an Action Potential

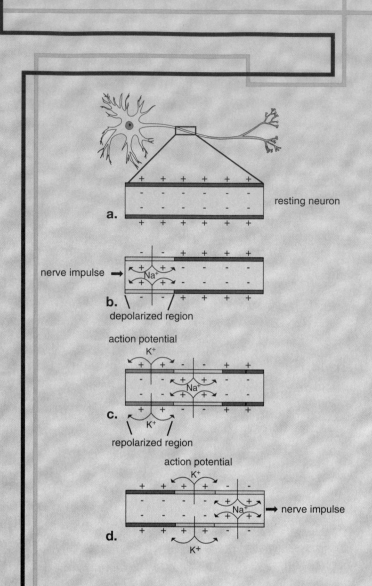

Nerve impulses travel along the neuron from the dendrites to the end of the axon. Once the distribution of ions returns to the resting state, another action potential can be transmitted along the neuron.

Will any signal cause a neuron to generate an action potential? The answer is no—an action potential will begin only when the stimulus is strong enough to cause the sodium ion channels to open. However, when an action potential is generated, it is the same amount of depolarization as another action potential (see figure 8.31). In other words, a neuron either generates an action potential or it doesn't. There are not any intermediate sizes of action potential in a neuron. Scientists call this the *all-or-nothing* event. A neuron either responds fully or does not respond at all.

Although the events that produce a nerve impulse are very complex, they happen very quickly. In fact, a nerve impulse can make it from your foot to your head in less than two-tenths of a second. Think about the importance of rapid transmission of nerve impulses the next time someone steps on your toe.

Chemicals Bridging the Gaps

What happens when a nerve impulse reaches the end of one neuron and moves to another? You will notice in figure 8.25 that an axon ending does not actually connect with the ending of a dendrite. There is a space, called the **synaptic space**. The electrical signal cannot cross the synaptic space. So how does a signal from one neuron reach the next neuron? The communication between neurons is done by specific chemical messengers called **neurotransmitters**.

Once the nerve impulse (the electrical signal) reaches the endings of the axon, it triggers the release of the neurotransmitters into the synaptic space. As shown in figure 8.32, the molecules of a neurotransmitter move

▲ **Figure 8.30 Propagation of the action potential.** (a) The plasma membrane of a resting neuron is more positive on the outside than on the inside. The entire neuron is said to be *polarized*. (b) A stimulus opens the sodium channels in part of the membrane, sodium rushes in, and part of the neuron is *depolarized*. (c) Potassium diffuses out, and this area again becomes *polarized*. (d) The impulse moves as a wave of electrical changes along the neuron. Another action potential cannot pass until potassium flows out of the cell and restores the electric potential of the resting neuron.

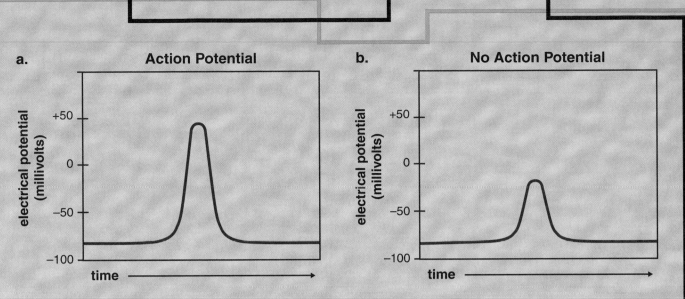

a. **Action Potential**

electrical potential (millivolts)

+50

0

−50

−100

time

b. **No Action Potential**

electrical potential (millivolts)

+50

0

−50

−100

time

▲ **Figure 8.31 All-or-nothing.** (a) An action potential occurs when the depolarization (inside of neuron becomes more positive) of a neuron is enough to cause the voltage to spike. (b) Some signals do not cause an action potential. If less sodium enters the neuron, the cell is not as positively charged (less depolarized). Without sufficient depolarization, an action potential does not occur.

across the synaptic space and bind to specific receptors on the dendrites of the next neuron. This binding then triggers the action potential in the receiving neuron, and it continues as an electrical signal passing through that neuron. Some neurons pass their signal to muscle cells or gland cells instead of other neurons. The neurotransmitters released from these neurons cause the muscle cells to contract or the gland cells to release their hormones.

Scientists have discovered a large number of different neurotransmitters. Different neurons make different neurotransmitters as their signaling chemical. Usually, a neuron makes and uses only one specific neurotransmitter. Some neurotransmitters are **excitatory** (can excite a neuron); that is, they cause a neuron to be more likely to initiate a nerve impulse. Other neurotransmitters inhibit a neuron; they are **inhibitory** neurotransmitters. They cause a neuron to be less likely to generate a nerve impulse. A number of helpful medicines and harmful drugs have been found to affect the brain by altering the release of neurotransmitters. Nicotine, for example, causes more

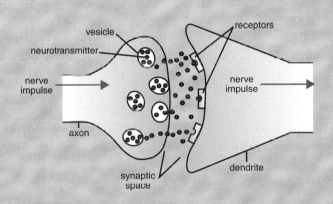

▲ **Figure 8.32 Neurons communicate with each other by releasing chemical messengers.** In response to an electrical impulse, neurotransmitter molecules released from the axon of one neuron bind to receptors on the dendrites of another neuron.

neurotransmitter to be released from an axon ending. This increased amount of neurotransmitter in the synaptic space increases the signaling rate to the receiving neuron. Studies of neurotransmitters also have helped researchers understand some diseases that affect the nervous system, such as Parkinson's disease and depression.

SCiLINKS®
NSTA
Topic: neurotransmitter
Go to: www.scilinks.org
Code: 1Inquiry393

4. Answer the following questions using what you learned from the reading. Record your answers in your science notebook.
   a. How does a stimulus result in a nerve impulse that travels from one neuron to another? Give your answer as a paragraph and a labeled diagram, using the following words:
      - Stimulus
      - Neuron
      - Nerve impulse
      - Sodium
      - Potassium
      - Neurotransmitter
   b. What are the roles of diffusion and active transport in neurons?
   c. Where does the energy come from to fuel cell activities, such as transmission of nerve impulses?
   d. Why do you think it is important that your nervous system have both excitatory and inhibitory neurotransmitters?
5. Now that you know how neurons send signals, read Making It Work to learn how signals are sent through your nervous system.
   a. Look ahead to Step 6 to guide your reading.
   b. Add to or redraw your diagram of the nervous system and your concept map as you continue to read and learn more details.
   c. As you read, keep track of questions that arise. See which questions are answered by the end of the reading.

Making It Work

So far you have learned a lot about how neurons are connected and how they send signals. But how does the nervous system work on a more practical level? For example, what happens when you touch a hot stove? To answer this question, consider the three major types of neurons in the nervous system—sensory neurons, motor neurons, and interneurons (see figure 8.33). **Sensory neurons** respond to stimuli from the external environment or from other parts of the body. They pass their signal to neurons in the brain or spinal cord, which process the signal and generate instructions for how the body should respond. These "processing and signal-integrating" neurons are called **interneurons**. Interneurons connect with motor neurons. The **motor neurons** carry the signal to muscles or gland cells, which cause those cells to respond by contracting or by releasing hormones, respectively.

Think again about the complexity of the nervous system. One neuron may connect with thousands of different neurons. Think about how you respond to touching a hot stove. Think about how you might respond when someone gently touches your hand. Are there similarities or differences in your responses to those two stimuli? Some responses are involuntary; you respond before you have time to think about an action.

The example of your hand touching a hot stove is an example of a **reflex** action. You pull your hand away from the

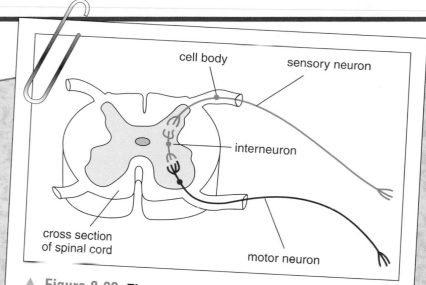

▲ **Figure 8.33 Three types of neurons.** Three types of neurons work together to transmit nerve impulses. Where does a nerve impulse start?

stove before you have time to think about and then decide on an action. The neuron pathway for a reflex is among the simplest. A sensory neuron picks up the signal, sends it to the spinal cord, and then transmits the signal to a motor neuron that signals your arm muscles to contract and pull your hand away (see figure 8.34). Most neuron pathways for reflexes also have a

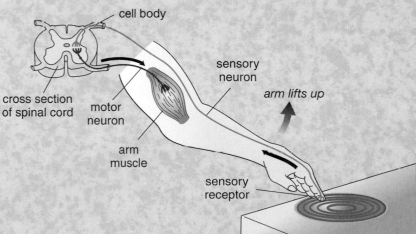

▲ **Figure 8.34 Reflex action.** The simplest pathway for a reflex involves a sensory and a motor neuron. The sensory neuron stimulates the motor neuron directly. The same sensory neuron might also send a signal to an interneuron, but the reflex action does not depend on conscious perception of the sensation.

connection with an interneuron between the sensory and motor neurons. Interneurons send the signal to the brain that allows you to know that you experienced heat, and you realize that you pulled your hand away. You consciously feel the heat, but your hand has already moved in response before you feel the sensation.

Other internal body functions that are involuntary are also regulated by neurons. For example, neurons in your brain regulate your heartbeat and your breathing rate. Other neurons control the secretion of digestive fluids in your stomach and intestines.

Other responses that you have are voluntary—you have conscious control over them. Those neuron pathways usually involve more neurons and more connections. It is through the different neurons signaling different parts of the brain that you make a decision and then figure out how to respond. When someone touches your hand, do you want to leave it where it is? Do you want to move it? Should you move it fast?

The Vertebrate Nervous System

The nervous systems of vertebrates are more complicated and specialized than those of other animals. Because of this complexity, scientists often talk about specific parts of the nervous system based on where the neurons are in the body or what their function is. The nervous systems of vertebrates are divided into two main parts: a central nervous system and a peripheral nervous system (see figure 8.35). The central nervous system is made up of the brain and the spinal cord. The neurons in the central nervous system are primarily interneurons. The central nervous system integrates information that comes from the peripheral nervous system and signals how the body should respond.

The peripheral nervous system is made up of neurons that receive information from the external or internal environment of the body and the neurons that carry information out to muscle or gland cells that respond to a change in the body's

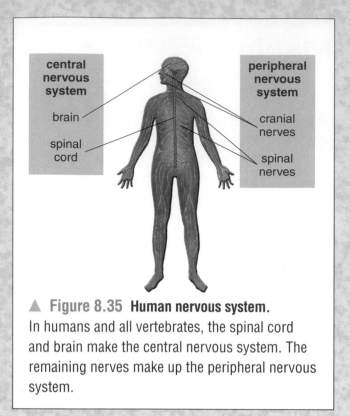

▲ **Figure 8.35** **Human nervous system.** In humans and all vertebrates, the spinal cord and brain make the central nervous system. The remaining nerves make up the peripheral nervous system.

environment. In other words, the peripheral nervous system is made up of sensory and motor neurons. Read the sidebar, Learning and Memory, to learn how the brain stores information.

Taking It All In

Since you were a young child, you have learned about the five senses that humans have—sight, sound, smell, touch, and taste. How does your body, specifically your nervous system, sense these things? The nervous system gathers and interprets sensory stimuli through the sensory neurons. Some sensory neurons have specialized endings on their dendrites called **sensory receptors** (see figure 8.36). Each sensory receptor picks up one specific type of stimulus. These receptors can be distributed broadly, such as the ones under your skin that sense touch, or they can be collections of many sensory nerve endings that are very close to each other, as is the case for the light receptors in your eyes. Different types of sensory receptors transmit information about different types of

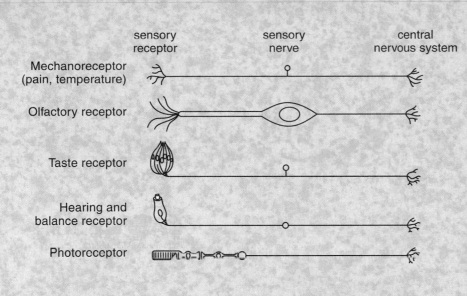

sensory receptor   sensory nerve   central nervous system

Mechanoreceptor (pain, temperature)

Olfactory receptor

Taste receptor

Hearing and balance receptor

Photoreceptor

▲ **Figure 8.36 Receptors on sensory neurons.** Sensory receptors are specialized endings on sensory neurons. Each ending is structured differently to respond to different stimuli.

environmental stimuli, including light, pressure, and chemicals. Read the sidebar, The Eye, to learn about receptors for light in your eyes.

There are five major types of sensory receptors. Figure 8.37 describes each type. For example, taste and touch receptors on your tongue gather stimuli about the chemical composition of the food you eat. Animals differ in how they interpret the environment depending on what sensory receptors they have. Bees and other insects have special receptors for ultravio-

let light and see flowers in a different way than you do. Also, unlike bats, you have no receptors for ultrasound.

The dendrites of sensory neurons are specialized to collect and transmit information about environmental stimuli. For example, when you hear a siren, sensory receptors in your ears vibrate in response to the mechanical energy of sound. The receptors convert this energy to a series of nerve impulses that travel through the axons of sensory neurons to your brain. Groups of neurons in your brain receive those impulses and interpret their pattern as sound. Other parts of your brain interpret what the sound means. Those areas of your brain have developed, in part, as a response to what you have learned during your life. Still other parts of your brain then signal your muscles to begin the appropriate response—to look around for the source of the sound and to get out of the way.

SCI**L**INKS®
NSTA
Go to: www.scilinks.org
Topic: nervous systems
Code: 1Inquiry397a
Topic: sensory receptor
Code: 1Inquiry397b

Type of Receptor	Sense	Examples	Stimulus
Mechanoreceptors	Touch, pressure Hearing Balance	Special cells in skin Hair cells in ear Hair cells in ear	Pressure against body surface Vibrations (sound) Fluid movement
Chemoreceptors	Taste Smell Internal chemical senses	Taste buds on tongue Olfactory receptors in nose Specialized cells inside body	Substances in mouth Odors Substances inside body
Photoreceptors	Vision	Rods and cones in the eye	Light
Thermoreceptors	Temperature	Receptors in skin and in a region of the brain called the hypothalamus	Change in radiant energy (heat)
Nociceptors	Pain	Nerve endings	Any stimuli that cause damage

▲ **Figure 8.37 Types of sensory receptors in humans.** Where are these receptors located in your body?

6. To show what you have learned about the nervous system of animals, work in teams of 3 to develop a comprehensive plan for a human model of a neural circuit.
   a. Use the following scenario: Imagine that you prick your finger and this causes your arm to pull away from the stimulus. How might you use people to model this reflex reaction?
   b. Consider what roles you would need students to play and what action each student would perform to represent the role.
   c. Write a script that includes lines for each role and each action.
   d. Record all of the details of your plan in your notebook.
   e. Exchange plans with another team and evaluate its plan.
      • Are all of the necessary roles accounted for?
      • Are all of the necessary actions included?
      • Is the script complete and accurate?
      • Is the plan comprehensive enough to demonstrate the team's understanding?

► **Figure 8.38**
Students playing the role of neurons. What do the students' bodies represent?

Reflect and Connect

Organize into teams of 3 and discuss the following questions. Record your answers in your science notebook.

1. Use a labeled sketch to illustrate the neural circuit for which you developed a model in Step 6. Indicate the direction of the nerve impulse.
2. How do animals sense the environment, and why is this an important behavior? Give at least two examples.
3. Write a paragraph and use a labeled diagram to explain how electrical energy in neurons is transferred to mechanical energy as a muscle cell contracts. Include what you know about how cells get this energy in the first place.
4. Select a specific behavior of a specific organism. Describe as much as you can at this point in your learning about the relationship between the nervous system and the behavior.

Learning and Memory

The brain has a remarkable ability to store information for years and to recall it at will. Unlike information stored on a computer, memory is not stored in specific places. Rather, memory seems to be stored in many places. The same region of the brain may house many types of memories.

Psychologists have divided memory into two types. Explicit memories, which include facts and events, involve regions of the cerebrum called the temporal lobe and hippocampus (see diagrams of the brain). Implicit memories, which include how to do something, such as riding a bicycle, are housed in the sensory or motor systems of the central nervous system. Both types of memories are formed by the same chemical and cellular processes.

Biologists have begun to understand how short-term memory storage leads to long-term memory retention. Short-term memory lasts only a few minutes, and unless additional changes take place, the memory is lost. You rely on short-term memory to store telephone numbers just before dialing. Short-term memory has a small capacity, and distraction or new information will cause you to lose information stored earlier. When you use the same information often or decide that it is important, additional molecular changes take place in the brain. An important result of those changes is that interneurons involved in storing the memory become more sensitive to impulses from certain axons that connect to their dendrites.

The results of some experiments suggest that the changes begin with activation of an enzyme protein. Those proteins also make cells more responsive to impulses from other neurons in the memory pathway. The changes strengthen the pattern of impulse transmission from neuron to neuron, forming memories that can last for many years.

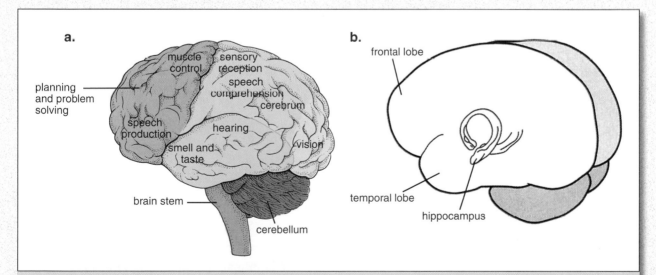

Brain structures involved in memory and learning. The (a) temporal lobes are regions located just above the ears and seem to be responsible for storage of long-term memory. The (b) hippocampus is tucked behind the temporal lobes. It may be especially important in transferring information from short-term memory to long-term memory.

The Eye

The human eye is sensitive to almost 7 million shades of color and about 10 million variations of light intensity. What makes this sensitivity possible?

The lens focuses light on a thin tissue called the retina (see diagram of the eye). The iris (the colored part of the eye) consists of muscles that can contract and relax, changing the size of the opening, called the pupil. This regulates the amount of light that enters the eye. The incoming light stimulates receptor cells, called rods and cones, in the retina (see diagram of the retina). Rods are responsible for black and white and peripheral vision (the edges of the field of vision). Cones are responsible for color vision.

Rods contain a protein that absorbs light from all visible wavelengths. Cones require brighter light than rods do. There are three types of cones, each containing a different pigment that absorbs red, green, or blue light. This absorbed light energy then signals the cell to begin an electrical impulse. Nerve impulses from the rods and cones travel through the optic nerves (one from each eye) to the brain. At the molecular level, light absorption is similar even in distantly related species. For example, some photosynthetic bacteria contain a form of a protein that absorbs light. This same protein is found in humans.

Neurons in the retina encode visual information before it is sent to the brain. For example, both red and green cones absorb yellow light. When they do, they act together to stimulate neurons that carry the perceptions of yellow light to the brain. However, red and green cones inhibit the transmission of each other's impulses, so you cannot see an object as both red and green.

The front-facing position of your eyes allows you to see objects from two slightly different angles. Comparing information from the two eyes allows the brain to perceive depth and to estimate distance. This adaptation is typical of predators. Many herbivores, such as horses, have eyes on the sides of their heads. This placement gives them a wide view of their surroundings. Why might this ability be useful for herbivores? Because their eyes see two different scenes, however, herbivores have a more difficult time judging distances.

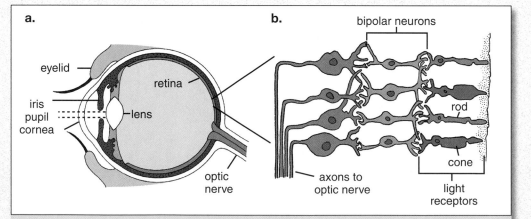

A cross section of the human eye. (a) Light passes first through the transparent cornea and then through the pupil, the adjustable opening in the iris. The light then reaches the lens, which focuses the image sharply on the retina. (b) In the retina, rods and cones absorb light, sending impulses to neurons in the retina. Connections among these neurons form interacting circuits that process visual information. The output of the circuits eventually goes to the brain through optic nerve fibers, enabling vision of the image.

Trapping Flies

Of course you have heard of mousetraps, but have you heard of flytraps? What type of mechanism would that require? Could a plant do that? Well, animals are not the only organisms that display behaviors. So far, in this chapter, you have been exploring and examining behaviors in a range of animals. However, bacteria, protozoans, fungi, and plants behave, too. For example, mobile bacteria change their direction of movement when they encounter food (see figure 8.39). Some predatory protozoans engulf other protozoans as food. A predatory fungus wraps itself around a microscopic nematode worm and absorbs its body fluids. The leaves of a sensitive plant close when touched, exposing sharp thorns that grow on the plant's stem.

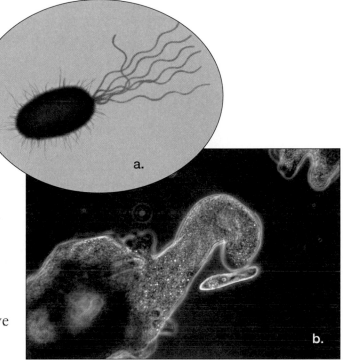

Unlike animals, bacteria, protozoans, fungi, and plants do not have nervous systems. This means that their behaviors are not controlled by nerve cell activity. How do you think their behaviors occur if they do not have nervous systems? In Trapping Flies, you will have an opportunity to learn how a certain interesting behavior occurs in a particular plant, the Venus flytrap (*Dionaea muscipula*).

▲ **Figure 8.39**
Behavior of single-celled organisms. (a) Mobile bacteria such as *Pseudomonas* can change their direction of movement by changing the direction that their whiplike flagella rotate. (b) The protozoan *Amoeba* preys on the protozoan *Paramecium*.

The Venus flytrap (see figure 8.40) is an exotic-looking plant that grows near the coast in a small area of North Carolina and South Carolina. What makes this plant so unusual is that it is a carnivore. It eats insects. In this activity, you will have an opportunity to design an investigation to learn how the Venus flytrap captures and digests insects. Your observations will help you explain how this behavior occurs in an organism without a nervous system. You also will

◄ **Figure 8.40**
Venus flytrap. The Venus flytrap is a carnivorous plant that captures and digests insects.

consider how this behavior is adaptive (that is, how it promotes survival and reproduction).

Materials
For each team of three students

1 forceps

1 Venus flytrap plant

3 toothpicks

access to immobilized insects

other miscellaneous materials

Cautions

Do not touch the Venus flytrap plants until you begin your experiment. (If you touch it and it responds, you will not be able to complete your investigation.)

Process and Procedure

1. Organize into teams of 3 and obtain a Venus flytrap plant from your teacher.
2. Observe the plant without touching it and complete the following in your science notebook.
   a. What behaviors, if any, does the plant display?
   b. Consider what part or parts of the plant might be adapted for catching insects. Explain your reasoning.
   c. Agree on one area of the plan to investigate.
3. With your teammates, review the materials that your teacher has available and design a simple investigation to test your idea about what part of the plant catches insects.
   a. Record your design and detailed procedure in your notebook.
   b. Have your teacher approve your work.
   c. Obtain your materials.

The insects have been stored in a refrigerator for a short period of time to slow their movement.

4. Conduct your investigation and record your observations. You may need to make observations for more than one day.
5. What do you think allowed for this behavior of the Venus flytrap? What caused the traps to close? Discuss your ideas with your classmates. Then read Venus Flytrap Closure to find out what scientists currently understand about Venus flytraps.

Plants do not have nerve cells. So how does a trap close on the Venus flytrap? This is an interesting question that scientists are still trying to answer. Inside the traps are trigger hairs. Many studies indicate that touching the trigger hairs causes an electrical potential to spread across the trap. Recall from the last activity, Neuron Networks, that electrical potential is the difference in charge across a membrane.

The mechanism for trap closure is less clear. One explanation for trap closure is a combination of growth and turgor pressure. **Turgor pressure** is pressure inside plant cells caused by the uptake of water. Water enters plant cells through osmosis. Remember that osmosis is diffusion of water across a membrane. Review Movement through Membranes in chapter 6 to refresh your memory.

Growth of the cells is caused by the release of acidic compounds. A decrease in pH loosens fibers in cell walls, making it possible for the cells to expand. Changes in the concentrations of ions increases turgor pressure as water enters cells through osmosis.

The trap closes as cells on opposite sides of the trap change relative size. When the trigger hairs are stimulated, cells on the *outer* surface of the trap increase in size, forcing the two halves of the trap together. The trap opens when the cells on the *inner* surface of the trap enlarge (see figure 8.41). Once the cells expand, they remain a larger size.

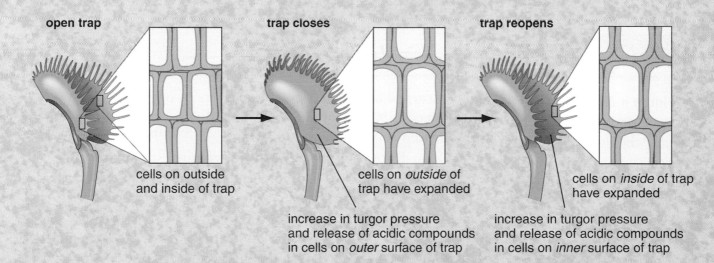

open trap

cells on outside and inside of trap

trap closes

cells on *outside* of trap have expanded

increase in turgor pressure and release of acidic compounds in cells on *outer* surface of trap

trap reopens

cells on *inside* of trap have expanded

increase in turgor pressure and release of acidic compounds in cells on *inner* surface of trap

▲ **Figure 8.41 Opening and closing traps.** Osmosis causes a change in turgor pressure, which expands the cells in the trap.

Reflect and Connect

Organize into teams of 3 and discuss the following questions. Record your answers in your science notebook. Notify your teacher when you are done reflecting and connecting.

1. What stimulus is the Venus flytrap responding to when it captures an insect?
2. Describe what changes take place in the plant that cause it to capture the insect.
3. How might the capture of insects by the Venus flytrap be an adaptation for living in a low-nutrient habitat? That is, how might this behavior promote survival and reproduction? Explain your reasoning. The following paragraph provides information that might be helpful.

   Venus flytraps grow in wet bog habitats and seepage areas on acidic soils (see figure 8.42). Those habitats do not provide plants with some of the nutrients they need to survive. Those habitats are low in plant nutrients, particularly nitrogen, because nutrients produced by decaying vegetation are carried away by water that is flowing constantly through the soil. Acidic soil conditions also hinder the uptake of nutrientsby plants.

4. What other stimuli do plants respond to?

▲ **Figure 8.42**
Venus flytrap habitat.
Venus flytraps grow in wet habitats such as this seepage area.

What Do You Know?

▼ **Figure 8.43**
Making observations.
Use your knowledge of scientific inquiry to investigate the behavior of a new species.

You have learned about a range of behaviors of organisms, and you know how behavior is generated. Now it is time to demonstrate your understanding and to learn more at the same time. In Part I, Getting to Know Another Organism, you investigate the behavior of an animal and communicate your findings to your teacher in writing. Your investigation gives you an opportunity to study behavior in the same way scientists do. It also helps you build on your understanding of the process of scientific inquiry that you began in chapter 1. Part II is a test designed to give you and your teacher feedback on what you have learned about behavior and nervous systems. As in chapter 4, Organizing the Elements: The Periodic Table, you examine the results of your test and revisit some of your answers. This feedback leads to improved understanding.

Part I: Getting to Know Another Organism

Materials

For each student or team of two to four students

zebra fish, mealworms (*Tenebrio*), or hermit crabs (if available)

a wild animal that lives in your local area (optional)

1 aquarium

1 video of animals exhibiting behaviors (optional)

habitat materials appropriate for each available species, except the wild animal (for example, water, rocks, sand, gravel, plants, food, shells, and wood shavings)

1 copy of Scoring Rubric for What Do You Know? handout

Cautions

Treat your study animals humanely. Handle them gently and provide them with adequate food, water, shelter, and appropriate environmental conditions. Do not approach wild animals. Many birds and animals such as squirrels carry diseases. Discuss an appropriate viewing distance with your teacher. You can also use binoculars to get a closer look at animals.

Process and Procedure

1. At the direction of your teacher, organize into teams of 2–4 or conduct your investigation by yourself.
2. From the animal species available (see Materials), select 1 to study. If you choose zebra fish, mealworms, or hermit crabs, create a habitat for your species in an aquarium. If you need information about a species's habitat requirements, search for it on the Internet. If you choose a wild animal, get approval from your teacher to study it in its natural habitat.
3. Study the scoring rubric for this activity and make sure you understand how your teacher will evaluate your performance.
4. Use the following questions as a guide while you design your animal behavior investigation.
   - What animal will you study?
   - Where will you make observations of the animal?
   - What aspect of the animal's behavior will you focus on?
   - During what time of day and for how long will you observe the animal?

- How many individuals will you observe?
- How will you collect data on the behaviors the animal displays?

5. Record the design and procedure of your investigation in your science notebook.
6. Have your teacher approve your design and procedure.
7. Place your animal in an aquarium or visit your animal's natural habitat and conduct your investigation. Record your observations in your science notebook according to the procedure you developed.
8. Answer the following questions in your science notebook.
   a. What behaviors did you observe?
   b. What external stimuli did your animal respond to? How did it respond to those stimuli?
   c. What behavior did you observe that you think might be innate? Explain why you think so.
   d. Did you observe any behavior that you think might be learned? If so, describe that behavior. Explain your answer.
   e. How might one or more of the behaviors you observed helped the animal survive and reproduce in its environment?

Part II: Testing for Understanding

In Part I, you had an opportunity to work alone or in teams to demonstrate your understanding of behavior by designing and conducting an investigation. Now you will take an individual test on the concepts that have been presented in this chapter. Then you will follow the Learn from Mistakes Protocol with each question that you missed.

Materials
For each student

1 copy of Test Your Knowledge of Nervous Systems and Behavior handout

Process and Procedure

1. Follow your teacher's instructions for preparing your desk for the test.
2. Read each question carefully and pinpoint exactly what is being asked.
3. Inspect any figures or diagrams for additional information and read through each response before marking your answer.

4. Turn your answers in to your teacher when you are finished.
5. Your teacher will score your test and give you feedback. Part of that feedback will be a discussion of the concepts important to each question.
6. Listen as your teacher explains how to demonstrate that you have learned from mistakes.
7. Follow the Learn from Mistakes Protocol for *each* question that you missed and turn in your paper as instructed by your teacher. You can find the protocol in the evaluate on page 196 for chapter 4.

Life's Work

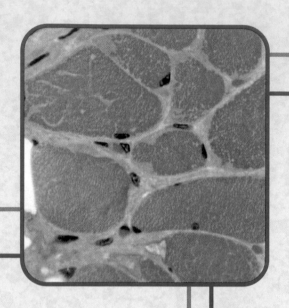

Life's Work

In unit 2, The Machinery of Life, you have been learning about different kinds of cells in organisms and the processes that take place in those cells. In chapter 9, Life's Work, you use everything you have learned to understand how muscle cells contract and cause movement.

You know that muscle cells contract in response to a signal from the nervous system. What happens once this signal is received? You also know from experience that movement requires energy. You learned in chapter 7, Cells Are Busy Places, that this energy is supplied through cellular respiration. Does the supply of energy determine when muscles feel fatigued? What other factors might cause muscle fatigue? You answer those questions as you complete this chapter.

To understand how animals move, you need to know about more than muscle cells. You need to understand the mechanics of movement. You already know something about mechanics if you have studied simple machines such as levers, pulleys, and inclined planes in previous science classes.

In the same way machines are designed to do work in an efficient way and for a specific purpose, animals also are structured to move efficiently in specific ways. Animals must move efficiently to survive in their environments. For example, animals move to gather food and to avoid predators. To ensure their survival, they must do those and other activities in a way that maximizes the movement for the amount of energy put in.

There are many common features to the structure of animals. One of these is levers. A **lever** is a bar that moves about a pivot point (fulcrum). In vertebrate animals, limbs act as levers when a force is applied to the bone by muscle. Levers are important for movement in animals. In chapter 9, you design your own lever system to accomplish a specific task. Design is an important part of biological science as well as engineering. For example, in the field of medical technology, artificial (prosthetic) limbs are an essential development for amputees.

By designing a lever system and comparing it to levers in an animal, you will demonstrate an understanding of both biological and physical systems. This is similar to the process that medical engineers go through when developing a prosthetic limb. In order to design a limb that moves effectively and efficiently with the amputee, they must understand what the mechanics of movement are and how that movement occurs. Listen as your teacher describes the design problem.

Make a sketch of the catapult launch mechanism and label each part. Sketches help you remember what you saw. They also help you think ahead about the design you will construct.

Goals for the Chapter

In chapter 9, you will design a lever system and investigate how movement occurs in animals. By the end of this chapter you will be able to answer the following questions:

- How do I plan and design a piece of technology to meet specific criteria?
- How does the structure of a muscle cell enable it to contract?
- How is energy involved in movement, and how is it related to work and power?
- How does an understanding of biology and physical science help me understand how animals move?

You will be better able to answer those questions by participating in the following activities.

ENGAGE	How Much Energy?
EXPLORE	Cellular Workout
EXPLAIN	Mechanics and Muscle
ELABORATE	Muscle Power
EVALUATE	Design Work

How do you transfer energy when you move?

EXPLORE

Cellular Workout

Key Idea:
Levers help us transfer energy to lift a bucket.

Do cells get tired during physical activity?

ENGAGE

How Much Energy?

Key Idea:
Different movements require different amounts of energy.

Life's Work

EXPLAIN

Mechanics and Muscle

Key Ideas:
- Simple machines affect the amount of force and distance required for us to move our limbs.
- To contract, muscle cells require energy in the form of ATP.
- Muscle cells fatigue as energy is depleted, and conditions in muscle cells change with exercise.

triceps muscle

tendon

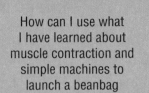

Design Work

Key Ideas:

- Muscular-skeletal systems and simple machines transfer energy to do work.
- Designs should meet a set of agreed upon criteria.

Linking Question

How can I use what I have learned about muscle contraction and simple machines to launch a beanbag as far as possible? ▲

ELABORATE

CHAPTER 9

Major Concepts

Muscle Power

Key Idea:

The relationship between energy and time determines power output.

▶ **Cell Function**
- **The structure of a muscle enables it to contract.**
- **Muscle contraction requires energy.**

▶ **Science Disciplines Connect**
- **Lever systems and molecular inter-actions in muscle cells explain move-ment in animals.**

▶ **Technological Design**
- **Using specific criteria to propose and implement a design is an important part of the design process.**
- **Communicating the steps in developing a design, as well as the results, is an important part of the design process.**

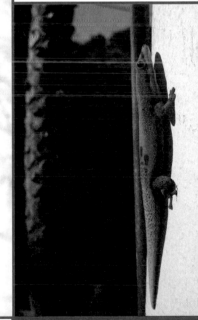

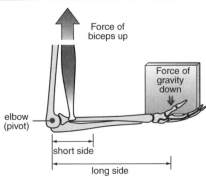

biceps muscle

tendon

Force of biceps up

Force of gravity down

elbow (pivot)

short side

long side

Linking Question

How does the power output of your muscles compare with that of a machine?

How Much Energy?

In chapter 7, you learned that your cells get the energy they need through the process of cellular respiration. For example, your muscle cells need energy to produce movement. Do you think that the amount of energy required for different activities might vary? Why might some activities require more energy than others? In How Much Energy, you work individually and as a class to consider those questions.

Materials

For each team of two students

1 stopwatch or timer

access to mats, jump ropes, and stairs or fitness steps

weights (optional)

Cautions

Don't perform any exercises if you have a medical condition that is aggravated by physical activity.

Process and Procedure

1. You know from looking at food labels that foods contain different amounts of energy. This energy is measured in kilocalories (kcal). How many kcal do you think it takes your body to do different activities? Think about that question as you study the activities listed here:

   - Deep knee bends
   - Lunges
   - Stair stepping
   - Sit-ups
   - Jumping rope

▲ Figure 9.1 **Energy to move.** Why do some movements require more energy than others?

2. Predict which activities will burn more calories by ranking the activities in Step 1 from least to most calories burned in 1 hour. The activity that burns the least calories should be ranked 1, and the activity that burns the most calories should be ranked 10. Be prepared to explain your decisions.
3. Work with a partner and discuss your rankings and your justification for those rankings.
4. How could you estimate the relative amount of calories burned during exercise? Read Measuring Your Response to Exercise to get some ideas.

READING

Measuring Your Response to Exercise

When you exercise, you notice that your heart beats faster and your breathing rate increases. Energy needs increase during exercise. As a result, the rate of cellular respiration increases to supply muscle cells with ATP. Remember that oxygen is used during aerobic cellular respiration. Increasing your breathing rate causes oxygen levels in the blood to rise and helps remove the carbon dioxide produced by cellular respiration. To supply your cells with more oxygen, your heart beats faster to pump more blood to your muscles. The increased blood supply provides your muscle cells with more oxygen.

Scientists measure the calories burned by measuring heat loss or the amount of oxygen consumed by a person during physical activity. This is difficult to do in the classroom. When measurement of a variable is not practical, another variable that behaves in a similar way is used as a substitute. The substitute variable is called a proxy variable. In this example, a proxy variable must have a similar relationship to exercise as calories burned. What do you think you could use as a proxy variable for calories burned?

5. Using a proxy variable, how could you determine which of the exercises listed in Step 1 will burn more or fewer kcal? Participate in a class discussion of how to design an investigation to answer that question. Answer the following questions as a class. Write your answers in your science notebook.

The unit of measure for food energy is the kilocalorie (kcal). On food labels, it is written as Calories, with a capital C.

a. How could you remove or reduce the variation in the data for different individuals?
b. How many repetitions or how much time for the exercise would you include in your design?

▲ **Figure 9.2**
Heavy loads. You have experienced carrying a load when carrying several grocery bags or a heavy backpack. Do you move differently when carrying a load? What other changes do you notice in your body?

⚠ Caution Do not perform any exercises if you have a medical condition that is aggravated by physical activity.

6. Decide with your partner which of the exercises from Step 1 you will do. Take turns doing the exercise while the other records data.
7. How might carrying a load while doing the exercise affect your results? Give your prediction in a sketch, a graph, or a couple of sentences. Record your prediction in your science notebook.
8. Repeat the exercise you did in Step 6—this time carrying a load. Take turns doing the exercise and recording data.
9. Share your results with the class and listen to the results from other teams. Record the data from the class in a data table.
10. Review your rankings from Step 2. Decide whether you would like to make changes using the new information you gathered as a class. Record any changes in your science notebook.

Reflect and Connect

Participate in a class discussion of the following questions. Record your ideas in your science notebook.

1. Watch as your teacher displays the number of calories burned for different exercises. How do your rankings compare? What similarities and differences do you notice?
2. What might influence the amount of energy (in kilocalories) required for different exercises? Consider both biological and physical influences.
3. Why does your body require more energy to do an exercise while carrying a load?
4. The goal of your catapult design is to toss an object as far as possible. What physical influences do you think you can adjust to maximize the distance of the toss?

Cellular Workout

In How Much Energy?, you recalled how important energy is to all life. You have already learned about photosynthesis and respiration in cells. Both processes convert energy from one form to another. That way the energy does something useful for the organism. For example, plants convert solar energy, water, and carbon dioxide to chemical potential energy stored in the bonds of molecules such as sugars, starches, and proteins. Animals use the chemical potential energy stored in foods and oxygen gas to do useful work such as running, keeping their heart beating, and helping to stay warm. But what happens when the energy conversion stops or changes? Do cells get tired? How do tired cells affect your whole body?

Without energy transfers, your muscles could not do work. Imagine not being able to lift your backpack from the floor to your back. To do that work, your muscles have to apply a force for some distance. When that happens, you transfer energy from your muscles to the backpack. The result of work is a change in the energy state of the backpack. It has greater potential energy on your back than on the floor. Remember that potential energy refers to the work that the backpack can do because of its new height, not the work it has done by falling.

Do cells get tired when they transfer energy to do work? Since cells are so small, how would you know? What factors affect the work cells can do?

In Cellular Workout, you and your team design an investigation to answer those questions. You use knowledge about simple machines, which you acquired in middle school, and your understanding of inquiry from this program to explore how a system of cells in your arm transfers energy to do work.

Part I: Workout Designer

Materials
For each team of four students

1 stopwatch

1 meterstick

1 bucket with handle
(approximately 2-gallon capacity)

dumbbell weights

1 lab apron (used as a cushion for
the bucket handle)

▲ Figure 9.3
Animals do work to lift objects. To survive, animals have muscles that do useful work. How does that survival depend on simple machines?

Cautions

Do not perform the lifting portion of this activity if you have a health problem that might be aggravated by exercise. Do not allow the weight to fly out of the bucket. To prevent this from happening, use a weight large enough to prevent you from lifting it quickly enough to make it leave the bucket.

Process and Procedure

When muscle cells in your arm transfer energy, they perform work. Doing work requires muscles to apply a force for some distance. So what factors affect the work that muscles in your arm can do? Is the amount of work that muscle cells can do always the same? How would you measure the result of different amounts of work done by muscle cells?

When you are lifting a weight with your forearm, your muscles must apply a force. To investigate how your muscles respond to different amounts of work, you could lift a *constant* amount of weight several times from different positions on your arm. How would the time required to complete 20 repetitions vary at different lifting positions along your forearm? In a team of 4, you answer this question through an activity you design.

1. Individually, read *each* design question and write an answer in your science notebook.
   a. How will you measure the amount of time it takes to lift a weight 20 times?
   b. How will you decide the amount of weight to use?
   c. How many lifting positions will you investigate?
   d. How will you test whether cells are getting tired at *each* lifting position?
   e. How will you standardize the lifting position along your arm to form a common basis of comparison with the entire class?

   Everyone's forearm is a different length. So using length units does not allow the class to compare results on a common scale. To standardize the lifting position, you need a unitless measure of forearm length, one that compares your total forearm length to the lifting position during a given trial (see figure 9.4).

   f. How will you standardize the number of trials per lifting position and the amount of resting time between trials so the entire class can compare results?

▼ **Figure 9.4**

Forearm measurement. Measure the entire forearm from elbow to palm. Then determine the percentage of forearm length that each lifting point represents.

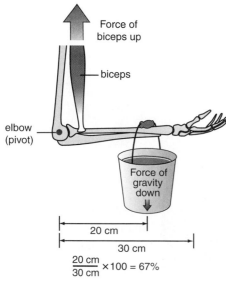

Force of biceps up

biceps

elbow (pivot)

Force of gravity down

20 cm

30 cm

$\dfrac{20\text{ cm}}{30\text{ cm}} \times 100 = 67\%$

g. Does beginning at your palm and progressing toward your elbow produce the same effect as starting near your elbow and progressing toward your palm?

h. How will you record the information in a useful way?

2. Meet with your team and listen carefully to all team members' answers.

3. Decide as a team the best combination of ideas for each answer and record those ideas next to your original answers.

4. Bring your ideas to a class discussion on the activity design and reach a consensus before collecting data.

5. Record the class' final design, meet with your team, and conduct your investigation.

6. Answer the Stop and Think questions after your team has finished collecting all of the data and before you conduct your analysis of the data in Part II.

Caution Do not perform any exercises if you have a medical condition that is aggravated by physical activity.

Part I

Meet with your team and conduct your preliminary analysis of your data by answering the Stop and Think questions in your science notebook.

1. Under what circumstances did your arm feel most tired? How might graphs show this?

2. Did your level of tiredness vary between trials? How could graphs show this?

3. Did your level of tiredness vary according to the lifting position on your forearm? How could graphs show this?

4. Why might the weight feel different when at different lifting positions on your forearm?

   Remember how weight is a measure of the force of gravity on an object and that simple machines can multiply either force or distance.

5. Which arm muscles were you using during your investigation? Draw a sketch indicating where the muscles are on your arm. Also, indicate which muscle is contracted when you move your hand toward your body and which muscle is contracted when you move your hand away from your body.

   Feel the front of your upper arm. Now bend your opposite arm so that your hand reaches toward your shoulder. This should be the same motion you did during the investigation. Now move your hand from your shoulder to your side to straighten your arm. Feel the back of it. You should be able to feel the muscles on the back of your arm relax.

Part II: Work Analysis

Materials
For each team of four students

graph paper

colored pencils

calculator

Process and Procedure

Graphs tell a story of experimental results. In this investigation, he story that graphs tell helps you see factors that influence the work that muscle cells can do. Often, graphs show relationships among factors, leading to deeper understanding. First, you graph your team's observations. Then you begin to analyze the graphs by determining what questions they generate.

1. Work together with your team, but produce individual graphs by accomplishing Steps 1a–d.
   a. On one side of your graph paper, design a layout for 2 graphs. Use the same scales to make comparison easier.

   In your design, include space for highlight comments and a caption for each graph.

   b. Make 2 graphs of time for 20 repetitions (vertical axis) versus standardized length (horizontal axis). The first graph shows your start-at-palm data. The second graph shows your start-near-the-elbow data.

   If your class decided to standardize the number of repetitions differently, use the class number.

   c. Include error bars equal to ± 5 percent of the value of *each* point.

   Error bars show how much variation might occur in the value of any point. Your teacher will give you an example to get you started.

   d. Include an appropriate title and legend.
2. Write "What I see" by any feature of the graph that draws your curiosity and describe that feature. You must have at least 1 comment on your graph.
3. Compare your graphs and "What I see" comments with other graphs—first within your team, then among the class.

   Make sketches of any graphs that are very different from yours.

4. Analyze your graphs and generate at least 4 questions about the data. Include words such as *points, error bars, trend, increase, decrease, spread out, close together,* and *overlap* in your questions.

Be sure to refer to exact features in your data. For example, this is a specific question: Why do times increase as they approach the end of the arm regardless of where data collection began? This question is too general to be useful: Why are the points the way they are?

5. Discuss your questions as your teacher directs.

Reflect and Connect

Answer these questions in your science notebook and be prepared to share your ideas in a group discussion.

1. How does standardizing forearm length on the graph affect your ability to form questions about work and about muscles getting tired?
2. Write a short paragraph that tells the story of your graphs. Make sure you address the question, Do cells get tired? Incorporate the words *energy, force, distance,* and *work* in your paragraph.
3. The introduction to this activity asked questions about cells, which are very small. Yet you designed an investigation involving arms, objects that are much larger than cells. What justifies using something so big when the original question was about something so small?

Mechanics and Muscle

In Cellular Workout, you investigated how cells do work in your arm. Why are humans and animals structured to do work in a similar way? What is the advantage of this structure? In Part I, you expand your understanding of simple machines, which helps explain the advantage of how animals are structured. Then in Part II, you learn how muscle cells convert chemical energy into mechanical energy to do work.

Part I: The Strong Arm

Materials
For each team of four students

meterstick

Leverage Your Effort

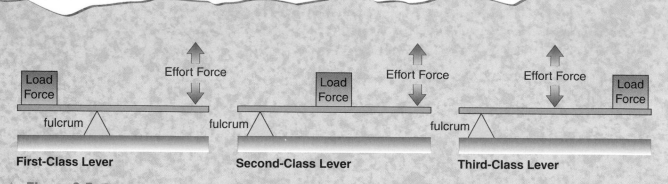

First-Class Lever   **Second-Class Lever**   **Third-Class Lever**

▲ **Figure 9.5** **Three types of levers.** There are three types (classes) of levers. In two classes, your effort force is less than the load force. In which two classes of levers is this true? What is the advantage of the third type of lever?

In middle school, you likely learned how simple machines help you do work. Examples of simple machines are levers, pulleys, and inclined planes. But remember, simple machines do not decrease or increase the amount of work required to do a job. They often make it possible for you to apply a smaller force than would be necessary without the machine. Figure 9.5 shows the three types of levers.

Figure 9.6 illustrates how machines make it possible for you to apply a smaller force. The minimum force required to lift the rock without the lever is equal to the block's weight, 3,118 newtons (N). An average ninth-grade student weighs about 624 N (140 pounds). But when you apply a force of 520 N (less than the weight of the student) to the long end of a first-class lever, the block lifts. This simple machine is

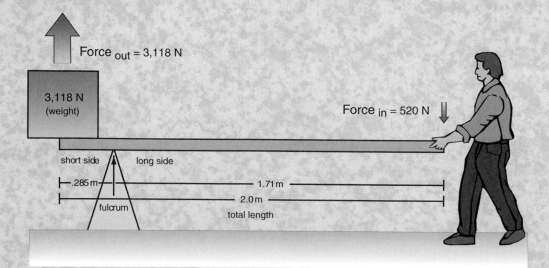

Force $_{out}$ = 3,118 N

3,118 N (weight)

Force $_{in}$ = 520 N

short side   long side

.285 m   1.71 m

2.0 m

fulcrum   total length

▲ **Figure 9.6** **First-class lever multiplies force.** Simple machines can increase the force that you can apply. Do they decrease the amount of work you have to do?

Work short side	=	Work long side
Force short side × Distance short side	=	Force long side × Distance long side
(3,118 N)(.285 m)	=	(520 N)(1.71)
889 joules	=	889 joules

▲ **Figure 9.7 Energy conservation in simple machine.** The work done on both sides of the fulcrum is equal. That means energy is conserved. If energy is the same on both sides, what is the purpose of a simple machine?

sometimes called a force multiplier because it increases the amount of force a human can apply.

But notice how the total amount of work done to lift the block has not changed. You can confirm this by inspecting figure 9.7.

A simple ratio helps you know by what factor a lever can multiply your force. The ratio is called the **mechanical advantage** (MA). In figure 9.7, the mechanical advantage is this:

$$MA = \frac{(\text{lever distance from fulcrum})_{long\ side}}{(\text{lever distance from fulcrum})_{short\ side}}$$

When you substitute values,

$$MA = \frac{1.71\ meters}{0.285\ meters} = 6.$$

This means that you could multiply a force by a factor of 6. Now that could be an advantage!

Not all simple machines increase the force that you can apply. Your arm, for example, is a third-class lever that decreases the force your biceps muscle applies to your forearm (see figure 9.8).

The distance your biceps moves is much less than the distance a weight in your palm moves. How does this affect the force your biceps can apply? How does your arm system affect the amount of work your biceps can do?

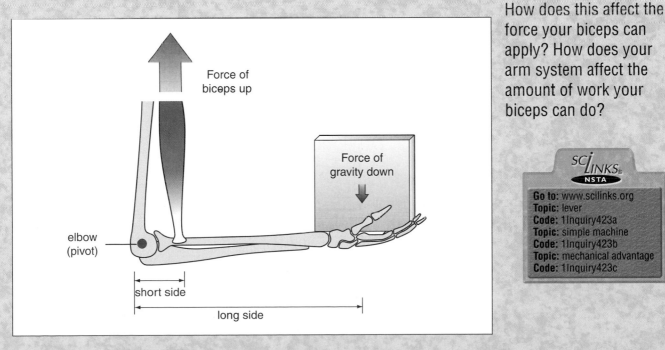

elbow (pivot)

short side

long side

Force of biceps up

Force of gravity down

SCI LINKS®
NSTA
Go to: www.scilinks.org
Topic: lever
Code: 1Inquiry423a
Topic: simple machine
Code: 1Inquiry423b
Topic: mechanical advantage
Code: 1Inquiry423c

▲ **Figure 9.8 Arms are distance multipliers.** The biceps applies a force close to the elbow. How does this affect the amount of weight that you can lift in your palm?

Chapter 9 Life's Work **423**

▲ **Figure 9.9**
Wheelbarrows are simple machines. Which force is greater, the force of gravity on the load or the force on the handles?

▲ **Figure 9.10**
Steam shovels are simple machines. Wheelbarrows, steam shovels, and human arms are simple machines. Which simple machine is the human arm most like—wheelbarrows or steam shovels?

Part I

Work individually to write answers to these questions in your science notebook before discussing them with teammates.

1. Sketch a wheelbarrow in your notebook and label the fulcrum, lever distance from the fulcrum for the long side, and lever distance from the fucrum for the short side. Then sketch a load of rocks in the wheelbarrow and you lifting the wheelbarrow handles in a normal fashion. Use arrows to represent the size and direction of force applied to the rocks and by your hands.

2. Use sketches to explain the similarities and differences between the way your arm and a wheelbarrow function as simple machines.

3. Suppose a steam shovel bucket could lift a maximum of 1,500 pounds (lb). The entire lifting arm measured from the pivot point to the center of the bucket is 30 feet (ft). The lifting motor can produce a maximum of 2,500 lb of lift. Where along the lifting arm should the lifting cable be attached?

   Consider the steam shovel as a third-class lever exactly like your arm.

4. Sketch the steam shovel in Question 3 and your arm, one above the other. Use arrows and highlight comments to point out similarities between the 2 simple machines.

5. Make the necessary measurements to estimate the mechanical advantage of your leg. Study figure 9.11 and assume your hamstring attaches about 4 centimeters (cm) below the back of your knee joint. Include your measurements and your calculation of mechanical advantage in a sketch.

▶ **Figure 9.11**
Legs are levers. Hamstrings bend your lower leg back from a straight position. The hamstring muscle group is comprised of several muscles.

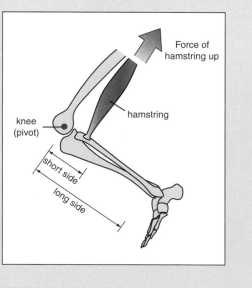

Force of hamstring up

hamstring

knee (pivot)

short side

long side

Part II: Muscular Machines

In Part I, you were reminded how simple machines such as levers help you do work. But how does your biceps muscle apply a force to create a lever? Two body systems are necessary for parts of your body to act as simple machines—the muscle system and the skeletal system (see figure 9.12). You might have heard them called collectively the muscular-skeletal system. In Part II, you learn how muscle cells produce movement at the microscopic level and how muscles together with bones produce movement at the macroscopic level. You learn how energy is transferred in the process of generating movement. You also revisit the question, Do cells get tired? You learn scientists' current ideas about what causes fatigue of muscle cells.

Work with a partner, taking turns reading the following sections about how muscles generate force. Then answer the Stop and Think questions to show what you have learned.

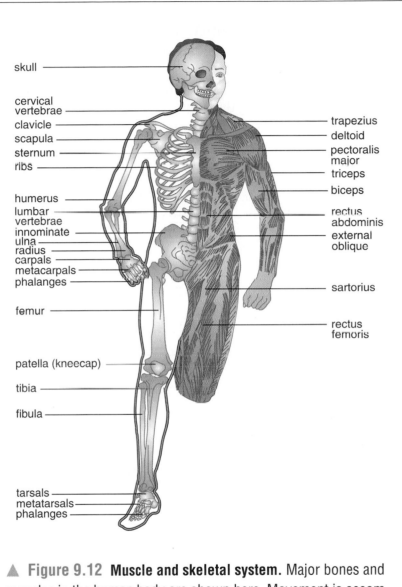

▲ Figure 9.12 **Muscle and skeletal system.** Major bones and muscles in the human body are shown here. Movement is accomplished through interaction of the bones, the joints, and the contraction of muscles.

Muscle and Skeletal Systems

All vertebrates have an internal skeleton that is made of bones. Vertebrates include amphibians, reptiles, birds, mammals, and most fish. The skeleton is an internal framework for the body (figure 9.13). To understand what this means, imagine what you would look like if someone removed all of your bones. You would look like a shapeless blob of skin, muscle, organs, and fat!

The skeletons of mammals (like you) are made up of more than 200 bones. Some of those bones are fused together, but others are connected together, bone to bone, at joints by ligaments. Joints are the places where two bones come together and body movement can occur.

Movement occurs through the coordinated interaction of the bones of an animal's skeleton, the joints between the bones, and the contraction of muscles that span the joints. Muscles are attached to bones by flexible cords of connective tissue called tendons (see figure 9.14). Tendons span joints so that when a muscle contracts, the force is applied at the joint and movement occurs.

Humans and other vertebrate animals have three types of muscles, as shown in figure 9.15. Each has a different structure and function. **Smooth muscle** is found in the walls of blood vessels, the digestive tract, and portions of the respiratory tract. Smooth muscles are involuntary. They operate body organs and regulate the internal environment of animals. **Cardiac muscle** is found only in the heart, and its contraction also is involuntary. **Skeletal muscle** moves the bones of the skeleton and is voluntary because it is under conscious control. This activ-

▶ **Figure 9.13**
Dinosaur skeleton. A skeleton is similar to a framework for a house—it provides support. What do you think this dinosaur looked like with muscles and skin?

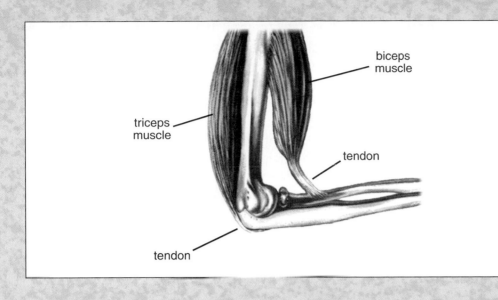

Tendon attachments. Muscles attach to bones by tendons. Notice how the tendons of the biceps and triceps muscles extend across the elbow joint.

biceps muscle

triceps muscle

tendon

tendon

ity focuses on skeletal muscle because it causes movement, such as the flexing of an arm to lift a weight.

When skeletal muscles contract, they shorten and change the position of the bones to which they are attached. A muscle attached to a bone is like a rope attached to a wagon. You can pull, but not push, a wagon with a rope. To move the wagon back to its original position using a rope, you must attach the rope to the other end and pull it. Muscles act in the same way—in opposing pairs (see figure 9.16). To touch your hand

to your shoulder, you contract your biceps and relax the triceps, producing the flexed position. When you return your hand and arm to the extended position, you contract the triceps and relax the biceps. Those two sets of muscles work in opposition to each other. All of your skeletal movements are performed by contraction and relaxation of opposing sets of muscles.

Bones can act as levers when the muscles that are attached to them contract. Your arm acts as a lever because muscle contraction causes one or more bones to rotate around a pivot point

b.

a.

c.

▲ **Figure 9.15** **Three types of muscle.** Each type has a different structure and function. (a) Skeletal muscle cells fuse end to end, forming a long fiber with characteristic striations. (b) Smooth muscle is made of long, spindle-shaped cells arranged in parallel sheets. (c) Cardiac muscle cells are organized in interconnecting chains that form a lattice.

(see figure 9.17). For example, your biceps muscle contracts and applies a force that causes the bones in your forearm to pivot around your elbow (see figure 9.16). But how does your muscle apply a force? You will find out in the next reading.

▶ **Figure 9.16**
Muscle pairs.
Muscle pairs enable the human arm to bend and straighten. Biceps bend your arm and triceps straighten your arm at the joint.

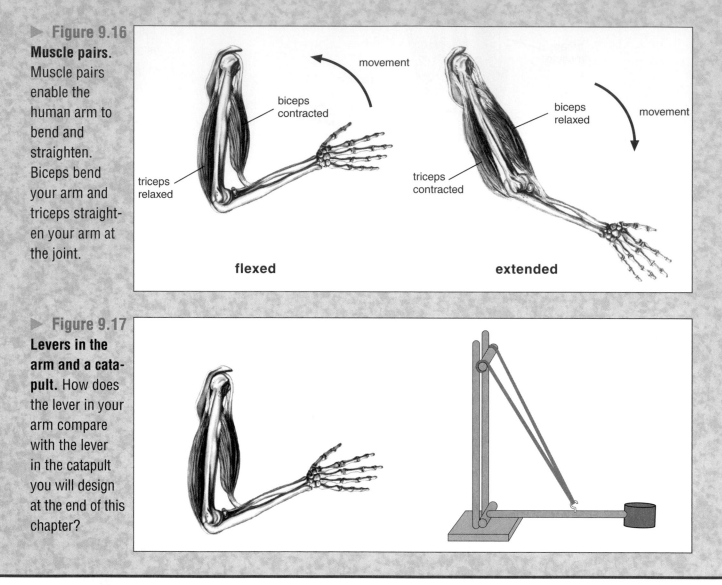

movement

biceps contracted

triceps relaxed

flexed

biceps relaxed

movement

triceps contracted

extended

▶ **Figure 9.17**
Levers in the arm and a catapult. How does the lever in your arm compare with the lever in the catapult you will design at the end of this chapter?

Stop & THINK
Part II

1. Could you move your arm if it had muscle but no bone? Describe in 1 or 2 sentences how bones and muscles interact to produce movement. Use what you know about levers.

2. What would happen if you had only biceps muscles in your arm and no triceps? Study figure 9.16 to help you answer the question.

Powerful Muscle Cells

Skeletal muscles are collections of muscle cells called fibers (see figure 9.18). These fibers run the length of the muscle. Your calf muscle contains about 1 million muscle fibers. Each fiber is made up of bundles of a thousand or more myofibrils. Each myofibril is divided into smaller units called **sarcomeres.** Contraction that you can see as movement of your arm occurs within the sarcomeres of your muscle cells.

Sarcomeres are made up of primarily two proteins—actin and myosin (see figure 9.19). Myosin makes up the thick filaments in the

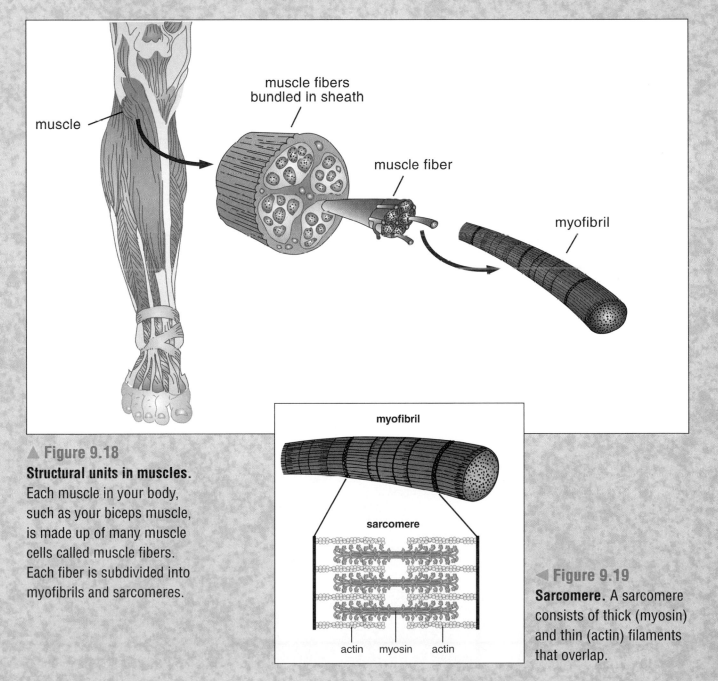

muscle

muscle fibers
bundled in sheath

muscle fiber

myofibril

myofibril

sarcomere

actin   myosin   actin

▲ Figure 9.18
Structural units in muscles.
Each muscle in your body, such as your biceps muscle, is made up of many muscle cells called muscle fibers. Each fiber is subdivided into myofibrils and sarcomeres.

◄ Figure 9.19
Sarcomere. A sarcomere consists of thick (myosin) and thin (actin) filaments that overlap.

► **Figure 9.20**
Sarcomere contraction. When myosin and actin interlock, the filaments are pulled together in a power stroke. A series of many power strokes causes the sarcomere to contract. What initiates the contraction of a sarcomere? Where does the energy come from?

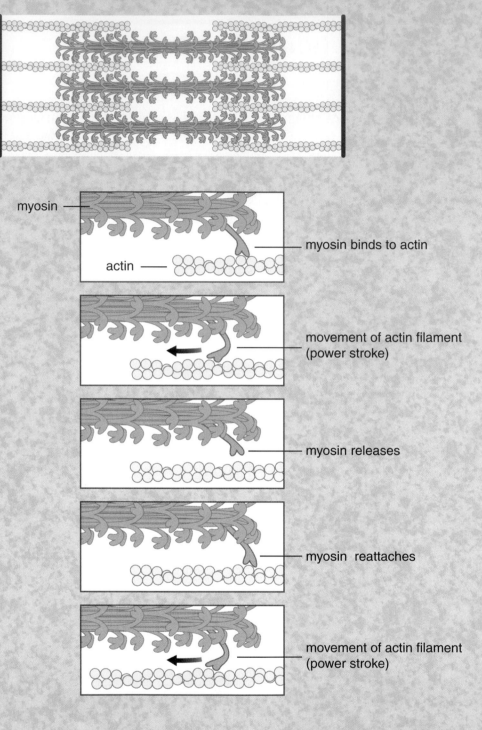

myosin

actin

myosin binds to actin

movement of actin filament (power stroke)

myosin releases

myosin reattaches

movement of actin filament (power stroke)

contracted sarcomere

middle of each sarcomere. Myosin molecules are large proteins that are nearly 500,000 times larger than a hydrogen atom. Actin is much smaller and makes up the thin filaments that form the ends of the sarcomere. The thick and thin filaments in sarcomeres give skeletal muscle its light- and dark-band appearance.

Muscle contraction occurs when the myosin and actin molecules interlock. During muscle contraction, myosin bonds to actin and *pulls* the two sets of thin filaments together (see figures 9.20 and 9.21). This creates a power stroke. The myosin releases and then reattaches to actin in another position in another power stroke. A single contraction of a sarcomere can take many power strokes.

In chapter 8, The Nature and Networks of Behavior, you learned that muscles contract in response to signals from the nervous system. A motor neuron sends a signal to a muscle cell, which rapidly spreads throughout all of the myofibrils in the muscle cell. The signal triggers the release of calcium ions through active transport. The increased concentration of calcium ions makes it possible for myosin to bond with actin (see figure 9.21). Therefore, calcium concentrations regulate muscle contraction. Movement of ions is important for many cell functions. Review chapter 8 to recall how active transport of sodium and potassium ions is important for sending signals through nerve cells.

Even with a high concentration of calcium ions triggered by nerve impulses, muscles still require energy to contract. Muscles use energy in the form of ATP. Energy from ATP helps release myosin from actin. The release of actin is necessary to initiate more power strokes or to allow the muscle to relax.

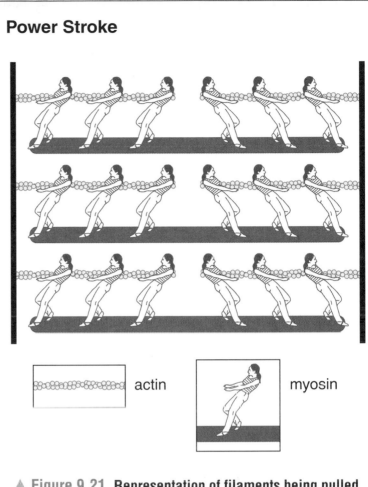

Power Stroke

▲ **Figure 9.21 Representation of filaments being pulled together.** Imagine myosin pulling the actin filaments closer together. This is how the muscle contracts.

Although the nervous system controls whether muscle contraction occurs, the availability of ATP in muscle cells determines how long a contraction can proceed. Muscle cells contain very little ATP. The supply of ATP in a single muscle cell can sustain a full contraction for only about 1 second. For a muscle cell to continue contracting, ATP must be regenerated rapidly. Most ATP is produced through cellular respiration, specifically aerobic respiration.

SCI*LINKS*
NSTA

Topic: muscle contraction
Go to: www.scilinks.org
Code: 1Inquiry431

3. Why are proteins important in muscle contraction?

4. Describe how energy is transferred during muscle contraction. Include what form the energy is in before and after contraction takes place.

5. What cellular processes are necessary for muscle contraction to occur? Keep in mind what you know about the transport of molecules and energy.

READING

Tired Cells

In Cellular Workout, you felt your arm get tired as you completed more repetitions. You even may have started to feel weak and may have had difficulty lifting the weight. What happened? Your muscle cells became tired, or fatigued, when the muscles were less able to contract. Many factors influence whether muscle cells become fatigued.

One cause of muscle fatigue may be reduced availability of ATP. Another cause may be changes in ion concentrations in muscle cells during exercise, which affect the ability of signals from the nervous system to spread throughout the muscle cell. A third reason may be related to the by-products of anaerobic respiration.

Remember from chapter 7 that ATP is supplied through cellular respiration. Cellular respiration requires glucose and oxygen:

$$C_6H_{12}O_6 + 6\ O_2 \rightarrow 6\ CO_2 + 6\ H_2O + ATP.$$

When there is not enough oxygen present for aerobic respiration, your cells temporarily undergo anaerobic respiration. During anaerobic respiration, cells produce lactic acid, which splits into lactate and hydrogen ions. Buildup of hydrogen ions causes a reduction of pH in muscle cells—the environment is more acidic. The change in acidity might interfere with the interaction of calcium ions and proteins and prevent myosin from bonding with actin. If myosin cannot bond with actin, muscle contraction will not occur.

Muscle fatigue is a complex phenomenon. Scientists continue to conduct research to determine what causes it to occur. Scientists do know that with regular exercise, muscles become resistant to fatigue. Regular exercise causes muscle cells to get bigger. Larger muscle cells can generate more force. Exercising also increases the number of mitochondria in muscle cells. Recall that cellular respiration, which supplies ATP to muscle cells, occurs in the mitochondria. Learn how scientists study the effect of resistance training on muscle by reading the sidebar, Muscle: Use It or Lose It?

Reflect and Connect

Work with a partner to answer the following questions in your science notebook.

1. How is muscle fatigue similar to an engine running out of fuel? How is it different?
2. Study the dog ankle joints shown in figure 9.22.
   a. Which has the largest mechanical advantage, the front or back leg? Show your calculations.
   b. How do you think the structure of the back leg might help a dog run faster or jump higher?

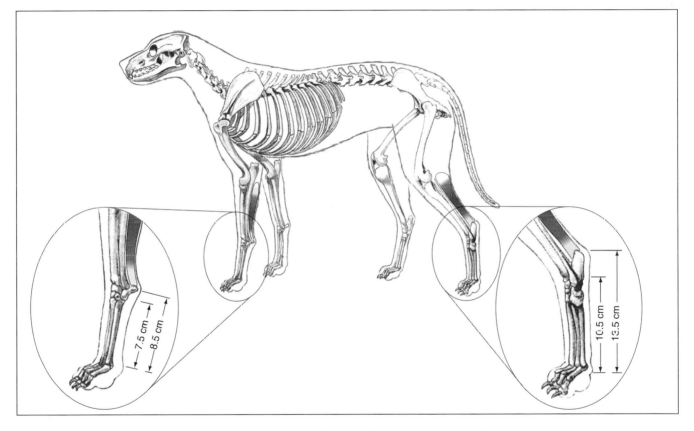

▲ Figure 9.22
Dog ankle joints. Use the measurements given here to calculate the mechanical advantage of the front and back leg at the ankle joint. Notice how the foot bones of a dog are elongated and positioned differently than human foot bones.

3. Medical engineers use an understanding of levers and muscle function to help design prosthetic limbs.
   a. Explain how this is a good example of one important relationship between science and technology.
   b. Give another example of this relationship.
4. Machines often transfer energy from one object to another. Your arm is a third-class lever and, therefore, a simple machine. Given this fact, do you think muscle cells are machines? Place your answer in a T-table with the headings "Yes, Muscle Cells Are Machines" and "No, Muscle Cells Are Not Machines." Include in each column specific examples from readings.

Muscle: Use It or Lose It?

Do you think you lose muscle if you don't use it? Scientists have conducted research to investigate the effects of both resistance training and detraining on muscle. Resistance training is exercise that causes your muscles to pull and push against a force. You have experienced detraining if you ever intensely trained for a sport or race for months and then stopped after the season or race was over.

Scientists have conducted experiments to study the effect of resistance training on muscle. For example, in one experiment, they measured the muscle mass of rats after a period of resistance training and detraining. The chart outlines the timeline for the experiment. The five rats in the control group did no resistance training for eight weeks and then had their muscle mass measured. There were 15 rats in the treatment group. They performed resistance training for eight weeks. The resistance training consisted of rats climbing a ladder with weights attached

to their tails. Training was conducted twice a day every three days. The weight on the tail was increased gradually during the eight weeks of training. After the eight weeks of training, five of the rats, called group 1, had their muscle mass measured. Another five rats, called group 2, received no training for four weeks and then had their muscle mass measured. The remaining five rats, called group 3, received no training for eight weeks and then had their muscle mass measured.

At the times indicated on the chart, the mass of one leg muscle of the rats was measured. This muscle is known as the flexor hallucis longus (FHL). The FHL is located on the back of the lower leg and across the bottom of the foot. This muscle flexes the foot and toes in rats. To measure muscle mass, rats were euthanized, the FHL muscle was removed, and its mass was measured. Animals often serve as model systems for the human body. This study is a good model system because rats and humans respond simi-

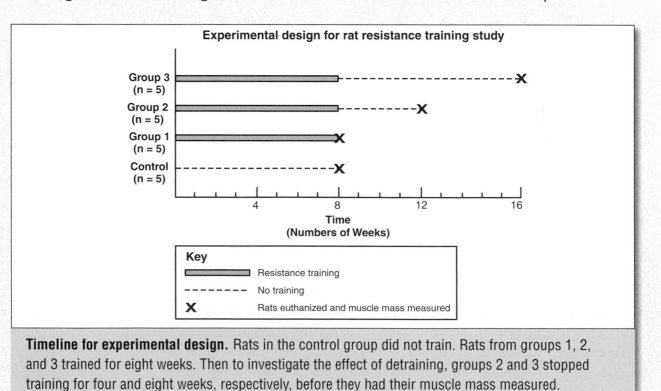

Experimental design for rat resistance training study

Time (Numbers of Weeks)

Key
— Resistance training
- - - - No training
X Rats euthanized and muscle mass measured

Timeline for experimental design. Rats in the control group did not train. Rats from groups 1, 2, and 3 trained for eight weeks. Then to investigate the effect of detraining, groups 2 and 3 stopped training for four and eight weeks, respectively, before they had their muscle mass measured.

larly to training. Like the training program in this rat study, human training programs usually involve training two or three times a week while gradually increasing the weight. Using animals in research studies of the muscular-skeletal system has potential benefits for, among other things, improving rehabilitation for people after they have sustained an injury or been diagnosed with a disease.

Study the graph of the results. The results of the experiment are given as the percent increase in muscle mass over the control group. As expected, the muscle mass of rats did increase as a result of resistance training. Rats in groups 2 and 3 that experienced detraining showed a smaller overall percent increase in muscle mass. This indicates that muscle mass is lost when training is stopped. Animals do *lose muscle* when they don't *use it.*

How do your muscles get bigger or smaller? You might have heard friends say that their muscle is *turning into* fat. They might have said that because they noticed their muscles getting smaller and weaker. Muscles get smaller when the volume and diameter of the muscle fibers (cells) decrease. The strength of your arm is directly related to the size (cross-sectional area) of the muscle. Muscles get bigger when the volume and diameter of the muscle fibers increase. Muscle cells can increase and decrease in size, and fat cells can increase and decrease in size; but muscle doesn't become fat, and fat doesn't become muscle.

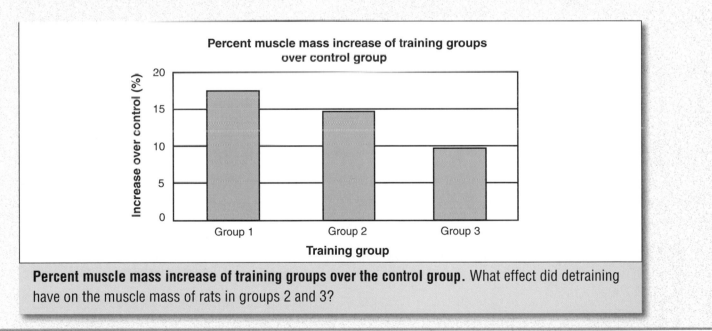

Percent muscle mass increase of training groups over the control group. What effect did detraining have on the muscle mass of rats in groups 2 and 3?

Muscle Power

ELABORATE

In How Much Energy? and Cellular Workout, your muscles were doing work by contracting. The rate at which work gets done is power. Power is the amount of work done divided by the time to do the work: power = $\frac{\text{work done}}{\text{time}}$. The average power is measured in the unit **watts**.

One watt (W) is equal to 1 joule (J) per second. You are familiar with watts if you have ever changed a lightbulb. Did you use a 40-, 60-, or 100-W bulb? A 100-W lightbulb converts 100 J of electrical energy to 100 J of electromagnetic radiation (light energy) in one second.

Most machines are designed to do work. Machines usually have a power rating that indicates the rate that the machine can do work. For example, the power rating of car engines is given in horsepower (hp). Horsepower is defined as 746 W. Cars with more horsepower can do more work in a given amount of time. For example, a 160-hp engine produces a greater acceleration than a 40-hp engine for the same car. Do you think the design of machines affects their power output?

Are some people more powerful than others? What might make them more powerful? In Muscle Power, you work in a team to calculate your own power output while climbing stairs.

Materials

For each team of three students

1 stopwatch or timer

1 meterstick

3 calculators

access to staircase

access to scale with metric units

Cautions

Do not run up stairs if you have any health problem that might be aggravated by exercise. Be careful when walking or running up stairs.

▼ **Figure 9.23**
Power. How much power could a person generate running up stadium stairs?

Process and Procedure

1. Organize into teams of 3 students.
2. How much power do you think your muscles deliver during physical activity? Read the following paragraph to learn how to calculate your power output while climbing stairs.

   Most of the work done in climbing stairs is due to moving the body against gravity. The force exerted against gravity while climbing stairs is very close to a person's weight. A common unit of force is a newton (N) (1 kg of mass has a weight of 9.8 N). The lemon you pick up in the grocery store weighs about a newton. To calculate the work done, you need to know the force exerted by a person and the distance that the force was exerted (in meters). When climbing stairs, the distance is vertical since your muscles apply a force against the pull of gravity. Remember from the introduction that

$$\text{power} = \frac{\text{work done}}{\text{time}} \text{ or } \frac{(\text{force} \times \text{distance})}{\text{time}}.$$

3. Discuss as a team how you will determine your power output while climbing stairs. Record your procedure in your science notebook. Your procedure should include how you will calculate power.

Consider these questions: How many stairs should you climb? Will you repeat trials?

4. Have your teacher approve your procedure.
5. Carry out your procedure for each member of the team. Record all of your measurements and calculations in your science notebook. Give your power output in watts.
6. How many kcal would you have to consume to provide the energy you need to climb stairs? How does your body compare to other machines? Complete the following tasks to find out. Figure 9.24 provides the conversion factors you will need. Show your work and record your answers in your science notebook.

   a. A protein bar contains 150 to 200 kcal. Convert your *work* done climbing stairs to kcal. The equation for calculating work is work = force × distance.

   b. A typical refrigerator uses 250 kilowatt-hours (kWh) per year. Convert your *work* done climbing stairs to kilowatt-hours and compare it in a ratio to the refrigerator energy.

   c. A mid-sized car engine has 110 hp. Convert your *power output* to horsepower and compare it in a ratio to the car engine.

   d. How could a student change his or her power output?

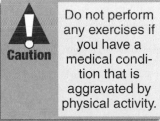

Caution Do not perform any exercises if you have a medical condition that is aggravated by physical activity.

Conversion factors
1 kilocalorie = 4,184 joules
1 kilowatt hour = 3,600,000 joules
1 unit of horsepower = 746 watts

▲ **Figure 9.24 Conversion factors.** Use the information here to complete calculations for Step 6.

7. Participate in a class discussion of the results.

Reflect and Connect

Work in a team to complete the following tasks and questions. Record your ideas in your science notebook.

1. Imagine that 2 students completed the same activity that you just did. The 1st student weighs twice as much as the 2nd student. The 2nd student climbed the same distance in half the time. Which student did the most work? How do the power outputs of the 2 students compare? Explain your answer.
2. What biological influences might have affected the power output for each individual? Other than weight, what might have been different about the students' bodies?
3. What is the relationship between energy and power output? Use graphs to show your answer.
4. What could you change in the design of your catapult to change its power output?

EVALUATE

Design Work

How do you know when the energy you put into something pays off? Many would say it is when something works the way you intended or when the job is done right. For example, painting your room takes a lot of work. But when you evaluate the results, you're happy with the product.

If the energy to do a job results in what you want or need, then the effort is worthwhile. The test is simple—does it work? A scientist or an engineer might ask the question this way: Does the device perform the way I designed it?

Scientists and engineers think of a task worth doing, design a way to do it, and then see if their design works. During this process, they

A Career in Biomechanics

Biomechanics is the application of mechanics and physics to the study of living systems. Biomechanics is a broad field covering a wide range of topics, including mechanics of human movement, artificial limbs, animal flight, swimming, and robotics. People who work in this field, whether studying humans or insects, are called **biomechanists**.

Biomechanists who study human movement work in a variety of careers. Some specialize in sports, whether that involves improving performance of an athlete or designing running shoes and other sports equipment. Others in this field design artificial (prosthetic) limbs and organs and other medical devices. A growing field is the development of ergonomics—the design and arrangement of things such as office furniture and equipment to increase productivity, safety, and comfort. For example, ergonomic office chairs support your body in a way that promotes good posture and reduces fatigue while you are working at a computer.

The study of animal movement is just as diverse. Some examples of research include how geckos grip surfaces, how insects fly, and how extinct animals such as *Tyrannosaurus rex* (*T. rex*) moved when they were alive. Studying biomechanics of animals helps scientists better understand how animals move, and the information scientists gather can be used to develop new technology. For example, geckos can hang from the ceiling because their feet are covered with millions of tiny hairs that can bond with any surface. Using this information, scientists are developing adhesive tape that is covered with millions of plastic "hairs." Scientists hope the adhesive can be used for a variety of applications, including surgical tape and sticky gloves for rock climbers.

Gecko. Geckos can walk on the wall and even on the ceiling because their toes are covered with millions of hairs.

Animals also are the inspiration for the design of robots. For example, models of the joint and leg structure of cockroaches help scientists develop six-legged running robots. Studies of elephant movement have shown that elephants always have one limb on the ground and have a bouncing motion when they run. By studying large animals such as elephants, scientists hope to use what they learn to develop robots that walk and run across rough terrain.

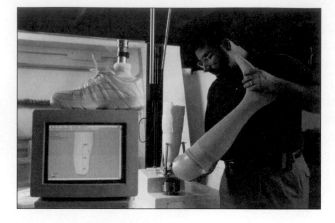

▶ **Figure 9.25**
Engineers use nature's designs. If you understand simple machines, you can design useful products. Where else in the human body are simple machines used?

revise their designs and test them again and again. For example, suppose you wanted to design a mechanical arm for a friend who suffered an amputation. What important design criteria would you use? What knowledge would you need? Would you need to know only about the muscular-skeletal system? Or might you need to know about simple machines, too? It seems that everything you learned in this chapter might be useful. In fact, you have been learning some concepts related to biomechanics. Read the sidebar, A Career in Biomechanics, to learn what scientists who study biomechanics do.

Organisms in nature are equipped with structures that give them specific functions. For example, a crab with a better claw might be able to capture more food and be more likely to survive in its environment. A rabbit with stronger hind legs might more effectively dodge the jaws of a pursuing coyote. What do the structures of the crab and the rabbit have in common? As with all structures in nature, they change and adapt with time. Some changes occur over millions of years. Scientists develop designs in a period of years. In this activity, you develop a design over a period of days.

▼ **Figure 9.26**
Structure of organisms. Sometimes the structure of an organism makes it more successful.

In Design Work, you work individually and in a team to apply the process of design to a specific design task. Then you evaluate your design based on how it performs. Along the way, you demonstrate what you know and understand about energy transfers in both biological and mechanical systems.

Part I: Scope Out the Design

Materials
For each student

1 copy of Design Work Scoring Rubric handout

Process and Procedure

What does the saying "I never hit a target that I couldn't see" mean? One interpretation is that you have to know where to aim if you intend to hit a target. This is especially true for design tasks.

In Design Work, your intense focus on design goals and expectations helps keep your eye on the target. When you understand the target clearly, you have a much better chance of hitting it.

1. Meet as a team of 3 and read the design goal aloud.

   Design Goal: Use the energy of 1 rubber band to launch a small bag of beans as far as possible. Teams will report the average of 3 tosses.

2. Sketch in your science notebook as many design ideas as you can think of in 5 minutes.

Brainstorming is an effective way of generating creative ideas and solutions as a group. Do not worry about your ideas being right or wrong. Remember, all scientists and engineers think of things that do not work. In fact, making mistakes is a part of getting the right answer. Translating what is in your mind to paper is the key task in the brainstorming process.

3. Read the following design constraints so you know what you can and cannot do to accomplish the design task.

Every job has constraints. You can think of constraints as rules of play. Soccer fields with no out-of-bounds lines or theatrical plays without scripts would produce inconsistent results. Constraints tell you what you can and cannot use to get the job done.

- All teams must use the same energy source—a #33 rubber band.

Study figure 9.27 to determine the maximum amount of energy 1 rubber band can supply. Remember, your design task is to transfer as much energy stored in the rubber band to the beanbag as possible.

▶ **Figure 9.27 Force versus stretch.** As you stretch the rubber band, it pulls back with a force. The more you pull, the greater the force of the rubber band and the more work the band can do. The shaded triangle represents the energy stored in the band when it is stretched 30 cm. What is true when you stretch the band half as much? Is the amount of energy stored in the band cut in half? To check your thinking, find the area of the new triangle using the equation: area$_{triangle}$ = $\frac{1}{2}$ (base) (height).

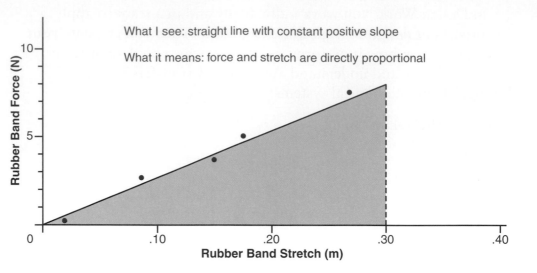

What I see: straight line with constant positive slope

What it means: force and stretch are directly proportional

- Each team will have 1 band and may alter the band in any fashion it deems best to accomplish the design goal.
- Your teacher will provide the launch mechanism framework. The team designs and provides the catapult arm, including the means of attaching the rubber band to the arm and the method of holding the bag of beans. Figure 9.28 shows the mechanism framework with measurements.

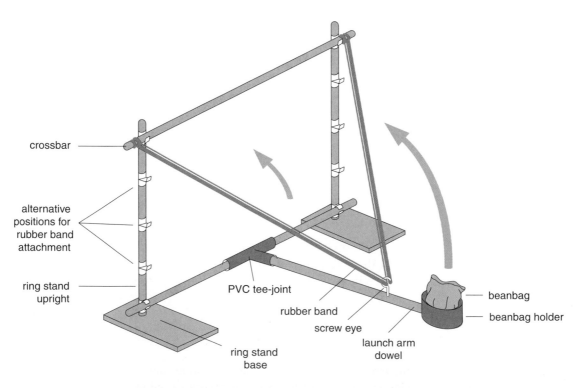

▲ **Figure 9.28 Ring stand catapult.** Your teacher will report the exact dimensions for this catapult. Record them in your science notebook so you can design your catapult arm effectively.

4. *Before* your team begins constructing your catapult arm, read the Design Work Scoring Rubric handout and Part I and Part II of the activity to understand all evaluation expectations.

Part II: Design Documentation

Materials
For each team of three students

3 pairs of safety goggles

launch mechanism framework (provided by teacher)

beanbag

wooden dowel

screw eye

#33 rubber band (provided by teacher)

device to hold beanbag (provided by students)

means of attaching bean bag holder to dowel (provided by students)

Cautions

Always wear safety goggles in laboratory settings. Beanbags launched through the air present potential eye injury hazards.

Process and Procedure

Design is not a random trial-and-error process. Instead, you use the tools of inquiry to apply knowledge in order to accomplish a stated goal. When you are done, you evaluate your efforts and make changes as needed. For example, engineers test a new air bag design by constructing prototypes. They test the prototypes on crash test dummies and improve the design with each test. Finally, they can place the air bags in new cars to be sold to consumers.

An early step in good design work is documenting your design ideas. Documentation is a tool of inquiry that involves recording what you intend to do and why, followed by what happened. Detailed documentation allows you to evaluate your results and compare them with your original ideas. This process helps you use the principles of nature to guide improvements. But when you do not document your predictions and results, you lose the connection to your original thinking. Often, this results in a trial-and-error approach to problem solving, which usually takes more time and produces poor results.

1. Meet as a team and document your ideas regarding your design by writing answers to Steps 1a–k in your science notebook.

Many design documentation questions are best answered in a sketch with highlight comments. For example, sketching your data table is better than describing it in words and makes it easier for your teacher to evaluate.

    a. How much will you stretch the rubber band? Why?

    b. Where on the launch mechanism will you attach the rubber band? Why?

    c. Where on the dowel (catapult arm) will you attach the rubber band? Why?

    d. How will you attach the rubber band?

    e. Will you cut the rubber band? Why or why not?

    f. Will you keep the rubber band as a loop (uncut)? Why or why not?

    g. Will you double over the rubber band? Why or why not?

    h. Will you twist the rubber band? Why or why not?

    i. Will you stretch the rubber band between the upright ring stands? Why or why not?

    j. How will you record important measurements required for the engineering report?

    k. How will you record the results of 3 tosses for both the preliminary and final design?

2. Ask your teacher to approve your design documentation before constructing your catapult arm.

3. Work with your team to construct your catapult arm according to your design documentation.

4. Conduct a preliminary test of your design as instructed by your teacher.

Launch the beanbag 3 times to test your initial ideas. Then modify your design based on the preliminary performance.

5. Document all modifications to your design, especially *why* you made each change.

6. Meet with other teams at the launch mechanism framework and document how your final design performs.

Remember, you report the average of 3 trials. What would improvement in launch distance between preliminary and final design mean regarding the process of design?

Caution — Be sure to wear your safety goggles.

Part III: Engineering Report

Materials

Process and Procedure

People who design processes and products communicate what they discover to a variety of audiences—colleagues, supervisors, and potential customers. When the communication is clear, it is easier to learn from and improve the design. The entire process forms a learning cycle. This cycle of design, evaluate, and modify repeats continuously until design goals are met.

In Part III, you work individually and in a team to communicate the findings resulting from your design effort. The communication takes the form of an engineering report, which you submit to your teacher for feedback.

1. Meet with your team and discuss answers to the questions in Steps 1a–d to determine the format for the engineering report, which has 3 parts: summary data table, calculations, and questions.
   a. How will the team ensure that all numbers have units and labels?
   b. How will the team ensure that data tables have easy-to-understand headings?
   c. How will calculations convey the relationship between the concepts needed to perform the calculation?
   d. How will the team ensure that answers to questions respond completely to the specific question posed and are easy to understand?
2. Work individually on answers to calculations in Steps 2a–f. Record them in your science notebook. Then meet with your team to reach a consensus answer. Show units in all of your calculations.

Calculations communicate well when they include governing equations in math symbols, substituted numbers, and final answers with units and labels.

   a. Calculate the maximum force applied to the catapult arm at the point of your rubber band attachment.

b. Calculate the maximum force applied to the beanbag due to your rubber band.

c. Calculate the maximum work done on the bag by your rubber band.

d. Compare the mechanical advantage of your arm to your catapult.

e. Pretend that your biceps could apply only the same maximum force as your rubber band. Calculate the maximum weight you could support in your hand when your forearm is at a right angle to your upper arm.

f. Suppose the time required to launch the beanbag is 0.10 seconds. Calculate the average power of your catapult.

g. How does the power you calculated in Step 2f compare to the average power your body produced climbing stairs? Use a quantitative comparison and discuss why your comparison does or does not make sense.

3. Work individually on answers to the questions in Steps 3a–f. Record them in your science notebook. Then meet with your team to reach a consensus.

   a. Explain what theoretically happens to the launch distance due to each of the following changes:
   - Double the mass of the beanbag (nothing else changes)
   - Double the number of rubber bands (nothing else changes)
   - Double the catapult arm length, keeping the rubber band attachment point the same (nothing else changes)
   - Double the mechanical advantage (nothing else changes)

   b. How does your mechanical advantage affect the force applied to the beanbag compared to the force applied by the end of the rubber band?

   c. Suppose your arm applies a constant force as it lifts an object. What are the similarities and differences between your arm and a rubber band-powered catapult? Use a Venn diagram to answer this question.

   d. Imagine 2 motions. Motion 1 is loading a catapult for launch, then launching it. Motion 2 is lowering a weight in your hand, then returning it close to your shoulder. Both motions involve energy transfers. Compare and contrast all of the energy transfers in those 2 motions.

e. Use your knowledge from the other activities in this chapter to design a prosthetic forearm that would hold 22.7 kilograms (50 lb). Show your design in a sketch with quantitative labels. Under your sketch, list all assumptions that you made.

f. Use a labeled diagram with a caption to describe what happens in muscle cells (the microscopic view) when you move your arm (the macroscopic view).

4. Produce your final engineering report, using your team answers, and turn it in to your teacher. The order of the report is title page, summary data table, calculations, and questions.

UNIT 3

The Earth and Beyond

The Earth and Beyond

As you lie on your back in your yard, gazing at the dark sky above, you may wonder how it all began. How and when did Earth and the universe form? What conditions evolved for life to exist on Earth? Scientists before you asked the same questions. What do scientists currently understand about the universe, and how do they know what they know? Modern science has some answers for those questions, and you discover them in unit 3, The Earth and Beyond. Like scientists, you also discover that as you learn more, new questions emerge that guide your curiosity and learning.

Your journey has taken you to the infinitesimal world of atoms and cells. Two important areas of exploration are the small worlds of cells and atoms and the huge world of the universe. Both stretch the limits of the imagination. Researchers who study either cells or stars encounter similar problems. They would like to be able to touch, sample, and observe directly the individual parts of those objects, but even with improved technology, much remains impossible. The parts that make up the cell are too small, and stars are too large and distant. Both, in different ways, remain too inaccessible to study completely.

You saw in unit 2, The Machinery of Life, that in spite of the difficulties, biologists are making rapid progress toward unlocking the mysteries of the cell. Astronomers are also unlocking the mysteries of the universe with advances in imaging from both land- and space-based telescopes.

In this unit, you journey through the universe, learning about structures in the universe, including stars and galaxies. Your journey takes you to stellar nurseries and colliding galaxies. You end your journey with a look at how life on planet Earth depends on the balance and mechanism of the Earth-Sun system.

Goals for the Unit

In unit 3, you and your classmates will explore a part of what scientists currently understand about the universe. By the time you finish the unit, you should understand

- the properties of stars, including luminosity, apparent brightness, temperature, and color, and revelations those properties can make about the stars;
- the properties of light, including speed, wavelength, and frequency, and ways astronomers use star spectra to analyze stars;
- the forces and processes that drive star and galaxy formation;
- the way those forces and processes shape and continue to shape the universe;
- the age of the universe and the way it formed;
- the Earth-Sun system and how this system relates to the biosphere.

As you explore those concepts, you learn more about the following concepts in scientific inquiry:

- Scientific explanations must be logically consistent, supported by evidence, open to questions and modifications, and based on current scientific knowledge.
- Mathematics is essential in scientific inquiry.
- Advances in technology lead to advances in science.

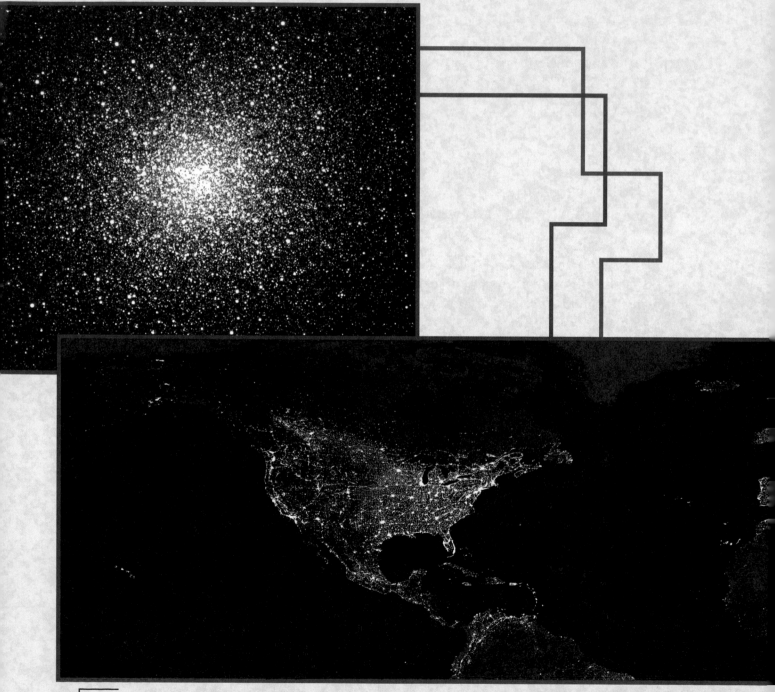

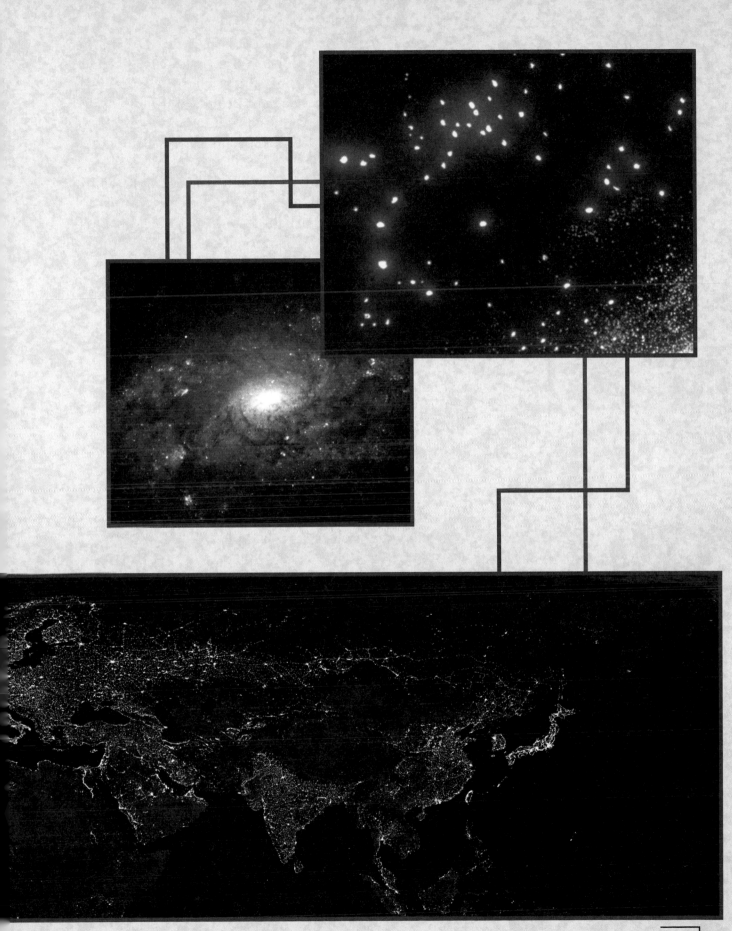

The Stars

Stars, like people, are unique in many ways, with their own set of special properties. Stars are also like members of a family, sharing similar characteristics. On a dark night, you can see the light produced from the stars in the sky. Did you notice in the opening photographs that some stars appear to be different colors? What does the color of stars tell us? The light that stars produce gives astronomers information about the properties of stars. For example, starlight helps scientists measure the vast distances in space. That starlight also indicates the temperature and color of a star. Astronomers can even use the light from a star to identify what elements make up the star.

Astronomers study the properties of the stars by measuring distances, analyzing the light from the stars, and looking for relationships in the data that they collect. This information gives scientists evidence for understanding what happened to stars in the past and for predicting what will happen in the future.

Goals for the Chapter

In your study of the stars, you model some of the measurements that astronomers make, examine light in a way that is similar to how astronomers examine light, and build your own understanding of the role that stars play in the universe. You also have the opportunity to develop answers to questions such as these:

- How and why do astronomers study the stars?
- What properties are used to describe stars?
- What properties do all stars share?
- How is the Sun similar to or different from other stars in the sky?
- What properties of stars provide information for learning more about the universe?

Astronomers learn more about stars every year. What they know now is based on many observations and analyses of the properties of stars that they can observe from Earth. What do you notice about stars as you look at the night sky? You will learn to think like an astronomer by participating in the following activities:

ENGAGE	Star Pictures
EXPLORE	Stars at a Glance
EXPLAIN	Stellar Parallax
EXPLORE	Springing into Action!
EXPLAIN	Much Ado about Waves
EXPLORE	Star Light, Star Bright
EXPLAIN	
ELABORATE	Putting It All Together
EVALUATE	The Night Sky Star Company

You will want to use the chapter organizer to help you with your learning. Check the organizer each day before you come to class and after you have finished the day's lesson. It will help you see where you are in the flow of the chapter. If you do not believe that you have mastered the content previously covered, consult with your teacher for clarification. Use the organizer to see where you are headed in your study of earth and space science.

ENGAGE

Star Pictures

Key Ideas:

- Stars occur in patterns across the night sky and historically the patterns have been given names.
- These patterns help us navigate the night sky.

How can scientists use these stars to determine distances in space?

EXPLORE

Stars at a Glance
Key Idea:

Near objects will appear to shift in relationship to distant objects when viewed from two different locations.

Linking Question

How can scientists use this shift to determine distances to stars?

EXPLAIN

Stellar Parallax
Key Ideas:

- When viewed from two different positions, near stars appear to shift against distant background stars.
- This shift can be used mathematically to determine the distance to stars.

The Stars

Linking Question

How can astronomers study properties of objects as far away as stars?

EXPLORE

Springing into Action!
Key Ideas:

- Light is a wave and travels at a constant speed.
- Models help us study abstract concepts.

Linking Question

What properties of waves and light are essential to understanding light from stars?

NIGHT SKY OBSERVATORY

EVALUATE

◀ **Linking Question**

The Night Sky Star Company

Key Idea:
We can gather much information about our universe by studying the properties of stars.

How can I use what I have learned to demonstrate my understanding about stars?

ELABORATE

Putting It All Together
Key Idea:
Astronomers use some important relationships among the properties of stars to study them.

Linking Question

What are the relationships among the properties of stars?

EXPLORE

CHAPTER

10 Major Concepts

▶ **Properties of stars supply key information to study the universe.**

▶ **Light is a wave and a form of energy that reveals a star's chemical and physical properties.**

EXPLAIN

Star Light, Star Bright
Key Ideas:
- Stars appear brighter due to both their distance and their luminosity.
- Light from stars can reveal a star's color, temperature, and luminosity.

EXPLAIN

Much Ado about Waves
Key Idea:
Light has properties such as speed, frequency, and wavelength that are essential to understanding the spectra from stars.

▶▶

Linking Question

How can astronomers use these properties to understand more about brightness, color, and the temperature of stars?

Star Pictures

▲ **Figure 10.1 The constellation Orion.** People throughout history have seen pictures defined by the brightest stars in the sky.

What do you know about the bright objects that you can see at night from your place on Earth? Do you ever observe patterns in the sky such as those in figure 10.1? For thousands of years, people have looked at the night sky with a wonder that generated countless questions. Let's take a look at some of the patterns that you and your ancestors have observed.

Materials

For each student

1 Star Pictures handout

Process and Procedure

1. Read It's a Bird . . . It's a Plane! with your class. What constellation names in figures 10.3 and 10.4 do you recognize?

READING

It's a Bird . . . It's a Plane!

Throughout the ages, when people have looked up at the night sky, they have seen distinctive patterns defined by the stars. Certain stars and patterns of stars are visible at various times of the year. Some stars are brighter than others, so they stand out, as in figure 10.1. Eventually, people named groups of stars that reminded them of a bear, a scorpion, or a person. Those groups of stars define regions of the night sky and are called **constellations**.

The 88 constellations that are recognized today were described by people from many different cultures, most notably the Greeks and Romans. Many figures reflect the myths of ancient Greece.

Astronomers use constellations as reference points in the sky. They have mapped the constellations in the summer and winter. Figures 10.3 and 10.4 show the 2 maps. Which constellation names do you recognize?

2. Participate in a class discussion of the following questions:
   a. Are constellations actual features in space? Explain your reasoning.
   b. A notable constellation is Orion, the Hunter, with his 3-star belt. What time of year, summer or winter, can you see Orion? How might people use this information as a point of reference?
   c. Orion's shield protects him from the bull, Taurus. Locate Taurus.
   d. Would everyone agree that the Orion constellation looks like a hunter and the Taurus constellation looks like a bull?
   e. What might people from another culture have seen in the stars that make up those 2 constellations?

You might have trouble picking out Taurus, the Bull, or Orion, the Hunter. Figure 10.2 may help. To see what the constellations look like in the sky, compare the three stars in Orion's belt with the three stars in the center of the picture in figure 10.1.

N

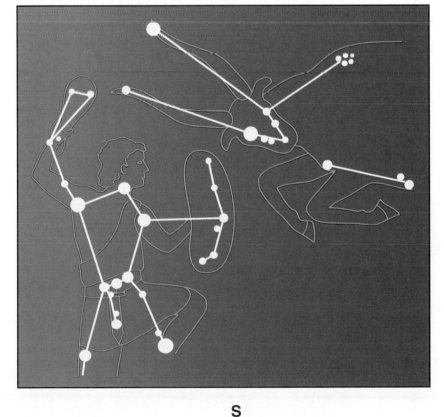

E   W

S

◄ **Figure 10.2**
Orion and Taurus.
Orion holds a shield and a club. Taurus represents only the head and shoulders of a bull. You can also see the stars of Orion in figure 10.1, especially the three bright stars of his belt in the center of the picture.

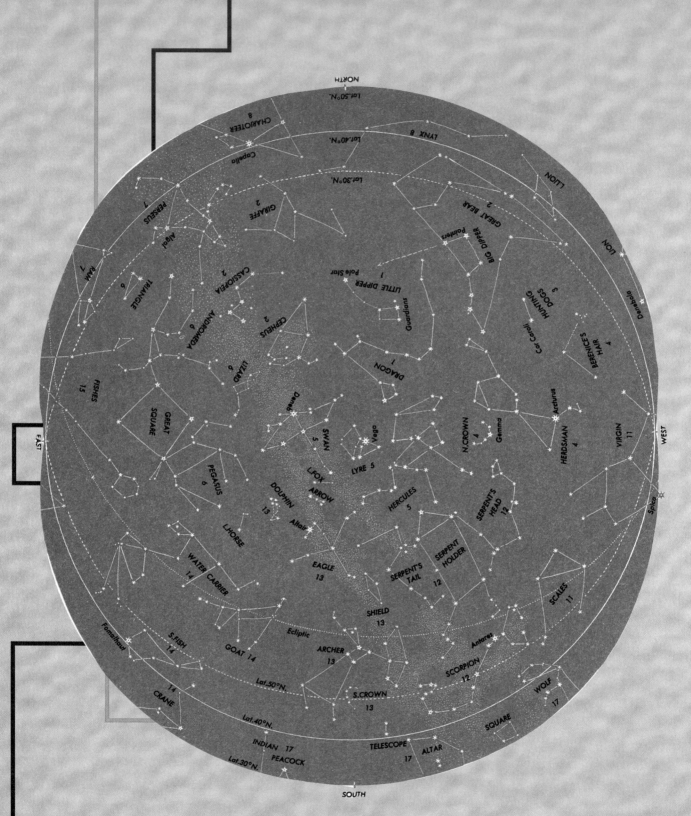

▲ **Figure 10.3 Summer sky map.** This map shows the constellations you can see from the Northern Hemisphere in the summer.

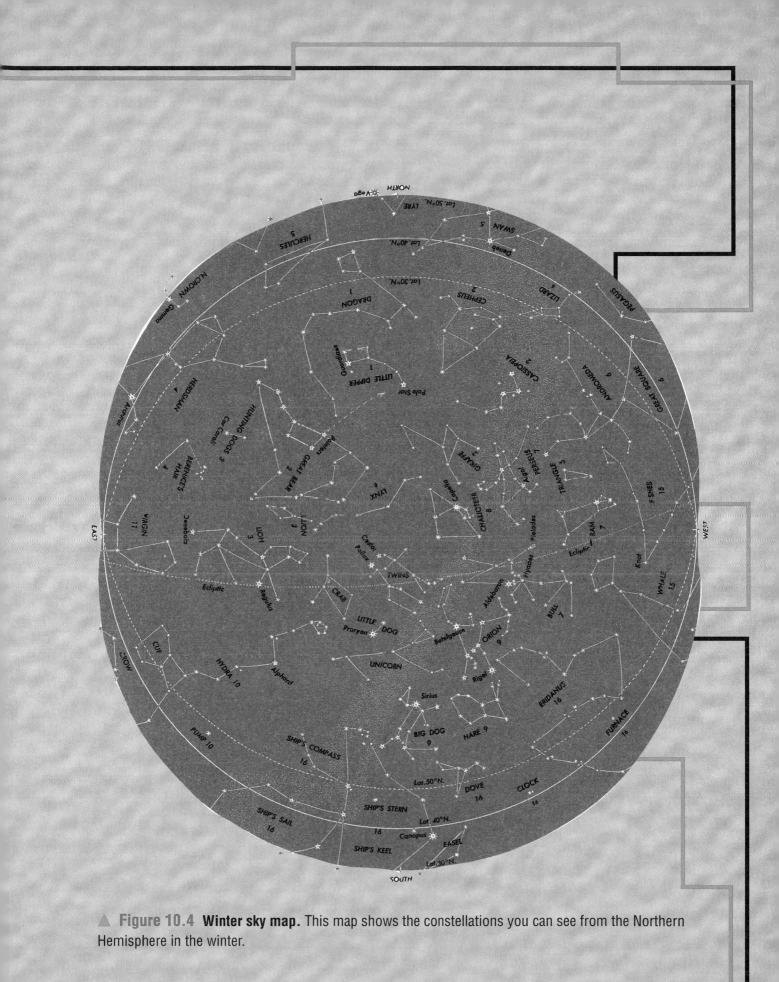

▲ **Figure 10.4 Winter sky map.** This map shows the constellations you can see from the Northern Hemisphere in the winter.

Reflect and Connect

Work individually to complete these tasks. At night, take time outside your home away from bright lights to look at the stars from your location.

1. Look at the stars on the handout titled Star Pictures.
   a. What images or pictures can you envision in these stars? Imagine a picture in the stars that is your own original constellation. Outline the picture on your handout.
   b. Select a name for your constellation. In your science notebook, write why you chose that name and briefly describe your constellation.

2. On a clear night, what constellations are you able to see from your location? With the help of figures 10.3 and 10.4, identify at least 3 constellations and record them in your science notebook.

3. What do you know about individual stars? List in your notebook 3 things that you know about stars and 3 things that you would like to learn about stars.
   a. Share your list with a partner and listen as your partner reads his or her list.
   b. Add to your list anything you learned from your partner.

4. The positions of constellations change in the sky during the night and from season to season. Yet the relative positions of the stars remain the same. What does this fact say about the motion of Earth? Compose your answer either in words or as a sketch of the position of Earth, the Sun, and stars at different times of the year.

Dark Skies

Earth at night. Look for your location on the map. Is your area affected by light pollution?

When you walk outside on a clear, dark night, can you see the stars distinctly in the sky? If you can, consider yourself lucky. In a recent astronomy journal, scientists report that nearly 70 percent of all Americans cannot see the Milky Way.

So what is getting in the way? Clouds, dust, air pollution, and lights! City lights, gas station canopies, and streetlights shine so brightly that it is difficult to see the light from stars. Astronomers call the problem light pollution because it obscures the night sky and makes it hard to see the stars, just as air pollution obscures the day sky.

People who own businesses and houses tend to like the increased lighting around their buildings. It helps prevent crime and makes them feel safe at night. It draws people to their businesses or welcomes them to their homes. But not everyone is happy about all of the light.

Astronomers in Flagstaff, Arizona, believe that light pollution is a major problem in their city. This is because Flagstaff is the home to at least six major telescopes. In fact, it was a Flagstaff astronomer who discovered Pluto in 1930.

Looking at the stars is important not only to the local astronomers of Flagstaff, but also to the citizens. People there have founded a group called the Flagstaff Dark Skies Coalition. This group believes that people of the city should be able to look up at the stars and be awestruck. They believe that people should be able to experience the imaginative potential that comes from looking at the stars. The Flagstaff Dark Skies Coalition thinks that people are missing out on an important human experience when they live in a place where light pollution obscures the stars.

To help control light pollution, the city of Flagstaff has begun to regulate the kind of lighting that building owners can install. Owners need to use fewer lights (which saves energy, too), use glare-free lighting, and use lower wattage lights. Because of the restrictions, the International Dark-Sky

Association has formally recognized Flagstaff as the first "International Dark-Sky City." Following Flagstaff's example, cities in Utah, Washington, and Idaho are also darkening their skies.

Controlling light pollution makes it easier for people to view objects and events in the night sky. As a result, many more discoveries may be made from locations on Earth that restrict outdoor lighting.

Light pollution. How can this light pollution be reduced?

Stars at a Glance

As you learned in the previous activity, people have often looked up at the night sky and tried to make sense of what they saw. They have wondered why some stars are brighter than others, how far away they are, how old they are, and what they are made of. People might have wondered how many stars there are. The curiosity people have about stars is no different today. In the Stars at a Glance activity, you work with a partner to discover a method that astronomers use to answer one of the questions they ask most often: How far away from Earth are objects in the sky?

Materials

For each team of two students

1 sheet of blank paper

1 clipboard

1 metric ruler

tape

1 wide-tipped marker

Process and Procedure

1. Be sure you and your partner have all of the materials you need.

2. Complete the following steps and think about how a process like this might be useful to astronomers as they try to determine the distance to objects in the universe. Record answers to questions under the heading "Stars at a Glance" in your science notebook.

It might be helpful for 1 of you to read the procedure and the other to do the activity. Then switch roles so each of you has a chance to experience the activity.

a. With your blank sheet of paper in a vertical position, use a ruler and marker to draw a vertical line in the center of the paper approximately 20 centimeters (cm) long. Place your paper on a clipboard.

b. Tape a ruler to the paper perpendicular to the bottom of the line, placing the center of the ruler at the line.

c. Hold the paper at arm's length in front of you with the line vertical and facing you.

You should try to hold the paper in this same position for the entire activity.

d. Hold the index finger of your other hand in front of your eyes, about halfway between you and the paper.

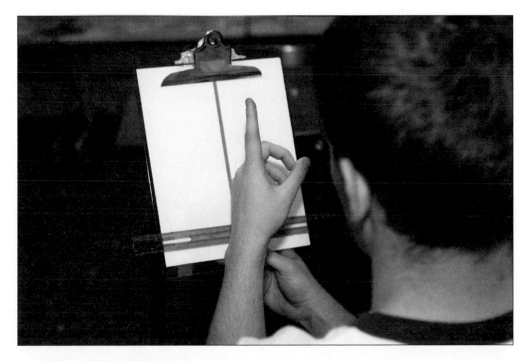

▲ **Figure 10.5 Experiment setup.** Hold your index finger in front of your nose and look at the line on your paper.

Both eyes should be open and your nose pointed at the line.

e. Close your left eye and observe the apparent movement. Use the numbers on the ruler to note the distance your finger appears to move with respect to the line. Open your left eye and close your right eye. Note the distance your finger appears to move in relation to the line. Record those measurements in your notebook.

f. Move your finger closer to the paper. Open and close each eye as before. Record measurements as before. What do you notice about the apparent movement of your finger relative to the line when your finger is closer to the paper? Record your answer in your science notebook.

g. Now move your finger closer to your nose. Open and close each eye as before. What do you notice about the apparent movement of your finger relative to the line when your finger is closer to your nose? Record your answer in your science notebook.

Reflect and Connect

Consider the following questions and record your answers under the heading "Reflect and Connect, Stars at a Glance" in your science notebook. Be prepared to share your answers in a class discussion.

1. Why do you think your finger appears to shift in position when you look at it first with 1 eye and then the other?
2. Compare the apparent shift of your finger at different distances. What did you notice about the shift when your finger was closer to and farther away from your eye? To answer that question, complete the following sentence:

As the distance from my eye to my finger increases, . . .

3. How might a similar process be useful to astronomers?

Stellar Parallax

READING

Stellar Parallax

There are many everyday examples of parallax on Earth just like the illustration in figure 10.6. How do astronomers use methods such as these to determine the distance to nearby stars? How have observations and mathematical relationships helped astronomers learn more about stars? Let's think about this more carefully.

In the Stars at a Glance investigation, did you notice that when you looked at your finger with first one eye and then the other that your finger appeared to shift to the left and right of the line you had drawn on the paper? In a similar way, when astronomers very carefully observe nearby stars first in the summer and again in the winter, they see that the positions of those stars relative to distant stars in the background seem to shift. This is because the scientists are looking at the stars in the night sky from two different positions. One position is from Earth in the summer, and the other is from Earth in the winter, which is an entirely different position in the sky. You modeled those two positions of Earth by looking at your finger—first with your right eye and then with your left eye. In your exercise, the distance between the two positions was only the separation of your eyes. For astronomers studying objects in the sky, the distance they use is the radius of the orbit of Earth around the Sun. This apparent shift of the position of stars is called **stellar parallax**.

▲ Figure 10.6 **Mountain and tree parallax.** How do astronomers use methods such as these to determine the distance to nearby stars?

Figure 10.7 shows the relationship from Earth to a nearby star at a six-month interval, such as December and June. The distance from Earth to the star is shown as *d*.

Topic: parallax
Go to: www.scilinks.org
Code: 1Inquiry467

The box insets show where the nearby star would be found in the sky compared to six distant stars. Astronomers use these measurements to determine the distances to the stars. The angle, *p*, is a measurement of the observed shift in position. It is called a **parallax angle**.

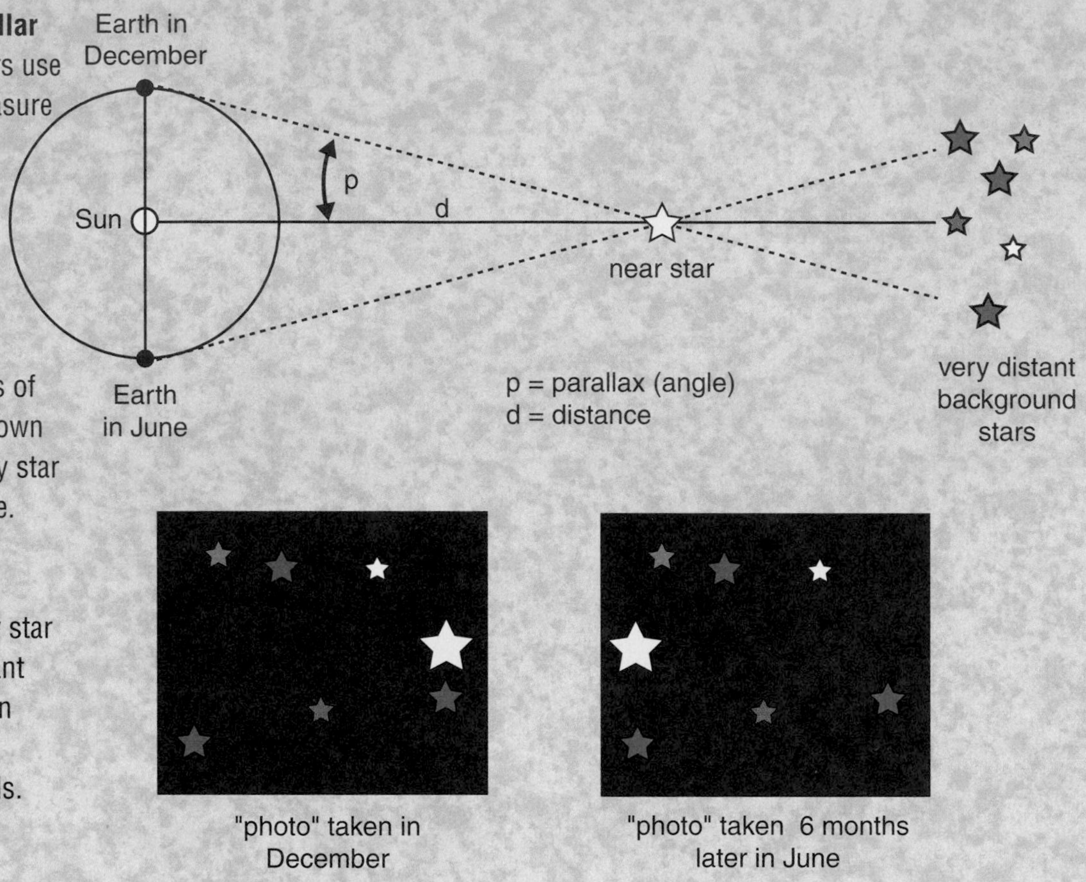

► Figure 10.7 **Stellar parallax.** Astronomers use stellar parallax to measure distances to nearby stars, such as the one shown here. Note that the distance to the background stars is not to scale. Two lines of sight (dashed) are shown from Earth to a nearby star in December and June. During the six-month interval, the apparent position of the nearby star compared to the distant stars changes, as seen in the "photographs" taken at these intervals.

p = parallax (angle)
d = distance

"photo" taken in December

"photo" taken 6 months later in June

Reflect and Connect

Work individually and record your answers in your science notebook under the heading "Reflect and Connect, Stellar Parallax."

1. View a simulation of stellar parallax as directed by your teacher. Make sure you click and drag the red star closer to Earth and farther from Earth. How is your model with your finger and line similar to this simulation of stellar parallax? To answer that, draw a T-table in your science notebook to organize your responses to Questions 1a–c. Label the top of the T-table with the 2 headings "My Model" and "Stellar Parallax Simulation." Write the words that appear in *italics* in the column labeled "My Model."

   a. What does your *finger* represent?

   b. What does the *line* represent?

   c. What do your *eyes* represent?

Monster Units

Would you measure the mass of this monster truck in grams? Would you measure its height in centimeters? You could, but the numbers would be very big. As you study science, you will learn to choose appropriate units in which to measure different things. Astronomers use their own set of units for the extreme measurements they must make in the universe.

If you were to use meters to measure the distance from Earth to its closest star, what would you guess this distance to be? Proxima Centauri is the closest star to Earth other than the Sun. If you were to measure the distance to Proxima Centauri in meters, it would be 39,900,000,000,000,000 meters (3.99×10^{16} m)! There is a better way to measure distances in the universe. Scientists use the unit **light-year (ly)** to measure distances to stars, galaxies, and other objects in the universe. One light-year is equal to the distance light can travel in one year. The speed of light in empty space is 3×10^8 meters per second (m/s) or 300,000 kilometers per second (km/s). In one year, light travels a distance of approximately 9.5 trillion kilometers, or 9.5×10^{12} km. Proxima Centauri is then 4.22 ly away. This number is much easier to work with! Don't make the mistake of thinking that a light-year is a measurement of time since it contains the term year. Remember that a light-year is a measure of distance.

Another unit of distance used by scientists is called the **astronomical unit (AU)**. One AU is the average distance from Earth to the Sun. That distance is about 150 million km (1.5×10^8 km). Distances in space much shorter than light-years are measured in astronomical units. For example, astronomers typically use AUs to measure distances within our solar system.

Another measurement made in astronomy is luminosity. Luminosity is the energy output of a star. For example, the luminosity of the Sun is 3.8×10^{26} watts (W). Again, this is an incredibly large number. Astronomers often use solar units to express a star's luminosity relative to the Sun. A solar unit for luminosity is simply a ratio of the luminosity of a star (L_{star}) to the luminosity of the Sun (L_{Sun}). Therefore, the Sun has a luminosity of 1 L_{Sun}. Proxima Centauri has a luminosity of 0.000138 L_{Sun} (1.38×10^{-4} L_{Sun}). Does that mean that Proxima Centauri is more or less luminous than the Sun? Proxima Centauri is much, much less luminous. In fact, if Proxima Centauri were the same distance from Earth as the Sun, the star would be barely visible to you.

On some of the graphs that you will be working with in this unit, you may notice that stars are labeled with a mass, using the unit M_{Sun}. Can you guess what that refers to? It is a ratio of the mass of the star to the mass of the Sun. For example, the mass of the bright summer star Vega is nearly three times the mass of the Sun, Vega so M_{Vega} is approximately 3 M_{Sun}. Those units help you get a feel for the sizes and luminosities of stars by comparing them with the most familiar star—the Sun.

2. Alpha Centauri, a nearby star, is 4.36 light-years (ly) from Earth, and Proxima Centauri is 4.22 ly from Earth. When viewed from Earth in June and again in December, which star appears to shift the greatest distance compared to very distant background stars? Explain your answer. If you are not familiar with the unit light-year, read the sidebar, Monster Units, to learn more about light-years and other units used in astronomy.

3. Both Alpha Centauri and Proxima Centauri are in the constellation Centaurus, the Centaur. How would you respond to a student who said that all stars in a constellation are the same distance from Earth?

EXPLORE

Springing into Action!

How do scientists study something as far away as the stars? One way is by analyzing the light from distant objects that comes to Earth through space. This light travels in the form of waves. You can learn a lot from studying the light waves from distant objects such as stars, but first, you will examine what is known about waves on Earth.

Indeed, you see evidence of waves every day. You are constantly experiencing waves that are both natural and human made. One type of wave travels through matter to reach you. You are very familiar with this type of wave. Examples include waves in a bathtub, pool, or lake; ground vibrations from a passing bus, truck, or train; and the sound waves that your ears receive. Those waves pass through matter such as water, the ground, or the atmosphere.

▶ **Figure 10.8**
What do all these photographs have in common?

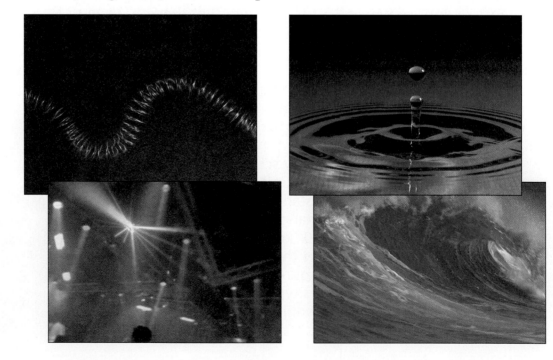

Other types of waves do not require matter to travel through. Visible light is a good example. Light waves can travel across a room to your eyes when you switch on a light, or they can zip across an auditorium as laser light at a concert. The waves travel through air in those cases, but light waves can also travel through outer space, where there is no atmosphere, or "air." If light waves needed air to travel through, you could not see beyond the boundary of the atmosphere. No light or energy would be able to travel from the Sun to Earth, and without this light energy, life would not have evolved on Earth. You would not be able to see that Earth has a moon or that there are other planets in our solar system. You also wouldn't be able to see the thousands of stars that are visible in a dark night sky.

Let's spend a few more minutes thinking about waves. Imagine sitting next to the ocean and watching the water. The surface of the water probably is not flat and mirrorlike. Rather, the surface of the water probably has a variety of ripples, waves, or swells. As the waves move through the water, they transport energy. You can see this as the waves move to the beach and crash on the shoreline.

Now imagine floating on the water in a kayak (see figure 10.9). Depending on how frequently the waves came by, you would bob up and down either slowly or quickly. If the waves were closely spaced, you would move up and down very rapidly. If the waves were spaced like ocean swells, you would move up and down more slowly as the swells pass beneath you. Does the speed at which you move up and down affect how fast the wave actually moves to the shore? In the Springing into Action! activity, you work with a team to learn about a key property of waves—speed—that helps you answer that question. You do this by observing how waves travel along a spring.

◀ **Figure 10.9**
Does the speed at which this kayak moves up and down with the waves indicate how fast the wave actually moves to the shore?

Materials

For each team of three or four students

spring

masking tape

1 measuring tape or meterstick

1 stopwatch

Process and Procedure

To help you understand how scientists use light waves to study objects in the sky, in this activity you will learn about the key properties of all waves. For example, did you know that all light waves in outer space travel at the same speed? They move incredibly fast—at about 300,000,000 meters per second (m/s), or 3×10^8 m/s. That's about 186,000 miles per second! You probably think that you could never see light moving at such speeds, but astronomers have captured images of pulses of light moving away from a star. Look at figure 10.10. It appears to be an explosion, spraying matter out into space. In reality, you are seeing a wave of light sweeping through clouds of dust after a stellar outburst. This image was taken by the Hubble Space Telescope in 2002.

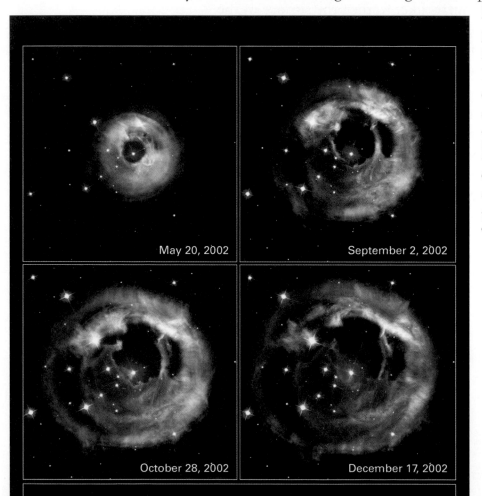

May 20, 2002

September 2, 2002

October 28, 2002

December 17, 2002

Light Echo from Star V838 Monocerotis
Hubble Space Telescope • Advanced Camera for Surveys

NASA, ESA and H.E. Bond (STScI) • STScI-PRC03-10

◄ **Figure 10.10 Echo of light.** This sequence of images from the Hubble Space Telescope shows a light echo. A flash of light from the star at the center (V838) is spreading into space and lighting up surrounding stellar dust. These images were taken from May to December 2002, and using the speed of light to calculate the distance of the largest light shell, astronomers determined that by December, the size of the light shell had reached a diameter of 4 to 7 ly. This star is in the winter constellation Monoceros (the Unicorn).

You cannot study the speed of something that fast in your science lab, so you will study a wave that moves much slower. Does the speed of all waves stay the same? What affects the speed of waves? If you could ride on a wave of light from the Sun to Earth, how long would it take you to get to Earth? Would it make any difference if you were riding on a red light wave or a blue light wave? You answer those questions as you work with a team to complete the following activities. Record your answers in your notebook under the heading "Springing into Action."

1. Work with your team and discuss the different variables that might affect the speed of a wave on a spring. Make a list in your science notebook and share your list with your classmates.

2. Participate in a class discussion on how to design your own experiment to investigate a variable that might affect the speed of a wave. Consider the 2 measurements that you need to make to calculate the speed of a wave. Also, consider how you will accurately measure those quantities.

3. With your team, choose 1 variable to test. Record this variable, as well as a list of materials that you need, in your science notebook.

4. With any variable you choose to test, you need to record the distance the wave travels and the time it takes the wave to travel that distance. Make a data table in your science notebook to organize the information that you collect.

Remember that it is best to do several trials and then take an average.

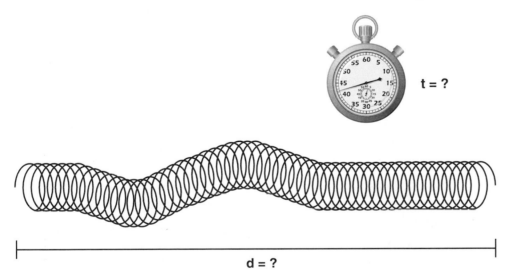

◀ **Figure 10.11**
Spring and speed.
What do you need to know to determine the speed of a wave?

5. In your science notebook, record your prediction about whether you think your variable will affect the speed of the wave.

6. Gather the materials that you need and conduct your investigation. Record all of your data in your science notebook.

7. After you have conducted your investigation, analyze your data to complete and answer the following questions. Record your answers in your science notebook.

   a. You are familiar with speed, such as the speed of a car, a train, or an airplane. Speed tells you the distance that something travels in a given amount of time. A car on the highway might have a speed of 97 kilometers per hour (km/hr, or 60 miles per hour)—it travels 97 kilometers (km), or 60 miles, in 1 hour. Use the distance your wave traveled and its average time for your trials to determine the speed of your wave. Use this formula to calculate average speed:

$$\text{speed} = \frac{\text{distance}}{\text{time}}$$

   b. Did the variable you tested affect the speed of the wave? Include evidence to support your answer.

8. When you are finished, contribute your data to a class data table and discuss your results with your classmates.

Reflect and Connect

Work with your team to answer the following questions. Record your best answers under the heading "Reflect and Connect, Springing into Action!" in your science notebook.

1. What variable changed the speed of the wave? Remember that there are variations in almost every test due to experimental error. You are looking for a significant change in the speed.

2. You learned earlier that the speed of light through empty space is about 3×10^8 m/s. The distance between Earth and the Sun is about 1.5×10^{11} m. If you were riding on a wave of light from the Sun to Earth, how long would it take you to get to Earth? Use the formula for speed to calculate the time needed to get to Earth. Convert your answer to minutes. Show all of your calculations and give your answer with the proper unit.

3. Sound waves in air have a velocity of about 340 m/s. How does the speed of your wave compare with the speed of sound? To compare, use a ratio to determine how much faster sound travels than your wave travels. For example, if your wave has a speed of 3.4 m/s, the ratio would be as follows:

$$\frac{340 \ \cancel{\text{m/s}}}{3.4 \ \cancel{\text{m/s}}} = 100$$

After dividing, you could say that the speed of sound is 100 times faster than the speed of your wave. Now use this method with your data.

4. How does the speed of sound compare with the speed of light? Using the same method explained in Question 3, determine how much faster light waves travel compared to sound waves. Be sure to show your work.

5. What features of thunderstorms help confirm your calculation in Question 4?

Much Ado about Waves

In the last activity, you learned how to measure the speed of waves in a spring. Did you find that the speed of a wave is different in a stretched spring compared to the same spring that is not stretched? In this case, the material is the same, but you have changed a property of the material so that the speed is different. The speed of a wave changes when the medium changes. A **medium** is the material through which a wave travels. Similarly, light waves travel at different speeds in different mediums. They travel the fastest in a vacuum of empty space and slow down somewhat in the atmosphere.

As you conducted your experiment with waves, you probably observed other features and properties of waves. In the Much Ado about Waves activity, you work with your team, using a spring to generate your own explanations for properties of waves.

Part I: Properties of Waves

Materials
For each team of three or four students

Slinky

1 measuring tape or meterstick

1 stopwatch

masking tape

Process and Procedure

As you do more experimenting with waves and learn more about wave properties, in your science notebook under the heading "Much Ado about Waves—Part I: Properties of Waves," record your ideas and answers to questions.

1. Watch as your teacher demonstrates how to make a complete wave on your Slinky.

You may have been making only a pulse in the previous activity, which is only one-half a wave.

2. Watch the piece of tape on your teacher's Slinky as your teacher makes another series of waves.
   a. What direction does the piece of tape move in relation to the wave? Those types of waves are called **transverse waves.** In a transverse wave, the matter (represented by the tape) moves at right angles (or perpendicular) to the motion of the wave.

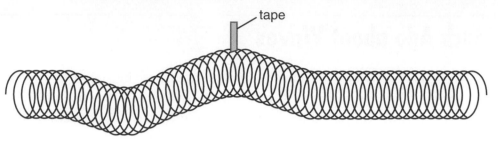
tape

► **Figure 10.12**
Wave and tape. Does matter (the tape) move in the same direction as the wave?

   b. Where is the tape after the wave passed?
   c. Draw this wave in your science notebook, using arrows to represent the motion of the wave and the motion of the tape. Label the wave as a transverse wave.
3. Now you will make your own waves to learn more about the properties of waves. Complete the remainder of the activity with your team and continue to record in your science notebook your answers to questions.
   a. Place a piece of tape on 1 coil of your Slinky.
   b. Stretch your spring at least 2 meters (m) and make a single complete wave on your Slinky as your teacher demonstrated.
   c. Now make another wave, but this time add a lot of energy to it, shaking the Slinky with more energy by moving your hand a greater distance.
4. After you observe these waves, answer the following questions and complete the following tasks:
   a. What characteristic of the wave did adding more energy change?
   b. The high part of the wave is known as the **crest,** and the low part is known as the **trough.** Draw a wave in your notebook and label those 2 parts.

Use a clean sheet in your notebook, turn your book horizontal, and use the entire page to draw your wave. Draw at least two wave crests and two wave troughs. You will label several features of waves on this drawing during the remainder of this activity.

   c. How did adding more energy to the wave affect the crest of your wave?
   d. When you measure from the midpoint of the wave to the top of a crest or the bottom of a trough, you know the **amplitude** of the wave. See figure 10.13. Measure and label in

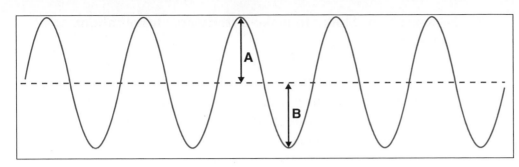

◀ **Figure 10.13**
Amplitude of a wave.
You can measure the amplitude by measuring distance A or distance B.

centimeters the amplitude of the wave that you drew. Label the amplitude on your picture with the measurement and unit.

e. How did adding energy to the wave affect the amplitude?

5. Read the following paragraph to learn about a different type of wave.

In a sound wave, the amplitude of the wave indicates the loudness of the sound. Sound waves are different from transverse waves. Sound waves are called **compressional waves** or **longitudinal waves.** You can make those waves with a Slinky by pushing the spring along the same line as the spring and then pulling your hand back while still holding on to the Slinky. Those types of waves must have matter through which to travel. Otherwise, there is nothing to compress. Try making a longitudinal wave with a Slinky. How does the motion of the wave compare with the motion of the tape? To answer that question, draw a picture of the longitudinal wave in your notebook and use arrows to label the direction of the motion of the wave and the motion of the tape.

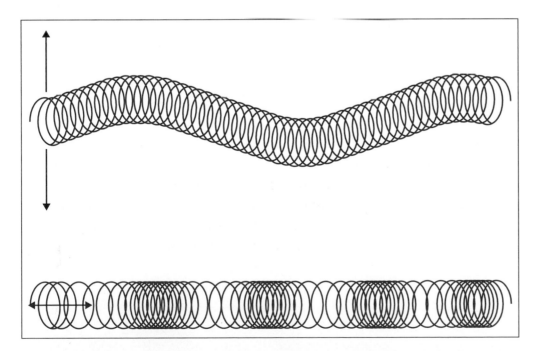

▲ **Figure 10.14 Two types of waves on a Slinky.** How are these types of waves different? How are they alike?

6. Now use your Slinky to make 2 transverse waves about 1 second apart.
   a. If you measured from a point on 1 wave to the corresponding point on the adjacent wave, you would be measuring the **wavelength** of your wave. An easy way to do this is to measure from crest to crest or from trough to trough. In your science notebook, draw a line on your transverse wave to represent how you would measure the wavelength.
   b. Measure and record the wavelength of the wave you drew in your science notebook. Use centimeters to record this measurement. Scientists use the Greek letter **lambda** (λ) as a symbol for wavelength. Label your wavelength with this symbol.
7. You can investigate other properties of waves. Continuously shake your Slinky from side to side as fast as you can, making transverse waves along the floor as you did before.
   a. Have your teammates count the number of waves that you make in 10 seconds. Your teammates should look at the number of times you move your hand back and forth in a complete cycle. Record this number in your notebook.
   b. How many waves did you make in *1* second? You have just calculated the **frequency** of the wave, or the number of waves per second.
   c. Scientists use the unit **hertz (Hz)** to represent waves per second. Record your wave frequency in hertz in your science notebook.
   d. In Step 6, you made waves with your Slinky. In Step 7, you made more waves. How does the *total* amount of energy you added to the Slinky compare in Step 6 and Step 7?
   e. How do the wavelengths of your waves compare in Step 6 and Step 7?
   f. How do the frequencies of your waves compare in Step 6 and Step 7?
8. What other questions arise that you could test now? Discuss this with your team and list them in your science notebook.
9. You have identified some properties of waves-speed, wavelength, and frequency. Read Waves to learn about the relationships between those properties.

Waves

In the previous activities, you calculated the speed of your wave by using the formula

$$\text{speed} = \frac{\text{distance}}{\text{time}}.$$

This method works well for waves that are not traveling very fast. What about waves traveling very fast? It would be impossible to use a stopwatch to time the waves. And if you could not see the waves moving, how could you measure the distance from where they started to where they ended? Scientists use properties other than distance and time to calculate the speed of very fast waves—they use wavelength and frequency. You learned in this activity that wavelength could be measured from corresponding points on the wave—you measured from crest to crest. You also learned that the frequency of a wave indicates the number of waves that pass in 1 second. The wavelength (λ) and the frequency (f) of a wave are related in the following equation: speed = $\lambda \times$ f.

You can use this equation to calculate the speed of a wave. If the wavelength is measured in meters per wave and the frequency in hertz (waves per second), the unit for speed will be in meters per second, or m/s.

You are already familiar with many types of waves that are measured in units of hertz; for example, your favorite FM radio station. Imagine a station with a tuning frequency of 96.1 FM. This is the same as 96.1 Megahertz (96.1 MHz), or 96.1×10^6 Hz. That signal vibrates at a frequency of 96.1 million times per second. That frequency is much higher than your Slinky's!

Sound waves are very different from radio waves. The frequency of a sound wave is related to the pitch of the sound. **Pitch** is the perception of how "high" or how "low" a sound is. In sound, the higher the frequency of the sound wave, the higher the pitch. For example, middle C on a piano has a frequency of 261 Hz, and an A, several notes higher, has a frequency of 440 Hz. You will learn later in this chapter how frequency is related to light waves as well as radio waves.

Speed, wavelength, and frequency are all related in a fundamental way. Think for a moment about large waves moving across water. For those waves, frequency is the number of times per second that a crest passes a person in a boat. The boat bobs up and down every time a crest passes. In figure 10.15, imagine the crests of the wave passing the eye of an observer once every 2 seconds. This is a frequency of 1 wave crest going by every 2 seconds, or f = 0.5 Hz. The distance traveled by the crest in that time interval is the crest-to-crest length, or $\lambda = 10$ m.

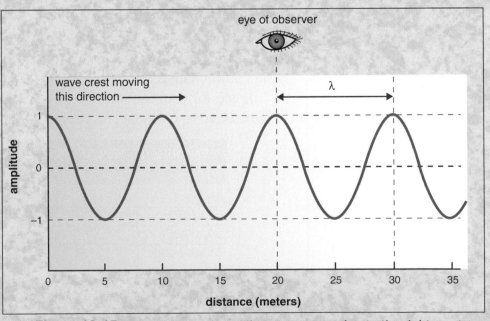

▲ **Figure 10.15** This diagram shows three waves moving to the right, past the eye of an observer. The wavelength, λ, is 10 m.

There are 2 ways to calculate the speed of a wave. The first way is by comparing a length of 10 m between crests divided by 2 seconds, giving 5 m/s. This is the formula you used in the previous activity:

$$speed = \frac{distance}{time}.$$

The second way is by multiplying wavelength by frequency, or

$$speed = \lambda \times f.$$

For figure 10.15, this gives the answer of speed = 10 m × 0.5 Hz = 5 m/s. To see how the units cancel, consider the equation

$$10 \ \frac{m}{\cancel{wave}} \times 0.5 \ \frac{\cancel{wave}}{s} = 5 \frac{m}{s}.$$

How do those 2 answers compare?

This relationship among frequency, wavelength, and speed is fundamental to understanding light, regardless of its source. Light from stars comes to Earth at the speed of light, which is much faster than waves in springs, waves across water, or sound waves. This light from stars holds vital clues that scientists need to understand the universe.

Topic: waves
Go to: www.scilinks.org
Code: 1Inquiry480

Stop & THINK

Part I

1. Imagine that you are creating a wave on a spring by shaking your hand from side to side. Without changing the distance your hand moves, you begin shaking the spring faster and faster. What happens to the amplitude, frequency, wavelength, and speed of your wave?

2. Waves are sent along a spring of fixed length. Explain how (or if) you could change the variables listed in figure 10.16. Cite evidence for your answers from the activity. Copy the chart in figure 10.16 to organize your response.

▶ **Figure 10.16**
Answer chart for Stop and Think Question 2.
Copy this chart into your notebook.

Variable	How to change	Evidence from activity
Speed		
Frequency		
Amplitude		
Wavelength		

3. Does a wave transfer matter, energy, or both? What is your evidence?

4. If you add more total energy to a wave (as you did in Step 7), what happens to the

   a. frequency of the wave?

   b. wavelength of the wave?

5. A wave moves 12 m in 5 seconds. There are 6 complete waves produced in that distance and time. Using this information, complete the tasks and answer the following questions.

   a. Sketch a picture of this wave and include all information given in the problem. Label your sketch with the values given to you. This will help you visualize the wave and solve the following problem.

   b. Calculate speed using the equation $\text{speed} = \dfrac{\text{distance}}{\text{time}}$.

      The information you need is given in the sentences above. Show all of your work and use the correct units in your answer.

   c. Now use your sketch and the information given to you to find frequency and wavelength. Then use the equation $\text{speed} = \lambda \times f$ to calculate speed another way. Again, show all of your work and use proper units.

   d. How do your 2 answers for the speed of a wave compare?

Part II: Starlight—Cell Phone Calls from Outer Space

READING

EM Waves in Space— Rainbows from Outer Space

Waves are everywhere! Imagine yourself in a grocery store when suddenly a nearby cell phone rings, crying beep-do-do-de-dooo. The person takes out the cell phone and begins speaking. But wait—how can the person's voice

▲ Figure 10.17 This teenager is using waves to communicate with her friends.

▲ **Figure 10.18** What do rainbows and the light from distant galaxies have in common?

enter the cell phone and then get transferred to the caller's cell phone somewhere else? How fast do voices move between wireless cell phones? As you might guess, the signal for that cell phone call is transported back and forth as waves. So waves from cell phones share many properties with waves in your Slinky.

You have learned about several types of waves that carry energy as they travel through matter. Examples are sound waves that travel through the air, ripples on a pond, and the pulse of a wave moving down your spring. Even seismic waves that travel through Earth require matter. Another important type of wave travels through space, between solar systems, and even across the universe. Those waves also carry energy and are a type of radiation. They are called **electromagnetic waves**, or **EM radiation** for short. Visible light in general and rainbows in particular are great examples of the EM radiation that your eyes can detect. The different colors indicate different wavelengths or frequencies of EM radiation.

Rainbows form when white light spreads into a spectrum of separated colors. When you look carefully at light as it exits a prism, you see the same spectrum of colors. In the air, water drops act like a prism and separate sunlight into rainbows. Those spectra always consist of the colors from red to orange to yellow, then green, blue, indigo, and violet. For any part of the rainbow, the color indicates waves of energy with a unique frequency, f, and wavelength, λ. The speed of light is a constant and is given the symbol **c**. The wavelength and frequency of light are related in the equation

$$c = \lambda \times f.$$

Does this equation look familiar? It is the same equation you used earlier to calculate the speed of a wave.

▲ **Figure 10.19** White light entering a prism is separated into different colors. Can you name the colors in order?

Since the speed of light is often given as the constant 3×10^8 m/s, you can look at the variables wavelength and frequency to discover some relationships. Remembering that $c = 3 \times 10^8$ m/s, what would happen to the wavelength if the frequency increased? Think back to Part I, Properties of Waves, when you made waves on a Slinky. The speed of your wave on the spring stayed constant as long as you kept the spring the same. When the speed of light is constant, as frequency increases, wavelength decreases. The opposite is true also—as frequency decreases, wavelength increases. Do you remember the amount of energy that you had to use to make waves with a high frequency and a short wavelength? Those waves of high frequency and short wavelength also are higher in energy.

To see how the equation $c = \lambda \times f$ is used, consider the color red. Red light is an EM wave with a wavelength of 700 nanometers ($\lambda = 700$ nm). Recall that 1 nm is 10^{-9} m. This means that when an EM wave of $\lambda = 700$ nm (or 700×10^{-9} m) enters your eyes, such as the light reflected from a red car, a signal to your brain is produced. Your brain assigns the color "red" to that car image. The frequency can be calculated using the formula $c = \lambda \times f$ and solving for frequency:

$$f = \frac{c}{\lambda} = \left(\frac{3 \times 10^8 \ \text{m/s}}{700 \times 10^{-9} \ \text{m/wave}} \right) =$$

$$4.3 \times 10^{14} \frac{\text{waves}}{\text{s}} \ \text{or Hz.}$$

That is 428 trillion cycles every second!

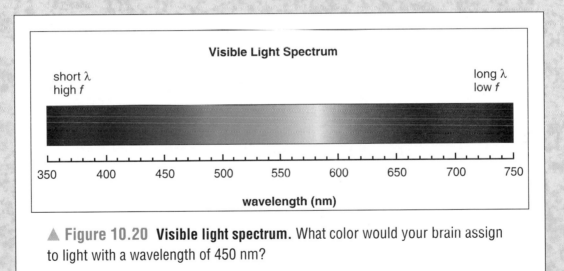

Visible Light Spectrum

short λ
high *f*

long λ
low *f*

wavelength (nm)

▲ Figure 10.20 **Visible light spectrum.** What color would your brain assign to light with a wavelength of 450 nm?

The wavelength of red light at 700 nm might seem short. As wavelength decreases even further, colors move through the spectrum to blue. For example, if the "light" (or EM waves) traveling from a car to your eyes had $\lambda = 450$ nm, what color would your brain assign to that image? Look at figure 10.20 to see.

Visible light waves are only a small fraction of a much larger array of EM waves. The whole spectrum of EM radiation with different frequencies and wavelengths is the **electromagnetic spectrum,** or **EM spectrum.** What is detectable, or "visible," to eyes is only a small part of that much broader EM spectrum. For longer wavelengths, your eyes cannot detect the EM waves and no signal is sent to your brain. For example, you don't see radio or cell phone waves, do you? Imagine that you could see the waves coming to a cell phone. Some radio wavelengths are about 1 km long! Similarly, your eyes cannot detect wavelengths shorter than visible light (higher frequencies), such as ultraviolet EM waves. Thus, no signal can be sent from your eyes to your brain for UV radiation when you are getting sunburned. The same is true for natural X-rays or gamma rays. Although you use many types of EM waves each day, you might not even know it.

All of the waves of the EM spectrum vary in wavelength and frequency. Interestingly, all of those waves travel at the same speed, 3×10^8 m/s. If waves of higher

frequency traveled faster, you would see blue light from the Sun before you would see red light. Since the waves all travel at the same speed, you see all colors of light at the same time, your eyes detecting this as white light.

SCILINKS®
NSTA

Go to: www.scilinks.org
Topic: electromagnetic waves
Code: 1Inquiry484a
Topic: electromagnetic spectrum
Code: 1Inquiry484b

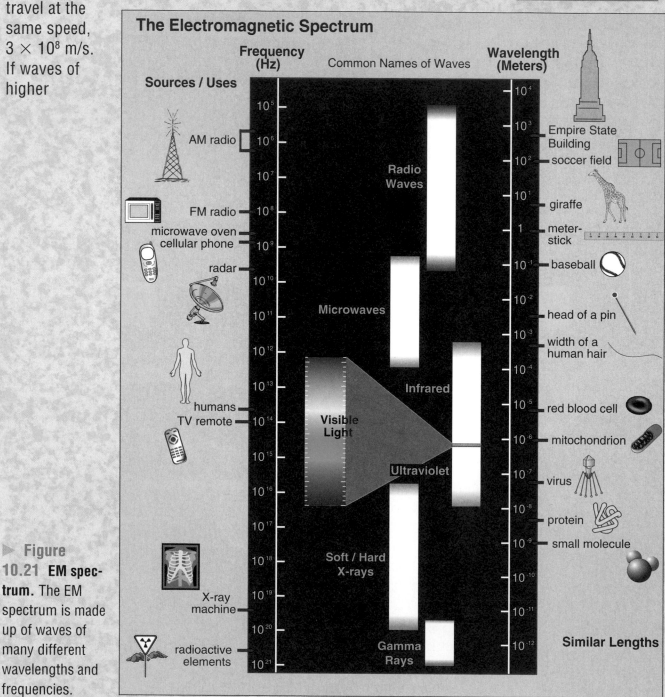

The Electromagnetic Spectrum

▶ Figure
10.21 **EM spectrum.** The EM spectrum is made up of waves of many different wavelengths and frequencies.

Waves to Music

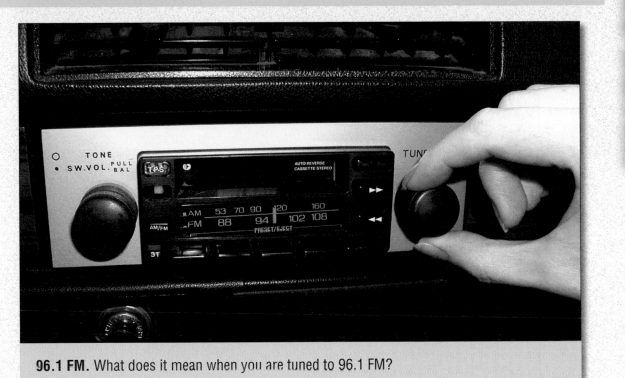

96.1 FM. What does it mean when you are tuned to 96.1 FM?

"You are listening to KWAV, K-WAVE, 96.1 on your FM radio station, where waves bring you your favorite music 24 hours a day!" Did you know that the music you hear from your radio starts out as EM radiation? Radio waves are much longer than the EM waves to which your eyes are sensitive. FM waves may be over 300 m long, and since they are part of EM radiation, they travel at the speed of light, about 3×10^8 m/s. Radio waves start out as sound waves, are converted to EM waves, and then are converted back to the sound waves that you hear from your radio.

You may listen to AM and FM radio stations. What is the difference? The difference is how the wave is carried from the station to your radio. Every commercial radio station in the United States is assigned a broadcast frequency by the Federal Communications Commission. This frequency is what you tune your radio to when you want to listen to your favorite station. In the station mentioned above,

you would tune to 96.1 on your FM radio. This means that the station's broadcast frequency is 96.1 MHz, or 96.1 million waves per second! FM stations broadcast in the range of 88–108 MHz. In contrast, AM radio stations broadcast in the range of 540–1,640 kilohertz. The radio station's assigned frequency is the frequency of the carrier wave, the wave that "carries" the information. The carrier waves for FM and AM radio stations are modified in different ways to transmit this information.

FM stands for frequency modulation, and FM stations send their information by modifying the frequency of the carrier wave. AM stands for amplitude modulation, and to send information, those stations modify the amplitude of the carrier wave.

You may have noticed while traveling in a car that you can pick up AM stations a long distance from the broadcast station, but your favorite FM station fades away when you are only 40–80 km (25–50 miles) away. That is because AM radio

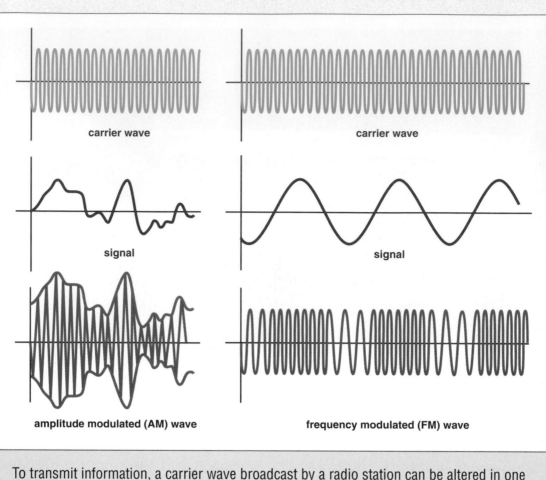

carrier wave   carrier wave

signal   signal

amplitude modulated (AM) wave   frequency modulated (FM) wave

To transmit information, a carrier wave broadcast by a radio station can be altered in one of two ways: amplitude modulation (AM) or frequency modulation (FM).

waves follow the curvature of Earth for some distance and bounce off charged particles in the upper atmosphere. That causes the AM radio waves to reflect back to Earth at a very long distance from their source. FM radio waves, however, neither follow the curvature of Earth nor reflect off the charged upper atmosphere. FM radio waves can be transmitted only in a simple straight line. Therefore, when you are farther than about 80 km (50 miles) from the broadcast station, you loose an FM radio signal.

Then why do people prefer FM radio stations for music if they cannot transmit long distances? Most people would say

that the sound is much better on FM than AM. That is because FM radio waves are transmitted at higher frequencies and the strength of the FM radio waves is constant. That allows for a clearer, purer sound from FM radio stations. The strength of AM signals does not remain constant because the amplitude varies.

The next time you listen to your radio, listen for these differences in sound quality. How far are you from the broadcast station? Which are clearer—the AM stations or the FM stations? Look at your radio to see the range of frequencies for AM and FM. Does it match what you learned here?

Reflect and Connect

Respond to the following tasks in a class discussion and record your best ideas in your science notebook under the heading "Reflect and Connect, Much Ado about Waves." Refer to figures 10.20 and 10.21.

1. What is the order of the 7 colors in the visible spectrum? Name them in order from longest wavelength to shortest wavelength.
2. Using the EM spectrum (see figure 10.21), consider X-rays and radio waves to answer the following questions:
   a. Which has the highest frequency?
   b. Which has the longest wavelength?
   c. Which has the greatest energy?
3. Make a T-table with 2 columns, labeling the headings "Red Light" and "Blue Light." In your table, indicate the differences, if any, in the following:
   a. Wavelength
   b. Frequency
   c. Energy
   d. Speed
4. Do cell phones use only EM waves in their operation? Think of the different steps in a cell phone conversation and think about the paths of all waves. Indicate in your answer all of the steps you can think of and all of the different types of waves involved.
5. These activities were about waves and the fact that waves have similar properties whether they are sound waves, waves on a Slinky, or light waves. In a Reflect and Connect question in the Springing into Action! activity, you imagined riding on a light wave from the Sun to Earth and calculated that your journey would take just over 8 minutes. Would it make any difference in time if you were riding on a blue light wave versus a red light wave? Give evidence that explains your answer.

Star Light, Star Bright

EXPLORE

EXPLAIN

The main thing that you can detect from stars is the EM radiation that they produce. This EM radiation includes the light that you see, as well as other types of radiation that you cannot detect with your eyes. You have learned that these waves have many properties that scientists can study. Can you name a few? These properties of light waves tell scientists many things about the stars from which the waves originate. What properties do you notice about stars when you look at them at night? Do you notice that in some constellations, some stars appear brighter than others? Does this mean they are closer, are bigger, or produce more energy?

In Part I of the Star Light, Star Bright activity, you investigate those questions by working with a model to look at the factors that can influence how bright a light appears to you and to relate that experience to stars. Astronomers have investigated those factors, too, and in Part II of this activity, you see how they use a mathematical relationship to answer questions about the brightness and distance of stars. Part III of the activity shows you how those relationships can help astronomers study other properties of stars, such as color and temperature. In this activity, you work individually and with your classmates as you watch a demonstration by your teacher.

Part I: Watt's Up?

Materials

Cautions

Do not touch hot lightbulbs.

Process and Procedure

1. Watch carefully as your teacher performs a demonstration with lightbulbs. Make a simple sketch in your science notebook of what you see, Label the heading "Star Light, Star Bright— Part I: Watt's Up?"
2. Discuss the following questions with your classmates and record your best answers in your science notebook.
   a. Which bulb appears brighter?
   b. Could these bulbs be identical? Explain your answer using the words *brightness, distance,* and *power.*
3. Observe the new demonstration that your teacher has set up. Make a new sketch of what you see. Discuss the following questions with your team and record your best answers in your science notebook.
   a. Which bulb appears brighter?
   b. Could these bulbs be identical? Explain your answer using the words *brightness, distance,* and *power.*
4. Observe the information marked on the bulbs that your teacher used in both demonstrations. Were you surprised by anything? You have probably replaced a lightbulb that burned out at some time. Some fixtures indicate the maximum wattage bulb that can be used. What do the watts have to do with the properties of the lightbulb? To find the answer, work with your class to explore more about light as your teacher continues this demonstration.

5. Observe as your teacher places 3 bulbs of *different* wattages at the same distance from you.
   a. Draw a diagram of the setup in your science notebook.
   b. Label each bulb with the watts that are printed on the bulb.
   c. Label the brightness of each bulb as it appears to you.

6. Place your hand *near* the 100-watt bulb that is on. Do the same for the 40-watt bulb.
   a. Other than light energy, what type of energy is being emitted by the bulbs?
   b. Do both bulbs seem to produce the same amount of energy during the time your hand is near the bulb? What is your evidence?
   c. How is this energy related to the wattage?

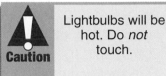

Caution — Lightbulbs will be hot. Do *not* touch.

Part I

1. How is the wattage of the bulb related to the brightness?

2. Could a lower wattage bulb ever appear brighter than a higher wattage bulb? Represent your answer with a labeled sketch.

3. Some lamp manufacturers warn customers to use only low-wattage bulbs in their lamps. Why do you think they do this?

4. When you look at the bulb, energy enters your eyes. When you place your hand near the bulb, energy hits your hand. Do your eyes or your hand receive all of the energy produced by the bulb? Explain your reasoning.

5. You saw in your teacher's demonstration that the energy output of a lightbulb is not always obvious when the lightbulb is placed at different distances. You also felt the heat given off by the bulbs.
   a. Would you expect to feel more heat, less heat, or the same amount of heat as you move your hand farther from the bulb?
   b. What does this tell you about the amount of energy striking your hand as you move closer to the bulb and farther from the bulb?

7. Read Watt's More to learn how this activity with lightbulbs connects to stars.

As you discovered with the demonstrations, apparent brightness can give you only limited information about the light from a lightbulb. You can gather more information when you know the energy output of the lightbulb—the wattage. A **watt** is a unit of power that indicates the transfer of energy per second. The higher the wattage, the higher the transfer of energy of the bulb. Just like you, from Earth, astronomers can see differences in the brightness of stars. It would be useful if they could determine that the brighter stars were closer to Earth than the dimmer stars. However, they know it is not that simple. Two stars can be the same distance from Earth but have different brightnesses. Or two stars can have the same brightness but be different distances from Earth.

Unfortunately, astronomers cannot walk up to the stars to read their "wattage," like you did with the lightbulbs in Part I. What astronomers can do is establish references. To establish references, astronomers first determine a star's brightness as it appears from Earth. What they see from Earth is a star's **apparent brightness.** It is called "apparent" because a star may appear to be very bright but only look that way because it is relatively close to Earth. A star also may appear brighter because it produces more energy than other stars. Astronomers refer to the power output of a star as its **luminosity.** For example, the Sun has a luminosity of 3.8×10^{26} watts, and it appears very bright to you. However, you are very close to this star! Other stars have luminosities much higher than the Sun, but they do not appear to be as bright because they are very far from Earth. Comparing a star's apparent brightness with its luminosity gives astronomers clues about how far away it is.

▲ **Figure 10.22 Lightbulbs.** What does the information printed on the bulb tell you?

You may be wondering about using stellar parallax to find the distances to stars. Why do scientists need to know apparent brightness and luminosity to find the distance to stars when they already can use stellar parallax? Remember, stellar parallax depends on distance, with nearer objects exhibiting greater parallax than more distant objects. Thus, parallax can be used to measure the distance only to relatively close stars. Current technology allows scientists to measure parallax for stars only within a few hundred light-years. There are a vast number of stars farther out in the universe that cannot be measured using parallax.

Scientists want to find out how far other galaxies are from Earth. To do that, they must measure the distances to stars within the galaxies. The parallax method will not work for those stars and galaxies because they are too far away. Some other method must be used to determine those great distances. This is an example of when the large distances in the universe challenge astronomers.

SCiLINKS
NSTA
Topic: luminosity
Go to: www.scilinks.org
Code: 1Inquiry490

Astronomers can use a light meter to determine a star's apparent brightness, but apparent brightness does not tell astronomers the luminosity of a star. Nor does apparent brightness indicate a star's distance from Earth. Instead, astronomers turn to closer sources of light to see how bright the light appears at different distances. In Part II of this activity, you learn how astronomers use apparent brightness and luminosity in a mathematical relationship to determine distances to stars that are very far away.

▲ **Figure 10.23 Spiral galaxy.** Scientists cannot use parallax to measure the distance to this galaxy because it is too far away. They must use another method to find the distance.

Part I continued

6. A friend sees a very bright star in the constellation Orion and tells you that it is very bright because it is much closer to Earth than the dimmer stars. Obviously, this friend is not in your science class! Could this statement be true? Or are there other factors to consider? Write a short paragraph explaining a better way to describe the apparent brightness of this star.

7. Why do astronomers need to know the apparent brightness and luminosity of stars?

8. You learned in an earlier activity about how scientists use stellar parallax to determine distances to stars. Does this method work for all stars? Explain your answer.

Part II: Starburst

You have already discovered that the farther you are from a lightbulb, the dimmer it appears and the less heat you feel. But how *much* dimmer does the light appear? Is there a pattern you can use that relates the distance from the source to the brightness?

Part II of this activity helps you model a fundamental law of math and science. It is a mathematical relationship that you will use many times not only when you study light, but also when you study such things as gravity, magnetism, and electric fields. In the study of stars, this mathematical relationship is the relationship that allows astronomers to determine the distances to stars that are very far away. Work in a team of 3 students to complete the steps that follow. Use your science notebook and the heading "Part II: Starburst" to organize and record all of your data and your answers to questions.

Materials
For each team of three students

3 pairs of safety goggles

1 Styrofoam ball at least 10 cm in diameter

25 bamboo skewers

string

1 marker

1 metric ruler

masking tape

graph paper

1 pair of scissors

calculator

1 tape measure (optional)

▶ **Figure 10.24**
View of night sky. Are the brightest stars always closer to you?

Cautions

Use care in handling bamboo skewers—they have sharp points. You should wear safety goggles while working with the skewers.

Process and Procedure

1. Make sure you and your team have all of the materials listed. Be sure you read and understand the caution statement.
2. Measure and record the radius of your Styrofoam ball.

The best way to do this is to measure the circumference of the ball with a tape measure or string and then solve for the radius using the formula $c = 2\pi r$. Remember that you need to record the radius of the sphere.

3. Stick the sharp end of the skewers into the Styrofoam ball following these directions.
    a. Cover only a small section of the sphere. (You do not have to cover the entire ball.)
    b. Use at least 20 skewers.
    c. Place the skewers no farther apart than 1 cm and as equally spaced as you can.
    d. Make sure the skewers are perpendicular to the surface of the ball.
4. Cut a piece of string 20 cm long. Measure 2 cm from each end and mark those points with a marker. Wrap the ends of the string with a small piece of tape so the ends will not ravel.
5. Use the string to "capture" several skewers near the surface of the ball by making a circle with the string.
    a. Line up the marks on the string and tape the ends together.

This will give you a circle of string with about a 16-cm circumference. You will have to take the tape off the string and retape several times. Each time, keep the circumference of the string the same. The value of the circumference is not important, only that the circumference stays constant throughout the activity.

    b. Invert the ball so the skewers are pointing toward the floor. Tap the ball gently so the string falls as far as it can along the skewers.

If the string falls off, you have not captured enough skewers. Try the procedure again, this time capturing more skewers.

    c. Measure the distance from the string to the surface of the ball. Add the *radius* of the ball and record this, along with the number of skewers you captured, in a data table in your notebook. This is your separation distance.

| ⚠️ Caution | You should wear safety goggles while working with skewers. |

▼ **Figure 10.25**
Starburst setup. Your model should look something like this.

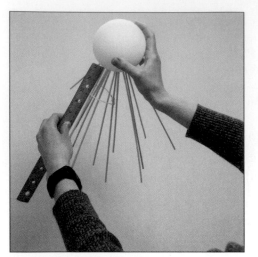

▲ **Figure 10.26**
Count the number of skewers captured with your string and measure the distance from the string to the ball.

    d. Repeat this procedure at least 5 times, capturing different numbers of skewers. Record the number of skewers captured each time and the separation distance.

6. You placed the skewers less than 1 cm apart on the Styrofoam ball. How does this distance compare with the distance the skewers are separated at the opposite end?

7. Answer the following questions about your model.

    a. If you placed the skewers exactly perpendicular to the surface and pushed them all to the center of the ball, what would happen at the center? Draw what you think that would look like (assume that skewers were distributed around the entire ball).

    b. You have been learning about stars and the light they produce. How is your model similar to a star?

8. Make a graph of your data from Step 5. On the *y*-axis, plot the number of skewers you captured; on the *x*-axis, plot the distance from the string to the center of the ball. Leave room below your graph for a caption.

    a. Draw a best-fit line for your data.

A best-fit line places approximately as many data points above the line as below it. It represents a type of average.

    Consider the key features, or *highlights,* of what you see and what those highlights mean.

    b. Write the phrase "What I see" by your best-fit line. Following this phrase, write your short description.

    c. Write the phrase "What it means" under your "What I see" comments. Explain what it means to have a graph of data with a line shaped the way you see it.

Consider using a phrase such as this: As the distance from the center of the ball (increases or decreases), the number of skewers (increases or decreases).

    d. Meet with your team and share what you have written on your graph. Decide as a team what to write as a caption under the graph.

Think back to other graphs and captions you have read. Captions often tell you, in sentence format, what you are looking at, what it means, and why it is important. Include those features in your caption.

    You have completed your highlight comments for this graph.

9. Add a column to your data table in your science notebook. Use your calculator to find the inverse square of each of your values for the *x*-axis.

On your calculator, enter your first value for the separation distance, square it, and then take the inverse of your answer ($\frac{1}{x}$). Record those values in the new column on your data table.

a. Now make a new graph, but this time use the inverse square values for your *x*-axis. For your *y*-axis, use the same values from Step 5. Remember to leave room for highlight comments and captions.

Due to the small values of the numbers, it might be helpful to use a graphing calculator or computer graphing program for this graph.

b. Make highlight comments on your graph, following the directions in Steps 8b–c, for the phrases "What I see" and "What it means."

c. Work with your team to write a caption for this graph.

10. Read The Inverse Square Law to learn about what you just modeled.

READING

The Inverse Square Law

The shape of your graph from Step 9 represents a fundamental law in mathematics and science. It is called the **inverse square law,** and it has profound implications for many fields of study in science. In the study of stars, you use it to explain the relationship between distance and the apparent brightness of a star. You use it again in another chapter when you study gravity.

Inverse relationships occur when one variable increases as the other

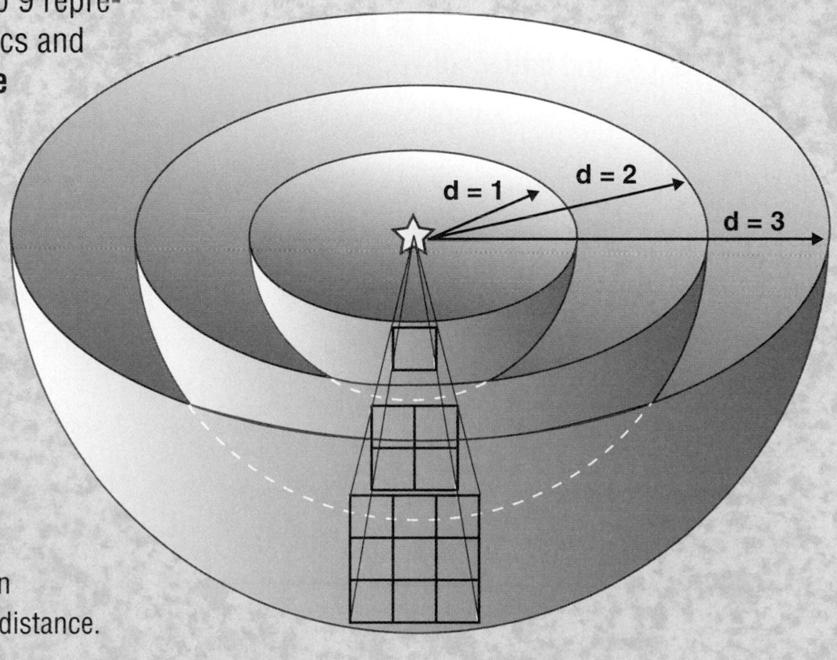

▶ **Figure 10.27 Inverse square law for light.** At greater distances from a star, the same amount of light passes through an area that gets larger with the square of the distance.

decreases. This is an inverse *square* law. When applied to stars, the law states that when the distance from a light (luminosity) *increases* by a factor of two (that is, it doubles), the apparent brightness of the light *decreases* by a factor of four (or two *squared*). The relationship holds true for other distances as well: when the distance from a light increases by a factor of three (that is, it triples), the apparent brightness of the light goes down by a factor of nine (three squared), and so on. This can be written as the following proportion (the symbol $\propto$ means "is proportional to"):

apparent brightness (AB) $\propto$

$$\frac{\text{luminosity (L)}}{\text{square of the distance (d}^2\text{)}} \text{ or } AB \propto \frac{L}{d^2}$$

This proportion relates the energy given off by a star (L) to the energy detected by your eyes at a given distance. For a star, the apparent brightness is measured with a light meter attached to a telescope. As light moves out from a star, the same amount of light must be redistributed to larger and larger areas. This is what makes a star look dimmer and dimmer at greater distances. Do you remember in Part II that as your loop of string was farther from the ball, there were fewer skewers in the loop? The decrease in apparent brightness of stars can be thought of as the spreading of light to larger and larger spherical shells around the star.

Because the area (A) of a sphere is $A = 4\pi r^2$, the amount of light at a given distance from the star must be the original luminosity spread over the area of a sphere at a distance d from the star. This distance is the same as the radius of the shell, or distance (d) = radius (r). This gives the inverse square law for brightness of a star as

$$AB = \frac{L}{4 \times \pi \times d^2},$$

where *AB* is apparent brightness as observed from Earth and *L* is the luminosity of the star. Luminosity is expressed in units of watts; distance, in units of meters. Apparent brightness, then, is expressed as watts per meter squared (W/m^2).

You can see from the equation that apparent brightness is just a portion of the total amount of energy that is produced. This portion is called flux. **Flux** is the rate of transfer of energy across a given surface area. For apparent brightness, this "area" is your eyes or a light meter. Consider this analogy: All of the rain falling per second from a rain cloud is to luminosity as the rain hitting a windshield is to apparent brightness or flux. Flux is an important concept in science—one that you will use again in this unit and in your future studies.

Topic: inverse square law
Go to: www.scilinks.org
Code: 1Inquiry496

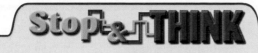

Part II

Work with a partner to answer these questions. Record your best answers in your science notebook under the heading "Stop and Think-Part IIa."

1. In an analogy map, compare the number of skewers captured by your loop of string (flux) with apparent brightness and your starburst model with luminosity. Use the chart in figure 10.28 to show how the two compare.

Something I notice in Starburst model	Something I notice about real stars	Why they are alike
Skewers captured by loop of string at distance 1		
Skewers captured by loop of string at distance 2 (farther from ball)		
Total number of skewers coming out of ball (compared with similar ball with different number of skewers)		

◀ **Figure 10.28**
Analogy map. Copy this chart in your science notebook.

2. If the distance from the source of energy increases 4 times, what happens to the apparent brightness, provided the luminosity remains the same?

3. What would happen to the flux or apparent brightness if the distance were cut in half?

4. In a previous analogy, apparent brightness and luminosity are compared to rain hitting a windshield and rain falling from rain clouds. As with all analogies and models, there are strengths and weaknesses to the comparison. Make a T-table in your notebook with the headings "Strengths" and "Weaknesses." Think about how the analogy is a good comparison and list those reasons as strengths. Also, consider how this analogy is not a good example for luminosity and apparent brightness and list those reasons as weaknesses.

11. Read Measuring Luminosity to learn how astronomers measure luminosity and use it to determine the distance to stars that are very far away.

Measuring Luminosity

The stars in the constellation Orion vary in brightness. If all stars were the same luminosity, you could simply conclude that the brighter stars were closer to Earth and the dimmer stars were farther from Earth. Then scientists could just use the inverse square law to determine the distance to all stars from Earth. It would be like lining up table lamps with 60-watt bulbs from 1 goalpost to another on a football field. The bulbs at the far end of the field would appear dimmest even though all of the bulbs had the same energy output.

Unfortunately, not all stars have the same luminosity. A dimmer star is not necessarily farther away than a brighter one because each may have a different luminosity. Lightbulbs can vary, too; they can have different wattages and, thus, luminosities. If you mixed in 100-watt bulbs with 60-watt bulbs on your football field, you would have difficulty using apparent brightness to judge distances to the lamps.

The inverse square law for the apparent brightness of a star can be used in several ways. If you are considering a nearby star, you can measure its distance using parallax and measure its apparent brightness using a light meter. Then it is a simple calculation to determine the star's luminosity. However, for stars that are great distances from Earth, determining the distance by parallax is not possible. Astronomers use the inverse square law to determine distances farther than the parallax method can accurately measure. To find those distances, astronomers have to know the apparent brightness and luminosity of a star. They can measure apparent brightness directly with a light meter; then they must determine, as accurately as possible, a star's luminosity before they can calculate its distance from Earth. But how can astronomers measure luminosity over such great distances?

Fortunately, in 1912, an American astronomer named Henrietta Swan Leavitt discovered a way to measure luminosity for a certain type of star. Leavitt was an astronomer at Harvard College Observatory who was studying a unique type of star called a variable star. Over time, variable stars fluctuate in their brightness. They cycle from bright to dim to bright again. The **variable stars** that Leavitt studied were called **Cepheid variable stars.** Cepheid variable stars are special variable stars because they cycle from bright to dim to bright in a very regular pattern. Leavitt discovered that the Cepheid variable stars go from bright to dim to bright in a cycle called their **period** (see figure 10.29). A period is a length of time—typically, a few days to 100 days for Cepheid variables.

A very familiar star, Polaris (the North Star), is a Cepheid variable star with a period of 4 days. Leavitt studied over 1,500 variable stars and discovered that Cepheid variable stars demonstrate what is called the period-luminosity law. Cepheid variable stars that vary in brightness over a short period of time (a few days) have lower luminosities than Cepheid variable stars that vary in brightness over long periods of time. Simply put, stars with longer periods are more luminous—they have more power.

12. Make a list of the stars in figure 10.29 and determine their period from the graphs.

Remember the period of a variable star is the time of one cycle.

13. Using your data from Step 12 and figure 10.30, determine each star's luminosity. Record your answers in the form of a chart in your science notebook.

Use the period values from Step 12 and find each value on the *x*-axis of figure 10.30. Put your finger on this spot on the *x*-axis. Move your finger up the graph until you touch the data line and read the *y*-axis value for luminosity.

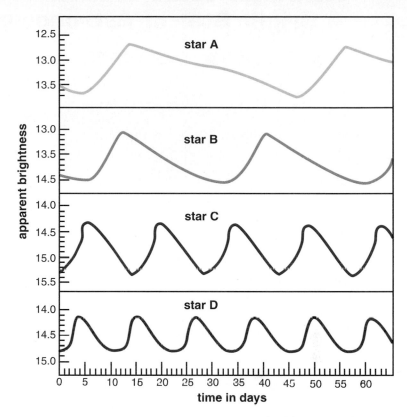

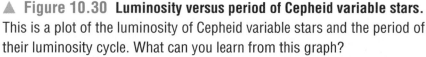
▲ Figure 10.29
Periods of Cepheid variable stars. Can you determine the period of the variable stars depicted in the graphs above?

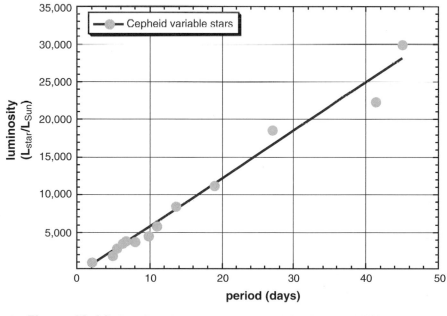

▲ Figure 10.30 **Luminosity versus period of Cepheid variable stars.** This is a plot of the luminosity of Cepheid variable stars and the period of their luminosity cycle. What can you learn from this graph?

Henrietta Swan Leavitt:
A Bright Star of Astronomy

HENRIETTA SWAN LEAVITT
At about 30 years of age.

Henrietta Swan Leavitt, 1868–1921.

Have you ever been outside on a clear, starry night and wondered how far away the stars are? Henrietta Swan Leavitt wondered, and what she discovered added greatly to astronomers's understanding of distant stars.

Leavitt was born in 1868 in Lancaster, Massachusetts. After high school, she continued her education at Oberlin College and the Society for Collegiate Instruction of Women (later known as Radcliffe College, part of Harvard University). It was there that Leavitt became interested in the stars.

Leavitt graduated from college in 1892. Shortly after she graduated, she became very sick and spent the next few years at home. Her illness left her deaf, but true to her nature, Leavitt refused to be held back. She became a volunteer at the Harvard College Observatory. By 1902, she became a permanent staff member at a wage of 30¢ per hour. Eventually, Leavitt became the head of the department of photographic photometry. Her group studied photo images of stars taken through telescopes to determine how big they were. It was during those studies that Leavitt made her famous discovery of the relationship between Cepheid variable stars's period and their luminosity. During her career, she discovered some 2,400 variable stars.

Henrietta Leavitt died of cancer at the age of 53. She was still working in the Harvard College Observatory. Leavitt's work played a very important role in scientists's ability to use the inverse square law equation to determine distances in the universe. Her work at the observatory laid a foundation that supports many ideas in modern astronomy.

14. Read the following paragraphs to learn how astronomers use information like you determined in Step 13 to know more about our universe.

You found the luminosities of variable stars in the previous steps in the same method that astronomers use today. Knowing the luminosity of Cepheid variable stars in distant galaxies helps astronomers map the distances to stars too far away to use the parallax method. They apply the inverse square law by measuring the apparent brightness using a light meter and comparing it to the luminosity according to Leavitt's scale. They then are able to solve for the 1 missing variable: distance to the star in question.

Leavitt's work in the early 1900s supported much of the growth in knowledge about distances in the universe during the next several decades. In fact, measurements from Cepheid variables have become an important tool for measuring distances up to about 10–20 million ly. This includes the work of astronomer Edwin Hubble, after whom the Hubble Space Telescope is named.

Cepheid variable stars represent some of the later stages of a star's life cycle. You may remember the Recipe for a Star activity from chapter 5, Star Material. In that activity, you began to study what makes up a star and the life cycle of a star. You learn more about the life cycle of a star in the next chapter.

Stop & THINK
Part II continued

Discuss the following questions with your team and record your thoughts in your science notebook under the heading "Stop and Think-Part IIb."

5. To find the distance to a star using the inverse square law, what 2 things do you need to know?

6. How would scientists use the inverse square law to find the luminosity of a nearby star?

7. If the distance to star A is 10 times greater than the distance to star B, and the 2 stars have the same luminosity, how would their apparent brightness compare?

Part III: Colorful Characteristics

By looking at a star with just your eyes, you can tell certain things about it. You can see how bright it appears, and you may even notice that it seems to be a certain color. However, by looking at stars with just your eyes, you cannot tell what they are made of or what their temperature is. For this type of information, astronomers need to observe a spectrum of the star's electromagnetic radiation. See the FYI, Types of Spectra, to learn about the different spectra scientists use and how the spectra are produced.

Types of Spectra

Astronomers have learned a great deal about the nature of stars by analyzing stars's EM spectra. You are most familiar with a continuous spectra—one produced as a rainbow from a rainstorm or prism. In the Matter Is Marvelous unit, when you conducted flame tests of certain elemental salts, you learned that elements can produce light. Do you remember the colored line patterns caused by emission lines—the emission spectra? Those fingerprints, or colored bar codes, are used to identify elements. Astronomers use **absorption spectra** rather than emission spectra. Study the figure in this FYI. It graphically shows the difference between two spectra and compares them to a continuous spectra. The EM radiation (including visible light) from stars is produced in the interiors of stars. In the Matter Is Marvelous unit, you saw that this energy is one of the products of nuclear reactions in a star. This radiation passes through the outer

layers of a star, where certain wavelengths of light are absorbed by elements. As scientists examine this radiation when it reaches Earth, they see dark bands in the spectrum that indicate the radiation that has been absorbed. Scientists can determine the elements responsible for those dark bands by studying the characteristic banding patterns.

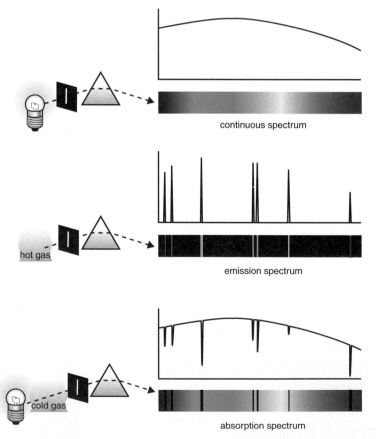

continuous spectrum

emission spectrum

absorption spectrum

Sources of continuous, emission, and absorption spectra. There are many ways to study spectra. Astronomers use absorption spectra to study starlight. The light produced inside a star passes through cool gas in the atmosphere of the star, producing an absorption spectra.

As astronomers in the past gathered spectral data from many stars, they noticed differences and similarities. They tried to find patterns that would help them understand the stars. In this part of the activity, you work with a team to look specifically at star spectra to see patterns. Those patterns help astronomers understand and classify stars.

Materials
For each team of three students

1 calculator

3 Intensity Graphs handouts

3 Spectra from Stars handouts

3 Mystery Star Intensity Graphs handouts

Process and Procedure

1. Obtain a Spectra from Stars handout for each team member and study them together. The handout shows representative spectra from different types of stars. The distinctive hydrogen lines are marked along the top. Those lines are common to many stars due to the abundance of hydrogen in the outer layers and atmosphere of stars. A color version of those spectra is included in figure 10.31 to help you analyze this data.

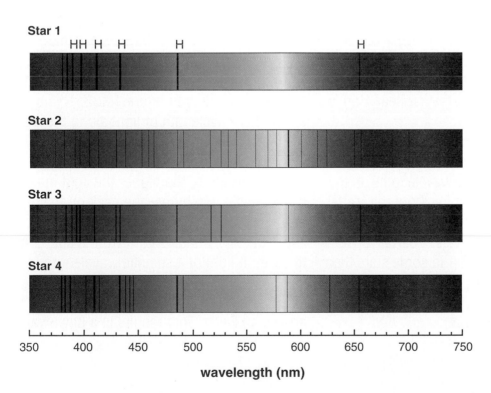

◄ **Figure 10.31**
Stellar spectrograms.
Use these spectra as you complete Steps 1 and 2. These are the same spectra as the ones on your handout, Spectra from Stars.

2. Discuss with your team the following questions about the star spectra. Record your thoughts in your science notebook under the heading "Part III: Colorful Characteristics."

   a. What are some features of the spectra?

   In your answer, consider such things as color, number and location of lines, and thickness of lines.

   b. What are the values of wavelength in nanometers (nm) for the 5 main hydrogen spectral lines shown?

   c. What are some similarities and differences among the spectra?

3. Astronomers can study spectra in more detail by representing the information they receive from them in the form of a graph. Read Spectral Patterns to learn more.

READING

Spectral Patterns

Astronomers analyze star spectra in detail to learn more about the lives of stars. One way to do this is to measure precisely the wavelength where spectral lines occur and to graph their "brightness," or how intense they appear. Here's how astronomers do this.

Different spectral lines in a spectrum correspond to elements present in the star. Those lines occur at specific positions, or wavelengths, in the EM spectrum. (Do you remember from the Matter Is Marvelous unit that those lines are caused by electrons changing energy levels?) Certain spectral peaks can be slightly wider in some stars than in others. The combinations of spectral lines for stars can tell astronomers a great deal about the elements that make up the star.

Spectra can also tell astronomers about the brightness of the light the star emits. Astronomers can graph the varying intensity of different wavelengths of light, as illustrated by the intensity graph in figure 10.32. This plot shows the wavelength of light along the x-axis plotted against the intensity, or brightness, of the light at each wavelength on the y-axis. For a given wavelength, the higher the light intensity from the star, the higher the peak on the graph.

What does the shape of the plot tell astronomers? Imagine light from a star coming to Earth. If light of a specific wavelength is absorbed on its way to Earth, that wavelength will not be present in the spectrum of light that arrives on Earth. That results in a downward

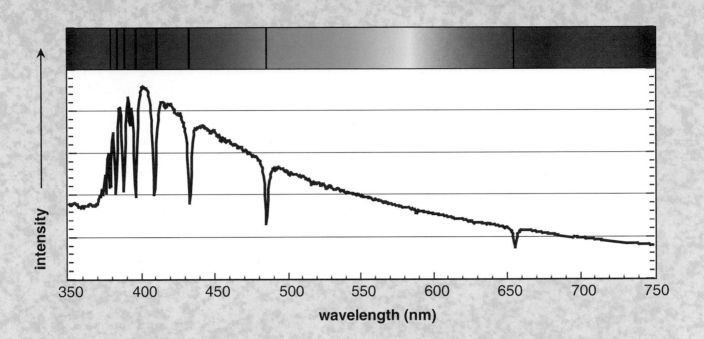

▲ **Figure 10.32 Spectra and intensity graph.** Astronomers represent what they see in a star's spectrum by graphing the intensity of the different wavelengths of light that the star emits. This intensity graph shows two key features: (1) an overall spectral peak of intensity at about 400 nm and (2) six downward absorption spikes between 390 and 500 nm. The absorption spikes in the plot correspond with the dark absorption lines in the star spectrum above. They give a fingerprint that tells about the elements in the atmosphere of the star.

light absorption spike, which is seen as a sharp *decrease* in intensity for a given wavelength. That decrease is called absorption. In figure 10.32, for example, a sharp absorption spike lies at λ = 486 nm because specific light with λ = 486 nm has been absorbed elsewhere. That wavelength is absent from the spectrum. The position of spikes gives a distinctive pattern of spectral lines for the star—or a spectral fingerprint. That fingerprint is due to gases in the cooler, outer regions of the star's atmosphere that absorb light emitted by the hotter, inner parts of the star. Some lines may also be due to absorp-

tion by gases in Earth's atmosphere. Look at the figure in the FYI, Types of Spectra. Do you see the cloud of gas that would account for the absorption lines? Recall that the absorption lines can tell astronomers what elements are present in the atmosphere of stars.

The other key feature to note in intensity graphs is the wavelength of light at which the intensity is the highest. For example, in the intensity graph in figure 10.32, what is the approximate wavelength of light with the highest intensity? Read the wavelength measurements on the *x*-axis to see that the peak is just less than 400 nm.

4. Obtain and study the Intensity Graphs handout. Can you see patterns on the graphs that match those from specific spectral groups on the Spectra from Stars handout? Discuss with your team what you see. Then match the star spectrum with the letter of the graph that you believe most closely matches it. Check your match with your teacher.

You can match spectra to graphs by noting the wavelengths of key spectral absorption lines. It might be helpful to cut the spectra into strips to help you match them to the graph.

5. Obtain a copy of the Mystery Star Intensity Graphs handout from your teacher, which shows 2 star spectra. Compare each of those intensity graphs with the previous 4 types of spectra. Which of the previous 4 are the graphs most like? Give 2 reasons for your answer.

Once again, think in terms of wavelengths at a specific spectral line, in addition to the wavelength indicating the peak intensity of the spectrum.

6. You will be able to use these graphs to determine the color of stars. To understand more, read the following paragraph.

Astronomers can determine the color of a star by looking at an intensity graph. Color, in turn, helps astronomers determine the temperature of the star. The wavelengths of light that have the highest intensity in star spectra correspond to the color and temperature of the stars. For example, if the red part of the spectrum has the greatest intensity, the star is cooler than if the blue part of the spectrum is most intense. You may be familiar with the relationship between color and temperature. If you have ever noticed a metal object being heated, you know that it starts out red and keeps changing color as it gets hotter, until it becomes a blue-white color at its hottest. Similarly, the blue flame of a laboratory burner is much hotter than the yellow flame of a candle.

7. What are the colors of the stars on the Intensity Graphs handout? To answer that question, do the following:
   a. Look at the wavelength units on the *x*-axis of the graphs on your handout. On which end of the axis are the wavelengths shorter? On which end are they longer?

   Think back to previous activities and the lesson on properties of waves. Which has a longer wavelength-red light or blue light? Label the blue end and the red end of each graph's *x*-axis.

b. Look at the intensity graphs and notice which wavelengths are most intense in each.

c. Number from 1 to 4 to order the graphs from those representing the hottest stars (1) to those representing the coolest stars (4).

d. Your eyes see the different wavelengths of visible light as colors. Label each graph with the color of the star it represents. Use figure 10.33 to help you link a color with the intensity peak on the spectrum. The intensity peak will be the highest part of the line.

Wavelengths peak of emission for star (nm)	Apparent color of star
650–750	Reddish
620–650	Orange
530–620	Yellowish
450–530	White
400–450	Bluish

◀ **Figure 10.33**
Starlight wavelength and color. Certain wavelengths in the electromagnetic spectrum produce these approximate colors in stars. These ranges of color do not have a distinct separation in the spectrum, and people have different perceptions of color.

Interestingly, even though the color green comes from light with wavelengths of around 500 nm, we see no green stars. That is because green is in the middle of the visible spectrum. Therefore, a star with an intensity peak in the green part of the spectrum also gives off much red, orange, yellow, and blue. When we see this mixture of colors, it usually appears white.

8. Determine the temperatures of the stars on the Intensity Graphs handout by reading and completing the following.

Once astronomers determine the wavelength of highest intensity coming from a star, they can calculate its surface temperature using the following formula (Wien's law):

$$T = \frac{2.9 \times 10^6 \text{ K} \times \text{nm}}{\lambda_{max \text{ (nm)}}}$$

In the formula, T is temperature in Kelvin (K). The sidebar, How Warm Is Warm?, explains how the Kelvin scale works. The symbol λ_{max} represents the wavelength of the peak in intensity in nanometers. The constant 2.9×10^6 has the units of K × nm.

Use the wavelength of the peak intensity to calculate an estimate for the surface temperature of the star represented in each of the graphs on your handout.

Remember, the only variables in the equation are T and λ_{max}. The K × nm are units of the constant in the equation and do not contain variables.

Topic: spectra
Go to: www.scilinks.org
Code: 1Inquiry507

Reflect and Connect

Work individually to answer these questions. Record your answers under the heading "Reflect and Connect, Star Light Star Bright" in your science notebook.

1. Describe what you can learn about stars by looking at their spectra. Give examples of what astronomers look for in spectra.
2. The Sun is a yellow-white star. What range of surface temperatures would you expect for the Sun?
3. Spectral analysis of a particular star reveals that its light has a peak in intensity at a wavelength of $\lambda = 640$ nm. Draw a sketch graph of the spectrum from this star and describe its temperature and color.
4. In each activity in this chapter, you learned certain characteristic properties of stars and the information that scientists can learn from these properties. Make a chart in your science notebook using the guide in figure 10.34. Fill in the chart with the properties that were addressed in each activity and the significance of each property to astronomers. You may look back in your book or science notebook to compose your best answer.

Activity	Property or properties	Significance to astronomers
Stars at a Glance and Stellar Parallax		
Springing into Action! and Much Ado about Waves		
Starlight: Cell Phone Calls from Outer Space		
Watt's Up?		
Starburst		
Colorful Characteristics		

▲ **Figure 10.34 Review chart.** Make a chart in your science notebook that is similar to this one to help you organize your response to Reflect and Connect Question 4.

How Warm Is Warm?

Scientists use a special temperature scale when working with very cold and very hot temperatures. This scale uses a unit called a Kelvin. The word *degrees* or its symbol ° is not used in the Kelvin scale. The British physicist Lord Kelvin developed the scale.

The lowest point on the Kelvin scale is the coldest temperature possible. Therefore, 0 K is absolute zero, the lowest available temperature. The table in the figure shows an approximate comparison of the three temperature scales—Kelvin, Celsius, and Fahrenheit.

Kelvin (K)	Celsius (°C)	Fahrenheit (°F)	Common example
0	–273	–459	Absolute zero
273	0	32	Water freezing point
310	37	98.6	Human body temperature
373	100	212	Water boiling point
5,840	5,567	10,053	Sun's surface temperature

Temperature scales. How do the temperature scales compare?

Putting It All Together

ELABORATE

Astronomers classify stars by recognizing patterns in the wavelengths of the light that the stars emit, in their temperatures, and in their spectra. Astronomers also are able to determine a star's distance, apparent magnitude, and luminosity.

So now what? Is it possible that relationships exist among those properties of stars? Scientists in all fields look for patterns and relationships. Recall from the The Machinery of Life unit that you learned about Robert Hooke and the patterns that he looked for in thin sections of cork. In the Matter Is Marvelous unit, Dmitri Mendeleyev looked for patterns and relationships in the chemical and physical properties of elements. He developed a periodic table that has proven to be an invaluable tool for all scientists. Astronomers also look for patterns, and they have looked at all of the properties you have been studying about stars to determine if relationships exist. In the Putting It All Together activity, you become the scientist and work with a partner to compare information about stars to discover relationships that exist among the properties of stars. The result of your efforts will generate an important tool that astronomers find very useful.

Materials

For each team of two students

2 Star Data handouts

1 Distance versus Temperature graph

1 Luminosity versus Temperature graph

Process and Procedure

1. Participate in a class discussion about the importance of graphs and ways they can be used. Then work with a partner to complete Steps 2–5.
2. Obtain the Star Data handout from your teacher.
3. Decide which member of the team will make each graph as described in the following:
   - One of you will plot distance from Earth on the *y*-axis versus star temperature on the *x*-axis. You will note and label the units shown on your Star Data handout.
   - The other will plot luminosity of the star on the *y*-axis versus temperature on the *x*-axis. Note that luminosity is given in solar units because each star's luminosity is given as a ratio to the Sun's luminosity (L_{star}/L_{Sun}). Refer to the sidebar, Monster Units, for more information.

These graphs are often called *xy* plots because you plot data from stars as pairs of values (as pairs of *xy* coordinates). After plotting data, it is important to look for trends and patterns in the data of your completed graph.

4. Make a prediction about which graph will show a stronger relationship between the 2 stellar characteristics you are graphing. Record your prediction in your science notebook and state your reason for choosing the graph that you did.
5. Graph your data on the appropriate graph paper handout. As you set up your graph, you should know that there is an important convention for these star data: place the high temperatures on the left-hand side of the *x*-axis, decreasing to low temperatures on the right-hand side of the *x*-axis. This means that you will put the hottest stars on the left end of the *x*-axis.
6. Compare your graph with your partner's graph. Which graph seems to show a more regular pattern? Describe in your science notebook the patterns that you see and explain why you think the patterns exist.

7. Read the following paragraph. Then discuss the answers to the questions with your class. Be sure to record answers to the questions on your graphs and in your science notebook.

Early in the 20th century, 2 astronomers working separately discovered the relationship between the temperature of stars and their luminosity. These 2 men, Ejnar Hertzsprung and Henry Russell, developed a powerful method for studying stars. Their plot of star data, known as the Hertzsprung-Russell diagram (or H-R diagram), is one of the most important tools used in astronomy. You will investigate this diagram further in the next chapter.

   a. Which of your 2 graphs could be labeled an H-R diagram? Why? Label this graph "H-R Diagram."

   b. Using the graph you labeled "H-R Diagram," predict the range of temperatures for stars with a luminosity (L_{star}/L_{Sun}) of about 3×10^4. Explain your reasoning and give a few examples.

   c. Must a star of this luminosity ($3 \times 10^4\ L_{Sun}$) be in that range of temperatures? What is your evidence?

8. Turn in both of your graphs to your teacher. You will revisit the graphs in the next chapter.

Reflect and Connect

Answer these questions on your own. Record your answers in your science notebook under the heading "Reflect and Connect, Putting It All Together."

1. Even though there did not appear to be a relationship between distance and temperature, why is it important to know the distances to stars when trying to understand their characteristics?

2. Recall that in Part I of the previous activity, you compared properties of distance, apparent brightness, and luminosity. You also felt the temperature of the air around different wattages of bulbs. What data could you have collected in Part I and plotted on a graph that would have resembled the data you used to make your H-R diagram?

3. One of the first things scientists do when they look at unfamiliar things is to classify them. Why would astronomers want to classify stars?

The Night Sky Star Company

Do you know someone who has adopted a star? This kind of adoption isn't a real adoption—a person doesn't take care of a star and make it part of his or her family. But the idea of being personally connected to a star is popular.

▶ **Figure 10.35 Night Sky Observatory.** Your company, the Night Sky Star Company, is working for this observatory. How much money will your adopt-a-star program raise for the observatory's new telescope?

In this activity, as a way to demonstrate your understanding of the important ideas in this chapter, you are going to imagine that you are involved in a project to support the fictional Night Sky Observatory. Your class represents the Night Sky Star Company, which has been hired to set up an adopt-a-star program to raise money for the observatory's new telescope. You need to provide the following items to your potential client:

- Certificate
- Constellation map
- Information page for each of the stars the observatory has listed

Those are the materials that a person receives in exchange for the money he or she pays to adopt a star.

The observatory prides itself on being an educational facility. Therefore, your company needs to provide materials that help people understand stars—their luminosity, apparent brightness, distance from Earth, and spectra. The Night Sky Observatory would not be happy if your company simply named the star and located it in a constellation. The person adopting a star would not learn much. Instead, your company must try to educate people about stars and the way they fit into the universe. If you don't, you might lose the adopt-a-star contract to another company.

Materials
For each team of two students

reference materials	1 A Season of Stars handout
access to the Internet	2 H-R Diagram handouts
variety of materials for making certificate, constellation map, and information page	2 Scoring Rubric for the Night Sky Star Company handouts

Process and Procedure

1. With a partner, select a star from the handout, A Season of Stars. You may want to choose a star that you can see in the night sky at the time you are doing this activity.
2. Obtain a copy of the scoring rubric for this activity to see what your teacher expects of you.
3. Use reference materials in your library or the Internet to find the following data about your star. Check off each piece of information as you find it.
   - Temperature
   - Luminosity (compared to the Sun)
   - Apparent brightness
   - Color

- Spectra and what it says about color, temperature, and elements present in the star
- Location in a constellation
- Location of the constellation in the night sky
- Distance from Earth and how it is determined
- Position on an H-R diagram

4. Use the information you find about your star and other things you learned in this chapter to write the educational section of the star material. Make sure you answer the following important questions (especially if you want to keep your job!). Check off each question as you answer it. (You do not have to answer the questions in the order shown.)

- What information can you communicate after looking at the spectra of your star?
- How do you use that information to determine the apparent color and surface temperature of the star?
- What elements are present in your star?
- Does your star appear dim or bright when viewed from Earth?
- How does that fact relate to the luminosity and the Earth-to-star distance? (Use your understanding of the inverse square law to communicate to the general public what you know about distance, apparent brightness, and luminosity.)
- Can scientists use parallax to determine the distance to this star? Why or why not? What is parallax?
- Where in the Milky Way galaxy is your star found?
- What evidence can you use in the form of mathematical calculations to support your data?
- How does understanding about waves help in solving those calculations?

5. Prepare to present your star to the rest of the company. Here is your chance to impress your boss and the people at the observatory. Use the information you found in Step 3 and the interpretation you wrote in Step 4 to create the 3 items that the observatory wants to give to people who adopt a star:

- *Certificate of adoption.* You should be creative.
- *Constellation map.* You should label your star.

- *Information sheet.* You should include as many facts and as much educational information as you can that are not reported in the certificate or the constellation map. Include an argument for why someone would (or would not) want to adopt this star.
- *Complete list of references.* You are required to include a complete list of all references used in your research. Your teacher will suggest a format for listing and documenting them.

6. Post your items on a bulletin board in your classroom as your teacher directs. Then tour the stars your company has prepared for adoption.

7. Be prepared to present your material and answer questions about your work.

Coming Attractions—Gravity!

Coming Attractions— Gravity!

In chapter 10, The Stars, you explored some of the properties that are used to study stars. You learned some of the information that you can collect by looking at starlight. But how did stars form? Are stars still forming in the universe? In chapter 5, Star Material, you learned about the life cycle of stars in the activity, Recipe for a Star. However, what is it that drives the steps in the life cycle of stars? In chapter 11, Coming Attractions—Gravity!, you learn about one of the fundamental forces that is responsible for the formation of stars and galaxies—gravity. Actually, you are feeling this force right now as you read.

The first image in the opening art shows a giant cloud of gas and dust. This is a photo of a region in space in which new stars are being born—a stellar nursery. What is it about this region in space that makes it suitable for the formation of new stars? What forces are involved in bringing this matter together into stars?

Stars are not the only structures in the universe. As astronomers look deeper and deeper into space using the newest and most modern telescopes, they can see more than just stars. They can see great clouds of gas and dust, such as a stellar nursery, and countless galaxies in addition to the Milky Way. Does the same force that pulls matter together into stars influence the formation, shape, and distribution of those galaxies?

In this chapter, you continue to explore stars and other amazing structures in the universe. With the help of a new generation of telescopes, astronomers are fortunate to be able to see many of these structures, even those that are incredibly far away—even to the edge of the universe. But just seeing the structures does not give astronomers all of the answers. Even if astronomers know what the structures look like, they still need to come up with ideas about how the structures formed. Those ideas often have their roots in observations that astronomers make here on Earth.

Goals for the Chapter

As you progress through chapter 11, you have the opportunity to explore the following questions:

- What kinds of structures do astronomers observe in the universe? How have modern telescopes such as the Hubble Space Telescope helped astronomers make observations?

- What tools do astronomers use to help them understand the properties and life cycle of stars?

- What is gravity? What variables factor into the strength of this force?

- What role does the force of gravitation play in the formation of stars and galaxies?

- What model can astronomers use to explain the arrangement of structures in the universe? What evidence did astronomers have that led them to the model?

- What new questions are astronomers asking about the universe and the structures in it? How are astronomers attempting to answer their questions?

You will be better able to answer these questions by participating in the following activities:

ENGAGE	Gravity Rules!
EXPLORE	Collision Course
EXPLAIN	Star Attraction
EXPLORE	Galactic Gravity
EXPLAIN	Neighborhoods of the Stars
ELABORATE	Guiding Equations
EVALUATE	Cosmic Dance

What conditions in space are necessary for gravity to initiate star formation?

Gravity Rules!

Key Idea:
Students have many different ideas about gravity.

EXPLORE

Collision Course

Key Idea:
A target-rich environment is necessary for the formation of stars.

Linking Question

What role does gravity play in the life cycle of stars?

EXPLAIN

Star Attraction

Key Ideas:
- Gravity plays a significant role in the progression of a star through its life cycle.
- We can use the H-R diagram to predict the life cycle of stars.

Coming Attractions— Gravity!

Linking Question

How can I apply what I have learned about stars to galaxies?

EXPLORE

Galactic Gravity

Key Idea:
Galaxies are abundant in the universe, and we can use models to study their distribution.

Cosmic Dance

Key Idea:

Gravity influences the interactions of galaxies.

How can I demonstrate what I have learned about gravity in the universe to solve problems related to colliding galaxies?

ELABORATE

Guiding Equations

Key Ideas:

- Mass and distance are quantities that influence the force of gravitation.
- The mathematical equation for the universal force of gravitation can be used to determine the force of gravity between any two objects.

CHAPTER

11 Major Concepts

▶ **Gravity is the force by which every object in the universe attracts every other object.**

▶ **Gravity is a significant factor in the birth of stars and the formation, shape, and distribution of galaxies in our universe.**

▶ **The H-R diagram is a useful tool for astronomers.**

▶ **Models help us understand the universe.**

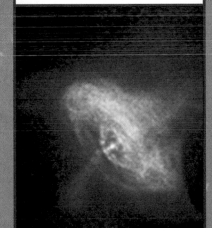

How does this model of galaxy distribution relate to gravity?

EXPLAIN

Neighborhoods of the Stars

Key Idea:

Gravity plays an important role in the formation, shape, and distribution of galaxies in our universe.

What is the mathematical relationship between mass and distance as it relates to the force of gravitation?

Gravity Rules!

▶ **Figure 11.1**
Dave Scott from *Apollo 15*. Astronaut Dave Scott from the *Apollo 15* mission conducted an experiment on the surface of the moon. Scott talked about testing Galileo's discovery of falling objects in gravity fields and wanted to test it on the lunar surface. He said to the cameras that were broadcasting his lunar experiment to the entire planet, "we thought we'd try it here for you. The feather is, appropriately, from an Air Force Academy falcon. I'll drop the hammer and the feather and . . ." What do you think happened? The painting is by artist and former astronaut Alan Bean, who also walked on the moon during the *Apollo 12* mission.

Why is Earth round? If Earth's gravity is stronger than the moon's gravity, why doesn't the moon come crashing into Earth? Those are questions you might have thought about when you were considering what you know about gravity. In this chapter, you answer those questions and others as you learn about the role of gravity in the formation of structures in the universe.

What are your ideas about gravity? In Gravity Rules!, you have the opportunity to express your thoughts about gravity. You also hear other ideas about gravity as you participate in a class discussion. Use this activity to think about what gravity is and how it influences the motion and shape of objects in the universe. If you are unsure about your answers to some of the questions, don't worry. Your teacher will not grade you on your responses; rather, you and your teacher will use them to discover your current understanding about gravity. You will discover the correct responses as you work through the chapter.*

Materials
For each student

1 What Are Your Ideas About Gravity?* handout

Process and Procedure

1. Individually, answer the questions on the handout, What Are Your Ideas About Gravity?
2. Share your responses with the class in a discussion about gravity.

*Adapted from *What Are Your Ideas About Earth?* and *What Are Your Ideas About Gravity?* which are the property of Great Explorations in Math and Science (GEMS), Lawrence Hall of Science, University of California, Berkeley, 1986 The Regents of the University of California, and used with permission. Further information is available from: The Lawrence Hall of Science, University of California, Berkeley, CA, USA 94720-5200, http://www.lhsgems.org. Also adapted by permission from Adler Planetarium.

Reflect and Connect

1. Satellites orbit Earth—in fact, the moon is considered a satellite. Looking back to Question 6b on the handout, propose an explanation for why objects can stay in orbit around Earth.
2. Explain why it is more accurate to say that astronauts experience weightlessness when they are orbiting Earth rather than saying there is no gravity in the spacecraft.
3. In chapter 5, you learned how stars were affected by the density of their layers. What is the connection between density and gravity?

Collision Course

EXPLORE

Now that you have spent some time thinking about what you know and remember about gravity, you will explore gravity's role in star formation. **Gravity** affects all types of matter whether it is on Earth or in outer space. What role does gravity play in the formation of a star? How do stars form? You began to explore star formation in chapter 5 when you learned that stars form layers because of different densities of the matter in the stars. How are density and gravity related? In Collision Course, you work with a partner to discover what happens when matter in the universe comes together.

Materials

For each team of two students

1 dime

1 die

1 marker

2 pieces of graph paper

1 playing grid: Collision Course Grid—7-H Experiment handout

2 playing grids: Collision Course Template handouts

▲
Figure 11.2
Horsehead Nebula. This interstellar dust cloud was sculpted by stellar winds and radiation into the shape of a horse's head. This Horsehead Nebula is found within the Orion Nebula and is one of the countless regions of the universe where new stars are being born. What is it about this region that makes it suitable for new star birth?

Process and Procedure

Scientists have viewed the environment in which atoms from the universe clump together into clouds of gas. Scientists imagine the clouds of gas collapsing, causing the atoms inside to become closer and closer. The result is that the density of the cloud continues to increase. Eventually, the matter in the collapsing cloud becomes a star. However, what conditions are necessary for the gases to come together? In this investigation, you work with a partner to simulate what happens as particles in a cloud of gas interact.

► **Figure 11.3 Spitzer Space Telescope image of a nebula.** This image taken by the Spitzer Space Telescope using infrared light shows clouds of stellar gases and dust. It is in these regions that astronomers see the birth of new stars. What is it about this region that makes it favorable for star formation?

▼ **Figure 11.4**

Collision Course moves. When you are playing the game, move up the board and then to the left with each roll of the die. Play until your playing piece exits the board.

1. Working with a partner, obtain the materials for this activity.

The playing boards are marked with squares, each square containing the letter *H*. The *H*s represent hydrogen atoms that would have made up most of the matter in early clouds of gas.

2. Lay out the playing board labeled "7-H." (You should see 7 *H*s in a selection of squares.) Place the dime in the box marked "Start."

This is your playing piece. To move the dime toward the upper left-hand corner of the grid, you alternate a move straight up the grid with a move straight to the left.

3. To become familiar with the rules of the game, try practicing the moves. Roll the die to determine how far to move in each direction. Then practice moving your playing piece in this way:
   • For your 1st turn, the number that you roll with your die is the number of spaces you move straight up the column on the grid.

   • Then roll again. This time move the appropriate number of spaces straight to the left.
   • With each roll, alternate moving up the grid and then to the left.
   • Keep track of the number of times your dime either crosses or lands on an *H*.
   • Continue until your playing piece moves off the grid. This signals the end of the game.

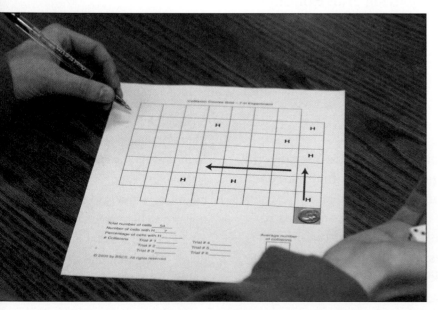

As you play the game, use a pencil to mark the path your dime takes on the playing board given your rolls of the die.

4. Note that 7 squares have an *H* on them. The *H*s were placed randomly on the grid using a random number generator. Write the following on your grid sheet and in your notebook.
   a. The total number of squares on the grid
   b. The number of squares with an *H*
   c. The percentage of total squares with an *H*

Remember, to calculate percent, divide the part (number of squares with an *H*) by the whole (total number of squares on the grid) and multiply your answer by 100.

5. Now it's time to play the game! Move your dime back to the starting position. Your dime represents a hydrogen atom zipping through a collapsing, spinning cloud of gas. The squares with an *H* represent hydrogen atoms in the cloud. Roll the die and move your playing piece as described in Step 3. As you play the game, remember that you are exploring what happens as atoms, ions, and molecules move through clouds of stellar dust and gas. Your dime will be colliding with other hydrogen atoms. Think about what this represents in the formation of a star.

You might recall that hydrogen usually combines, or bonds, with itself to form a stable gas molecule, H_2. As a gas cloud collapses, however, temperatures are too hot for H_2 to be stable. All hydrogen exists as single H atoms in early clouds of gas and H^+ inside a star.

6. Tally how many times your playing piece either crosses or lands on an *H* during the course of a game. Those encounters represent atomic collisions. Record the number of collisions for trial 1.
7. Repeat the game 5 more times for trials 2–6.
   a. Record on your handout the number of collisions for each trial.
   b. Calculate the average number of collisions for the 7-H grid and record this average on the handout.
8. Now it is time to explore the conditions when more hydrogen atoms are present in the cloud of gas.
   a. Work with your partner and decide how to *randomly* select 14 squares to mark with an *H* on the Collision Course Template. Record your selection method in your notebook and get your teacher's approval.
   b. Use the Collision Course Template to make a new playing board with 14 *H* spaces. Use a marker to label the squares with an *H*. Title this game board "14-H Experiment."
   c. Repeat the game with 6 trials on your new grid.
   d. Record the number of collisions for each of the 6 14-H trials.
   e. Calculate the average number of collisions.

9. Get another blank Collision Course Template and select 21 squares using the same method you devised previously. Use a marker to label the 21 squares with an *H*. Title this game board "21-H Experiment."
   a. Repeat the game with 6 trials on your new grid.
   b. Record the number of collisions for each of the 6 21-H trials.
   c. Calculate the average number of collisions.

10. Look at the sample bar graph that your teacher shows you. Use a piece of graph paper to make a bar graph of your data for the 7-H, 14-H, and 21-H trials, leaving room to include data from 1 other team.

11. Add the data from 1 other team to your graph.

12. Discuss with your team the trends you see in your graph. Prepare a T-table with the headings "What trend I see" and "What this trend means." The first trend is already shown in figure 11.5 to help you get started. Add more trends as you discuss your graph with your team.

▼ **Figure 11.5**
T-table for Step 12.
Copy this table in your notebook and complete it with additional trends.

What trend I see	What this trend means
I see the number of collisions increasing with more Hs	As there are more Hs, there are more particles to hit and the number of collisions will increase
Add more trends here	

Reflect and Connect

Discuss the answers to these questions with your class. Record your best answers in your notebook.

1. In which of the 3 games—7-H, 14-H, or 21-H—is the following true? Explain your answers to each statement.
   a. The matter is most dense.
   b. The matter is least dense.
   c. The number of collisions is greatest.

2. Astronomers who study star formation say that stars form in "target-rich environments."
   a. In which of the 3 games—7-H, 14-H, or 21-H—would you say that you have a target-rich environment?
   b. Recall from the Recipe for a Star activity in chapter 5 that you analyzed different density layers of a star. Where would the most target-rich environment be in a star? Answer that question with a sketch of a star showing density layers. Label the sketch with the *densest layer* and the *least dense layer*. Also, label the area that would have the most target-rich environment. Below your sketch, explain your reasoning.
3. In a star's target-rich environment, what objects are colliding? What might happen as a result of that collision?
4. How do you think the Collision Course game and gravity are related? How can they help you understand an important concept about stars?
5. Why are models useful to astronomers when they are studying stars?

Star Attraction

Up to this point in chapter 11, you have explored two of the conditions that must be met for a star to form—there must be a target-rich environment and the gases must come together. As that happens, the density increases within the cloud until the center of the cloud gets hot. After a great deal of time, sometimes millions of years, the star finally "turns on." You learned in Recipe for a Star in chapter 5 that when a star "turns on," nuclear fusion takes place; fusion releases an enormous amount of energy.

What triggers that process? One event that may trigger the conditions for star birth is star death. Recall from chapter 5 that a high-mass star eventually explodes into a supernova. That explosion triggers the birth of new stars in a process illustrated in figure 11.6.

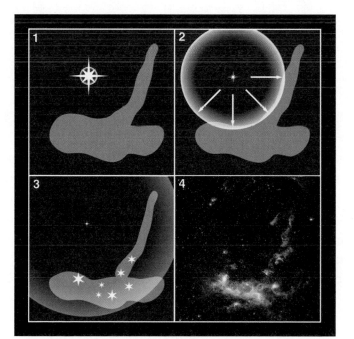

▲ **Figure 11.6 Star formation.** A dying massive star initiates a process of star formation. As a dying star explodes, it produces a supernova that propels matter into space, producing a target-rich environment. It takes millions of years for this sequence of events to take place. But the supernova explosion itself is very fast—just minutes.

▲ Figure 11.7
Patterns help you find a friend's home. You see patterns every day. What type of patterns do scientists look for in studying the universe?

What does gravity have to do with this process? Gravity pulls the matter together so tightly that the core of the star gets hot enough for nuclear fusion to begin. You may have thought of gravity as a force that pulls things only down. However, in reality, gravity is a force that pulls things *together*. This is a pattern that astronomers observe in the universe.

Patterns are useful to people who are trying to make sense of different types of systems. For example, when trying to find the house of a new friend, isn't it helpful that the number patterns along the streets follow a numerical order, with even numbers on one side of the street and odd numbers on the other side?

Astronomers also see a pattern in the universe; that is, matter gathers together to make stars. What causes this pattern of matter in the universe? How can astronomers' understanding of matter help them arrive at a reasonable explanation for the formation of stars? In Star Attraction, you begin to develop good answers for those and other questions. In Part I, you read about gravity and watch a video clip about how the information you read about was confirmed in a lab. Then you apply what you have learned about gravity to its role in the formation of stars, their life spans, and their life cycles.

Part I: A Universal Force

Materials

SCI LINKS
NSTA
Topic: life cycle of a star
Go to: www.scilinks.org
Code: 1Inquiry528

Process and Procedure

1. Read A Universal Force to learn more about the force of gravitation.

A Universal Force

You probably know the name of the force that causes things to fall to the ground—the force of gravitation. On the surface of Earth, you feel the force as gravity. The force of gravitation on Earth seems very strong. The last time you tripped and fell to the ground, you certainly felt its strength. However, when you pick up a pencil that you dropped, for a short time, you easily produce a force greater than gravity. It turns out that the force of Earth's gravity on a pencil is much weaker than your own strength when you pick up the pencil. Even for small metal objects on your lab table, the force of a tiny magnet is greater than that of Earth's gravity. This means that you can use the magnet to lift a paper clip off the table. The magnet pulls the paper clip in the opposite direction from which gravity pulls it. The magnet pulls the paper clip up even though gravity is pulling the paper clip toward Earth.

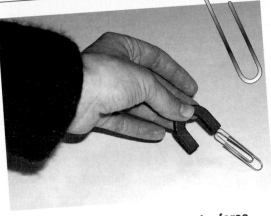

▲ **Figure 11.8 Magnets exert a force.** Which force is stronger—the force of the small magnet on the paper clip or the force of Earth on the paper clip?

Sir Isaac Newton noticed the attraction of all objects to Earth. As the legend goes, he sat under an apple tree in the mid-17th century and was struck by a falling apple. He realized that a force pulled the apple to Earth. His experiences led him to propose that the force of gravitation is a universal force.

What did Newton mean when he described the force of gravitation as a universal force? He believed not only that things fall to the ground on Earth, but also that everything in the universe attracts everything else. In other words, gravity is a force that pulls things together throughout the universe. On Earth, your experience of this universal force of "pulling together" is the experience of "pulling down" because you observe things falling to the ground. By applying a law that humans could investigate on Earth, Newton was able to explain things that he observed beyond Earth, such as the moon revolving around Earth instead of spinning off into space.

Have you ever seen evidence that the tree in your backyard is attracted to your house through gravitation? Do you feel pulled toward the building on the corner through gravitation?

▲ **Figure 11.9 Sir Isaac Newton.** As the legend goes, Sir Isaac Newton used a simple observation about a falling apple as evidence to support his ideas about the universal force of gravitation.

The answer is no because people on Earth rarely feel the universal nature of the force of gravitation due to everyday objects. The force of gravitation of small objects such as your body and a building are weak compared with the force exerted by the much more massive Earth. Nonetheless, the universal force of gravitation is still present. Everything (including you!) is attracted to everything else.

You would be acting like a scientist if you were somewhat skeptical about the universal force of gravitation. You might say, "Show me!"

A man named Henry Cavendish did just that a century after Newton explained universal gravitation. Cavendish set up a device called a torsion balance, which responded to differences in gravitational attraction only between easily movable, small objects. Because of the way the torsion balance was set up, it ignored the much stronger gravity of Earth. With the balance, Cavendish could observe the gravitational attraction between two objects, such as a couple of lead weights. His torsion balance provided evidence of the universal nature of the force of gravitation.

▶ **Figure 11.10**
Model of Henry Cavendish's torsion balance. Cavendish used equipment like this to show that even objects with relatively small masses exert a force of gravitation on other objects.

2. Watch as your teacher shows a video clip of a replication of Cavendish's experiment.
3. Sketch the setup in your notebook and label all parts.
    a. Use arrows to represent the movement of the balance.
    b. Write highlights under your sketch, using 2 columns. Use the column headings "What I see" and "What it means."
4. To show your understanding of Cavendish's experiment, answer the following questions:
    a. How would an experiment like the one in the video clip support Newton's idea of universal gravitation?
    b. Why is it important to test the torsion balance in a controlled environment? What variables were the scientists trying to control?

5. Read the following paragraph to learn more about the universal force.

You can see that the mass of an object determines the force of gravity that it will exert on another object. The moon is much less massive than Earth; consequently, the force of gravity that the moon exerts on an object at its surface is much less than the force of gravity that Earth exerts on the same object at its surface. However, is mass the only thing that determines the force of gravity between 2 objects? Think about the Sun. The mass of the Sun is over 300,000 times the mass of Earth! If mass was the only factor that determined the force of gravity between 2 objects, Earth along with all of the other planets in the solar system might hurl into the Sun. There must be other factors. Can you think of one? That's right—distance. The distance between 2 objects plays a big role in the force of gravity between them.

Stop & THINK
Part I

1. Consider a suitcase sitting on the floor.
   a. How fast is it moving in a vertical direction?
   b. Does it change velocity when you pick it up? Explain your answer.
   c. What must your arm supply to change the velocity of the suitcase?
   d. Is this force greater than, equal to, or less than the force of gravity on the suitcase?

2. Is there an instance in which you could be holding the suitcase and the force of gravity and the force that your arm is applying are equal? Explain your answer and include a sketch using arrows to represent the forces.

   Use longer arrows to represent stronger forces, shorter arrows for weaker forces, and arrows of the same length for equal forces.

3. Complete the following sentences:

   As the mass of an object increases, the gravitational force between that object and another object will _____.
   As the distance between 2 objects increases, the gravitational force between the object _____.

4. You may be "attracted" to another student in a number of ways. Explain why you do not feel the attraction due to gravity.

5. If everything is attracted to everything else, how might matter in the universe behave?

Part II: Gravitating toward Stars

Materials

For each student

colored pencils

graphs from the Putting It All
Together activity in chapter 10

1 H-R Diagram Showing
Evolution of the Sun handout

1 Stages of Solar Evolution—
The Sun's Scrapbook handout

Process and Procedure

1. Read Gravity and Mass with a partner to learn more about
   how gravity affects stars. Take notes in your science notebook
   of the main ideas. After each paragraph, stop and share with
   your partner what you have written. Add to your notebook any
   new ideas that your partner may have written down.

READING

Gravity and Mass

So what does gravity have to do with star formation? Recall the Collision Course game that you played in an earlier activity. Gravity begins to pull the particles together into smaller and smaller spaces. This means there is more mass in a smaller volume. As the density of the cloud increases, more H atoms collide. The density, pressure, and temperature of the star increase. When the temperature gets high enough, the star "turns on." Recall that this occurs when nuclear fusion begins in the core. None of this would be possible without the force of gravity!

In a star, gravity pulls matter inward toward the center. At the same time, another force pushes out. That opposing force is the result of thermal pressure. This thermal pressure is similar to the pressure inside a balloon, which will increase as you heat it up. **Thermal pressure** is due to the increase in temperature and pressure

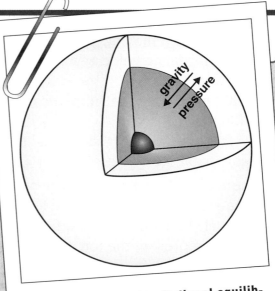

▲ Figure 11.11 **Gravitational equilibrium.** At each point inside this star, the pressure pushing outward balances the force of gravity pulling inward.

as gravity pulls all of the matter together. It is also due to the nuclear fusion taking place inside the core once the temperature is high enough. When the force due to thermal pressure is weak compared to the gravitational force, the matter continues to come together until the temperature at the core is high enough for fusion to begin. At this point, the star "turns on" and a star is born.

When the inward force of gravity balances the outward force resulting from thermal pressure, the star is in gravitational equilibrium. This is similar to the **gravitational equilibrium** that was produced in the earlier example of holding a suitcase. As you are lifting it from a resting position, your force is greater than gravity. However, if you are just holding it stationary off the floor, it is in gravitational equilibrium. The force of your hand on the suitcase balances the force of gravity on the suitcase.

A star's birth mass determines the outcome of this struggle between gravity and pressure. In the Recipe for a Star activity in chapter 5, you were introduced to the life cycle of stars of different masses, and you continue your learning here. You may want to review that section of chapter 5 before you continue.

Mass is a key factor in the time required for a gas cloud to collapse to a star and "turn on" by fusion. Gas clouds with small masses collapse, or pull together, slowly (over tens of millions of years) because the gravitational attraction is low. Gas clouds with high masses collapse quickly (over tens of thousands of years) because the gravitational attraction is high (see figure 11.12).

In chapter 10, you plotted the luminosities versus the temperatures of stars and found that your graph showed some interesting trends. Do you remember what that type of graph is called? The graph is called an H-R diagram, and it is a valuable tool for astronomers. The stage in the life cycle of a star, which is driven by gravity, can be determined by the star's position on the diagram.

Mass of gas cloud (compared with Sun)	Time for collapse (years)
0.5	1.5×10^8
1	4×10^7
2	8×10^6
3	3×10^6
5	700,000
9	150,000
15	60,000

▲ **Figure 11.12 Collapse time of gas cloud to the main sequence star.** Mass is a key factor in the time required for a gas cloud to collapse to a star and turn on by fusion. What does gravity have to do with the time it takes for a star to turn on?

The pattern that is revealed in an H-R diagram is illustrated in figure 11.13. You will notice that most stars fall along a distinct trend, or line, in the diagram. Those stars are called **main sequence stars.** Main sequence stars are stars undergoing fusion at a relatively steady state, forming layers, and maintaining a balance between the outward force produced from thermal pressure due to fusion reactions and the inward force due to gravity—they are in gravitational equilibrium.

Topic: H-R diagram
Go to: www.scilinks.org
Code: 1Inquiry534

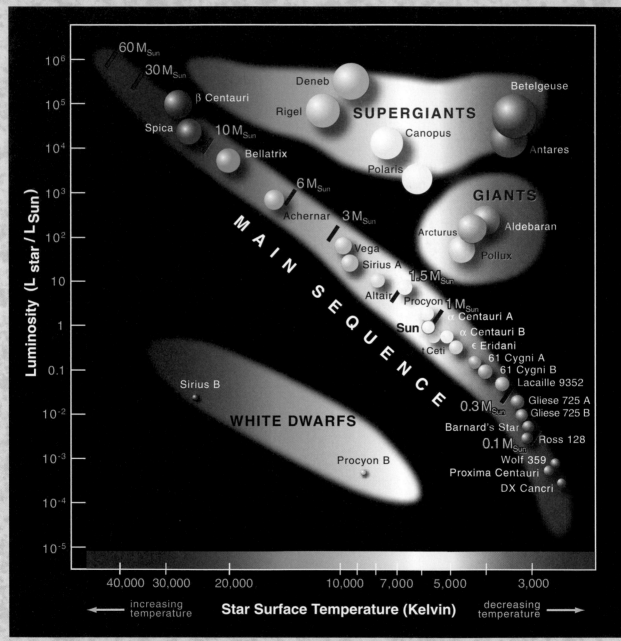

▲ **Figure 11.13 This is an H-R diagram.** This diagram plots a star's luminosity (solar units) versus its surface temperature Kelvin (K). Note that temperature increases to the left (hotter stars are on the left-hand side). A star's luminosity is shown in relation to the Sun's luminosity, or the ratio L_{star}/L_{Sun}. This H-R diagram shows fields for four main groups of stars (main sequence, giants, supergiants, and white dwarfs). H-R diagrams help astronomers as they determine where a star is in its life cycle.

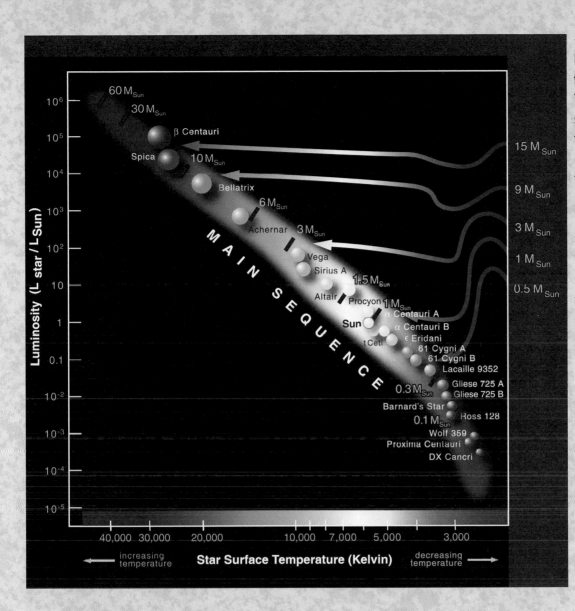

Luminosity-temperature paths. This H-R diagram shows the luminosity-temperature paths of clouds of gas as they collapse into main sequence stars. Example paths begin with a gas cloud with half the mass of the Sun (0.5 M_{Sun}) up to a gas cloud with 15 times the mass of the Sun (15 M_{Sun}).

Mass is an important factor in the lives of stars. When stars begin fusion, they are plotted on the main sequence of the H-R diagram at various points depending on their mass. Higher-mass stars are positioned on the main sequence further up the sequence and to the left on the diagram. They have high temperatures and luminosities. Low-mass stars appear on the main sequence further down and to the right on the H-R diagram. Figure 11.14 illustrates where stars of different masses enter the main sequence.

Life on the main sequence as a fusion-fueled star cannot go on forever. A star's balance is sometimes interrupted, such as when the gravitational equilibrium is affected. What can affect this equilibrium? The star can run out of the fuel that drives the nuclear fusion reactions. When that occurs, the outer layers of the star begin to change. The layers begin to expand, and the star becomes more luminous because it is larger. As the luminous shell expands, it cools slightly. During those changes, the stars are no longer on the main sequence. They are now red giants or even supergiants (see figure 11.13). Here, fusion reactions accelerate inside the star, once again depending on whether the star is a low-mass or high-mass star.

In low-mass stars, outer layers of hydrogen gas are pushed away, creating an expanding gas cloud, or **nebula**, that surrounds the star. The remaining core of the star becomes a white dwarf (see figure 11.13). In high-mass stars, fusion reactions can accelerate uncontrollably, leading to a massive-star supernova explosion (figure 11.15). During those spectacular events, much of the mass of the star is blown away into space, leaving just a small, very hot core of the star. The remnants of the atoms "die" as neutron stars.

a.

b.

▲ **Figure 11.15 Before and after photos of a supernova.** In the before picture (a), the arrow indicates the star that exploded (b) as a supernova.

2. You will find it very helpful to use your notes and, in particular, the concept maps that you made in the Recipe for a Star (elaborate) section of chapter 5. Those tools will help you connect your previous learning to the H-R diagram. Answer the following questions with your class to make sure you understand the H-R diagram.
   a. A particular star is plotted on the H-R diagram according to its luminosity and temperature. If the star is located at the bottom right-hand corner along the main sequence, what does that position tell you about the star's mass?
   b. A high-mass star that is 15 times more massive than the Sun (15 M_{Sun}) appears in what position on the main sequence?
3. Your teacher will distribute your graphs from the activity, Putting It All Together, in chapter 10. Determine which one is your H-R diagram and on that graph, do the following:
   a. Shade and label the main sequence stars on your graph.
   b. Use the temperature ranges along the x-axis to color the graph so that it indicates the color of the stars in the different temperature ranges. Look at figure 11.16 for more information about star temperature and color.

Star surface temperature (K)	Color
11,000 to 50,000	bluish
7,500 to 11,000	blue-white
6,000 to 7,500	white
5,000 to 6,000	yellow-white
3,500 to 5,000	red-orange
2,000 to 3,500	reddish

▲ Figure 11.16 **Star temperature and color.** Use this table to determine the color scale for your H-R diagram.

   c. Along the y-axis, indicate with an arrow the direction of increasing luminosity.
   d. Along the x-axis, indicate with an arrow the direction of increasing temperature.
   e. Circle and label the region on your graph where you would find red giants.
   f. Circle and label the region on your graph where you would find white dwarfs.

4. Get the 2 handouts for this activity: Stages of Solar Evolution—The Sun's Scrapbook and H-R Diagram Showing Evolution of the Sun. On the H-R diagram, note a counterclockwise path numbered 1 to 11. This shows either a numbered position or a numbered transition, with the stage number embedded in an arrow (for example, stage 2 is a transition between positions 1 and 3). On your handout, Stages of Solar Evolution—The Sun's Scrapbook, note the empty cells.

   a. For the position of each number in the H-R diagram, work with your partner to fill all empty cells for the Sun's evolution in these categories:

   - H-R fields that the Sun will occupy as it evolves (5 empty cells)

   - Surface Temperature of the Sun at each number on the H-R diagram

   - Luminosity (versus Sun's current luminosity) at each number on the H-R diagram

   - Radius (versus Sun's current radius) at each number on the H-R diagram

   b. What stage in the Sun's evolution lasts the longest? How many years?

   c. At what stage would the Sun's surface have the highest temperature? How hot?

   d. At what stage would the Sun have the highest luminosity? Explain your answer.

   e. At what stage will the Sun be the largest? How large?

   f. When the Sun finally cools to a black dwarf, what will its approximate radius be compared with its current radius? How many times smaller?

   g. What do you think is the life span of the Sun? How did you determine this?

Reflect and Connect

1. You just studied the life cycle of the Sun. What role does gravity play in this cycle?

2. Where do you think you would find neutron stars on the H-R diagram? Explain your reasoning.

3. Explain how scientists can use the H-R diagram to help determine the history of a star. What do they need to know about the star to use the diagram?

Did You See That?

Imagine a woman going about her business nearly 1,000 years ago. Perhaps she is shopping at a village market or collecting firewood in the desert. Suddenly, the woman sees a brilliant burst of light from up in the sky. The light keeps the same position relative to the stars, but it is so bright that the woman can see it during the day. As night falls, she sees that it looks like an enormously brilliant object in the constellation Taurus (see the supernova image below).

People in the woman's community see the bright light, too. They are fearful. What could this fiery object be? They continue to watch it for 23 days and nights. It appears to die out, leaving in its place what looks to be an average star. The people survive the event, but they wonder what caused the mysterious light.

The woman and her neighbors were not the only people to witness the extraordinary event. It was viewed from places on opposite sides of Earth and was well documented by several people.

One account was from the court astronomer to the Song emperor in China. He had been keeping track of the constellations that he could see from the palace. One day he noticed a brilliant new star close to the moon. It was so bright that it was clearly visible even in daylight. It was four times brighter than Venus, and it resided in the constellation Taurus. He wrote about the event in the court records:

> In the 1st year of the period Chih-ho, the 5th moon, the day chi ch'ou, a guest star appeared. It was visible in the day like Venus, with pointed rays in all four directions. The color was reddish-white. It was seen altogether for 23 days. (Yang Wei-te, Court Astronomer)

Around the world, in the desert Southwest of North America near present-day New Mexico, people also may have recorded the event. This time an Ancestral Puebloan (Anasazi) artist may have seen a brilliant star close to the crescent moon. The star remained

Bright light from a supernova. What is this brilliant light? For about 23 days, it was visible to the eye in the daytime sky in the year AD 1054.

An Ancestral Puebloan cave drawing.
Archaeologists found this rock drawing in Chaco Canyon National Historical Park in New Mexico. They believe that this could be a depiction of the AD 1054 event. The crescent represents the moon, which would have just been entering the first quarter at the time of the event. Calculations indicate that the moon would have been within 3 degrees of the bright exploded star, a position similar to that pictured on the rock.

Crab Nebula. Today astronomers can see the remnants of the massive-star supernova of AD 1054, the remarkable Crab Nebula.

of the lower horn of the bull, near Orion's club). Astronomers call the remnant the Crab Nebula.

visible for 23 days. To record this unusual event, on a rock near his dwelling, he etched a many-rayed star next to a crescent moon (see the photograph of cave drawings).

Today you still can see the glowing remnants of this extraordinary event close up with a telescope (see the image of the Crab Nebula). We now know that what people saw in AD 1054 was a massive-star supernova, or exploding star, that produced a light 10 billion times more powerful than that of the Sun.

The explosion left behind a neutron star in the constellation Taurus (which you can find in the picture near the end

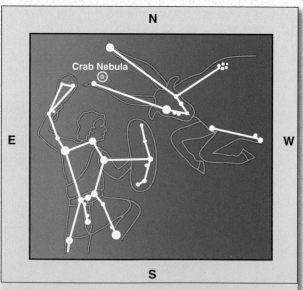

Crab Nebula in Taurus. The Crab Nebula can be found near the tip of the lower horn of Taurus.

Galactic Gravity

The Whirlpool galaxy. These galaxies are about 35 million light-years (ly) away. The bigger galaxy is known as the Whirlpool galaxy and appears face on from Earth. There are a couple of hundred billion stars here. What causes these stars to clump together in a galaxy?

Wow! You have learned a lot about stars! So why has so much of this unit focused on stars? Stars are probably the most familiar structures in the night sky outside of our solar system. Even within our solar system, the closest star, the Sun, is very familiar. Nevertheless, are there other structures in the universe that astronomers study? Sure there are, and gravity plays a big role in determining their shape and distribution in the universe—as it does with stars.

Galaxies are one of the main structures in the universe. **Galaxies** are huge collections of stars bound together by gravity. You have already seen in chapter 10 that stars in other galaxies can help astronomers determine distances in the universe. In Galactic Gravity, you learn about galaxies other than our own Milky Way galaxy. Modern technology is helping astronomers see more galaxies in the universe than ever before. How many other galaxies are there, and how are they spread out in the universe? In Part I of this activity, you look deeper into the universe using images from the Hubble Space Telescope. In Part II, you investigate the arrangement of galaxies in the universe. Believe it or not, you can understand that concept better by making a simple model with soap bubbles.

Hubble Trouble

Space telescopes are superior in many ways to ground-based telescopes because they do not have to contend with interference from Earth's atmosphere. Trying to see distant objects through the thick atmosphere is like trying to see through the water in a deep swimming pool or lake—the farther you have to look, the more difficult it is to see objects underwater. Some people think astronomers get better images with space-based telescopes because they are closer to the stars, but this is not true. The Hubble Space Telescope (HST) orbits about 600 kilometers (km) above Earth. This is only a small fraction of the distance to the structures in the universe that the telescope images.

The HST, originally designed in the 1970s and launched in 1990, has changed astronomers' understanding of the universe. On-orbit service calls by Space Shuttle astronauts have kept the telescope in top-notch condition by allowing astronauts to take it apart, replace worn-out equipment, and upgrade instruments. Regular servicing of the telescope is essential to keep it operational.

Despite the amazing insights from the HST, its fate remains uncertain. Policy makers and National Aeronautics and Space Administration (NASA) administrators will determine whether the HST will remain functional. In January 2004, NASA announced that it was canceling plans for a final upgrade of the $1.3 billion telescope by the Space Shuttle. Without an upgrade, the telescope will become unusable. NASA's choices are to perform an upgrade with robots or destroy the telescope.

Traditionally, the HST was upgraded by astronauts on the Space Shuttle. With the grounding of the Space Shuttles following the 2003 *Columbia* disaster, the earliest proposed flight date for the next mission was to be spring 2007—too late for a manned mission to save the HST. Therefore, the word from NASA was that there would be no shuttle missions to repair the HST. However, new developments in July 2004 kept the hope of the HST's future alive. At that time, NASA was considering proposals to upgrade the telescope using a robotic mission. This would be safer than a manned Space Shuttle mission and could be in place soon enough to salvage the telescope. As you are reading this, you may already know the fate of the HST. If not, search the World Wide Web or check the newspapers for current updates.

The HST is not the only space-based telescope. You have seen images in your book taken from the Spitzer Space Telescope, a telescope that takes images that detect infrared radiation. The Chandra X-ray Observatory, another space-based telescope, is designed to observe X-rays from high-energy regions of the universe, such as the remnants of exploded stars. Those are only a few of the space-based telescopes. What will be next—telescopes on the moon? Some astronomers hope so.

Part I: Take a Closer Look

Materials

Process and Procedure

Welcome to the universe! What can you see of it? From where you stand right now, probably not much. However, if you were lucky enough to be using the Hubble Space Telescope, you would have plenty to observe (see figure 11.18). You might see large structures, with many tiny lights, that appear to be swirling. You might also see deep black space with nothing in it—or is something there? Look closer. Look even closer. Now what do you see? In this activity, work with your class to find the answer to that question!

▲ **Figure 11.18**
The Hubble Space Telescope (HST).
Telescopes like the HST help astronomers see structures in the universe that they cannot see with Earth-bound telescopes.

1. With your class, look at Image A of the Take a Closer Look transparencies. Discuss the following questions:
   a. What image is on the transparency?
   b. What structures do you see in Image A?
   c. Are there any visible structures in the marked box on the image?
2. Now, look at Image B of the Take a Closer Look transparencies. This image is a closer look at the boxed area in Image A.
   a. Now that you have taken a closer look at the area of space in the marked box, how would you change your answer to Question 1c? What do you see in this enlarged view of the marked box?
   b. Among the structures on Image B, what do you see? In particular, what do you see within the marked area on Image B?
3. Let's take a closer look. Study Image C of the Take a Closer Look transparencies. Image C is a closer look at the area of space that is outlined in Image B.
   a. As you observe Image C, how would you change your answer to Question 2b? What do you see now in the enlarged view of the marked area?
   b. Between the structures in Image C, what do you see?
   c. If you were able to look deep into the spaces between the structures in Image C, what do you predict you might find?

Stop & THINK

Part I

Image C is the Hubble Deep Field North, an image composed of 10 days of exposures of a small slice of the sky taken with the Hubble Space Telescope. The telescope is able to capture light from structures in the universe that are 10 times fainter than any light that ground-based telescopes can detect. By counting the structures in this slice of the sky and multiplying by the number of slices that make up the whole sky, astronomers estimate that there are 80 billion of these structures in the observable universe.

1. Describe in your science notebook what an image such as the Hubble Deep Field North means to you.

2. Think about what the image means to scientists and describe what you think scientists can learn from the image.

Part II: A Bubble Map

Materials
For each team of two students

2 pairs of safety goggles

2 lab aprons

masking tape

1 metric ruler

1 container of soap bubble solution

2 drinking straws or coffee stirrers

Cautions

Wear safety goggles while working with the soap solution. Do not share the drinking straws. Clean up as your teacher directs.

Process and Procedure

Astronomers are continuously adding to their observations of galaxies. An interesting observation was made even before you were born. This observation helped astronomers understand how gravity plays a role in the formation and distribution of galaxies. In 1983, Margaret Geller and John Huchra of the Harvard-Smithsonian Center for Astrophysics began mapping all of the galaxies in a specific section of the sky. Because the universe is so big, they decided to make a map of just 1 pie-shaped slice. It took them 6 months to make their initial observations. Figure 11.19 shows the results of Geller and Huchra's initial data and subsequent research to map 2 slices of a part of the universe.

Surprised at what the map showed, astronomers began to think of models that would explain it. The closest model seems to be a soap bubble map. Scientists often use simple models to understand complex concepts. Do you remember using a Slinky to understand the wave nature of light?

With your partner, you will make a soap bubble model that can help you understand this map of the universe and you will investigate the force that pulls matter together in the universe—gravity.

1. Use masking tape to make a large triangle on your desk to designate an area in which you will make your bubble map.
2. Spread a thin layer of soapy water inside the masking tape borders.
3. Taking turns with your partner, put one end of a small straw in the soapy solution and blow through it slowly to create a bubble.
4. Carefully remove the straw, moving it to another spot in the soapy solution to create another bubble.
5. Continue moving and creating bubbles until you have made several.
6. Draw a sketch in your notebook of the bubble sculpture that you have created. Include a scale bar to indicate the size of the bubbles.

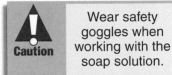

Wear safety goggles when working with the soap solution.

▼ **Figure 11.19**

A slice of the universe. Geller and Huchra's map depicts thousands of galaxies in a slice of the universe. The white dots are galaxies, and "MW" shows the location of our galaxy, the Milky Way.

If your bubbles pop too soon, look carefully at the bubble residue left on your desk. Sketch this if all of your bubbles have popped.

7. Follow your teacher's instructions for cleaning up your area.
8. Discuss these questions with your partner and record your answers in your science notebook.
   a. Where does the matter (the stuff that makes up the surface of the bubbles) exist in your soap bubble map? What is between the matter (inside the bubbles)?
   b. Look at Geller and Huchra's map of a slice of the universe. In what ways does it resemble your soap bubble map? What does that tell you about the arrangement of matter (galaxies) in the universe?

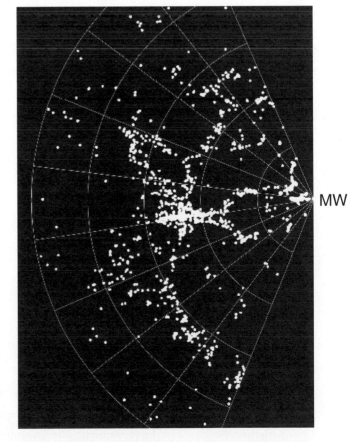

MW

9. Read the following 2 paragraphs that explain how Geller and Huchra made a model to explain their picture.

READING

Galaxy Distribution

To verify the arrangement of galaxies that they thought they observed in their slice of the universe, Geller and Huchra added more slices of the map, one on top of the other. Eventually, their 3-dimensional model revealed that the gaps, or voids, that they saw in their 2-dimensional map were actually spherical. The galaxies were located on the outer shells of the spheres. In 2003, the Anglo-Australian Observatory released a much larger survey of over 221,000 galaxies (see figure 11.20). Each blue dot is a galaxy. Can you see the connection between this map and your bubble map?

Geller and Huchra's work provides some of the best data from which astronomers can build explanations of the distributions of galaxies in the universe. There is still so much that scientists do not know about galaxies. As technology continues to advance, providing astronomers with direct evidence, they will be able to answer many questions.

Topic: galaxy
Go to: www.scilinks.org
Code: 1Inquiry546

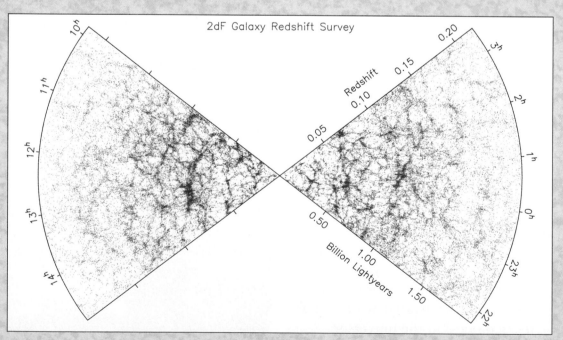

▲ **Figure 11.20 Map of galaxy distribution.** The distribution of galaxies in the universe is not random or uniform. Instead, galaxies cluster together, and these clusters are close together. Do you see the resemblance to your bubble map?

Reflect and Connect

Answer the following questions individually. Record your answers in your science notebook.

1. How has the Hubble Space Telescope helped scientists study the universe?
2. How does the bubble model support the theory that the force of gravitation plays a major role in the arrangement of galaxies in the universe?
3. Describe at least 2 methods that astronomers use to study galaxies.
4. Assume the role of an astronomer. What would you want to find out about galaxies? How would you go about trying to find the answers to your questions?
5. Use your understanding of the structure of the universe to comment on the following excerpt from a poem by the English poet Francis Thompson (1859–1907).

> "Mistress of Vision"
> All things by immortal power,
> Near or far,
> Hiddenly
> To each other linkèd are,
> That thou canst not stir a flower
> Without troubling of a star . . .

Neighborhoods of the Stars

You have just made a bubble model that represents how galaxies are distributed in the universe. Why are they distributed this way? The answer lies in the laws of gravity and the distribution of mass in the universe. Over the last century, astronomers have learned a great deal about galaxies, helping to explain the distribution of galaxies in the universe. Take a look at what astronomers have learned.

Remember that Newton's law of universal gravitation states that everything attracts everything else. The amount of pull depends on the mass of the objects and the distance between them. For example, when large masses are close together, the gravitational attraction between them is high. If the same masses are farther apart, their gravitational attraction is much lower. This is true even on the universal scale. Every mass in the universe attracts every other mass and is attracted to every other mass.

▲ **Figure 11.21**
Image of the universe from WMAP. The uneven colors of this map indicate how matter is spread unevenly across the universe. You will learn more about this image in the next chapter.

So why doesn't the mass in the universe gather into one big clump of matter? One reason is because matter is not distributed uniformly in the universe. In fact, astronomers have recently found evidence of "lumpiness" in the universe that has existed since just after the beginning of the universe. They have shown the uneven distribution of matter from the slight variations in background EM radiation. That background radiation is in the microwave part of the EM spectrum. Those variations are represented in a map of the entire sky (see figure 11.21) made with data collected by the Wilkinson Microwave Anisotropy Probe (WMAP). The apparent lumpiness illustrates the way that matter, attracted by the force of gravitation, gathered into structures out of small fluctuations in the density of the universe just after the beginning of the universe. Since then, the force of gravitation has enhanced the tiny fluctuations and formed clusters of galaxies, solar systems, stars, and planets.

The structure of the universe has always interested scientists. Stars were always a favorite topic of study, but clearly, many other types of objects were spread across the sky. Early in the study of astronomy, scientists discovered that most of the stars they could see were clustered in a visible band called the Milky Way. It was in 1609, when Galileo first used a telescope, that scientists recognized the fact that those stars formed a structure they called the Milky Way galaxy. For many years, they believed that the Milky Way galaxy was the only galaxy in the universe and that the Sun was in the center of it.

▼ **Figure 11.22**
Andromeda galaxy, M31. This galaxy is the closest large spiral visible from the Northern Hemisphere.

Astronomers in the past observed many smudges of light in the night sky. One such smudge is visible with the unaided eye from the Northern Hemisphere. Astronomers thought this faint smudge of light was like all others within our galaxy. It was not until Edwin Hubble picked out a Cepheid variable star in this smudge and used Henrietta Swan Leavitt's period-luminosity relationship that he discovered that this smudge was well outside the Milky Way. To his surprise, the smudge was light from another galaxy, the Andromeda galaxy (see figure 11.22). You will learn more about Hubble's discovery in the next chapter. Only within the last century, with continued advancements in technology, have astronomers identified thousands of other galaxies and observed billions more.

Designation for Deep Sky Objects

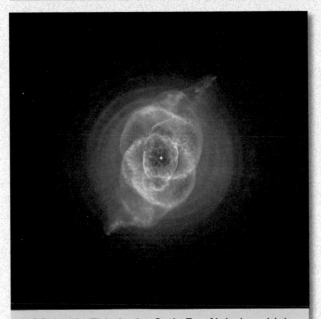

NGC 6543. This is the Cat's Eye Nebula, which is cataloged as NGC 6543. What do the letters and numbers mean?

Deep sky objects are astronomical objects beyond our solar system. In your book, you have seen many images of deep sky taken with some of the most sophisticated telescopes available. Those objects have common names, such as the Andromeda galaxy or the Orion Nebula, but often they are designated by another naming system. For example, the Andromeda galaxy is often given the name M31. What does the M31 mean, and where did the naming system come from?

The *M* in the M31 naming system for the Andromeda galaxy comes from the catalog of 18th-century astronomer Charles Messier. The 109 objects in the *Messier Catalogue* are designated M1, M2, and so on. They are often called the Messier objects and are cataloged as a result of Messier's attempt to list objects that could be confused as comets. While looking for comets in the mid 1700s, Messier was continually finding cometlike objects. He began his catalog so that others would not mistake these deep sky objects for true comets.

The Messier objects include some of the most well-known deep sky objects visible from the Northern Hemisphere. As more modern telescopes were used and interest in astronomy spread to the far reaches of the world, another naming system evolved. Several thousand deep sky objects are listed in the *New General Catalogue*, published over a century ago by English astronomer J. L .E. Dreyer. Those objects are prefixed with the letters *NGC*. Most of the Messier objects are included in the *New General Catalogue*, and many of them have a popular name as well. M1, for example, is known as NGC1952 and as the Crab Nebula. A few objects not listed in either of those major catalogs have different prefixes, such as IC or Col., identifying other lists. This text will use either the Messier object notation or the NGC notation.

Charles Messier (1730–1817). Charles Messier developed a naming system for many deep sky objects.

CLASSIFICATION OF GALAXIES

Astronomers have determined that galaxies can be classified by shape. One classification scheme puts galaxies into four categories: spiral, barred spiral, elliptical, and irregular. With a closer look, astronomers can learn even more about each of the galaxy types.

◄ **Figure 11.23** **Spiral galaxy (NGC 2997) viewed face on.** Spiral galaxies have a bulge at the center and a flattened disk containing spiral arms. This type of galaxy contains both old and young stars. While the core contains the older yellow and red stars, the arms contain young blue stars. Spiral galaxies contain a lot of gas and dust, providing the raw material in the arms for ongoing star formation. Can you tell by the picture that the galaxy is spinning much like a hurricane? The center of a spiral galaxy rotates at a faster speed than the arms, giving the galaxy its characteristic whirlpool shape.

▷ **Figure 11.24**
Sombrero galaxy (M104). This is a spiral galaxy seen edge on. You can see the brilliant white core encircled by the dust lanes that make up the spiral arms.

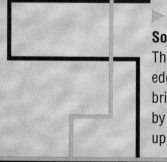

◄ **Figure 11.25** **Barred spiral galaxy (NGC 7479).** Barred spiral galaxies are a special type of spiral galaxy that have a bar-shaped collection of stars running across their center. The stars in this type of galaxy resemble those in a spiral galaxy.

Figure 11.26 Elliptical galaxy (NGC 4486 [M87]). Elliptical galaxies have a uniform appearance; they do not have a disk or arms. These galaxies are characterized by a smooth, ball-shaped appearance. They are made of old stars and contain very little gas and dust. No significant star formation takes place in these types of galaxies. The stars astronomers see in an elliptical galaxy are yellowish red; the hot-burning blue stars are gone, and only the slow-burning older stars are left.

Figure 11.27 Irregular galaxy (NGC 1705). Irregular galaxies are neither spiral nor elliptical. These galaxies are usually smaller and have no definite shape. Irregular galaxies tend to have very hot newer stars mixed in with lots of gas and dust.

Figure 11.28 Ring galaxy (AM 0644-741). Can a galaxy change its shape? This galaxy changed from a spiral galaxy to this beautiful ring galaxy. Another galaxy (not seen in the image) plunged through the center of this one. The aftermath of the collision formed a ring of new and very hot stars. You study more about galaxy collisions in the evaluate activity.

▼ Figure 11.29
Galaxy cluster. This image from the HST shows a massive cluster of galaxies.

Astronomers have found that galaxies are grouped into clusters (see figure 11.29). Studying the galaxy clusters, scientists have observed that members in a cluster orbit each other and sometimes even collide. That behavior shows scientists that members of galaxy clusters are pulled together by the force of gravitation (they are gravitationally bound). Clusters of galaxies also have their own shape. Even galaxy clusters are found in groups; they are called **superclusters**. Superclusters contain dozens of individual clusters.

Surprisingly, even though our solar system is within the Milky Way galaxy, scientists know less about some features of our galaxy than they do about neighboring galaxies. This is because it is difficult to get a good view of something when you are part of it. Seeing our galaxy would be like trying to see the top of your head without a mirror. In addition, gas and interstellar dust have prevented astronomers from seeing into dense regions at the center of our galaxy. It helps that astronomers have been able to identify other galaxies. When astronomers can view an entire galaxy, they can study it to add to their knowledge of our own Milky Way galaxy.

▼ Figure 11.30

Size of the Milky Way. This galaxy is similar in size and shape to our own Milky Way galaxy. Our solar system is located on a spiral arm of the Milky Way. The galaxy has a diameter of about 100,000 ly, and our solar system is about 28,000 ly from the center of the galaxy.

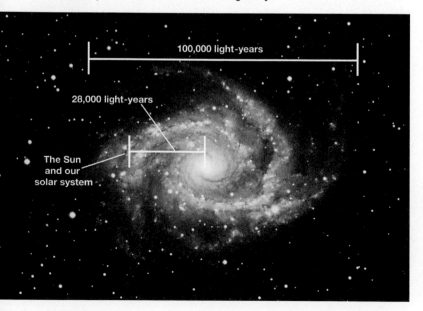

100,000 light-years

28,000 light-years

The Sun and our solar system

Applying their knowledge of nearby galaxies to our own galaxy, astronomers have determined that the Milky Way is a spiral galaxy. In fact, our solar system is located within one of the arms of the spiral, about 28,000 ly from the core of the galaxy. The core is 15–20 ly across (see figure 11.30). The entire galaxy is 100,000 ly from edge to edge. Our galaxy is a member of the cluster called the Local Group. Unfortunately, the gas and dust often found in spiral galaxies make it difficult for astronomers to see many of our galaxy's details. Because of this, they study radio and infrared EM waves that can pass through the gas and dust throughout the galaxy. See the FYI—Images from the EM Spectrum, for more information about how astronomers use radiation of wavelengths other than visible light to study structures in outer space.

Looking at many different galaxies helps scientists describe their similarities and differences and classify them based on their shape. Still, much is unknown about how galaxies form. To learn more, astronomers work to improve the technology that helps them look deeper into space. Because of the advancement of the Hubble Space Telescope, astronomers now have a picture of the universe that goes deeper into space than ever before. Figure 11.31 shows part of the Hubble Deep Field picture you saw in Part I: Take a Closer Look. As you know, previous pictures of this part of space appeared as if they were empty of structures. With the help of the Hubble Space Telescope, however, astronomers now see that this part of space contains a number of oval-shaped galaxies.

Recall from chapter 10 that the light that you see from distant objects in space takes time to reach you. As astronomers look deeper into space, they look farther back in time. Studying distant galaxies is like studying a fossil of the early universe. Perhaps as astronomers view more distant galaxies, they will see some in different stages of formation and come to understand more about the structure and formation of galaxies.

Hubble Deep Field
Hubble Space Telescope · WFPC2

▲ **Figure 11.31**
Hubble Deep Field image. There are many more galaxies in space than scientists first imagined. The area of the sky seen in this image is very small—about the size of President Roosvelt's eye on a U.S. dime when the dime is held at arm's length. The galaxy that appears so large near the center is 300 million light-years away. Some of the galaxies that look smaller are even farther away.

Reflect and Connect

1. Looking at faraway galaxies is like looking far back in time. Generate an analogy to describe why scientists can better understand how galaxies form when they are able to look far back in time. Think about home movies and photographs to answer this question.

2. The sidebar, Did You See That?, tells about a massive-star supernova witnessed by people in AD 1054. In fact, you can see remnants of the supernova today with a telescope. The supernova is 6,300 ly away. Explain why it is incorrect to say that the supernova occurred in AD 1054.

3. Why do astronomers study galaxies other than our own to learn more about the Milky Way galaxy?

4. How would astronomers classify our Milky Way galaxy based on its shape? What are some of the characteristics of this shape of galaxy?

5. You learned that the shape of a spiral galaxy is caused by its spinning, which appears similar to a hurricane. Think of other events in nature that have this same shape because the interior is spinning faster that the exterior. Record at least 2 examples.

FYI—Images from the EM Spectrum

As you have learned so far in your study of space science, astronomers use a variety of techniques to study the universe. Most of what astronomers know about stars, galaxies, and other components of the universe is based on their study of the visible light coming from those objects. While visible light is important, it is not the only way astronomers study the universe.

In fact, studying visible light can be difficult at times. Light pollution from human activities on Earth and interference caused by interstellar dust can prevent astronomers from seeing visible light emitted by distant objects. Also, visible light alone does not always tell astronomers about the nature of the universe. Therefore, what else can astronomers study besides visible light, and how do they conduct their studies?

Objects emit energy across the entire electromagnetic (EM) spectrum—not only at the wavelengths of visible light. Astronomers can study those radiated EM waves (or EM radiation) to help understand the nature of objects. The pictures generated by examining only certain types of EM radiation give astronomers different views and, therefore, different information about the same object. For example, this figure shows images of the Crab Nebula, which is what remains from a star that exploded nearly 1,000 years ago. Each image was generated by gathering EM radiation at a different range of wavelengths from the same object in the sky.

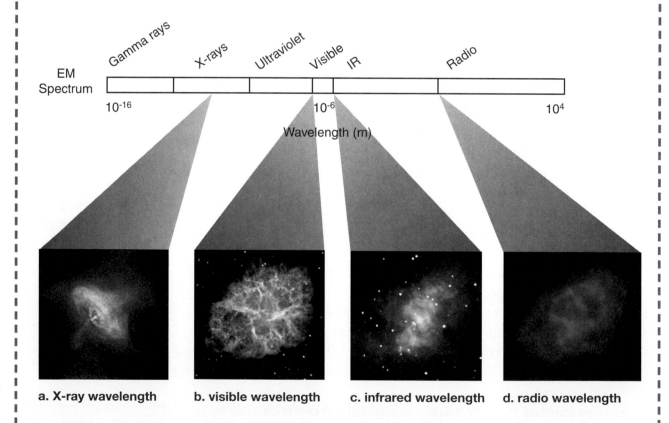

a. X-ray wavelength   b. visible wavelength   c. infrared wavelength   d. radio wavelength

▲ **Images of Crab Nebula.** These images were generated by collecting EM radiation at specific wavelengths. The scale is not the same for all images.

Guiding Equations

Gravity plays a vital role in the formation of stars. In the last activity, you saw that it also is key to the formation and distribution of galaxies in the universe. Your bubble map showed you a three-dimensional model of the way galaxies are distributed in the universe. What other models can help you understand more about gravity? As you saw in the previous chapter, mathematics is used to model concepts. There is more to gravity than just its influence on the formation of stars and the distribution of galaxies. You will take a closer look at gravity in a more precise way to learn how gravity influences all matter.

In Part I of Guiding Equations, you review the quantities necessary to build the mathematical relationships in the universal law of gravitation. You have to know how to make the measurements required by the equation, so you work with a partner to discover how the center of mass is determined on an irregular object. Knowing the center of mass is crucial to determining distance in the mathematical model. In Part II, you learn how this mathematical model of gravitation can help scientists better describe interactions among bodies in the universe. You also practice using this model as a class and individually.

Part I: Distance and Mass—Two Quantities That Measure Up!

Materials
For each team of two students

2 pairs of safety goggles

1 wire coat hanger with paper covering

50 cm of string

1 weight (can be washer or fishing weight)

1 pencil

Process and Procedure

1. Read Distance and Mass—Two Quantities That Measure Up! to better understand the importance of mass and distance as they relate to gravity.

Distance and Mass—Two Quantities That Measure Up!

Gravity is defined as the force between any two masses. The masses could be an object that is on or near the surface of Earth and Earth itself. Do you recall the two factors that determine the amount of this force? The mass of the two objects is one, and the distance between the objects is the other. If one of the objects is a person standing on Earth and the other object is Earth itself, what is the distance between the objects? Your first thought might be that there is no distance between the two objects. However, before you can properly use the mathematical model for gravitation, you need to know a few things.

You have already learned many important things to be successful in using the mathematical model. You have learned that the greater the mass of the objects, the stronger the gravitational force between the objects. Distance is something else you have learned about. You have learned that the greater the distance between the objects, the weaker the gravitational force. Another important mathematical concept you

have used is the inverse square law. Recall that the inverse square law states that the apparent brightness of a star decreases with distance. Like many things in the universe, the relationship of gravity and distance also follows the inverse square law.

How much do you remember? If the distance between two objects doubles, what would happen to the force of gravity between the objects? Remember that the force of gravity would be less, but how much less? By the inverse square law, the force of gravity would be four times less (or 2^2). Gravity would *decrease* proportionally with the *square* of the distance.

What if you were standing on Earth and there is no distance between you and Earth? In this mathematical model, you must measure the distance between the **centers of mass** of the two objects. So what is a center of mass? It is a point where the mass seems to be concentrated from the perspective of balance. The center of mass of a uniform, spherical object is the center of the sphere. The center of mass for an irregular object might not be at its center because of the uneven distribution of mass across the object. For example, if you tried to balance a 30 centimeter (cm) ruler on your finger, it would balance with your finger near the 15-cm mark—the middle. However, if you tried to balance a baseball bat or a broom on your finger, would it balance at the halfway point? Why not? The reason is because the mass is not evenly distributed throughout the object.

Topic: gravity
Go to: www.scilinks.org
Code: 1Inquiry556

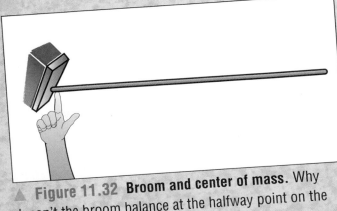

▲ **Figure 11.32 Broom and center of mass.** Why doesn't the broom balance at the halfway point on the handle?

2. Where is the center of mass for a wire coat hanger? Is it along one of the edges? Is it near the top where the hook of the hanger twists together with the sides? You will work with a partner to find the center of mass for a hanger.
   a. Tie the string to the weight.
   b. Make a loop in the end of the string opposite the weight.
   c. On your index finger, balance the hanger by the hook. Use figure 11.33 to help you with the rest of the procedure.
   d. Loop the string around your index finger and let the weight pull the string straight down.
   e. Draw along the string onto the paper on the hanger.
3. Make a space for your finger at one corner of the hanger by opening up the paper on the end (see figure 11.34).
   a. On your index finger, balance the hanger by the corner and loop the string around your finger so that the weight hangs straight (see figure 11.35).
   b. Draw along the string.
4. Repeat Steps 3a–b for the other corner.
5. Where the 3 drawn lines meet on the hanger's paper is the center of mass for the hanger. Use your finger to try to balance the hanger at this point.
6. Read the following paragraphs to learn more about centers of mass.
   Your own center of mass depends on your shape and size. In general, the center of mass for boys is higher on their bodies than it is for girls. Your body naturally knows its own center of mass. For example, when you bend over, your back end extends out behind you so that you keep your body's

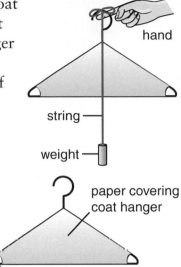

◀ **Figure 11.33**
Step 2. Your setup should look something like this. Draw a line on the paper wrapping along the position of the string.

◀ **Figure 11.34**
Step 3. Carefully tear away the paper on a corner of the hanger.

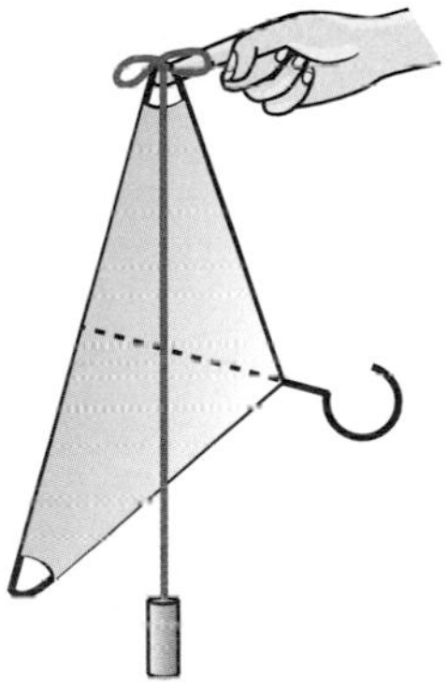

◀ **Figure 11.35**
Step 3a. Hold the hanger like this and draw a line on the paper along the string.

◀ **Figure 11.36**
Step 4. Hold the hanger on the last corner and draw a line as before.

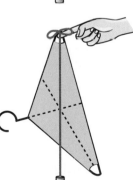

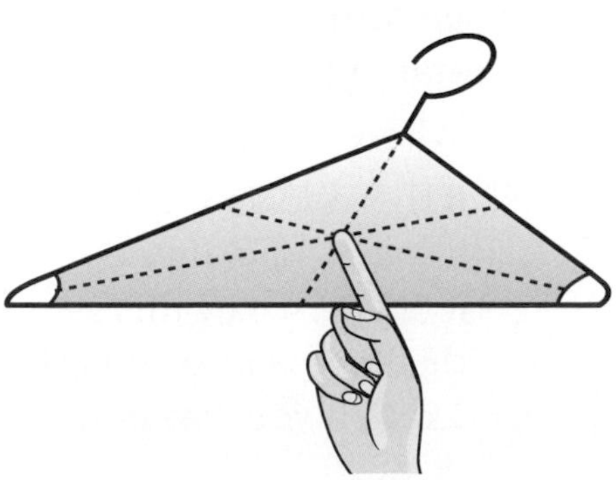

◀ **Figure 11.37**
Step 5. Can you balance the hanger at the point where all of the lines meet?

center of mass over your feet. If you didn't, you would tip over. You may want to try these activities to demonstrate how your body works with its center of mass:

- Place a chair firmly against a wall. Sit in the chair with your feet flat on the floor in front of you. Have a friend place his or her thumb on your forehead. Now try to stand up. Can you?

- Place a chair sideways against a wall. Stand facing the wall with the chair between you and the wall. Bend over the chair, keeping your toes out from under it. Touch your head to the wall. Try to lift the chair and stand up. Can you do it?

- Stand with your back against the wall. Have a friend place a quarter on the floor directly in front of your feet. Can you pick up the quarter?

- Stand with your side against the wall, with your arm and leg touching the wall. Can you lift your other leg straight out away from the wall?

Have you heard parents and teachers say that the backpacks that students carry to school are too heavy for them? How do heavy backpacks change your center of mass? Put on a backpack and try the activities above again. What happens?

Activities adapted with permission from GRACE Educational Curriculum, Texas Space Grant Consortium.

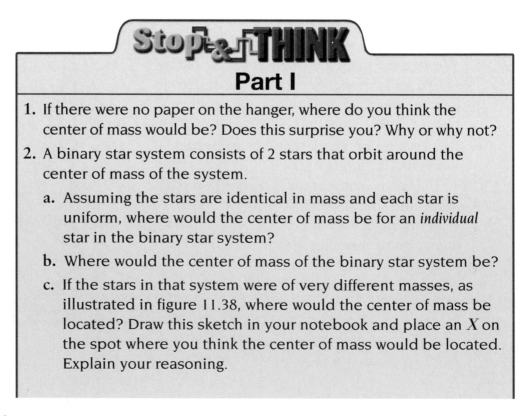

Part I

1. If there were no paper on the hanger, where do you think the center of mass would be? Does this surprise you? Why or why not?

2. A binary star system consists of 2 stars that orbit around the center of mass of the system.

   a. Assuming the stars are identical in mass and each star is uniform, where would the center of mass be for an *individual* star in the binary star system?

   b. Where would the center of mass of the binary star system be?

   c. If the stars in that system were of very different masses, as illustrated in figure 11.38, where would the center of mass be located? Draw this sketch in your notebook and place an *X* on the spot where you think the center of mass would be located. Explain your reasoning.

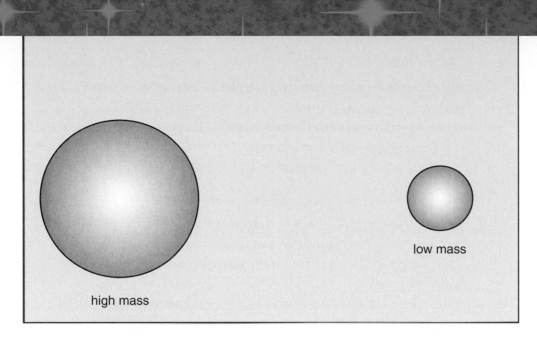

◀ **Figure 11.38**
Binary star system.
Where would the center of mass be for this system? Use this with Stop & Think Question 2c.

Part II: Using Equations

Now that you know how to measure distance between two objects correctly, you can learn how to put that knowledge to use. Cavendish's experiment with a torsion balance allowed him to view the universal attraction between objects. This is the relationship Newton described 100 years earlier, but no one had been able to confirm his ideas experimentally. Cavendish was able to measure the amount of attraction between the objects on the balance as well as determine experimentally the value for the universal gravitation constant. You see how this constant is used in the mathematical equation in this activity. When scientists are able to see the effects of a force and measure its magnitude, they can better understand the force. When they can use actual data to describe the force of gravitation, for example, they can use math to help them investigate its effects in many different situations.

Work with your classmates to see how scientists use information such as the mathematical relationship called the universal law of gravitation, first described by Newton.

Materials

For each student

1 scientific calculator

Process and Procedure

1. Think about the 2 things you have already learned that will affect the force of gravity on an object. Write them in your science notebook under the title "Universal Law of Gravitation."
2. Check with your classmates and with your teacher to see that you answered Step 1 correctly.

3. Now consider these questions to help you refine what you have written in your notebook.

   a. How many masses do you need to know to determine the force of gravity between objects?

   b. How would you measure the distance between the 2 objects?

Think back to the activity with the hanger to find your best answer.

4. By now, you should realize that you know quite a bit about what affects the amount of gravitational force between 2 objects. Check your understanding by doing the following tasks:

   a. In your science notebook, write a sentence to describe the relationship between mass and the force of gravitation. Do the same for distance and force due to gravitation.

Don't forget that the forces due to gravity and distance follow the inverse square law.

▶ **Figure 11.39**
Universal law of gravitation illustration.
Use this illustration to help you formulate your answers to Step 4a.

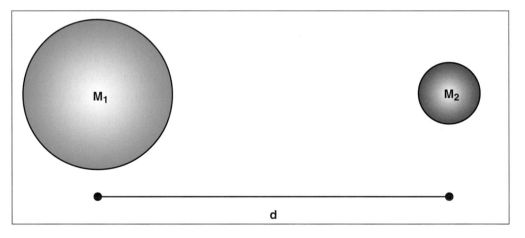

b. Compare your sentences to the following mathematical equation. With your partner, talk about your understanding of the equation.

$$\text{force of gravitation } (F_{grav}) = \frac{G \times m_1 \times m_2}{d^2}$$

To understand this mathematical equation, you have to know what all of the symbols stand for and in what units they are measured:

- G is the universal gravitation constant that Cavendish measured with his torsion balance. It has a value of $6.67 \times 10^{-11} \frac{m^3}{kg \times s^2}$. This is a very small constant—$0.0000000000667 \frac{m^3}{kg \times s^2}$. It is a constant—it will remain the same in every equation.

- Mass (m) is measured in kilograms (kg). There are 2 masses—1 for each object. Does it matter which mass goes first?

- Distance (d) is the distance in meters from the center of one mass (m_1) to the center of the other mass (m_2).

- Finally, gravitational force (F_{grav}) is measured in a unit called a newton (N). By canceling units in the equation above, you should be able to demonstrate that forces given in newtons have units of. In other words, 1 N is the same as or equal to $1 \frac{kg \times m}{s^2}$.

5. Now practice using real numbers in the equation. Consider the following problem:

   Two balls have their centers 2.0 m apart. One has a mass of 8.0 kg, and the other has a mass of 6.0 kg. What is the gravitational force between them?

To help you organize all of the information given to you in a problem, in your science notebook, make a computation chart like the one in figure 11.40.

Name of variable	Value	Unit	Variable in equation
Distance	2.0	m	d
Mass	8.0	kg	m_1
Mass	6.0	kg	m_2
Universal gravitation constant	6.67×10^{-11}	$\frac{m^3}{kg \times s^2}$	G

▲ **Figure 11.40**
Computation chart.
Use this chart to help you organize the information given you in the problem.

Remember that the constant G will always be the same number and will be in every problem you do using the equation.

6. Now it is time to put the values into the equation.
   a. Copy the equation in your notebook.

   $$F_{grav} = \frac{G \times m_1 \times m_2}{d^2}$$

   b. Put the information from the problem into the equation.

   $$F_{grav} = \frac{6.67 \times 10^{-11} \frac{m^3}{kg \times s^2} \times 8.0 \text{ kg} \times 6.0 \text{ kg}}{(2.0 \text{ m})^2}$$

   c. Calculate your answer. All calculators work differently. For some brands, you need to use parentheses; for other brands, you do not. Check with your teacher if you do not get the correct answer and practice putting the numbers in your calculator correctly.

The correct answer for this problem is $8.0 \times 10^{-10} \frac{kg \times m}{s^2}$.

Do you remember what the unit $\frac{kg \times m}{s^2}$ is called?

It is called a newton and has the symbol N. So your answer can be written as 8.0×10^{-10} N.

d. Work with a classmate to figure out how the units cancel out in the equation to give the units $\frac{kg \times m}{s^2}$. Check with your teacher if you do not understand.

7. Try this example problem. Follow the same problem-solving strategy that you used before and copy everything in your note book.

   Sarah has a mass of 50.0 kg, and Earth has a mass of 5.98×10^{24} kg. The radius of Earth is 6.38×10^6 m. Calculate the force of gravity between Sarah and Earth.

With numbers as large as the radius of Earth, you may use as the radius the distance between the centers of mass of Earth and Sarah.

a. Make a computation chart, copy the equation, rewrite the equation with values given in the problem, and calculate your answer.

b. Show your answer with the proper units. Did you remember to cancel the units in the equation?

c. Check to see that you got 490 N for your answer. If you did not get the right answer, ask a classmate for help. If you still do not understand or cannot get the correct answer, check with your teacher.

Weight and Gravity

If you are like many people, you measure the force of gravity on your body on a regular basis. How do you do that? You weigh yourself! Scales measure the force of attraction between you and Earth. Remember that the force of gravity is measured in newtons. A "scientific" bathroom scale also would measure your weight in newtons. Different people's bodies contain different amounts of matter, which means they have different masses. That is why you and your friends weigh different amounts on a scale even though you all feel the attractive force of the same Earth.

What would happen if you traveled to a different planet in the universe? According to the law of universal gravitation, you would be attracted to that planet just as you are to Earth because both you and the planet have mass. The measure of that attraction would depend on the mass of the planet and the distance from your center of mass to the center of mass of the planet.

Let's look at a specific example. Have you seen pictures of astronauts walking on the moon? They experience a lower gravitational force on the moon than on Earth. The reason is because although the moon is much smaller than Earth (its diameter is 3,476 km as compared with Earth's diameter of 12,756 km), the moon is almost 100 times less massive. Therefore, astronauts are closer to the moon's center of mass, but the smaller mass does not exert nearly the force that Earth does. A person who has a mass of 50 kg would weigh 490 N on Earth but would weigh only 81.3 N on the moon. The person's mass would remain the same because he or she has the same amount of matter, but his or her weight would change because the force of gravity changes.

The following table charts the data for the mass and diameter of the planets in our solar system and the Sun. Also included on the chart is the weight of a 50-kg person (on Earth) standing on the surface of the structures in space.

Structure	Mass (kg)	Radius (m)	Weight of 50-kg person (n)	Weight of 50-kg person (lbs)
Mercury	3.30×10^{23}	2.44×10^6	185	41.5
Venus	4.869×10^{24}	6.05×10^6	444	99.7
Earth	5.98×10^{24}	6.38×10^6	490	110
Mars	6.4219×10^{23}	3.40×10^6	185	41.5
Jupiter	1.900×10^{27}	7.16×10^7	1,236	277
Saturn	5.68×10^{26}	6.00×10^7	526	118
Uranus	8.683×10^{25}	2.59×10^7	432	97
Neptune	1.0247×10^{26}	2.48×10^7	556	125
Pluto	1.27×10^{22}	$\sim 1.17 \times 10^6$	31	7.0
Sun	1.989×10^{30}	6.95×10^8	13,732	3,083

The force of gravitation between two bodies depends on the masses of the bodies and the distance between their centers of mass. If a 50-kg person on Earth could travel to other structures in our solar system, he or she would find that the gravitational attraction between his or her mass and the mass of the structure would be different than it was on Earth. Therefore, his or her weight also would be different. Would the person's mass be different?

Reflect and Connect

Answer the following questions in your science notebook.

1. Try some more calculations, this time on your own. For Questions 1a and 1b, set up a computation chart and show how your units cancel for a final answer in newtons, or $\frac{kg \times m}{s^2}$.
   a. You and a classmate next to you both have a mass of 50 kg. Your centers of mass are 1 m apart. What is the force of gravitation between your 2 bodies?
   b. Earth has a mass of approximately 5.98×10^{24} kg. If you stand on the surface of Earth, you are 6.38×10^6 m from the center of its mass (Earth's radius). What is the force of gravitation between you and Earth?
   c. How does the force of gravitation between you and Earth compare with the force of gravitation between you and your classmate? How many times larger is it?

Remember, to compare values by finding out how many times larger one value is over the other, simply divide the larger value by the smaller value.

2. Jupiter is a very large planet. Its mass is 317 times greater than Earth's, and it has a diameter more than 11 times greater. However, an object in Jupiter's atmosphere (Jupiter has no surface) is only 2–3 times heavier than it would be on Earth.
   a. How is that possible?
   b. Use the data from the table in sidebar, Weight and Gravity, to calculate the force of gravitation on a 50-kg body on Jupiter.

3. If Earth began to shrink but its mass remained the same, predict what would happen to the value of the force of gravity (F_{grav}) on a person standing on the surface. Explain your answer by drawing a before and after sketch of the shrinking Earth. Use highlight comments to express "What I see" and "What it means."

4. Answer the following questions about the way scientists work and the nature of science.
   a. Why do you think scientists use patterns that they observe on Earth to explain things that they observe in the universe?
   b. What is good about this practice?
   c. What sort of problem could arise by using this practice?

Now You See It

In early 2003, astronomers used new infrared technologies to make surprising observations of the universe. What they saw made them ask new questions about the formation of galaxies.

Astronomers can see more easily into the universe at infrared wavelengths because of the advent of new, larger infrared detectors. Observing the universe with infrared radiation allows astronomers to see past the dust and gas that block visible light. In the past, the only infrared detectors had been small and astronomers could not conduct large surveys to look for distant galaxies. However, with large-format infrared cameras on a high-precision telescope in Paranal, Chile, astronomers recently took another look at the universe. The observations that astronomers made are some of the farthest-reaching near-infrared observations ever.

The area of sky the astronomers looked at had been studied by the Hubble Space Telescope for a week to make up the image of visible light known as the Hubble Deep Field South (an image like the Hubble Deep Field—see Galactic Gravity, Part I: Take a Closer Look—but focused on the southern sky). As seen in the image here, astronomers observed that the earliest-forming galaxies appeared to have small populations of young, hot stars. In contrast, when they looked only at infrared light emitted by galaxies, astronomers saw that many of the earliest-forming galaxies already contained mature stars that made up as much as half of the mass of the galaxies.

In addition to the surprising old age of the stars in these earliest galaxies, the

Hubble Deep Field South. This image taken with the Hubble Space Telescope shows the earliest-forming galaxies with young, hot stars as well as mature stars.

galaxies were unexpectedly large. This observation seemed to conflict with the ideas astronomers had about the formation of galaxies in the early universe. Astronomers had always thought that galaxies took billions of years to pack on mass by pulling in gas from the surrounding space or merging with neighboring galaxies. The new infrared image made astronomers wonder how galaxies managed to grow to a massive size in a relatively short period of time.

Astronomers now question their original ideas about galaxies. Is it possible that the extraordinarily dense regions of the early universe gave rise to the quick formation of mature galaxies? To find out, astronomers need to survey more of the universe than just the Hubble Deep Field

South. (In fact, the original Hubble Deep Field image from the northern skies does not reveal the same number of mature galaxies under infrared analysis, leaving astronomers wondering which view best represents the universe at large.)

On August 25, 2003, NASA sent into space the Space Infrared Telescope Facility. This telescope was renamed the Spitzer Space Telescope (SST). The space-craft is viewing the universe at infrared wavelengths that cannot reach Earth-bound telescopes because of Earth's atmosphere. With this new technology, astronomers are surveying a region of space 30 times larger than both of the Hubble Deep Fields combined. What astronomers see might just "shed some new light" on the origin of the structure of galaxies in the early universe. Some of the images in your book come from the SST. You may want to search the World Wide Web for additional images from the SST.

Spitzer Space Telescope. In 2003, NASA launched the Spitzer Space Telescope (SST). The SST views the universe at infrared wavelengths—longer than the visible light your eyes can detect. This is an artist's rendition of the telescope. It is impossible to get a true photograph of the SST in orbit since it does not orbit Earth—it orbits the Sun!

EVALUATE

Cosmic Dance

It is not difficult to picture the universe as a dynamic, changing place. If you can picture 80 billion galaxies swirling in space, you might also imagine that they sometimes collide, just as moving objects sometimes do. Collisions may be even more likely when the galaxies are being drawn together by the force of gravitation. Scientists were not surprised, then, to find galaxies in various stages of interaction even when they collided. In figure 11.41, the Hubble Space Telescope captured several galaxies in a "cosmic dance" with other galaxies. In the Cosmic Dance activity, you work individually to demonstrate your understanding of the concepts in this chapter by analyzing an image of two galaxies.

▶ **Figure 11.41**

Images of the interactions of galaxies. (a) Galaxies NGC 5426 and 5427 and (b) galaxies NGC 4038 and 4039; both of these images depict what can happen when two galaxies come into close contact. What happens when two galaxies encounter each other?

a.

b.

Materials
For each student

1 calculator

1 Galaxy Crash handout

1 Scoring Rubric for Galaxy Crash handout

Process and Procedure

1. Obtain the Galaxy Crash and Scoring Rubric for Galaxy Crash handouts from your teacher.
2. Read through both handouts before answering the questions. Check with your teacher if you do not understand any of the questions.
3. Complete the questions on the Galaxy Crash handout. Turn in the handout to your teacher when you are done.

In this test of your understanding, work alone to answer the questions on the Galaxy Crash handout. Explain your answers completely by using words and numbers. Show all of your work when you are solving mathematical equations. Check that you use the proper units in your answers.

▼ **Figure 11.42**

Spiral galaxies on a collision course. As you complete the activity, you may want to look at this color image of the two galaxies NGC 2207 (on the left) and IC 2163 (on the right).

CHAPTER 12

Cosmic Questions

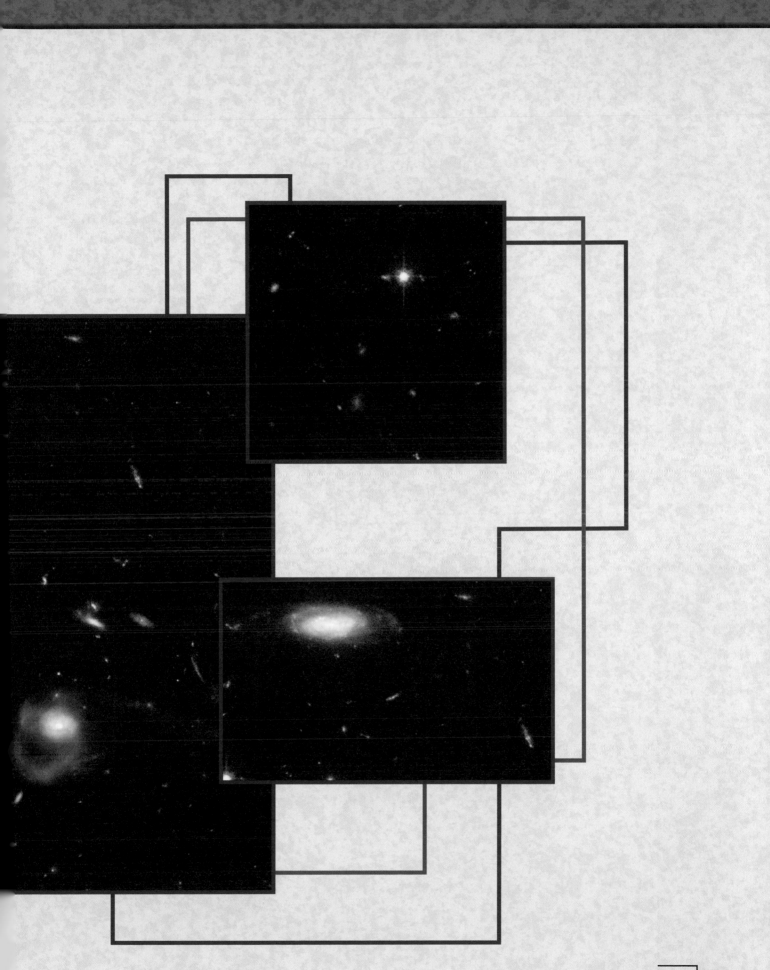

Cosmic Questions

You have learned a lot about the universe. In chapter 10, The Stars, and chapter 11, Coming Attractions—Gravity, you studied stars and the role gravity plays in their formation as well as the formation of galaxies. Stars and galaxies are familiar structures in the universe. You have seen how scientists answer questions about them. As you learned more about stars and galaxies, you may have thought of other questions about the universe. Have you ever looked into the night sky and wondered how far the universe extends or how old it is or whether there is other life in the universe? You may have heard scientists' ideas about the universe and wondered how they came up with their ideas.

In chapter 12, Cosmic Questions, you add to your knowledge about the parts of the universe. You learn how scientists study the vastness of the universe and how they test their theories about the universe. As you study the structure of the universe, you find that its current form gives scientists clues about its origin and evolution. In fact, the science of **cosmology** integrates all three areas of study—origin, evolution, and structure of the universe. As a student in cosmology, you explore the past, present, and possible future of the universe.

In this chapter, you learn about the universe on a scale of things that range from very small to very large in distance, time, and space. How do scientists explore something as immense and as old as the universe? How can scientists predict what will happen to the universe in the future? Scientists base their studies of the universe on their understanding of matter and energy. By learning about matter and energy, you develop an understanding of how scientists establish their theories about the universe.

Goals for the Chapter

When you finish this chapter, you should be able to answer the following questions:

- What skills, tools, and knowledge do scientists use to develop theories about the universe?
- What is the current scientific theory about the origin, evolution, and structure of the universe?
- What evidence do scientists have that supports their theory of the origin, evolution, and structure of the universe?

To help you answer those questions, you will participate in the following activities:

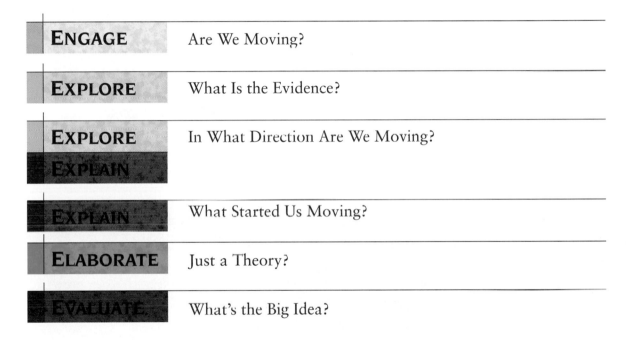

ENGAGE	Are We Moving?
EXPLORE	What Is the Evidence?
EXPLORE / EXPLAIN	In What Direction Are We Moving?
EXPLAIN	What Started Us Moving?
ELABORATE	Just a Theory?
EVALUATE	What's the Big Idea?

Are We Moving?

How many times have you heard this question: Would you please sit down and be still!? You must have been moving around when you heard those scolding words. However, when you actually did sit down, were you really still? Even if you didn't move any part of your body, were you really motionless? To answer those questions, you need to consider frame of reference. **Frame of reference** is the context in which you observe motion. Pretend you are sitting very still in your seat on a bus. Your friend sitting next to you observes that you are still. You and your friend are observing from the same frame of reference. But what if someone observes you from the sidewalk as the bus passes by at 48 kilometers per hour (km/h), or 30 miles per hour (mph). What would that person see?

In Are We Moving?, you work with a partner and your class to determine whether you are moving from a frame of reference outside of your classroom. You also determine approximately how fast you are moving. The motions of the planets, stars, and galaxies give cosmologists information necessary to determine the age and evolution of the universe.

▼ **Figure 12.1**
Student sitting at desk after scolding. Can you ever really be still?

Materials

For each student

1 calculator

For each team of three or four students

several globes

sticky dots

Process and Procedure

1. Pick a partner and discuss the following questions. Record your thoughts in your science notebook.
    a. Gravity acts between you and Earth, holding you to the surface. Therefore, if Earth is moving, you are, too. How many different ways is Earth moving? List all of the ways you can think of.
    b. Where would you have to be to observe each of those motions—what would be your frame of reference?
    c. Be prepared to share your ideas with the class. Add any new information to your notebook that you learn in the discussion.

2. First, you will consider your speed as Earth rotates on its axis to determine how fast you are moving on this spinning planet. Look at the globe that your teacher has provided.
    a. Place a sticky dot at the North Pole and at the equator below the United States.

▼ **Figure 12.2**
Globe with sticky dots.
Your globe should look similar to this.

You might have to cut the sticky dot in half so that it fits around the axis holding the globe to the stand.

b. Now find the lines that go east and west on the globe. What are they called?
c. Find a latitude on your globe that passes through both Texas and Florida. What is this latitude? Place a sticky dot on the line directly in line with your other 2 dots.
d. Now find a latitude on your globe that passes through the Hudson Bay in Canada. What is this latitude? Place a sticky dot on the line directly in line with your other dots.
e. Your globe should look like figure 12.2.

3. Discuss the following questions with your partner. Record your best ideas in your notebook.

   a. How long does it take Earth to make 1 complete rotation?

   b. Turn your globe to represent 1 complete rotation while you view from above the North Pole. Do all of the sticky dots make 1 complete rotation?

   c. Do all of the sticky dots travel the same distance in 1 rotation? Explain your answer.

   d. Are all sticky dots traveling at the same speed? Explain your answer.

   e. Be prepared to discuss your answers as your teacher directs a class discussion.

4. The rotational speed of Earth is the same at all locations—Earth makes 1 rotation every day. As you rotate with Earth, you are not moving relative to the center of Earth. However, you have determined that the surface speed at different locations is changing with latitude. You observed the surface speed of your sticky dots as you looked at them from a frame of reference above the globe. Therefore, from a frame of reference outside Earth, you would be moving. How quickly are you moving? Follow these steps to find out.

   a. Find the latitude for your location on the globe.

▶ **Figure 12.3**

Globe showing rotation of Earth. The distance around Earth varies with latitude.

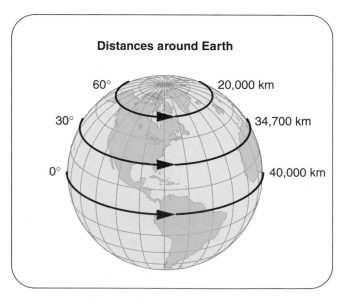

Distances around Earth

60°   20,000 km

30°   34,700 km

0°   40,000 km

   b. Use the table in figure 12.4 to find the distance traveled in 1 rotation at your location.

Latitude	Distance around Earth (km)	Distance around Earth (mi)
0°	40,000	24,900
15°	38,700	24,100
30°	34,700	21,600
45°	28,300	17,600
60°	20,000	12,500
75°	10,400	6,500
90°	0	0

c. Use that number to calculate your speed in *both* kilometers per hour and miles per hour. Use the formula

$$\text{speed} = \frac{\text{distance}}{\text{time}}.$$

Show all of your work.

▲ **Figure 12.4**
Distances at different latitudes. Use this table to find your approximate distance.

5. Is your speed on the rotating Earth the only motion involved with Earth? You probably thought about the revolution of Earth around the Sun. How fast is Earth moving in this type of motion? Follow these steps to find out.

a. The circumference of Earth's orbit around the Sun is 940 million kilometers (km), or about 584 million miles. That is the distance you need for your calculation. What is the time? Consider how long it takes Earth to make 1 complete revolution around the Sun. How many days is that?

b. Since you used hours for the time in the previous step, convert the days for 1 revolution into hours. All you need to know is how many hours are in a day. Show your work, including the cancellation of units.

c. Now use the equation to find your speed in a revolution around the Sun. Find your speed in both kilometers per hour and miles per hour. As before, show your work and use proper units with your answer.

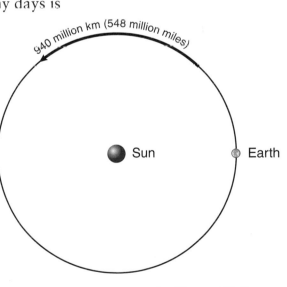

▲ **Figure 12.5**
Earth's revolution around the Sun. What is the speed of the orbiting Earth? Note: Illustration not to scale.

Reflect and Connect

1. Explain the difference in speed for people living in Mexico versus people living in Canada related to the rotation of Earth. Explain your reasoning.

2. Are there places on Earth where you would have no speed due to the rotation of Earth?
3. Are there places on Earth (another frame of reference) where you would have no speed due to the revolution of Earth around the Sun?
4. Imagine that you are riding on a bus with no vibration and you look out the window to see a cow go by. How can you tell if it is you or the cow that is moving?
5. Often when you learn new things, you generate more questions. Record at least 2 new questions you thought about regarding Earth's motion from different frames of reference.
6. Think about the main idea of this activity. Summarize the main idea in 1 sentence.

You need to keep track of your answer to this last question because you use it later in the chapter. Consider highlighting it in your notebook or placing a star beside it. You will find similar questions at the end of each Reflect and Connect section that you will want to mark. You use those answers in the evaluate activity at the end of the chapter.

EXPLORE

What Is the Evidence?

You really are moving fast while you are sitting in your classroom! Do you think the Sun is moving? What about the Milky Way? Are other galaxies moving, too? Obviously, you cannot go to a frame of reference outside the universe to see if stars and galaxies are moving. So what evidence do scientists have that tells us if stars and galaxies are moving? Recall that scientists measure a star's apparent brightness and compare it with its luminosity to determine the star's distance from Earth. At the same time, they look closely at the light that comes from the star to learn even more about objects in the universe. Scientists have made observations of the light emitted from stars in distant galaxies to analyze the movement of structures in the universe.

In What Is the Evidence?, you work as a class and with a partner to explore the characteristics of light that help scientists detect motion in the universe. Before you study this characteristic of light, you will study evidence of motion in another type of wave—a sound wave. By studying that characteristic with sound first, you have the opportunity to experience it firsthand. After hearing changes in moving sources of *sound* in Part I, you apply what you have learned to moving sources of *light* in Part II.

Part I: Doppler Effect—Evidence of Motion

Materials

Process and Procedure

1. To understand how scientists look for evidence of motion from
   distant galaxies, read the following paragraph about sound
   waves. You will be able to hear this evidence in your classroom
   in the next steps.

   Studying sound waves can help you understand some other
   important features of waves. Like electromagnetic (EM) waves,
   sound waves have a range of frequencies and wavelengths.
   Recall from chapter 10 that with sound waves, pitch corresponds directly with the frequency of the waves. A high-pitched
   sound has a high frequency and a short wavelength. A low-
   pitched sound has a low frequency and a long wavelength.

▲ **Figure 12.6**

Spectators at a race.
How does the sound of
these race cars change
as they approach the
spectators? How does
it change as the race
cars move past the
spectators?

2. Look at figure 12.7. Discuss with your class which drawing represents a high-pitched sound and which drawing represents a low-pitched sound.

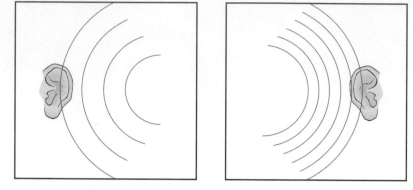

► Figure 12.7
Different frequencies.
Which diagram represents a high-pitched sound, and which diagram represents a low-pitched sound?

3. Copy the diagrams in figure 12.7 in your science notebook. Label one "High-Pitched Sound" and the other "Low-Pitched Sound."
4. Continue to learn more about sound by reading the following paragraphs.

READING

Wave Frequencies

What is a "high-frequency" sound? Recall that frequency is how often the peak of a wave passes a point in space in a given amount of time. For a high-pitched sound (high frequency, short wavelength), the wave peaks pass that point very frequently. If that point in space is your eardrum, the waves pulse against your eardrum very rapidly. In contrast, low-pitched sounds have waves that pulse against your eardrum with a low frequency. For example, you may be familiar with the musical note A440. With this note, sound waves are hitting your eardrum with a frequency of 440 hertz (Hz). The pitch of the note you hear is an A on the musical scale.

Like EM waves, your ears are sensitive only to a limited range of frequencies of sound.

Most people cannot hear sounds with frequencies below 20 Hz or above 16,000 Hz. There are sound waves outside this range, but human ears cannot detect them. Dogs can detect sounds with much higher frequencies than humans can (figure 12.8). Frequencies higher than humans can hear are called ultrasonic. Do you remember what EM radiation with frequency just higher than visible light is called? The range of EM radiation with frequency just higher than visible light is called ultraviolet light. What do you think sound with lower frequency than humans can detect is called? Refer back to the EM spectrum (figure 10.21) on page 484 for a hint about using frequencies of EM radiation just lower than visible light.

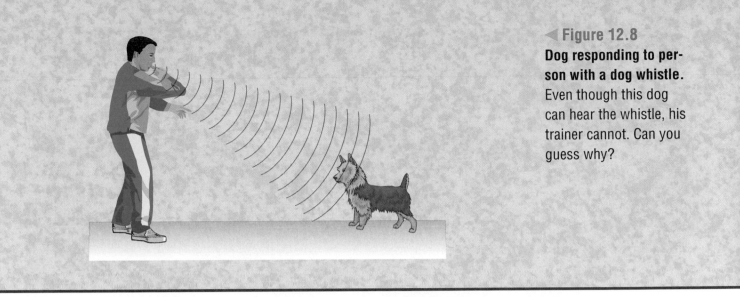

◀ **Figure 12.8**
Dog responding to person with a dog whistle.
Even though this dog can hear the whistle, his trainer cannot. Can you guess why?

5. Gather around your teacher. He or she has a source of sound, such as a buzzer or sound ball. Listen to the sound.
   a. How would you describe the sound? Try to hum the pitch the sound is making.
   b. Move to a different position around the buzzer. Does it sound the same from that new position? Hum the pitch that you hear.

6. The sound from the source creates sound waves that move outward from the source. This is similar to the ripples in water that move out from the spot where a rock is thrown into a lake. Use this analogy to make a sketch in your science notebook of sound waves moving outward from the source. To make the sketch, do the following:
   a. Draw a sketch of the sound source and show sound waves as evenly spaced rings around it.
   b. Add arrows to show the direction of motion of the sound waves outward from the source. How far do the waves go in your classroom? Does your sketch show this?
   c. This is your model for what sound waves look like when they move out from a *stationary* object. Label your diagram "Sound Waves from a Stationary Sound Source."

▲ **Figure 12.9**
Teacher swinging a sound ball. What do you notice about the sound when your teacher twirls the sound ball?

7. Next, you participate with your teacher in a demonstration. Your teacher will move the sound source quickly. Your job is to listen very carefully to the sound source as it moves. Your teacher will stage the experiment where the sound source moves rapidly toward you and rapidly away from you. During the demonstration, record your observations in your science notebook for the following questions:

   a. What do you notice about the sound when the source is moving toward you?

   b. What do you notice about the sound when the source is moving away from you?

8. After your teacher completes the demonstration, discuss the answers to these questions as a class.

   a. Recall that pitch describes the frequency of sound waves (high-pitched sound is high-frequency waves). You have also probably experienced the sound of a vehicle (such as a train, bus, or car) as it travels toward you and then passes you while blasting its horn. How does the pitch of the horn change as it moves past you?

   b. Did the moving sound source have the same pitch as the stationary sound source in your teacher's demonstration?

   c. How is your experience with the moving sound source similar to your experience with the sound of the vehicle's horn?

   d. Changes in pitch tell you something about changes in frequency of sound waves. Do you think that the pitch of the vehicle horn or the buzzer actually changed while the sound source was moving?

Think about the pitch of the horn you would hear if you were riding in the car.

9. In your notebook, draw a diagram similar to that shown in figure 12.10. Title your drawing "Sound Waves from a Moving Sound Source."

   a. Add an arrow to your drawing to indicate that the sound source is moving toward listener A and away from listener B.

   b. Add circles to indicate sound waves reaching the ears of both listeners.

   c. Add highlight comments to your drawing. Title your highlight comments "What I see" and "What it means."

▲ **Figure 12.10 Two listeners with sound source between them.** Draw this diagram in your science notebook.

Remember, the sound source is moving. Consider the pitch and therefore the frequency detected by both listeners as the sound source is moving.

10. Look at the diagram in figure 12.11. It shows a fire engine blaring, racing down the street. The small arrows show the outward motion of the first sound waves the fire engine emitted. Each interior circle represents sound waves emitted at 7 different times as the truck moved forward. Answer the questions to compare this diagram with the one that you drew in Step 6a.

    a. How is this diagram different from the one you drew in Step 6a? Copy this diagram in your science notebook. Label the diagram "Sound Coming from a Moving Object."

    b. Draw a stick figure on your diagram to show where you would be standing to hear the sound of a fire engine coming toward you. Label your stick figure.

    c. Draw a stick figure on your diagram to show where you would be standing to hear the sound of a fire engine moving away from you. Label your stick figure.

▼ **Figure 12.11**

A moving fire engine with sound waves. When an object is moving, the wavelengths of sound it emits are distorted for a stationary listener, depending on whether the object is moving toward or away from the listener.

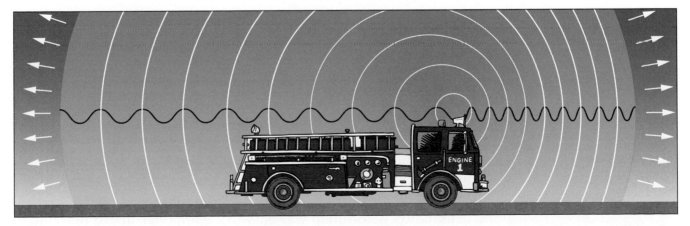

d. Add an arrow to indicate the direction the fire engine is moving. Label this arrow "Motion of Sound Source."

11. Discuss the following questions with your class. Record your ideas and answers in your science notebook.
    a. Look at figure 12.11 again. Are the wavelengths shorter (higher frequency) in one part of the diagram, yet longer (lower frequency) in another? How would this affect pitch?

Remember, you measure the distance between two adjacent waves to determine wavelength.

    b. Add the labels "Higher Pitch" and "Lower Pitch" to the diagram you drew in Step 6a.
    c. Add the labels "Higher Frequency" and "Lower Frequency" to the sketch you made in Step 10a.

Stop & THINK

Part I

To check your understanding of the activity in Part I, complete the following task. Record your description in your science notebook.

1. The **Doppler effect** is the term used to describe the *apparent* change in frequency with the relative motion of the source and the observer. Copy this definition in your science notebook. In your own words, describe what an observer notices about sound coming from a moving object and why he or she notices it. Distinguish between these two situations: when an object is moving toward an observer and when the object is moving away from the observer.

SCI LINKS.
NSTA
Topic: Doppler effect
Go to: www.scilinks.org
Code: 1Inquiry582

You can use your experience with your teacher's sound source to help you write your description.

2. It is possible to observe the Doppler effect even when the sound source is stationary. Describe an instance when this would be true.

Part II: The Doppler Effect . . . with Light Waves!

What do sound waves and the Doppler effect have to do with the universe? Recall that astronomers use the best evidence they have available to study objects beyond Earth and the solar system. This evidence is the light waves that those objects emit. As you know, light and sound travel in waves. Perhaps light from outer space has something in common with sound waves! Work with a partner to find out.

Materials

colored pencils or markers (optional)

Process and Procedure

1. Work with a partner and read Using Spectra to Study the Universe to see how the Doppler effect applies to light.

READING

Using Spectra to Study the Universe

When you see light from the Sun exit a rainbow or a prism, you see that light can be split into colors. Those colors define a spectrum of light that appears largely continuous to your eyes. However, when you use instruments that are more sensitive than your eyes, new details emerge. In particular, what at first appears to be a continuous spectrum actually consists of many lighter and darker bands of light across the visible spectrum. You have already seen several examples of those spectra from distant stars. Study figure 12.12 to see an absorption spectra of the Sun. Recall that the lines are specific for elements contained in the star. They have a characteristic wavelength.

Astronomers collect data on the spectral lines produced by stars. From the data, they determine what elements make up the stars. Those studies have shown another interesting pattern. Sometimes astronomers note that a distinctive spectral pattern for an element, such as helium, does not fall at the wavelengths it would if it were heated and observed on Earth. In fact, sometimes an

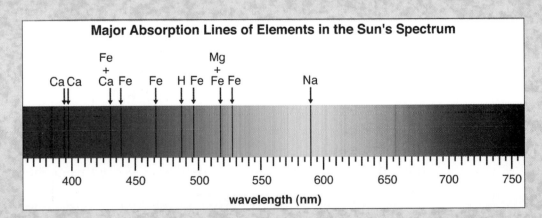

▲ **Figure 12.12 Major absorption lines of elements in the Sun's spectrum.** Many lines appear in the spectrum for the Sun, the star closest to Earth. The wavelengths of the lines tell astronomers what elements are absorbed in the cooler gases in the atmosphere of the star. The Sun shows distinct lines indicating the presence of elements such as calcium, iron, magnesium, sodium, and hydrogen.

entire family of spectral lines from stars is seen to shift over, either to the left or to the right—that is, to higher or lower wavelengths.

For example, look at the spectral line at wavelength (λ) = 590 nanometers (nm) in the middle of the spectrum in figure 12.13a. With what color in the spectrum would the line correspond? If those spectral lines were all shifted as a group to the right, the lines would move to longer wavelengths. This move is toward the red side of the visible spectrum. Astronomers refer to this shift in the line spectra to longer wavelengths as a **redshift.** An example is shown in figure 12.13b. In contrast, the spectral lines for helium can be shifted to the left to shorter wavelengths. For example, the spectral line at 590 nm shifts toward the blue side of the visible spectrum. Scientists refer to these spectral shifts as **blueshifts.** An example is shown in figure 12.13c.

▶ **Figure 12.13**

Emission spectra for helium. (a) Notice the line at a wavelength (λ) of 590 nm in the middle of the spectrum. (b) Notice that the line (as well as all of the other lines) is shifted to the longer wavelengths (toward the red end of the spectrum). (c) All of the lines are shifted to the shorter wavelengths (toward the blue end of the spectrum).

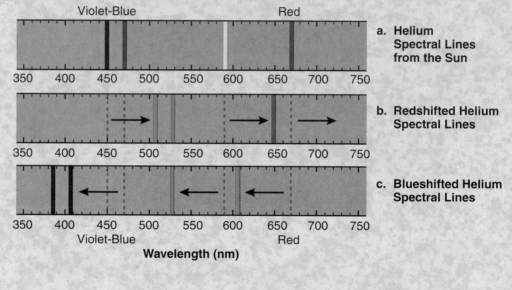

a. Helium Spectral Lines from the Sun

b. Redshifted Helium Spectral Lines

c. Blueshifted Helium Spectral Lines

2. Watch as your teacher performs a demonstration using the overhead projector.
   a. Sketch the setup in your science notebook. Label Earth and the distant star as your teacher instructs.
   b. Draw the result of the star moving *away* from Earth. Label your drawing "Star Moving Away from Earth."
   c. Draw the result of the star moving *toward* Earth. Label your drawing "Star Moving toward Earth."
   d. What would you call this effect? Write this at the bottom of your sketches in Steps 2b and c.
   e. Highlight your drawings by using the headings "What I see" and "What it means." Be sure to include how frequency and wavelength change in your "What it means" category.

f. What color of light has the shortest wavelength? What color of light has the longest wavelength (see figure 12.14)?

g. Label your drawings from Steps 2b and c with the terms *redshift* and *blueshift*.

3. Read the following paragraph to see how observing redshift and blueshift will deepen your understanding of the universe.

The redshift and blueshift in spectra is key evidence of motion within the universe. Scientists observe those shifts from a frame of reference that includes observers on Earth (or from a space-based telescope) and light coming from outside our solar system. Those observations include light from stars within our Milky Way galaxy and light from stars and galaxies well beyond the Milky Way. This evidence tells scientists about the relative motions of the stars and galaxies; that is, whether the observer and the source are approaching each other or moving farther away (see figure 12.15).

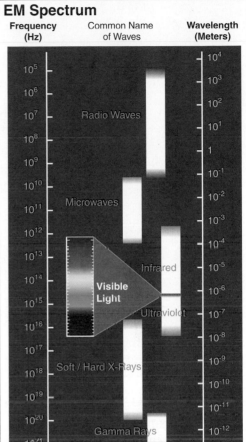

EM Spectrum		
Frequency (Hz)	Common Name of Waves	Wavelength (Meters)
10^5		10^4
10^6		10^3
10^7	Radio Waves	10^2
10^8		10^1
10^9		1
10^{10}		10^{-1}
10^{11}	Microwaves	10^{-2}
10^{12}		10^{-3}
10^{13}		10^{-4}
10^{14}	Infrared	10^{-5}
10^{15}	Visible Light	10^{-6}
10^{16}	Ultraviolet	10^{-7}
10^{17}		10^{-8}
10^{18}	Soft / Hard X-Rays	10^{-9}
10^{19}		10^{-10}
10^{20}		10^{-11}
10^{21}	Gamma Rays	10^{-12}

▲ **Figure 12.14**
EM spectrum. Use this diagram to answer Question 2f.

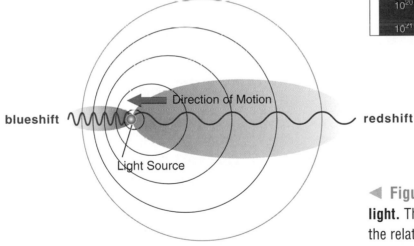

◀ **Figure 12.15 Doppler effect with light.** This evidence tells scientists about the relative motions of stars and galaxies.

4. Answer these questions with your partner. Then discuss your ideas with your class.

a. What does a shift of the line spectrum toward the red tell astronomers about the wavelengths of light that reach the observer on Earth? How do those wavelengths compare with wavelengths emitted by the same element on Earth?

b. Recall that the Doppler effect is the *apparent* change in wave frequency (and wavelength) when the source of the waves is moving with respect to the observer. That movement could be toward or away from the observer. If the wavelengths of light appear to shift as noted in the spectrum in figure 12.13c, is the object moving toward or away from the observer? How do you know?

c. In which direction (toward red or blue) do the spectral lines shift when the object is moving away from the observer? Why?

5. Imagine that scientists observe the line spectra of element X from different objects in space. The line spectra might look like those in figure 12.16. Study the figure and answer Questions 5a–i.

a. Which of spectra A–F can you use for a comparison? Why?

b. How many spectral lines do you see in your standard, and at what wavelengths do those spectral lines occur?

c. Is the spectrum measured for element X on Earth different from or the same as the spectral lines measured for object B?

d. Which objects are moving toward the observer on Earth? How do you know?

e. Which objects are moving away from the observer on Earth? How do you know?

▶ **Figure 12.16**

Spectra of element X.
Astronomers observe these spectral lines of element X from the light that objects B–F emit in space. Object A shows the spectral lines for element X when studied on Earth. Note: These are exaggerated shifts.

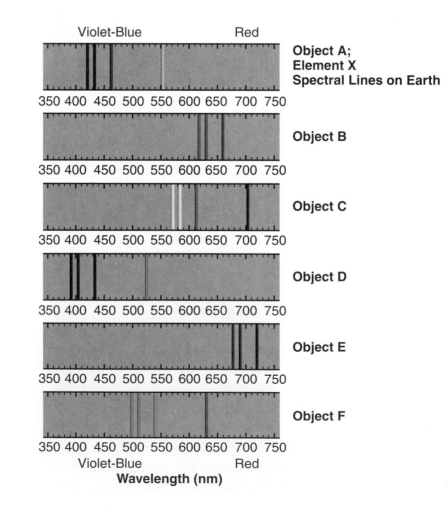

f. You have seen the evidence that astronomers see that shows that objects are moving either toward or away from you. You also have seen that the amount of redshift or blueshift is not always the same for different objects. What inference can you make regarding the motions of those objects based on the amounts of redshift or blueshift you see? Check your inferences with your teacher.

g. Rank the objects based on your inferences. Label your rankings.

h. Draw a model of the movement of object B, showing the shape of the light waves that it emits. Be sure to label where you would find Earth.

Compare your figure with that of figure 12.15.

i. Draw a model of the movement of object D and compare this model with the one in Step 5h. Should they look the same? Why or why not?

6. What conclusions could scientists who study these spectra draw from their observations?

Reflect and Connect

1. Complete the following task on your own. In your science notebook, create a concept map about what you have learned about the Doppler effect. Remember to use verbs to connect the concepts that show relationships. Your concept map should be arranged so that the most universal concept is at the top. Use the following list of words as a guide for your map. You may add more words if necessary, and you may use the words more than once. Try to use as many of these words as possible.

- Doppler effect
- Light
- Color
- Redshift
- Moving/motion
- Sound
- Frequency
- Blueshift

- Pitch
- Wavelength
- High/higher
- Source
- Observer
- Decreases/smaller
- Increases/larger
- Low/lower

2. Think back to both parts of this activity. What was the main idea? Summarize the main idea in 1 sentence.

Feel, Hear, and See the Shock Wave!

Have you ever heard a sonic boom? If so, you were experiencing an event that is sometimes called a shock wave. You can even feel the vibrations as a shock wave passes. Think a minute about what you learned about the Doppler effect and sound. You learned that as a source of sound is approaching you, the waves of sound "bunch up" in front of the moving source and spread out behind the mov-

ing sound source. What happens as the sound source moves faster and faster? What if the sound source were moving at the same speed as the sound? What if the sound source moved faster than the sound? *Supersonic* is the term given to objects that move faster than the speed of sound. Look at the illustration of sound waves to understand what sound waves look like when this happens.

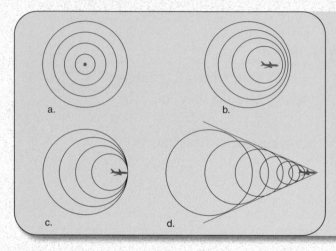

Sound waves. These four pictures illustrate sound sources moving at different speeds: (a) a stationary sound source, (b) a sound source moving slower than the speed of sound, (c) a sound source moving at the speed of sound, and (d) a sound source moving faster than the speed of sound.

If you have ever heard a sonic boom, what you experienced was the shock wave (created by the supersonic aircraft) reaching your ears. This is very similar to the wake produced by a speeding boat. Imagine that you are standing on the shore of a beach or lake. The water is calm as a fast-moving motorboat zooms by. As the boat goes by, you do not notice any waves at the shore. In time,

however, large waves from the boat's wake splash your feet.

Look at the illustration of sound waves coming from a jet and listeners on the ground. Some people have the misconception that a sonic boom is a single event that occurs as the plane breaks the sound barrier. This is not the case. Rather, a sonic boom is continuous as long as the aircraft is supersonic.

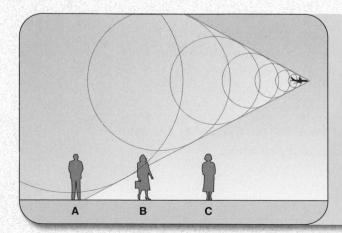

Listening to sonic booms. Sonic booms are not single events. Listener A has already heard the boom, while listener B is hearing it now. Listener C has not yet heard the sonic boom.

You may have heard a sonic boom, but have you ever seen one? The photograph shows an F/A-18 Hornet just as it goes supersonic. Atmospheric conditions must be just right for this unusual cloud to appear around the jet. A drop in air pressure occurs at the plane, allowing for moist air to condense in the cloud you see in the photograph.

Seeing a shock wave. This F/A-18 Hornet was photographed just as it broke the sound barrier.

In What Direction Are We Moving?

EXPLORE

EXPLAIN

In the last activity, you discovered how scientists use the Doppler effect with light waves to determine the movement of stars and galaxies. Understanding that galaxies are moving away from Earth at various speeds and knowing the distance to those galaxies are two pieces of evidence that scientists use to answer more cosmic questions. Scientists used those two pieces of scientific knowledge to make an important discovery about the universe.

The early part of the 20th century was a rich time for new discoveries in space science. Scientists began to ask more questions about the universe. They wondered whether a relationship existed between the distance from Earth to galaxies and the speed at which those galaxies were moving. History has shown that scientists made inferences and found evidence to support their ideas.

In this investigation, In What Direction Are We Moving?, you work with a partner and in teams of four to follow the discoveries of Edwin Hubble. Hubble worked to answer this question: What is the relationship between distance from Earth to galaxies and the speed at which those galaxies are moving? You will gain an understanding of astronomers' current model of the universe and the evidence they have to support that model. Understanding the current model of the universe is key to understanding how it all began.

▲ **Figure 12.17**
Edwin Hubble (1889–1953). Edwin Hubble worked to answer this question: Is there a relationship between the distance a galaxy is from Earth and the recessional speed of the galaxy?

Part I: Observing the Universe

Materials

graph paper

Process and Procedure

In the explore activity, What Is the Evidence?, you observed spectral data from various objects in the universe and saw how objects moving away from the observer showed a redshift in their spectra. In Part I of this investigation, you and your partner look at representative spectral data from galaxies in the universe. The observations you make will be similar to those made by astronomers when they study galaxies. Your observations will help you begin to understand the nature of the universe.

1. Read the following paragraphs and discuss them with your partner. As you are reading, think about the knowledge that astronomers had about the universe over 80 years ago. This was a time before the National Aeronautics and Space Administration (NASA), moonwalks, or space shuttles.

READING

Beyond the Milky Way

Before 1924, many astronomers thought that all objects in the universe were concentrated into one large cluster called a galaxy. They called it the Milky Way galaxy, and many astronomers thought it was the only galaxy in the universe. At the same time, some astronomers inferred that there were other galaxies beyond the Milky Way, but they had no evidence to confirm that conclusion.

When astronomers of that time studied the Milky Way, they called one type of object they observed a nebula. They gave it that name because the object looked fuzzy, or nebulous, in a telescope. Figure 12.18 is an example of one of the objects astronomers of that time thought were nebulae.

Some astronomers thought these nebulae were clouds of dust within the Milky Way. Others believed they were other objects, perhaps beyond the Milky Way. In 1923, Edwin Hubble took a historic photograph of an object in the night sky that he originally thought was a nebula within the Milky Way galaxy (see figure 12.19). When he looked at his photograph, he discovered a Cepheid variable star in the nebula. Using Henrietta Swan Leavitt's work with Cepheid variables, he gathered evidence that indicated the distance to the star (and therefore the distance to the nebula). His calculations revealed that the nebula was well beyond the Milky Way galaxy. Scientists now know that light arriving at Hubble's eyes had left that object about 2.2 million light-years (ly) ago. Much to his surprise, Hubble was not seeing a nebula, but an entire distant galaxy—the spectacular Andromeda galaxy. Figure 12.18 is a photograph of the Andromeda galaxy (M31).

Hubble's work demonstrated that there were galaxies beyond the Milky Way. Because of his observations, Hubble began to build a new understanding of the structure of the entire universe. His discovery prompted a new set of questions for astronomers to try to answer. What do you think some of those questions might have been?

▲ **Figure 12.18 Andromeda galaxy.** Astronomers once thought these objects were nebulae.

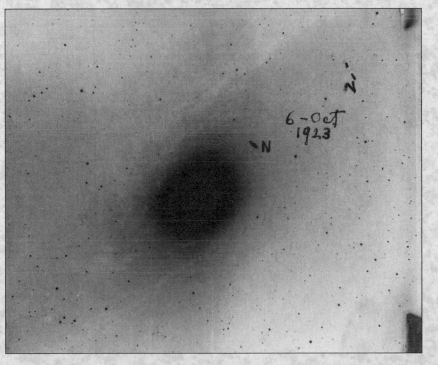

◄ **Figure 12.19 Edwin Hubble's photographic plate of the Andromeda galaxy.** In the 1920s, Edwin Hubble made observations with the Mount Wilson Observatory's 100-inch telescope, located in California, that would change the thinking of astronomers of the time. The idea then was that this figure (also pictured in figure 12.18, taken with more modern technology) was a nebula. Hubble searched for novae—stars that underwent a sudden increase in brightness. He found several on this plate and marked them with an *N*. He saw something in this plate and in plates taken earlier of the same object that made him ask questions. Hubble discovered a Cepheid variable star in this nebula. He crossed out his previous notation of "N" and replaced it with "Var!" (seen in the top right corner). His discovery of a Cepheid variable star and his subsequent calculations led him to discover that this nebula was not a small cluster of stars and gas within our own galaxy, but a large, distant galaxy in its own right.

2. Look at the intensity plots in figure 12.20. Imagine that you and your partner are astronomers studying the universe and you have gathered the spectral data from the five distant galaxies shown in figure 12.20. Answer these questions about your observations.

You see the unit Mly in figure 12.20. Recall that "M" before units indicates mega-, or a prefix of one million. For example, a distance of 40 Mly is the same as 40 million light-years (40×10^6 ly).

    a. Based on your study of these spectral data, what trends do you observe? To answer this question, make a graph with the recessional speed of each galaxy plotted on the y-axis and the distance of each galaxy plotted on the x-axis.

    b. What can you conclude about the behavior of these galaxies? What are these galaxies doing in relation to the observer?

As you develop your answer to these questions, consider the redshift patterns by studying the change in the peaks on the intensity plots for each galaxy. Recall what you have studied about redshift patterns in line spectra.

    c. Draw a simple sketch or diagram that might represent the behavior of these galaxies in the universe in relation to Earth. As you develop your diagram, think about your interpretation of the redshift patterns and the distances galaxies are from Earth.

    d. How much time did it take for light traveling from each of these galaxies to arrive at Earth?

Part I

Work with your partner to discuss these questions. Record your answers in your science notebook.

1. In your own words, describe how Hubble provided evidence that galaxies exist beyond the Milky Way.

2. Does it seem as though a relationship exists between a galaxy's speed and its distance from Earth? Explain how evidence leads you to this relationship.

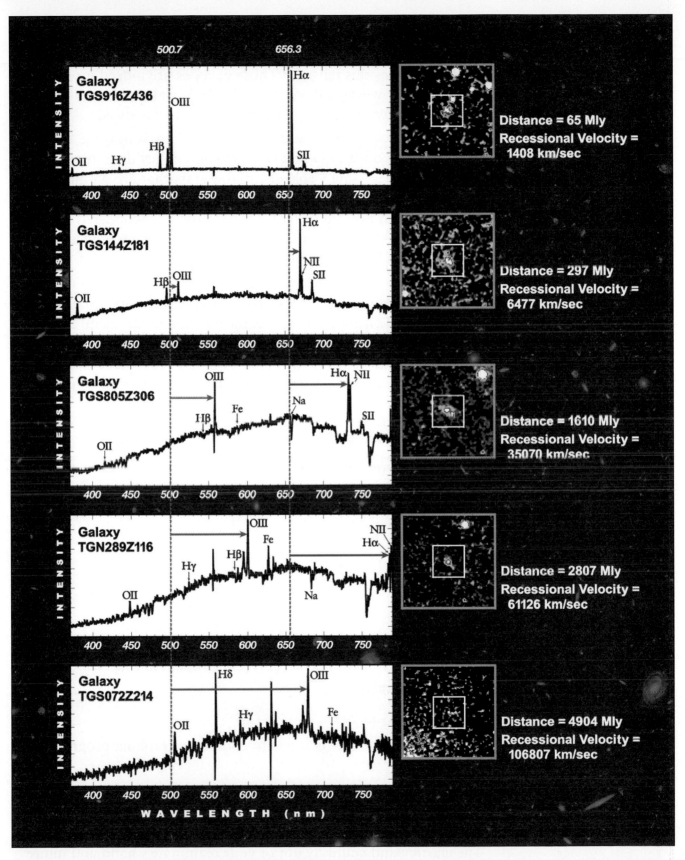

▲ **Figure 12.20 Galaxies and intensity plots.** What would this spectral data from distant galaxies tell scientists?

Part II: An Elastic Universe

Some galaxies within our Local Group show a blueshift in their spectra. What does this tell you? Those galaxies are indeed moving toward Earth. However, galaxies outside our Local Group exhibit a redshift and are receding away from Earth at various speeds.

Astronomers can determine a how fast a galaxy is moving away from Earth based on the amount of its redshift. They determine the distance to galaxies using Cepheid variable stars that are within those galaxies. Much like you did in Part I, Hubble studied the spectra of many galaxies and noticed the redshift patterns. He wondered whether a relationship existed between how fast a galaxy was moving away from Earth and what its distance from Earth was.

In Part II, you work in teams of four students to explore a model that might explain the spectra scientists observe from other galaxies outside our Local Group. You also determine the relationship between a galaxy's recessional speed (how fast it recedes or moves away from Earth) and its distance from Earth. By looking at this model, you make observations and measurements much like those that Hubble made.

Materials
For each team of four or five students

1 piece of elastic band

1 washable color marker

1 overhead marker

6 safety pins

1 meterstick or tape measure

1 metric ruler

masking tape

1 transparency of An Elastic Universe Graph handout

For each team member

1 pair of safety goggles

1 graphing calculator or access to computer graphing program (optional)

1 copy of An Elastic Universe Graph handout

Cautions

The elastic band could fly out of your teammate's hand and injure your eyes. Wear safety goggles during this activity.

Process and Procedure

1. Participate in a class discussion that will help you understand your model of the universe.
2. Select a length of elastic band that your teacher provides.
3. Pin 6 safety pins randomly along the length of your elastic band.

▼ **Figure 12.21**
Elastic band model.
Pin your safety pins perpendicular to the length of elastic in your model.

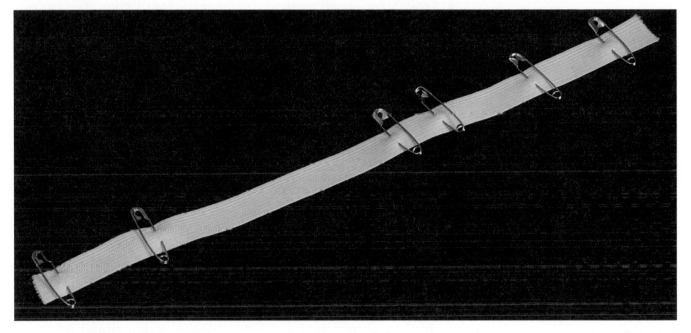

4. Meet with your team and answer the following questions:
   a. What do the safety pins represent?
   b. What does the elastic represent?
   c. Stretch the elastic and observe the motion of the pins. What happens?
5. Choose 1 safety pin to be the Milky Way and mark it with tape or a marker.
6. Your job is to design a way to measure the expansion of your "universe." Your universe is your elastic band and pins. Remember your frame of reference. You are observing the universe from Earth, and Earth is in the Milky Way galaxy. As an astronomer, you must make measurements from Earth.
   a. Astronomers use the term *recessional speed* to describe the speed that galaxies are receding, or moving away, from Earth. That is how they measure the expansion of the universe. What measurements do you think you need to find recessional speed?
   b. Write the formula for speed in your notebook.

Everyone will use the same time for calculating speed. Therefore, you do not have to measure time.

7. Meet with your team. Discuss a plan to measure and calculate the recessional speed of the galaxies in your universe. Record your plan in your notebook. As you are making your plan, keep the following guidelines in mind:
   - Use Earth as your frame of reference.
   - Keep track of each initial and expanded measurement.
   - Use metric measurements.
   - Stretch the elastic to twice its length (as will your classmates to keep things consistent).
   - Assign roles to each team member.

8. Consider all of the data that you have to record and make a data table to organize your measurements and calculations. Read the entire Process and Procedure to make sure you have thought of all measurements.

9. Have your teacher approve your plan *and* data table before you begin.

10. Conduct your investigation and record all of your measurements.

11. After you have conducted your experiment, discuss the following questions with your team and record your answers in your science notebook.

   a. What is the relationship between the starting position of a galaxy and the distance it moved from the Milky Way? Make a sketch in your science notebook that shows what happened to the galaxies.

   b. Imagine that it took 1 second to expand your universe from 3 meters (m) to 5 m. Then calculate how fast (the speed) each galaxy moved away from (receded) the home galaxy. To calculate the recessional speed (how fast galaxies moved away from the home galaxy) of each galaxy, use the following formula:

$$\text{recessional speed (moving away)} = \frac{\text{distance traveled (cm)}}{\text{time interval(s)}}$$

   Record in your data table the recessional speed for each of your galaxies.

   Do not forget to put in the proper units when you do your calculations. Also, remember that astronomers actually obtain recessional speeds when they look at the spectra of distant galaxies. The amount of redshift tells astronomers how fast a galaxy is moving away from Earth.

   c. What is the relationship between the distance a galaxy is from "home" and its recessional speed? To answer that

Caution

Wear your safety goggles as you work with the elastic bands.

question, complete this sentence: As the distance a
galaxy is from home increases, the recessional speed
_____.

d. Describe your observations about how the galaxies moved.
Consider the following questions as you write your description: Does there appear to be a center location on the elastic?
Did the galaxies appear to move from where they originally
started? How did the galaxies move in relation to the elastic?
What evidence do you have to support your ideas?

12. You learned in Part I that galaxies that were receding faster had
larger redshifts. Consider the spectrum in figure 12.22. If you
use this spectrum as a standard for comparison, what would
the spectra look like from each of your other galaxies?

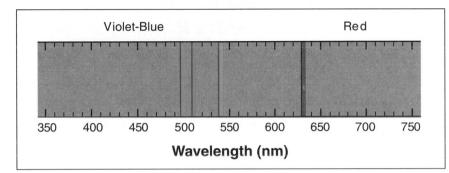

◀ **Figure 12.22**
**Standard galaxy
spectrum.** Use this
spectrum as your
comparison when you
draw spectra for your
receding galaxies.

To answer that question, follow these steps:
a. Copy the spectrum from figure 12.22 into your science notebook. Be sure to copy the scale and emission lines in the
proper place.
b. Draw what the spectral data for your galaxies might look
like from the Milky Way. Be sure to label each galaxy and its
corresponding spectrum.

13. Your teacher will distribute the An Elastic Universe Graph
handout to each team member along with 1 transparency of
the same graph to your team. Work with your team to do
the following:
a. On your own handout, plot your data from your elastic
band model and compare your graph with your teammates'
graphs. Since you worked as a team, you should have nearly
identical graphs. As a team, make sure all of you have similar graphs.

Notice that the y-axis on the graph is the recessional speed of each galaxy from
the home galaxy and the x-axis is the original distance of each galaxy from the
home galaxy.

b. As a team, make 1 graph of your team's data on the transparency. Have each team member label the graph with his or her initials and give the graph to your teacher.

14. Your teacher will post other teams' data on the overhead projector. Look at the transparencies of others teams' data. As you view their data, think about the following questions and record your ideas in your science notebook.
    a. What trends do you notice?
    b. Are any trends similar?
    c. Are any graphs exactly alike?

Stop & THINK
Part II

Discuss these questions with your team. Record your responses in your science notebook.

1. Why do different teams' graphs look similar when the teams randomly chose their initial placement of galaxies?

2. Does your elastic band model explain the spectral data from Part I of this activity? Discuss your reasoning.

3. If the elastic band model is an accurate model of the nature of the universe, what does it tell you about galaxies in the universe and, therefore, the nature of the universe?

4. As with all models, there are strengths and weaknesses to the elastic band model. Prepare a T-table in your notebook with the title "The Elastic Band Model." Use "Strengths of the Model" and "Weaknesses of the Model" as column headings. Complete the table by listing ways the model is a good representation of the universe and ways it is an incomplete representation of the universe. Give at least 2 examples of each. Use your knowledge about the discoveries of Hubble and your experiences with the elastic band model to support your comparisons.

Part III: Hubble's Discovery

In Parts I and II of this investigation, you observed a model of the universe and discovered the relationship between the distance a galaxy is from an observer and its recessional speed. In Part III, you read about how Hubble concluded that the universe is expanding and how he provided a way to calculate how fast it is expanding.

Materials

For each team of four students

completed An Elastic Universe Graph handouts and transparency from Part II

Process and Procedure

1. Read The Hubble Constant to learn how Hubble concluded that the universe is expanding.

READING

The Hubble Constant

Edwin Hubble (with help from Milton Humason) photographed and studied the spectra of many galaxies. Much of their work stemmed from the earlier discoveries of Vesto Slipher, an American astronomer working at Lowell Observatory in Flagstaff, Arizona. Slipher showed that many galaxies were rapidly moving away from Earth. This paved the way for Edwin Hubble's discovery of the expanding universe.

Hubble was not able to measure distances to stars or galaxies with a ruler (as you did along your elastic). Recall that Hubble determined the distances to the Andromeda galaxy (M31) by finding Cepheid variable stars within the galaxy. By studying those variable stars, Hubble showed that Andromeda was well beyond our galaxy. Scientists today have calculated that Andromeda is at least 2.2 million ly away.

Hubble made other significant observations about distant galaxies. He looked at the spectra of galaxies (which are made from the spectra of all of the stars in the galaxy) and noted that those galaxies that were farther away had larger red-shifts. Hubble noticed that the farther away a galaxy was from Earth, the larger its redshift. What do you think that means? Hubble deter-mined that galaxies that were more distant were moving away from Earth faster than galaxies that

▲ **Figure 12.23 Galaxy NGC 7217.** Edwin Hubble studied distant galaxies such as this one. He analyzed their spectra to determine the amount of redshift. What does the amount of redshift indicate about a galaxy?

were closer to Earth. He had discovered that the recessional speeds of the more distant galaxies were greater than the recessional speeds of the nearby galaxies.

Now Hubble had more questions. Was there a relationship between the distance from Earth to a galaxy and the galaxy's recessional speed? He made a graph of his data, plotting the distance to the galaxies on the *x*-axis and their recessional speeds on the *y*-axis. When the relationship plot-ted as a line, Hubble knew that the two variables were correlated (see figure 12.24). You will hear this relationship referred to as **Hubble's law.** It shows that the farther an object such as a galaxy

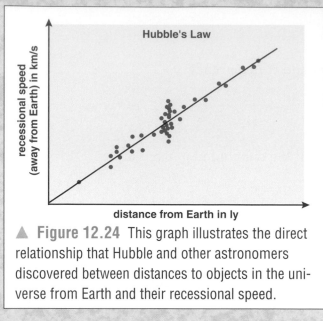

Hubble's Law

recessional speed (away from Earth) in km/s

distance from Earth in ly

▲ **Figure 12.24** This graph illustrates the direct relationship that Hubble and other astronomers discovered between distances to objects in the universe from Earth and their recessional speed.

is from Earth, the faster it is moving away (receding) from Earth.

Because of this linear relationship, Hubble concluded that the universe is expanding. His data showed that most galaxies are moving away from each other with space. You modeled this understanding with your elastic model: the elastic represented space itself. And as you observed, the galaxies moved with the elastic (space). Because the relationship between the distance and recessional speed of galaxies is a straight line, Hubble calculated the slope of the line. Scientists call the slope of this line the Hubble constant (H_0).

Hubble's data also had another very important implication. He realized that with Hubble's law, astronomers could determine the distance to faraway galaxies based on redshift alone. If they determined a galaxy's recessional speed based on the redshift and they knew the slope of the line (the Hubble constant), they could calculate the galaxy's distance from Earth.

The Hubble constant also indicates the rate at which the universe is expanding. That rate can be used to estimate the size and age of the universe. The inverse of the slope of the line tells astronomers additional information. That relationship shows how long ago it was that all of the galaxies were on top of each other—the

point in time before galaxies expanded out into the universe that exists today.

Astronomers have been able to gather and graph more data since the 1920s. An accurate value of the Hubble constant depends on Cepheids and accurate distance measurements. Astronomers have refined Hubble's law using other methods of obtaining distances, including studying a certain type of exploding star. They call these exploding high-mass stars Type Ia supernovae. These supernovae have similar physical properties, including brightness, which allows astronomers to calculate very accurately relative distances to galaxies.

In 1990, NASA launched the Hubble Space Telescope. The telescope provided crucial data for refining and improving the Hubble constant. Astronomers are now able to locate more Cepheid variable stars within faraway galaxies. In 2001, Wendy Freedman and other investigators studied 27 galaxies using Cepheid variables. They also studied Type Ia supernovae. Using the new data, they calculated a new value for the Hubble constant. Using their revised value of the Hubble constant, they estimate the universe to be about 13.7 billion years old. That estimate has been supported by results from several other methods.

▲ **Figure 12.25 Image of Galaxy NGC 4603 taken with the Hubble Space Telescope.** This spiral galaxy is one of the most distant galaxies in which astronomers have observed Cepheid variable stars.

2. Share your understanding with a partner and record the important ideas from this reading in your science notebook.

Reflect and Connect

Discuss the following questions with your class. Record your answers in your science notebook.

1. The elastic model is 1-dimensional, but the universe is not. How could you use elastic or another material to represent the 3 dimensions of the universe?

2. Prior to Hubble's time, most astronomers thought that the universe was static (the universe was not expanding). Imagine that an astronomer came back from the early 1900s. Using your elastic model, explain to him or her what Hubble's work showed.

3. How did the elastic model of the universe help you understand Hubble's ideas of the nature of the universe?

4. You studied 2 different types of motions in the engage activity, Are We Moving? The motions included your surface speed on Earth as it rotates on its axis and Earth's speed as a result of its revolution around the Sun. You also studied additional motions. Provide evidence of the fact that you are moving due to the expanding universe even while you are sitting still at your desk. Where would you have to be to observe this motion—what would be your frame of reference?

5. There are 3 parts to this activity. What is the main idea of the activity as a whole? Summarize the idea in 1 sentence.

What Started Us Moving?

EXPLAIN

If the universe is expanding, how did it begin? What did it expand from? How might scientists be able to figure that out? Scientists do this by imagining that they are "running the universe film backward" from the present to its origin.

Materials

Process and Procedure

Read The Big Bang to see how you can use a mental model to understand what has happened in the past.

The Big Bang

Have you ever watched a video played backward? You can use the rewind function on your VCR to watch events occur in reverse as the tape rewinds. Some scenes are particularly interesting (and funny!). Perhaps a diver moves backward from the splash into the water to standing calmly on the diving board. Maybe the splatter and mess of a broken egg on the counter moves backward until the egg is safely in its shell in the egg carton.

Cosmologists are scientists who study the origin and evolution of the universe. When they work to unravel the history of the expanding universe, they use the idea of running films in reverse. If they theorize that the universe is expanding and they can calculate about how old the universe is, they can "run the film backward" for that length of time to envision how the universe began.

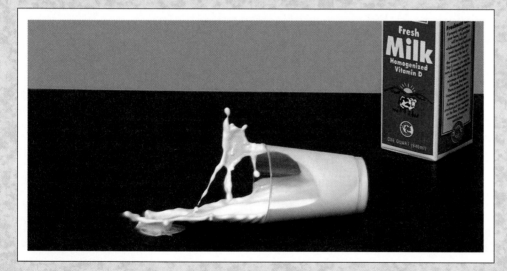

◄ **Figure 12.26 Glass of spilled milk.** What did this scene look like in the past?

Stop & THINK

Answer the following questions on your own. Then share your thoughts in a class discussion.

1. Examine the scene in figure 12.26 and think about how it might have looked in the past.
   a. If you "run the film backward" from the present to the initial state, what do you think an earlier image might have looked like?

b. What inference might you make about what happened?

c. Be prepared to share your ideas in a class discussion.

2. After you have listened to others' ideas, answer the following questions in your science notebook.

a. How does your inference compare with those of your classmates?

b. What evidence do you have that supports your inference of what happened? Is there any part of your inference that is not supported by evidence? List any inferences that are not supported by evidence.

c. If you run the "film" backward in your mind, will your "film" always tell the true story? Why or why not?

d. How could you get the story exactly right?

e. Can you do that for the story of the universe? Explain your answer.

"Running the film backward" to see how something starts sounds simple, doesn't it? The problem is that a "film" of the universe describes something that no one has ever before experienced or created in a laboratory. Nothing in scientists' current lives can help them visualize the opening frames of the "film." As much as ideas about the origin of the universe stretch the mind, however, astronomers can use evidence, measurements, and observations to try to build a picture of how the universe started.

As scientists "run the universe film backward," they see that galaxies move closer together. They see that the density of galaxies was greater and the universe was more compressed.

Scientists envision "running this film backward" approximately 14 billion years. In doing so, they see those visible galaxies that expanded billions of light-years outward come back together. Scientists propose that in the initial frames of the "film," all of the matter of the universe was once packed together into a state of astonishingly (maybe unimaginably) high temperature, pressure, and density. That hot, dense state of the early universe was too hot for basic atomic particles such as protons and neutrons to exist.

Now that scientists can envision the start of the "film," they can trace its origin and evolution to the present. From a tiny speck smaller than the size of an atom, scientists think that the universe rapidly expanded into existence in an event called the **big bang.** While you may imagine the big bang to be just like an explosion, it was different in one important way. Unlike an explosion, the universe did not expand into something. Instead, it expanded with all of the space, time, matter, and energy of the entire universe.

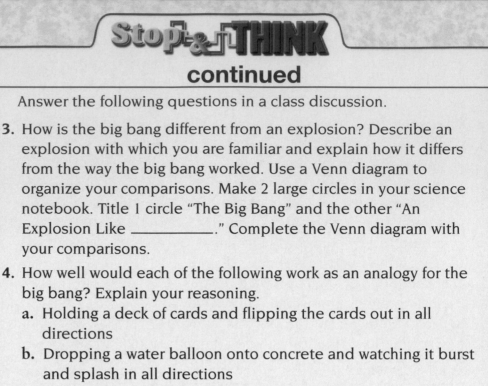

Stop & THINK

continued

Answer the following questions in a class discussion.

3. How is the big bang different from an explosion? Describe an explosion with which you are familiar and explain how it differs from the way the big bang worked. Use a Venn diagram to organize your comparisons. Make 2 large circles in your science notebook. Title 1 circle "The Big Bang" and the other "An Explosion Like _____." Complete the Venn diagram with your comparisons.

4. How well would each of the following work as an analogy for the big bang? Explain your reasoning.
   a. Holding a deck of cards and flipping the cards out in all directions
   b. Dropping a water balloon onto concrete and watching it burst and splash in all directions
   c. Allowing bread dough containing raisins to rise until it has doubled in size

Scientists have enough evidence and information to support the following theory about the evolution of the universe. During the initial second of its existence, scientists think that the universe experienced extremely rapid expansion. It ballooned outward in all directions, growing from a size smaller than a proton to a size billions of times larger (perhaps the size of a grapefruit).

At the first moment of the big bang, the temperature of the universe was extraordinarily high.

During the first second, the temperature of the universe cooled slightly to $10^{10}°$ Celsius (C). Although still incredibly hot, the universe had cooled down enough so that particles stopped colliding so violently. Now protons and neutrons could form. Space, at that time, was full of protons, neutrons, and electrons, all surrounded by photons (particles of EM radiation). However, the temperature was still so hot that protons, neutrons, and electrons could not combine to form simple atoms.

From this point (1 second into the existence of the universe) and through the next 380,000 years, scientists think that the universe was opaque, which means that light could not pass through it. Scientists refer to this time as the dark era. When the temperature of the universe fell below 3,000°C, protons, neutrons, and electrons cooled enough to form the simplest atoms. Hydrogen gas began to form at those temperatures. Hydrogen gas is clear; therefore, the universe became transparent. For the first time, the photons could stream unstopped across space.

You have already studied what happens when hydrogen gas is available in the universe. Gravity pulls the clouds of gas together, and stars are born. Groups of stars are gravitationally attracted to form galaxies. At the same time, planets form around some stars, and on at least one planet, life evolved. Now you are sitting here studying about how the universe began! The award-winning astronomer Carl Sagan once wrote, "These are the things that hydrogen atoms do—given 15 billion years of cosmic evolution."

Cosmic Evolution

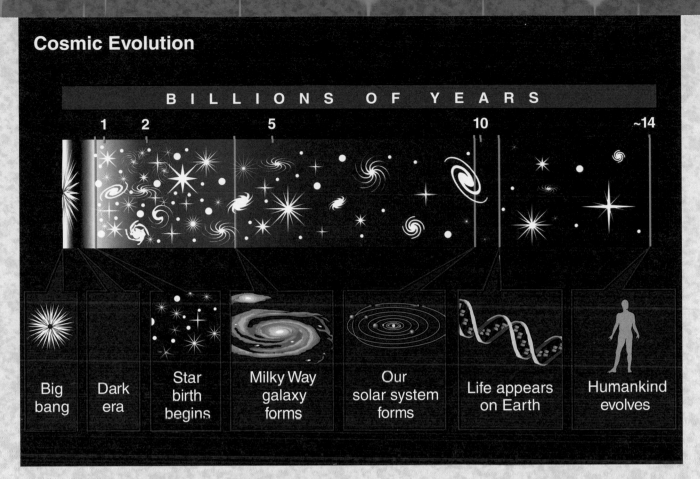

▲ Figure 12.27
Timeline from the big bang to present. What does this illustration tell you about the evolution of the universe?

continued

Complete the following tasks as a class.

5. Consider the last paragraph and the quote by Carl Sagan. You learned about life and living systems in the unit, The Machinery of Life. Discuss the role of the big bang in supplying all of the matter needed for life.

6. To help you get a perspective on the events in the early years of the universe, fill in the chart in figure 12.28 as a class. Imagine that each point in time is a "freeze-frame of the film of the universe." When you have completed the chart as a class, copy it into your science notebook.

Time	Event	Description
0 seconds	Big bang	
1 second		
2 seconds to 300,000 years		

▲ **Figure 12.28** Copy this data table into your science notebook and fill it in as you discuss the reading with your class.

Expanding balloon with waves. Wavelengths of high energy become stretched over time because they are emitted in an expanding universe. The waves stretch along with space and are detected as much longer wavelengths today. This is similar to the change you see in the wavy lines on this expanding balloon.

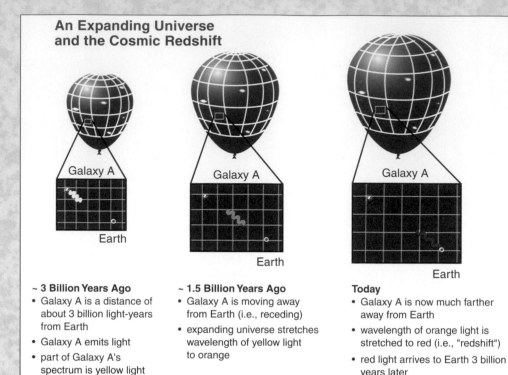

An Expanding Universe and the Cosmic Redshift

Galaxy A

Earth

Galaxy A

Earth

Galaxy A

Earth

~ **3 Billion Years Ago**
- Galaxy A is a distance of about 3 billion light-years from Earth
- Galaxy A emits light
- part of Galaxy A's spectrum is yellow light

~ **1.5 Billion Years Ago**
- Galaxy A is moving away from Earth (i.e., receding)
- expanding universe stretches wavelength of yellow light to orange

Today
- Galaxy A is now much farther away from Earth
- wavelength of orange light is stretched to red (i.e., "redshift")
- red light arrives to Earth 3 billion years later

Scientists recognized that they could determine whether their ideas made sense with regard to how the universe began. If they were correct, they should see evidence of the EM waves that could pass through the transparent universe beginning 380,000 years after the big bang. The remnants of the high-energy, short-wavelength radiation that began to stream through space at that time in history should still be evident. It should be coming toward Earth equally from all directions because it filled the entire universe at the same time. Because of the expansion of the universe, the wavelength of that high-energy radiation should have stretched to longer wavelengths by the same percentage that the universe expanded between 380,000 years after the big bang and now. It should reach Earth in the form of microwaves (see figure 12.29).

Sure enough, in the 1960s, scientists Arno Penzias and Robert Wilson of Bell Laboratories detected a faint background noise through their horn antenna, which was designed to relay telephone calls to orbiting satellites (see figure 12.30).

► Figure 12.30

Arno Penzias and Robert Wilson of Bell Laboratories. In the 1960s, Arno Penzias and Robert Wilson of Bell Laboratories discovered cosmic microwave background from the big bang.

◀ **Figure 12.31**

Artist's conception of the orbit of the Wilkinson Microwave Anisotropy Probe (WMAP). WMAP orbits at a distance of 1.5 million km (approximately 1 million miles) from Earth. The probe used the gravitation of the moon as a slingshot to send it into an orbit well beyond Earth and the moon. Notice that the probe does not orbit Earth, but rather orbits in a plane far from Earth.

They wondered whether pigeons that roosted on the antenna had left droppings that were causing the extra noise. When they shooed away the pigeons and cleaned up the droppings, the noise was still there. They learned that Princeton astronomers Robert Dicke and P. J. E. Peebles believed that something they called the cosmic microwave background should be found in the universe. Penzias and Wilson realized that this is what they were detecting. They were the first people to discover what scientists think is the radiation left over from the big bang.

Today the best data on cosmic microwave background measurements is collected from the Wilkinson Microwave Anisotropy Probe (WMAP) (see figure 12.31).

WMAP has made a very detailed map of the oldest light in the universe (see figure 12.32). It is a baby picture of the universe. The light that it captures is from a few hundred thousand years after the big bang, over 13 billion years ago! WMAP provides additional evidence for the theory that the universe started at one point and is expanding. The fact that the microwaves are the same from all directions in the universe suggests that the vast universe was once a tiny region of space with a single temperature. During initial rapid expansion of the universe, all of its parts maintained their original temperature, which has since cooled over 13.7 billion years. Amazingly, the radiation has cooled to the exact temperature that scientists predict it should be if their theory is correct.

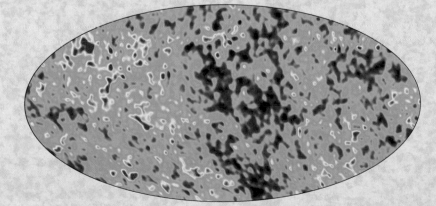

◀ **Figure 12.32**

WMAP image of the oldest light in the universe. Colors of this map indicate warmer (red) and cooler (blue) spots. The shape of this map is a projection of the entire sky much like a globe of Earth would look when projected on paper.

Answer Question 7 in a class discussion. Then at school or at home, do the task outlined in Question 8.

7. Think carefully about what you learned about waves and wavelengths earlier in this unit. Why were scientists looking for microwaves instead of the very high-energy, short-wavelength radiation they inferred was streaming through space from the big bang?

   Consider what you learned about how light waves change when they are moving away from you. You also may want to refer back to figure 12.29.

8. Have you personally ever seen cosmic microwave background? Read the Cosmic Leftovers sidebar to learn how you can see cosmic microwave background for yourself. Then look at cosmic background on a television at school or at home.

While the photons were finally traveling through space, the protons, neutrons, and electrons were combining to make the earliest atoms. The lightest nuclei—hydrogen and helium—combined with electrons to form hydrogen and helium atoms. Most of the matter in the universe is hydrogen and helium, which exist today because of the big bang. Recall that hydrogen and helium are the building blocks of the stars.

Scientists continue to find evidence that supports the big bang theory. However, they cannot yet "run the film backward" with total confidence. While scientists know that the big bang must have happened, their current explanation of its details is hindered by their lack of understanding of the physics and chemistry that would have taken place under such extreme conditions. Attempts to simulate the conditions under which the big bang happened have not yet occurred, so many questions remain.

Currently, the big bang theory states that 13.7 billion years ago the universe began as a small, dense, hot point that suddenly erupted and began expanding. The expansion created all matter, time, and space, and the universe has been expanding ever since.

The history and nature of science suggest that the big bang theory will be refined in the future by new discoveries, improved technology, better theoretical models, and more research. Remember, you can observe only those parts of the universe from which light has had time to reach Earth. New technologies may allow you to detect objects that are now too faint to see, meaning that someday you may be able to see further back into time. However, you may never see the whole universe. Because of this, you may never completely understand the entire "film" from the opening to the credits. Science, however, is adding details to the "film's" plot every day.

Topic: age of the universe
Go to: www.scilinks.org
Code: 1Inquiry608

Cosmic Leftovers

You have probably seen the remnants of the big bang, but you didn't know it. Cosmic microwave background shows up as snow (or static) on a television screen when you flip past an unused channel. To be sure that what you see is really this ancient energy from the universe, try the following.

With permission from an adult, disconnect any cable or satellite dish that is connected to the TV. Equip the TV set with a good antenna. Tune the TV to an unused channel. Set the contrast to its maximum and turn the brightness down to the point where the snow on the screen appears as white flecks on a black background. About one out of every 100 of the flecks represents the detection of an individual photon from the remnants of the big bang. You are seeing photons from the formation of the universe! The rest of the flecks are static and other environmentally produced interference. Once you have witnessed the photons from the big bang, return the TV to its original settings and reconnect it to the cable or satellite.

The number of photons left over from the big bang actually is quite large. Scientists calculate that there are now 550 million cosmic microwave photons in every cubic meter of space in the universe. In contrast, if all of the visible matter in the universe were spread evenly throughout space, there would be roughly one hydrogen atom in every 3 cubic meters of space. Clearly, photons outnumber atoms by roughly a billion to one. It's no wonder there is snow on so many TV channels!

Cosmic background radiation. Have you ever seen static like this on your TV? You are seeing cosmic leftovers!

Reflect and Connect

Discuss the following questions with your class. Complete the sidebar reading (Question 4) individually.

1. Some scientists estimate that the universe is about 13.7 billion years old. Why do they think this? Could it be older? Could it be younger? Explain your answers.

2. Scientists often refer to the "observable universe." Explain the significance of the distinction between *universe* and *observable universe*.

3. Describe 3 pieces of evidence scientists have to support the big bang theory.

4. What would happen if you ran the "film" forward into the future? What is the future of the universe? Read the sidebar, The Future of the Universe, to find out what cosmologists propose for the "film's" finale. Then state what they predict in answer to this question.

5. This activity was about the big bang theory and the evidence that scientists have to support it. Summarize the main points of the big bang in 1 sentence.

The Future of the Universe

What will become of an expanding universe? Will it keep expanding on into the future? Will the universe expand faster and faster until it rips apart? Or, like a balloon losing air, will it gradually slow and then collapse on itself?

Cosmologists are beginning to answer one of the most important questions in cosmology—how the universe will end. To do that, they gather information about the structure of the present universe. Each time they make new observations about the universe, they can provide evidence to support or refute their theories.

Albert Einstein developed one of the first theories in 1916. He predicted that there was some sort of strange "antigravity" in the universe. Antigravity is a force that keeps the universe from slowing down due to the pull of gravity. Eventually, he discarded his idea, believing that he had made a terrible mistake.

By 1998, scientists had made enough observations to begin to understand more about the nature of the expanding universe. Some objects that scientists studied included supernovae (very bright, exploding stars). Scientists determined the distance to supernovae from Earth and their recessional velocities. They compared supernovae in more distant galaxies with those closer to Earth to see how the rates of expansion of the universe were changing across time. What they found truly surprised them. They expected to see that the expansion rate was slowing down. Instead, they determined that it was actually speeding up. Einstein's idea of a force that worked against gravity no longer seemed so far-fetched.

Today scientists propose something like Einstein's antigravity called dark energy. Dark energy not only keeps the universe from slowing down, but also

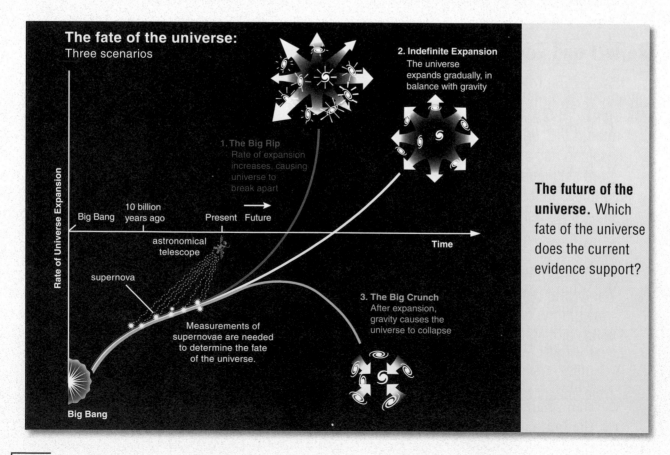

The fate of the universe: Three scenarios

2. Indefinite Expansion
The universe expands gradually, in balance with gravity

1. The Big Rip
Rate of expansion increases, causing universe to break apart

Rate of Universe Expansion

Big Bang   10 billion years ago   Present   Future

astronomical telescope

supernova

Measurements of supernovae are needed to determine the fate of the universe.

Time

3. The Big Crunch
After expansion, gravity causes the universe to collapse

Big Bang

The future of the universe. Which fate of the universe does the current evidence support?

makes it fly apart faster and faster. Dark energy grows as space expands. In the young universe, there wasn't as much space, so there was less dark energy to counteract gravity. As a result, the expansion of the young universe slowed down after its initial burst in the big bang. Then as the universe continued to expand, the increased dark energy acted like Einstein's antigravity and actually sped up the expansion. Since future expansion will yield even more dark energy, the "full speed ahead" effect of dark energy will only increase. One theory that scientists have about the future of the universe is that it will continue expansion indefinitely.

Other theories exist, and like the previous theory, most involve dark energy. Scientists believe that dark energy makes up about 70 percent of the universe. They also think that all of the mass in the universe could not account for enough gravity to stop the expansion and cause a "big crunch." But what if new evidence arises suggesting that there is more mass in the universe than scientists now know of? What if this dark energy fades away? Without dark energy, the universe may collapse in on itself, like the reverse of the big bang. Cosmologists like to call this the big crunch.

By studying distant supernovae, scientists have found that the expansion of the universe is accelerating. But will the universe continue to accelerate at the rate astronomers are now observing? If Einstein's prediction was correct (and there is evidence today that it is), the universe will take the path of indefinite expansion. However, if the repulsion from dark energy is or becomes larger than Einstein's prediction, the universe may be torn apart in a "big rip." If this is the grand finale of the universe, galaxies, stars, planets, and finally atoms will be ripped apart in a catastrophic end of time.

Currently, all of those theories are being pursued by scientists. Understanding the future of the universe will require many more observations. Modern telescopes capable of looking more than halfway across the universe will be needed to fine-tune the theories and may lead to new ones. Does all of this make you a little nervous? Don't worry, these events are not predicted to occur for billions and billions of years.

Just a Theory?

You have just read about the incredible evidence supporting the big bang theory. Some people may say, "Well, it is just a theory." But you could explain to them just how much evidence there is to support that theory. The problem comes about because of a misunderstanding of the term *theory*. The term *theory* is too often used today in a casual, nonscientific way, as though no evidence exists to support the theory.

What do you mean when you say that you have a theory about something? Usually, you mean that you have an idea about how to explain something. You may suggest a theory about who kidnapped the actress in the late-night thriller, or you may have a theory about why Ms. Figueroa always looks tired when she delivers the mail on Monday morning. You also may have a theory about what the coach of the baseball team said to his pitcher after the team lost the championship game.

▶ **Figure 12.33**
Grocery cart crash.
Do you have a theory about what caused the ding in this girl's car door?

The theories that you develop about things are often tentative. That is, when you say that you have a theory about something, you may mean that you don't have much evidence. When you don't have much evidence, other people won't always agree with or share your theories. Nevertheless, it is fun to suggest clever ideas.

Scientists use the word *theory* in a very different way than most people do. Scientific theories are explanations that have strong evidence to support them. Sometimes scientists propose different theories to explain the same data. Over time, evidence generally accumulates that supports one theory over another. Sometimes evidence arises that refutes existing theories in favor of a new one.

Think about the following questions. Then share your thoughts with your class. Record the best ideas in your science notebook.

1. What are some other theories you might develop throughout a typical day?
2. How is a scientific theory different from a guess?

A good example of a scientific theory is the atomic theory. The atomic theory was an explanation developed in 1803 by the British teacher and chemist John Dalton. You may already be familiar with one of the most important ideas of Dalton's atomic theory. Dalton postulated that all matter in the universe is composed of tiny particles called atoms. This idea was revolutionary at the time Dalton first suggested it, but since then, physicists have accumulated an enormous body of evidence to support it. Part of that evidence is the result of scientists' modern ability to detect, manipulate, and even subdivide atoms. Even though Dalton did not predict that atoms could be subdivided into smaller pieces such as electrons and protons, the general outline of his theory still stands.

Another example of a solid scientific theory is the cell theory. You were introduced to the cell theory in the sidebar, The Development of Cell Theory, in chapter 6, Cells: The Building Blocks of Life. Cell theory states that (1) all living organisms are composed of one or more cells, (2) cells are the basic unit of life, and (3) all new cells come from preexisting cells through cell division. This is an example of a biological theory that is supported by an enormous body of evidence.

Strong evidence supports the atomic and cell theories, and no modern scientist questions them. Nevertheless, people still refer to these ideas as theories. Clearly, scientists use the word *theory* very differently from the way most nonscientists do.

▲ **Figure 12.34**
John Dalton (1766–1844). John Dalton developed the atomic theory. What separates a scientific theory from a nonscientific theory?

continued

Think about the following question. Then discuss your answer with your class.

3. How is the big bang theory like the atomic and cell theories?

Now you can see that a scientific theory is an idea that has been extensively tested and is supported by a large body of observations and evidence. A good theory explains data that scientists already know, and it explains additional data as they become known. In fact, a good theory also predicts new data and suggests new relationships that scientists may not have recognized. When multiple lines of evidence continue to support a theory, scientists describe the theory as mature and robust. That evidence solves problems because it has predictive power and makes sense across scientific disciplines. For example, there is consistency between the estimates of Earth's age and the time required for biological evolution.

There are several reasons why the big bang theory has survived as a strong scientific theory. First, a significant amount of evidence indicates that the big bang theory is an accurate explanation. As you already have seen, there currently is no other explanation besides the big bang to account for the data that scientists have collected and analyzed from the universe. Second, the big bang theory explains the evidence that scientists have seen and recorded as well as the new data scientists continue to collect. Third, the big bang theory successfully predicts new phenomena. That is, cosmologists' explanation for the origin, structure, and evolution of the universe continues to be supported. This is true even for evidence collected after the theory was proposed. For those reasons and others, scientists accept the big bang theory as a valid explanation of the observable universe.

Does this wide acceptance of the big bang theory mean that scientists have explained everything about the origin and evolution of the universe? Does it mean that every part of the explanation is correct? No, not necessarily. Scientists will continue to gather data about the universe to see how the data apply to the big bang theory. As new information about the universe becomes available, it will support or contradict the original explanation. If some information does not fit with the theory, scientists will have to modify the theory accordingly. In addition, new technologies and advances in science will enable scientists to support or refute the big bang theory.

So when people talk about explanations for things in the world around them, they need to consider whether they are talking about a theory as merely a plausible idea (as people typically use the term) or about a scientific theory (as scientists use the term). The difference between the two is quite large, indeed.

Reflect and Connect

Think about the following questions. Then discuss your answers with your class.

1. How is a scientific theory different from a theory as nonscientists often use the term? Give an example of each type.
2. Review the sidebar, The Future of the Universe, from the previous activity. In your opinion, is there experimental evidence for ideas scientists have for the end of the universe?
3. Do you think the big bang theory has enough evidence to support it? What additional evidence should scientists look for?
4. The major concept of this activity was an understanding of the term theory. Summarize the main idea of this activity in 1 sentence.

What's the Big Idea?

The study of the universe is complex. In this chapter, you have seen that scientists use knowledge from many disciplines of science to understand the universe. To many people, it may seem like a jumble of ideas. How could you organize the ideas from this chapter to help people understand the main ideas about the origin and evolution of the universe and the evidence that scientists have for their explanations?

In What's the Big Idea?, you and a partner create a chapter organizer that makes sense of the big ideas and shows how other ideas are linked together to support the ideas. You have seen chapter organizers at the beginning of each chapter of this book. Did you notice that this chapter does not have one? It is because you are going to make the chapter organizer for chapter 12.

Look back at the chapter organizers in this book and use them to guide your work. Your organizer does not have to be exactly like the ones shown. In fact, to receive an excellent grade for your work, you will have to add a few features.

▼ **Figure 12.35**
Students working on a chapter organizer. You will work with a partner to make a chapter organizer for this chapter. What would help you understand the flow of the chapter concepts? Construct your chapter organizer to explain the concepts of chapter 12.

This chapter organizer will demonstrate your understanding of what scientists know about the origin and evolution of the universe and how they know it. It also will help others understand those ideas.

Materials

For each team of two students

scratch paper

1 piece of poster or butcher paper

sticky notes

markers

2 copies of the Scoring Rubric for What's the Big Idea? handout

Process and Procedure

1. With your partner, review the What's the Big Idea? Scoring Rubric, which presents your teacher's expectations for your chapter organizer.

2. You already have the building blocks for your chapter organizer. Look back in your notebook at your responses to the Reflect and Connect questions that came at the end of each activity. The last question in each of those sections asked you to record the main idea of each activity in 1 sentence. Make a list of your responses on a piece of paper. You should have 5 of them.

3. Compare your responses with your partner's. Look at any comments that your teacher may have made about your answers. You may want to review an activity and add to or change some of your ideas. Refine your main ideas and decide on 1 statement per activity. Record each statement on a separate sticky note.

4. Participate in a class discussion about the task of creating a chapter organizer. Think about and discuss some of the types of chapter organizers with which you are familiar. Remember to use chapter organizers from this book as a guide (not as a template) for your organizer. Record your ideas in your notebook.

5. Plan your chapter organizer on a piece of scratch paper. You may want to use sticky notes so you can move your ideas around until you find the best place to write them permanently. Take time to incorporate ideas from both team members. When you are satisfied with your plan, use the markers and a large sheet of paper to complete your organizer, keeping in mind the time frame that your teacher has set. Use your scoring rubric to focus your work.

When you have completed your organizer, go over it with your partner. Check for accuracy and neatness and, most of all, how well it meets the expectations given on the scoring rubric.

6. When your plan is complete, hang your chapter organizer in your classroom.

7. As a class, examine each other's work.

CHAPTER 13

The Earth-Sun System

The Earth-Sun System

So far in unit 3, The Earth and Beyond, you have focused your learning on things very distant from Earth. You have learned how gravity brings matter together to make objects such as galaxies and stars. Your learning has included understanding the process in which stars begin nuclear fusion and the way stars begin making the elements listed on the periodic table. Indeed, nuclear fusion in the cores of stars followed by stellar explosions makes *all* of the elements and then spews fragments of matter and gas back into space. The process is shown in figure 13.1.

Star Formation Region DR6   Spitzer Space Telescope • IRAC
NASA / JPL-Caltech / S. Carey (Caltech)   ssc2004-18a

▶ **Figure 13.1**
Star-forming region.
Can gravity recycle this dust and matter into a new star?

Can gravity bring that matter together again and initiate another big bang? Will that matter make another star surrounded by planets? Recently, astronomers have observed other newly forming star systems in the Milky Way galaxy. What would a new star and its solar system be like?

To answer questions such as those, you don't have to go any farther than your own solar system. At the center of the solar system lies a bright yellow-white star, the Sun. It has been burning brightly for about 4.6 billion years. As you know, planets surround the Sun, and you live on the third planet, Earth. You are able to observe Earth in much detail, and geologists can study the fascinating evolution of the Earth-Sun system.

You may think that you studied only earth science in unit 3. Not true. You studied many disciplines, including physics, chemistry, astronomy, and cosmology. In this chapter, you have the opportunity to make connections to even more science disciplines. You will see how your previous learning is connected to geology and to biology. Science is often separated into discrete disciplines, but you have the chance in this chapter to see how science is truly multidisciplinary.

Goals for the Chapter

As you look at the connections to other sciences in chapter 13, you learn about the origin of and some important changes in the Earth-Sun system. You also learn how this close interaction might be linked to the evolution of life. You will have the opportunity to explore answers to these questions:

- What matter came together to form the Sun and the planets in our solar system?
- In what major ways has Earth changed since it formed 4.6 billion years ago?
- How did Earth end up with so much water at its surface?
- What are the relationships between the earliest life on Earth and the development of the atmosphere?
- Would scientists expect to find evidence for life on other planets, such as Mars? Why or why not?

Scientists of every type in many disciplines are studying the complex relationship and long history of the Earth-Sun system. You will study many of those relationships as you complete the following activities:

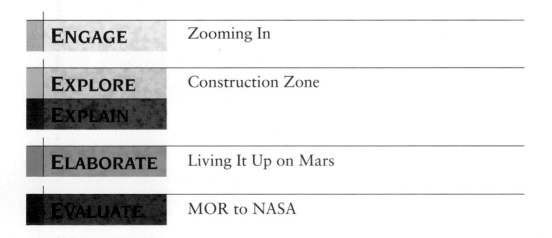

ENGAGE	Zooming In
EXPLORE	Construction Zone
EXPLAIN	
ELABORATE	Living It Up on Mars
EVALUATE	MOR to NASA

How can I better understand how Earth began, evolved, and became suitable for life?

◄◄
Zooming In
Key Idea:
We can use models and simulations to study how our solar system began.

The Earth-Sun System

EXPLORE

EXPLAIN ▶▶

Construction Zone

Key Ideas:

- Bodies in the solar system are made from different materials, all of which were originally in the protoplanetary disk.
- Earth has undergone major changes, which set the stage for it to become a life-supporting planet.

MOR to NASA

Key Ideas:

- Scientists must analyze data to make important decisions about life on other planets.
- Scientists must use evidence and reasoning to defend their ideas.

CHAPTER

13 Major Concepts

▶ The solar system formed from a disk of gas and dust 4.6 billion years ago.

▶ All elements in the universe are manufactured in stars and explosions of stars.

▶ Early Earth was very different from the Earth today.

▶ Life on Earth depends on energy from the Sun.

▶ Certain conditions are necessary for life.

Linking Question

How do conditions on Earth compare with conditions on Mars?

ELABORATE ▶▶▶

Living It Up on Mars

Key Idea:

Certain conditions are necesssary for life on our planet and those conditions may also support life on other planets.

Linking Question

How can I use what I have learned to predict and defend the possibility of life on Mars?

A key feature of the Earth-Sun system is life. As you will see, learning about the needs of life helps scientists think about the prospects for other life in other places. Those places could be in our solar system, in our galaxy, or in the distant reaches of the universe. Let's start by looking at evidence for formations of solar systems other than our own.

ENGAGE

Zooming In

Do you remember the Take a Closer Look activity in chapter 11, Coming Attraction—Gravity!? In that activity, you looked deeper into space around the Big Dipper. You were looking at images from the Hubble Space Telescope (HST), and you discovered that in an apparently empty area of the night sky, there were many distant galaxies and stars. Zooming In allows you to look again through the "eyes" of the HST. This time, however, you will visit the Orion Nebula. Recall that this nebula is an area of dust and gas where new stars are forming. Zoom in to this nebula with your class as you view a video clip made from images taken with the HST.

▶ **Figure 13.2**
Nebula NGC 3603. This spectacular image captures several stages in the formation of stars and other bodies in the star system.

Materials

For each team of two or three students

access to computer to view video clip from Student Resource CD (SRCD)

Process and Procedure

1. With your team, watch the video clip Zooming In on Orion. View the video clip several times.
2. Discuss with your team what you see in the video clip. Record your ideas in your science notebook.
3. Look closely at the last frame of the video clip.
   a. Draw a sketch of what you see.
   b. How is the last frame different from or similar to other features shown in the video clip? Note those differences or similarities in your sketch and highlight them.
4. Discuss with your team what you think this feature is and why you think so. Record your best ideas in your science notebook and be prepared to share them in a class discussion.
5. Participate in a class discussion about what you saw in the video clip. As a team, share what you think about the images and your responses to Steps 3–4. Add other ideas to your science notebook as you hear discussion from your classmates.

Reflect and Connect

1. What new knowledge or information has the HST provided? Base your answer on this engage activity and other activities in The Earth and Beyond unit.
2. You have seen evidence for the development of a solar system other than our own. What *conditions* would be necessary to *support life* as you know it on a planet in this distant solar system? To answer this question, complete the following steps:
   a. In your science notebook, make a list of conditions you think would be necessary to support life.
   b. Share your list with a partner.
   c. Add to your list any new conditions that you hear.
3. Watch the 2 video clips, Forming a Planetary Gap and Planet-forming Disks, found on your SRCD. The videos are artists' conceptions of what you saw in the actual images from the HST. Would you expect all of the planets that form to have the same chemical makeup? What might account for this?

Construction Zone

The last image of the video clip, Zooming In on Orion, was evidence of a region around a star that could be a newly forming solar system—a construction zone. Scientists call this area a **protoplanetary disk,** or **proplyd** for short. Figure 13.3 shows an image of a protoplanetary disk around a star 88 light-years away from Earth. This disk surrounds a star very similar to our Sun. As you have seen before, when new discoveries are made, new questions arise. You may be thinking of questions now.

When a solar system (or specifically, a planet) is in its very early stages of formation, what is its composition? Is it the same as the other planets in the solar system? From what you know about our solar system, what do you think? In Part I of Construction Zone, you have an opportunity to explore the answer to that question and others.

Early Earth was very different from what you see today. As you work through Parts II and III of this activity, you learn about what changes Earth has gone through and how geological processes have contributed to this changing planet. You also look at conditions that developed on Earth that made it "just right" for the beginnings of life.

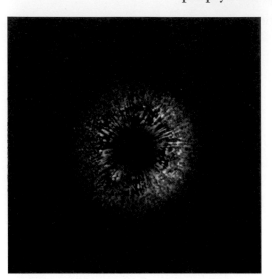

▲ **Figure 13.3**

Planetary systems in the making. This recent image from the HST reveals a protoplanetary disk surrounding a star very similar to our Sun.

Part I: A Stellar Snack Mix

Think back to that proplyd you first saw in the engage activity. Imagine the Sun as a newly forming star about 4.6 billion years ago. It is spinning, gathering in dust and gases and forming a proplyd. The Earth is one of those newly forming planets, or **protoplanets.** Also

▶ **Figure 13.4**

A distant solar system. In this artist's conception of a distant solar system, you can see the ring of dust that surrounds the central star. Planets are formed as dusty material in a large disk surrounding a star is pulled together by gravity.

within the disk are the beginnings of Mars, Jupiter, Saturn, and the rest of the objects in our solar system. Are all of the bodies in our solar system made of the same elements? Are those elements in the same proportion on each planet? Work with a team, using a model to study the distribution of matter in the new bodies of the solar system.

Materials
For each team of three students

1 scoop, about the size of a 16-oz margarine container

1 bowl or container to hold stellar snack mix

graph paper (optional)

computer with spreadsheet and graphing program (optional)

graphing calculator (optional)

Cautions

If you have food allergies, alert your teacher before getting any snack mix.

Process and Procedure

1. Assemble your team. Listen to your teacher's instructions for getting a big sample of stellar snack mix.
2. When it is your team's turn, go to the large container, scoop out some snack mix, and place it in your team's container. Don't eat any stellar snack mix yet!
    a. Work with your team to develop a plan to determine the percentage of each component of your stellar snack mix.

Caution If you have food allergies, alert your teacher before getting any snack mix.

Remember that a percent is a ratio of the *part* (the number of pieces of the component you are looking for) divided by the *whole* (the total number of snack mix pieces) multiplied by 100.

    b. Make a data table to organize all of your data and calculations.

    c. Have your teacher approve your plan and data table before you go to the next step.

3. After getting your teacher's approval, begin your procedure. As you work through your plan, keep asking yourself this question: How does this snack mix model represent a forming solar system?

4. Decide with your group the best way to represent your data with a graph. Each team member will make a graph. Consider these questions when you plan your graph.

- What type of graph will I make?
- Will I use a calculator or computer?
- Will I need graph paper?
- How will I label each part of my graph?
- Do I need a legend for my graph?
- What highlight comments will I make on my graph?

▶ **Figure 13.6**
Different types of graphs. Which type of graph best represents your data?

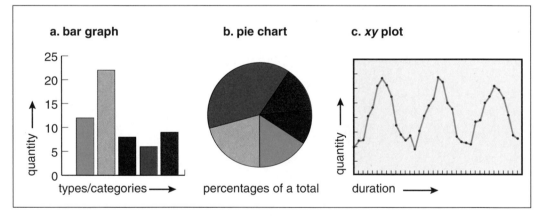

5. Have your teacher approve your plan before you make your graph. Gather your materials and graph your data. Everyone on the team must make a graph.

6. Discuss the following 3 questions with your team and record your own answers in your science notebook.

    a. What component of the stellar snack mix shows up most often? What percentage of the total is the component?

    b. What component is the rarest? What percentage of the total is the component?

    c. Do you think other groups will have the same results as your team? Why or why not?

7. Participate in a class discussion as each team reports its results.

8. Now that you have discussed results from each team, work with your partners to discuss how the activity compares with the formation of different objects that are found in solar systems.

   a. Your teacher came to class with a large container or bag of stellar snack mix. Imagine that your teacher's stellar snack mix represents all of the matter of the solar system. If the original container of stellar snack mix was all of the material in the solar system, what do you think the different pieces in the stellar snack mix represent? Explain your reasoning.

   b. Now imagine your teacher gathering items at a grocery store to make the stellar snack mix for your class. In the real "snack mix" of the solar system, where did the materials come from?

9. A solar system has a certain amount of matter that typically does not change. When a solar system forms, all of the ingredients are distributed among the different types of bodies in the solar system. Those bodies typically include a central star, planets, moons, and probably asteroids and comets.

   Now imagine that your teacher's initial container of stellar snack mix is all of the ingredients in a solar system and that your team represents a body in the solar system with its sampling of stellar snack mix. Think back to when your team got its scoop of snack mix and to the graphs created by different teams.

   a. How might your team's stellar snack mix be similar to how ingredients are distributed as bodies form in a new solar system? Use your graphs as evidence.

   b. How might your team's stellar snack mix be different from how ingredients are distributed during the formation of a solar system? Again, use your graphs as evidence.

10. What do you think Earth might have been like early in its existence? Write in your science notebook 2 changes that you think might have happened since then.

11. Scientists have also studied models to understand how Earth and the moon formed. The models are computer programs that allow scientists to use large amounts of data to simulate the early stages of solar system formation. Read Cosmic Recycling to learn the current theories about the formation of our solar system.

Cosmic Recycling

As you know, there may be many scientific theories to explain a phenomenon. Recall the theories for the end of the universe you read about in chapter 12, Cosmic Questions. One theory usually emerges as most accepted because of the evidence to support it. Like the theories you studied, there is convincing evidence in support of one theory for the formation of the solar system; it is called the nebular theory of solar system formation. The theory explains the formation of our solar system (as well as other similar solar systems) as emerging from a swirling cloud of interstellar dust and gas. The bodies that make up the solar system come from that cloud much like each sample of snack mix came from the same original sample.

The universe is a great example of a recycling plant. Raw materials of hydrogen and helium are in abundance, and eventually, gravity pulls them together to form a star. Nuclear fusion begins as the star turns on and the hydrogen and helium begin their nuclear transformations into heavier elements. You learned about those processes as you worked your way through unit 3 as well as other chapters. But have you ever thought of that overall process as a recycling process? You know that a star does not live forever. Depending on its mass, it may eventually explode as a supernova, causing rapid fusion of even heavier elements and spewing those elements out into space. Can you think of what might happen to this new cloud of gas and dust? Gravity may pull it back together to form another star or star system complete with planets! The cycle continues.

◀ **Figure 13.7**
Inside a forming solar system. In this artist's conception of a solar nebula, you can see the swirling gas and dust that will eventually come together as planets and other bodies in the system. How are these bodies like your stellar snack mix?

Part I

1. Think of the 2 descriptions mentioned in the last paragraph. The first part of the paragraph mentions a forming star and star system. The end of the paragraph mentions a star and star system complete with planets. What is the main difference between the original cloud of gas and dust and the second cloud that forms the star system with planets?

2. Continue reading Cosmic Recycling to learn how this recycling process leads to the formation of planets.

Topic: solar system formation
Go to: www.scilinks.org
Code: 1Inquiry631

The Milky Way, like other galaxies, originally contained just hydrogen and helium. With billions of years of cosmic recycling, our galaxy increased its content of heavier and heavier elements. Later generations of stars have a higher content of these heavier elements than the earlier generations. Our solar system is only 4.6 billion years old. When it was forming from recycled stellar litter, there were enough of the heavier elements to form the rocky planets in our solar system. Earth is one of those rocky planets, and the matter forming our planet came from this cosmic recycling plant.

This recycling process formed the cloud of gas and dust that eventually became our solar system. As the cloud of gas and dust collapsed, it started to spin. And much like an ice-skater pulling his or her arms in, the cloud of gas began to spin faster and faster, eventually flattening into a protoplanetary disk (see figure 13.8). Disturbances in this disk gave rise to the formation of the planets. Those processes—heating due to fusion, spinning, and flattening—explain the layout of our solar system. Our planets orbit in nearly the same plane, all in the same direction. Most planets spin on their axes in the same direction as well.

Since it takes billions of years for solar systems to form, scientists use computer technology to test their predictions. Scientists model these formations with computer programs that use large amounts of data to simulate the early stages of solar system formation.

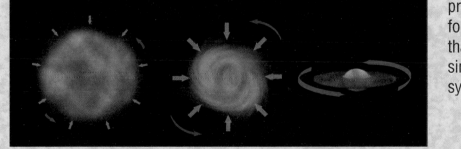

▲ **Figure 13.8 Collapsing cloud of dust to a protoplanetary disk.** This sequence of paintings shows the collapse of a cloud of gas and dust to form a protoplanetary disk. In (a), the original cloud is large and the rotation is very slow. The image in (b) shows how gravity causes the cloud to collapse, and like an ice-skater pulling his or her arms in, the cloud spins faster and faster. (c) The result is a spinning, flattened disk with the mass concentrated in the center. In our solar nebula, the hot, dense, central bulge became the Sun and the planets formed in the disk.

3. Could a solar system like ours have formed with the first generation of stars after the big bang? Explain your answer.

4. Think about the theory of the formation of our solar system. What role does technology play in allowing scientists to test this theory? Give specific examples of the technology used to test the theory.

5. How did our moon form? Read Moon Formation to answer this question.

READING

Moon Formation

Just as there are theories about the solar system, there are emerging theories about the formation of our moon. Several theories have been popular, including one that says that the moon formed from a chunk of Earth. According to that theory, a piece of Earth was blasted away during impact with a huge object about the size of Mars—the impactor. The impact would have generated enormous amounts of heat on both Earth and the impactor. What evidence do scientists have to support this theory? The composition of the moon is similar to that of the crust and mantle of Earth. An impact with such a large body could have sent a piece of Earth flying away from the surface. The gravity of Earth would have slowed it down and trapped it in an orbit around Earth.

▲ Figure 13.9 **Impact with Earth.** Current theories contend that the moon was formed as a result of an impact of a Mars-sized object with Earth.

Computer simulations have added to scientists' knowledge of the formation of our solar system as well as the formation of our moon. Recent studies using sophisticated computer simulations (and increased amounts of data) have led to a different theory. That theory asserts that the moon came not from a chunk of Earth that was blown away by an impact, but from the impactor itself. This new model claims that over 80 percent of the moon's composition came from material that was originally in the impactor. The new data explains some of the inconsistencies with the previous theory, including the chemical compositions of Earth and the moon. Currently, this is the most popular theory. As new and more advanced technologies become available (and new evidence is found), those theories will be carefully tested and likely modified and improved.

Topic: moon formation
Go to: www.scilinks.org
Code: 1Inquiry633

◀ **Figure 13.10**
Artist's conception of Earth half an hour after the giant impact. After this impact, did the moon form mostly from Earth's materials or from the impactor's materials?

Part I continued

6. Why might an impactor and Earth have different chemical compositions if they both originated in the same protoplanetary disk? Explain your answer.

7. The moon has no easily vaporized ingredients such as water and methane. Use your knowledge of the events that led to the formation of the early moon and your prior knowledge about gravity to explain why the moon has no easily vaporized ingredients on its surface.

Part II: Early Earth

You have learned that Earth was formed about 4.6 billion years ago from a protoplanetary disk that contained all of the matter that makes up our solar system. You also know that early Earth was very different from today's Earth. What might some of those differences be? One difference is that there was no life on early Earth. Life, however, did evolve, so the conditions on Earth must have changed. What conditions changed to make it possible for the evolution of life on Earth? One of those conditions was the presence of water.

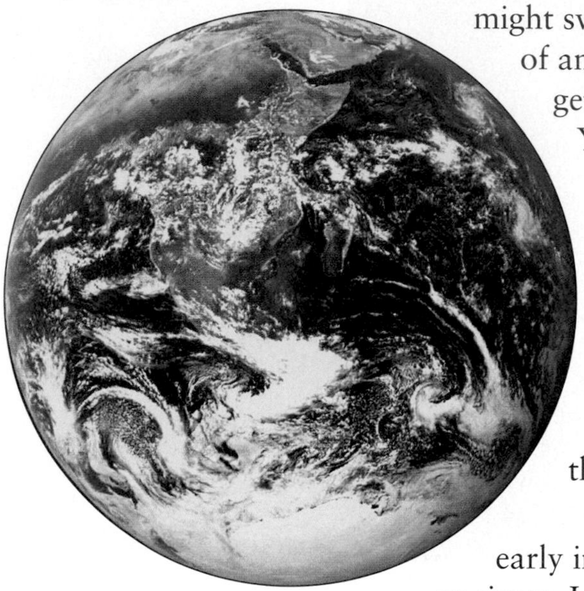

What would a warm summer day be like without any water? That might be hard to imagine. Depending on where you live, you might swim at a lake, river, or pool or run along the shore of an ocean. Even if no water is nearby, you still have to get a drink of water as you become hot and thirsty! You could not live without water.

You are used to having water at the surface of Earth. In fact, over 70 percent of Earth's surface is covered by water. However, water did not always cover Earth, particularly just after it formed. At that time, Earth was most likely hot and was being intensely bombarded by asteroids. Just look at the moon—its pocked and cratered surface is a relict of that time of intense asteroid bombardment.

So if there wasn't much water at the surface of Earth early in its history, there could not have been oceans, lakes, or rivers. How did water get to the surface of Earth? In Part II, you and your partner explore this question.

▼ **Figure 13.11**
Earth from the *Apollo 17* mission.
How was early Earth different from today's Earth?

Materials
For each team of two students

2 pairs of safety goggles

1 150-mL beaker

1 watch glass to fit on top of beaker

2 wire gauze squares

1 pair of beaker tongs or mitts to handle hot glassware

1 ring stand and ring

1 Bunsen burner

sample of copper sulfate

1 striker or matches

Cautions

Tie back long hair and secure loose clothing while working with a laboratory burner. Use caution while handling hot objects. Dispose of used matches properly. Copper sulfate is mildly toxic. Do not touch the chemicals. Wear your safety goggles. Wash your hands after conducting this experiment.

Process and Procedure

1. With your partner, participate as your teacher directs a class discussion.
2. Gather your materials and read the complete procedure for this activity. Ask your teacher for clarification of any step you do not understand.
3. Put on your safety goggles and look closely at your sample of copper sulfate. In your science notebook, write a complete description of the substance.
4. Place your sample of copper sulfate in your beaker and record in your science notebook the mass of the sample and beaker. Be sure to label your data with the proper units and descriptions.
   a. As you heat your sample, you will record any changes that you see in the sample of copper sulfate and in the beaker and cover.
   b. Place your beaker and sample on the wire gauze and place it on the ring and ring stand. Place the watch glass over the mouth of the beaker (see figure 13.12).

Wear safety goggles while working in the lab.

Caution

◀ **Figure 13.12**
Experiment setup. Your lab setup should look like this.

c. Light the burner and adjust it so that you have a blue flame.

d. Place the burner under the ring stand, ring, and wire gauze.

e. Record your observations in your science notebook.

f. After about 1 minute of heating, use tongs to carefully remove the watch glass from the beaker. Lay it aside but be careful; the watch glass may be hot.

g. Continue heating until the sample turns white. Record any additional observations.

h. When you finish heating the sample, turn off the burner and allow the beaker to cool. It will cool more quickly if it is removed from the ring stand and placed on a cool wire gauze.

5. Meet with your partner to make sure you both have the observations written in your science notebooks.

6. Answer the following questions as a team while your sample cools and record your best answers in your science notebook.

a. What did you observe forming on the bottom of the watch glass?

b. Where do you think it came from? Why do you think so?

c. Look back at your initial observations of the copper sulfate. Did you think that this new substance was initially present in the blue copper sulfate? Why or why not?

7. After your beaker has cooled, record the new mass. Be sure to label your 2 mass measurements so that you know which one was recorded before heating and which one was recorded after heating.

8. Work with your partner to answer these questions about your sample.

a. What happened to the mass of your beaker and sample?

b. What can account for this change in mass?

9. Do you think that all teams' samples have the same change in mass? Justify your answer.

10. How can you explain the change in mass during heating? Why did the mass change, and where did the missing mass go? Explain your answer using evidence and observations from your experiment.

11. Do you think that all materials change mass when they are heated? Why or why not?

12. You learned in the introduction to this part that early Earth did not have water on its surface. How might the investigation in Part II model how Earth came to have water on its surface? Think about geologic systems with which you are familiar to formulate your ideas.

13. Read Volcanoes and Icy Comets—They Make a Planet Wet! This reading will discuss current ideas about how the surface of our planet became over 70 percent covered with water. Take notes as you read, writing a sentence to summarize each paragraph.

READING

Volcanoes and Icy Comets— They Make a Planet Wet!

Early Earth was probably not a very hospitable place. The rocky outer part of Earth is called the **lithosphere.** The lithosphere of Earth was under siege from crashing chunks of rock from space. Those rocks are called **meteorites,** and they exploded on impact with Earth. What you think of as continents were only small fragments of their current size, and they were most likely shaken by volcanic eruptions and vast outpourings of lava. Because of the very different atmosphere, dangerous ultraviolet rays would have penetrated to all exposed surfaces on the planet. Moreover, until later, there were probably no large bodies of water such as oceans to harbor life.

In contrast, today people are very used to water at the surface of Earth. All of that water is called the **hydrosphere,** which includes all lakes, rivers, oceans, ice caps, and glaciers, in addition to water in the ground. But how did this change occur? That is one of the exciting questions that geologists ask.

Even though hydrogen and oxygen are common in the solar system and in the Milky Way, Earth is unusual because it has liquid water that covers the planet. Planetary geologists have evidence of two important ways that water could have built up and accumulated on Earth.

One line of evidence comes from the outer reaches of the solar system as **comets.** Comets consist largely of rock and ice (see figure 13.13). Early in the solar system, there were probably many more comets than there are today. Those comets would have been larger and would have contained more water in the form of ice than comets today. Some planetary geologists think that much of Earth's water could have come from comets crashing into Earth. That theory is certainly reasonable, but it is difficult to know how much of the water could have arrived here in that way.

Another line of evidence comes from meteorites. Most people think of meteorites as chunks of rock or metal that come from outer space, streak through the atmosphere, and then smash into Earth. What does that have to do with water on the surface of Earth? Meteorites are leftovers from the makings of the solar system over 4.6 billion years ago. Studying meteorites allows scientists to see the earliest matter in the solar

◀ **Figure 13.13**
Comet Hale-Bopp. Several comets are famous, but the last spectacular comet seen from Earth was Comet Hale-Bopp in 1997. What did the early bombardment of comets bring to Earth?

system. Some types of meteorites contain water. Scientists infer from this fact that early Earth was made from the same ingredients and, therefore, must have contained water as well. See figure 13.14 for a close-up view of water contained in a meteorite that landed near some boys who were outside playing basketball.

How would water get out of Earth to make standing water on Earth's surface? As you continue to read, think about how you got water out of your sample of copper sulfate. A likely way for this to happen to Earth is by volcanic eruption. Volcanoes spew hot, molten rock from Earth's interior to the surface as lava. Volcanoes also

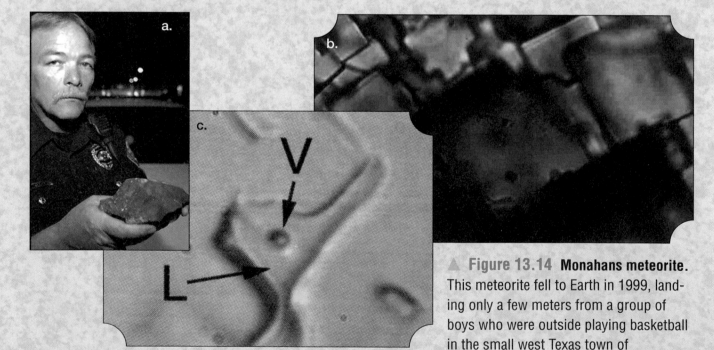

▲ **Figure 13.14 Monahans meteorite.** This meteorite fell to Earth in 1999, landing only a few meters from a group of boys who were outside playing basketball in the small west Texas town of Monahans. (a) Local law enforcement personnel took the meteorite into custody. Scientists from the National Aeronautics and Space Administration (NASA) cut the meteorite to examine the inside, which had not been contaminated by Earth. (b) Scientists discovered blue salt crystals inside the meteorite. The crystals were blue due to the intense radiation exposure in space. Upon closer examination, the scientists found evidence of (c) water droplets trapped inside the salt crystal. In (c), the area labeled "L" indicates the water droplet and "V" is a vapor or gas bubble in the water. The width of the area marked is only about one-fourth the width of a human hair.

emit massive amounts of gas to Earth's atmosphere. Those gases are mostly water vapor (H_2O steam), with lesser amounts of gases such as carbon dioxide (CO_2), sulfur dioxide (SO_2), hydrogen sulfide (H_2S), hydrogen (H_2), nitrogen (N_2), and methane (CH_4). This process of getting the gas out of a planetary body such as Earth is called **outgassing.** An example of gases leaving the Augustine volcano in southwest Alaska is shown in figure 13.15.

There are minerals in Earth's crust that contain water in much the same way the copper sulfate did in your previous experiment. The intense heat of the magma releases the water—just as you did when you heated the copper sulfate. However, the steam produced from the volcano shown in figure 13.15 is produced largely in another way. Magma (molten rock) moving from Earth's interior carries water molecules to Earth's surface. Those water molecules are released as a vapor (steam) by volcanoes (see figure 13.15).

How might volcanic outgassing have contributed to the increase in water on Earth? Scientists think that shortly after Earth formed, the planet would have contained a lot of water and other gases. Those gases would have been transported to Earth's surface by volcanic eruption. As the steam and water vapor built up in the early atmosphere, the water vapor would have gathered to make clouds. That process would have led to condensation of the water vapor, and the condensate would have fallen to Earth as rain. Thus begins the water cycle. If you had left the watch glass on your beaker in the activity with copper sulfate, you would have had "rain" in your beaker!

Volcanoes contributed not only to the water on our planet's surface, but also to our atmosphere. The first bits of atmosphere on Earth were probably linked closely to the earliest volcanic eruptions. The early atmosphere contained large amounts of water vapor and carbon dioxide due to the abundance of volcanic activity. After some time, water condensed as clouds and rain, which led to larger and larger pools of water on Earth. With more rain, the pools grew to oceans.

▲ Figure 13.15 **Augustine volcano in southwest Alaska.** Note the plume of volcanic gases, mostly steam, exiting the crater at the top of the volcano.

1. In what ways did erupting volcanoes change early Earth?

2. Recall your experiment when you heated copper sulfate. How was that experiment similar to the effect of volcanoes on the early atmosphere of Earth? How was it different? Make a T-table in your science notebook to organize your answers.

3. The images in figures 13.16 and 13.17 were taken from Mars. Figure 13.16 shows a view of the largest volcano in the solar system, Olympus Mons. This is one of several massive volcanoes on Mars. Olympus Mons is 26 kilometers (km) high, or about 3 times higher than the highest mountain on Earth, Mount Everest. Figure 13.17 was taken from the surface of Mars by the Mars Pathfinder. It shows gentle ripples of thin, high clouds. Scientists also know that Mars is now very cold. From these observations, what is your evidence about an atmosphere on Mars?

◀ **Figure 13.16 Olympus Mons on Mars.** This image shows the giant volcano, Olympus Mons, on the surface of Mars. The summit crater is on the upper left, and the flanks of the volcano spread away from the summit crater. Including the part of the volcano to the left (not shown), Olympus Mons covers an area about the size of Colorado. At 26 km high, it is about three times taller than Mount Everest.

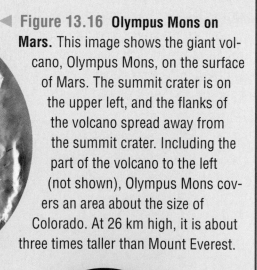

▶ **Figure 13.17 Thin, high clouds above Mars.** This image was taken from the surface of Mars by the Mars Pathfinder.

4. To learn more about how other bodies in the solar system formed similarly to Earth, read the sidebar, Geology in Outer Space.

Geology in Outer Space

Other bodies in the solar system probably formed in a similar way to Earth. How do geologists know this? The planets are made of similar materials (they all were separated from the same "stellar snack mix"), and in several cases, scientists can see clear examples of volcanoes on other planets (see the figures). Mars and Venus are adjacent to Earth, and they probably have histories most similar to that of Earth. For example, planetary geologists have shown that there are volcanoes on both Mars and Venus.

Maat Mons on Venus. The massive volcano Maat Mons is on Venus. Lava flows cover the vast plains at the base of the volcano for hundreds of kilometers and extend back to the summit of Maat Mons. Maat Mons is about 8 km high, larger than any volcano on Earth.

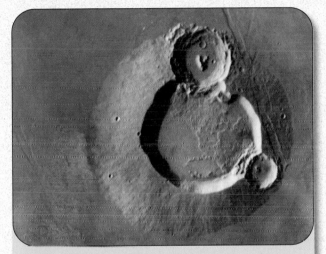

Ulysses Patera on Mars. This image is of the volcano Ulysses Patera on the surface of Mars. It is much smaller than Olympus Mons, shown in figure 13.16. This volcano has two impact craters on the sides of its summit. Which is older—the volcano or the craters? Can you tell?

A plume of gases has been observed erupting from a volcano on the surface of Io, a moon of Jupiter (see the figure). This volcano is known as Pillan Patera and has shown evidence of being an active volcano in every image taken since 1979. In fact, volcanoes are so active on the surface of Io that images taken of the surface have shown no impact craters. Lava flows have completely covered all impact craters! Io is the most volcanically active of all moons and planets in the solar system.

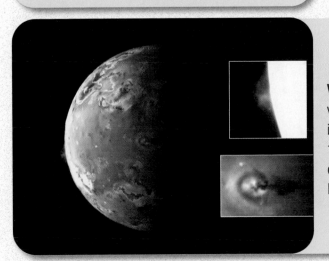

Volcano on Io, a moon of Jupiter. An erupting volcanic plume on the left side of the photograph is shown in a box. The volcanic plume is about 140 km high. The circular feature near the center of the image is another massive volcano, Prometheus.

SIDEBAR

Part III: Early Life

It would not have been fun to be alive on planet Earth in its infant stages! In fact, it would have been impossible to survive—the conditions were much too harsh. You require certain things to live, but you know that the first life on Earth was not human. Those first living organisms were much simpler than the plants and animals you see today. Can you imagine what early Earth would have looked like with no plants and animals and just the early development of water collecting on its surface (see figure 13.18)? What were the first organisms, and how did our Earth change to become favorable for that life to evolve? Work with a partner as you learn about the changes that created environmental conditions allowing life to evolve and be sustained. You already learned many of them in earlier chapters, so this will be a chance for you to demonstrate how much you remember and how well you can apply those things to new learning.

▼ **Figure 13.18**
Early Earth. Imagine Earth with no plants and animals. What would the first forms of life have been like?

Materials

For each team of two students

2 copies of Bare Elements of the Solar System handout

Process and Procedure

1. Meet with your partner and review the list you made in Question 2 from the Reflect and Connect questions in the engage activity, Zooming In. What conditions are necessary to support life? Add to the list anything new that you may have thought of. What you think is most important should be listed first. Be prepared to justify your list and the ranking.

2. Participate in a class discussion. Did everyone list the same conditions in the same order? What were the top 5 conditions listed by the class? List these in your notebook.

3. Obviously, living things have needs. In the previous steps, you may have thought about the things that you and your family members require to live. You may have thought of essential things in your life, such as food, shelter, and clothes. But you also may have thought about other living organisms on Earth. Obviously, the many types of organisms on our planet have different needs. To learn what some of those needs are, complete the following tasks:

   a. Join your partner and obtain copies of the Bare Elements of the Solar System handout.

   b. Look at the categories across the top of the table. Note that the meteorite is a rare type because of the amount of carbon it contains. The sample discussed in your handout and the photograph in figure 13.19 is the Murray meteorite.

   c. Discuss with your partner what each item is.

   d. Write in your science notebook possible similarities and differences among the objects.

4. Look at the list of elements down the left side of the table. Record in your science notebook your answers to the following questions:

   a. How many elements are listed? How many elements are there in the periodic table of the elements?

   b. From top to bottom, what pattern do you see in the arrangement of elements?

▲ **Figure 13.19**

The Murray meteorite. This sample of the Murray meteorite is about the size of a golf ball. This meteorite is a rare, carbon-rich variety that is featured in your handout, Bare Elements of the Solar System.

5. Write in your science notebook brief answers to the following questions. In each answer, use a figure or percentage from the table as your evidence.
   a. What are the 2 most common elements in the solar system?
   b. What are the 4 most common elements in bone or muscle tissue?
   c. Is iron more abundant in the solar system, the whole Earth, or a leaf? Explain why your answer does or does not make sense to you.
   d. In chapter 5, Star Material, you learned how nuclear fusion involving helium nuclei and hydrogen nuclei in the cores of stars produces higher-mass elements. Figure 13.20 shows some key reactions in the cores of stars.

$$3\,^{4}_{2}\text{H} \longrightarrow \,^{12}_{6}$$

$$^{12}_{6}\text{C} + \,^{4}_{2}\text{He} \longrightarrow \text{O}$$

$$^{16}_{8}\text{O} + \,^{4}_{2}\text{He} \longrightarrow$$

$$^{20}_{10}\text{Ne} + \,^{4}_{2}\text{He} \longrightarrow$$

$$^{16}_{8}\text{O} + \,^{16}_{8}\text{O} \longrightarrow$$

$$^{12}_{6}\text{C} + \,^{16}_{8}\text{O} \longrightarrow$$

▲ **Figure 13.20** **Table of reactions.** The table shows examples of key nuclear fusion reactions in stars. What are the fusion products for each reaction?

Copy the table in figure 13.20 into your science notebook. For each reaction in figure 13.20, write in the table what element is produced by the nuclear fusion reaction. Be sure to include the correct mass number and atomic number with the element symbol.
   e. Which of the elements listed in your Bare Elements handout are produced by the fusion reactions in figure 13.20?
   f. You have learned about the role of supernovae in making elements. (Remember that a supernova is the spectacular explosion of a high-mass star.) Is the rarity of high-mass stars and supernovae reflected in the contents of the solar system? Why or why not?
   g. Compared with the entire solar system, what materials or items in the table tend to have the highest contents of high-mass elements such as uranium and lead?

6. You learned in chapter 6, Cells: The Building Blocks of Life, that carbon is essential for life because all life is made up of carbon-based molecules such as those shown in figure 13.21. But is carbon in only living things? To answer that question, complete the following tasks.

Discuss the following with your partner and write brief answers in your science notebook. In each answer, use a figure or percentage from the table as your evidence.

a. Rank the 10 categories across the top of the table by the percentage of carbon, from highest to lowest.

b. Turn to 2 new facing pages in your science notebook. Make a T-table on the left-hand page using the headings "Things That Did Not Live" and "Things That Did Live."

c. Place each of the 10 items in the Bare Elements handout in the T-table by deciding if the item was ever alive.

d. On the right-hand page, write 1 sentence to explain why you placed each item in the column you did. If you were not sure about an item, write the reason for your uncertainty. It's OK to be unsure—what is important is to try to write your reason clearly.

Recall what you learned about the building blocks of life in chapter 6. Read the sidebar, Carbon Rocks!, to learn more about carbon in nonliving things.

e. Things that are alive must have carbon in them. On the other hand, is it true to say that if something has carbon, it must be alive? Explain your answer with evidence and examples from the table.

7. Discuss the following questions with your partner. Write in your science notebook thoughts and ideas from your class discussion.

a. Think back to Part I. Which column in the handout is most analogous to the large container of stellar snack mix that your teacher brought to class? Explain your answer.

b. Thinking back to Part I again, which column or columns of the handout are most analogous to the scoops of stellar snack mix obtained by your group? Explain your answer.

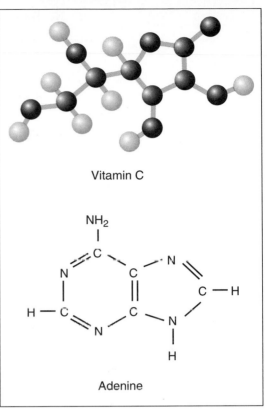

Vitamin C

Adenine

▲ Figure 13.21
Models of the molecule for vitamin C and adenine. These two models of molecules show examples of essential carbon-based molecules, vitamin C and adenine. Vitamin C (top) has the formula $C_6H_8O_6$, and the atom model of this molecule shows carbon (black), oxygen (red), and hydrogen (white) atoms. Adenine (bottom) is an essential building block of DNA and RNA in all organisms. The adenine molecule consists of five carbon atoms, five nitrogen atoms, and five hydrogen atoms.

8. Imagine an old carbon star that was in our neighborhood of the Milky Way. It was older than our solar system (older than 4.6 billion years) and was emitting carbon and other matter into space. How do you think the carbon could get from that star and then to the surface of Earth to be part of organisms such as forests and our bodies?

9. You have seen that carbon is essential for life and living things and that nonliving things have carbon as well. But where did the carbon come from? Is all of the carbon on Earth today from the original matter that made up our planet? The next reading, Carbon: Stellar Litter *and* a Building Block of Life, will answer those questions. Take turns reading each paragraph with your partner. One partner should read 1 paragraph, and the other partner should summarize the paragraph. Write these summaries in your science notebook. Switch roles for each paragraph.

Carbon Rocks!

Carbon is an element essential to life. So it's not surprising to see carbon in the chemistry of a living thing, such as a leaf or a human bone. But why would carbon also be found in a rock such as limestone or in a rock from outer space?

Well, carbon is found in virtually all geologic settings, whether or not there is life. Carbon is just another elemental ingredient of rocks formed in that geologic setting. For example, meteorites are fragments of rock that have fallen to Earth and been recovered. Some types of meteorites have a wide variety of carbon-based molecules, such as amino acids or sugars, mixed in with other rock and mineral pieces. Some meteorite minerals also consist of carbon, but scientists surely don't know of life in outer space that would have brought carbon to the meteorites.

Minerals are another geologic material that consists of carbon. For example, you may be familiar with diamonds, as seen in the figure. Diamonds are the hardest material in nature; they are used on saw blades to cut through rock and cement. Diamonds form at high temperatures and pressures deep within Earth, where there is no evidence for life. Diamonds are brought to Earth's surface in rare and spectacular volcanic eruptions. Most diamonds are mined in Africa and Russia, but they are also found on most other continents. This includes the central United States.

In contrast, living organisms are able to gather and concentrate carbon in their bodies. After the remains of the organisms are hardened to rock, that rock can display very high levels of carbon.

For example, coal is a familiar rock that consists mostly of carbon. The geologic record has abundant evidence for forests and swamps. With time, this plant material gets buried under more and more layers of rocks. The plants are compressed and heated, slowly turning into a soft, dark rock (see the figure of rock layers). This soft rock is coal. When

A spectacular diamond. Diamonds are the hardest material in nature, and they consist entirely of carbon.

taken from the ground, coal will burn and make a very hot fire, which is why it is an important source of energy for many people.

Limestone is another rock type with a lot of carbon. Most typically, limestone consists of fragments of shells that are "glued" together and hardened into a rock. The shell fragments are often from animals that lived in a marine setting, such as snails, clams, or corals. Those animals remove dissolved calcium (Ca), carbon (C), and oxygen (O) from the water in order to make their shells. That process is then reflected in the chemical formula of their shells. This is indicated by the formula $CaCo_3$. As you see from that formula and in the handout, carbon is an important element in limestone.

Black layer of coal sandwiched between other geologic layers of sandstone. Coal is the geologic evidence for an ancient forest or swamp that was compressed into a dense layer. Coal consists largely of carbon from trees and plants.

Carbon: Stellar Litter *and* a Building Block of Life

You learned earlier that meteorites often contain water. But what else do they contain? Recall that meteorites are leftovers from the formation of our solar system 4.6 billion years ago. An asteroid is one of those leftover chunks of rock still floating around the solar system. An example is the asteroid Gaspra, shown in figure 13.22.

Geologists study meteorites for many reasons. One reason meteorites are important to study is that some of them contain carbon-based molecules. In some cases, amino acids and sugarlike molecules have been found in carbon-rich meteorites. On Earth, compounds such You learned earlier that meteorites often contain water. But what else do they contain? Recall that meteorites are leftovers from the formation of our solar system 4.6 billion years

ago. An asteroid is one of those leftover chunks of rock still floating around the solar system. An example is the asteroid Gaspra, shown in figure 13.22. as those help to form the web of life. Careful work has documented that the carbon-based molecules are not from contamination after the meteorite landed. The molecules were part of the interstellar material that made up planets in the solar system.

You can see the ingredients of a meteorite when you cut it open. Note in figure 13.23 all of the little specks and blobs. This meteorite sample is somewhat wider than a golf ball, so the specks and blobs are about 1-3 millimeters (mm) across. When geologists look through a microscope at a meteorite (see figure 13.24), they can identify the blobs as small pieces of rock and minerals. Geologists call them chondrules.

◄ **Figure 13.22 A true leftover from the formation of our solar system.** The asteroid Gaspra has been orbiting the Sun for 4.6 billion years. An asteroid or a meteoroid is a body still in orbit—it becomes a meteorite when it hits Earth. Gaspra is about 18 km long from lower left to upper right, and the Sun is shining on Gaspra from the right. You can also see numerous craters, the result of Gaspra's impact with smaller rocks. This image was taken in 1991 during the Galileo mission. The primary goal of the Galileo mission was to study Jupiter and its moons.

◀ **Figure 13.23 Leoville meteorite.** The photograph shows a cut and polished surface of the Leoville meteorite. The total width of the slab is a bit greater than a golf ball. Note the light-colored globules and spheres. These are called chondrules. The darker material between them is called matrix.

Between the chondrules, geologists see dark material that they call matrix. What is this matrix made of? A lot of the matrix is carbon!

Most of the carbon in the matrix is the mineral graphite, which is what you use in your pencil. Another form of carbon in the matrix is much rarer: diamond. On Earth, diamond forms only at high pressures deep in Earth. The diamond included in this matrix also must indicate high temperatures and pressures from an ancient star explosion. Another carbon mineral in the matrix is extremely rare on Earth. It is silicon carbide (SiC), a mineral made up of silicon and carbon.

◀ **Figure 13.24 The Semarkona meteorite.** This is the Semarkona meteorite as viewed through a microscope. This meteorite is similar to the one shown in figure 13.23. The light gray blobs and circles are chondrules, and the dark material between the chondrules is matrix.

10. What can you learn from studying carbon-rich meteorites that you cannot learn by just looking at Earth?

11. Think back to the theories for the formation of the moon. Remember that some scientists thought that during the formation of the solar system about 4.6 billion years ago, the moon formed when a massive body, perhaps the size of a small planet, crashed into Earth. When you look at the moon, you see massive craters pocking the moon's surface (see figure 13.25). The craters are evidence that the moon has a long history of intense bombardment by meteorites, rocks, and dust.

    Would you expect to find any carbon on the moon? From the paragraph above, provide 2 lines of evidence for your answer.

12. Look back at your list that you made in Step 1. Did you list carbon? Maybe not, but you may have listed food. Recall from chapter 7, Cells Are Busy Places, that you get carbon from the food that you eat. Did you list air, carbon dioxide, or oxygen? Those are obvious needs for plants and animals. A Breath of Fresh Air describes how our atmosphere balanced in a way that led to the first life and eventually to the complex living organisms that are seen on Earth today. Continue reading with your partner following the procedure in Step 9.

▼ **Figure 13.25**
Moon's south pole. This is a view of the moon's south pole, which is not visible from Earth. Would you expect to find any carbon on the moon?

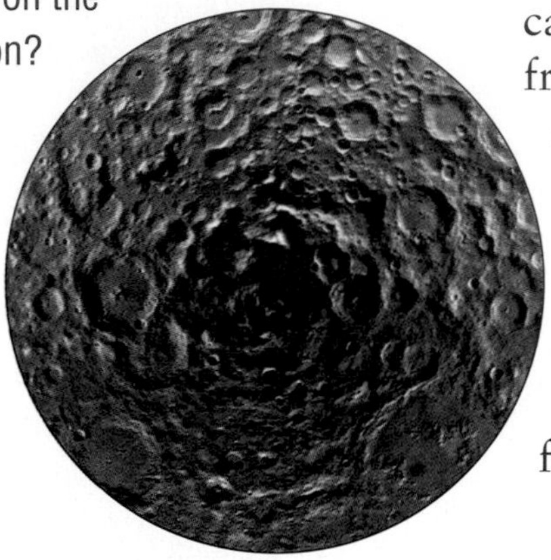

READING

A Breath of Fresh Air

"It's time for a breath of fresh air!" You can do this now by stepping outside your school building and taking a deep breath. But what if you tried this on early Earth? Would it have been possible for an organism like you to get some fresh air? To think more about that question, look at the pie charts in figure 13.26.

An **atmosphere** is a thin layer of different gases that surround a planet. The pie chart in figure 13.26a shows Earth's earliest atmosphere. Compare that atmosphere with the chemistry of our current atmosphere in figure 13.26b. Geologists spend a lot of time and effort gathering evidence about Earth's early atmosphere. From the pie charts, you should see a few key differences compared with today.

First, carbon dioxide and water vapor were more plentiful in early Earth's atmosphere than they are today. Both carbon dioxide and water vapor have been steadily removed from the atmosphere. Second, the level of oxygen has increased to 21 percent compared with the less

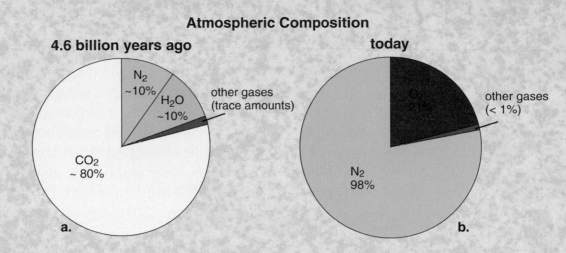

Atmospheric Composition

4.6 billion years ago

N₂ ~10%

H₂O ~10%

other gases (trace amounts)

CO₂ ~ 80%

a.

today

O₂ 21%

other gases (< 1%)

N₂ 98%

b.

▲ **Figure 13.26 Atmospheric composition of early Earth and today.** These two pie charts show estimates of the atmospheric gases (a) in the atmosphere of early Earth and (b) in our atmosphere today. What are the key differences in the two conditions?

than 1 percent on early Earth. In fact, it is this increase in oxygen that allows you to take a deep breath of fresh air today!

How did Earth's atmosphere become enriched with oxygen? Surely volcanoes have contributed huge amounts of gas to our atmosphere. Can volcanic outgassing be the only thing responsible for the change? Volcanoes add mostly water and carbon dioxide to the atmosphere. Scientists also know from observations that volcanoes do not add very much oxygen. So whatever took carbon dioxide out of the atmosphere removed carbon dioxide much faster than volcanoes could add it back. In addition, the process created a lot of oxygen. Volcanoes alone cannot account for this.

Think about your activities in chapter 7 with *Anacharis* and the reaction of photosynthesis. What are the reactants and what are the products of photosynthesis? That's right—photosynthesizing organisms such as *Anacharis* remove carbon dioxide from the atmosphere and give off oxygen. That overall pattern is consistent with the change from early Earth's atmosphere to our current atmosphere. In your *Anacharis* experiment, you actually simulated this change when you measured an increase in

oxygen level in the water. The process that caused this increase was photosynthesis. Your *Anacharis* removed carbon dioxide from the water and produced oxygen gas. In a sense, your experiment simulated a key process in the 4.6 billion years of evolution of our atmosphere!

When you think about photosynthesis, you probably recall organisms on Earth today—plants. Of course, your *Anacharis* is an aquatic plant, one that lives in water. And *Anacharis* produces oxygen during photosynthesis. However, there is one problem with the idea that photosynthesizing plants caused an increase in oxygen levels in the atmosphere. The snag comes from geologic evidence that shows that plants have been on Earth only during the most recent 10 percent of Earth's history. That is just the last 450 million years. How then can scientists account for the clear geologic evidence of photosynthesis over at least the past 80 percent of the history of Earth? That evidence indicates that photosynthesis has occurred for the past 3.5 billion years, much longer than the 450 million years that Earth has had plants.

Well, you are in luck. Again, the geologic evidence is strong in this regard. The answer is a common photosynthesizing bacteria called

cyanobacteria (blue-green algae). They use energy from the Sun, take in carbon dioxide, and give off gaseous oxygen. The oxygen gas that they release became concentrated in the early atmosphere. You may have examined cyanobacteria when you studied the cell in chapter 6. Study the graph in figure 13.27. What trends do you see?

Cyanobacteria have membranes that contain chlorophyll that are similar to the chloroplasts found in plants. The membranes allow cyanobacteria to carry out photosynthesis. Scientists hypothesize that chloroplasts in algae and plants originated as cyanobacteria. You can learn why scientists think cyanobacteria are the ancestors

of chloroplasts by reading the sidebar, The Origin of Eukaryotes, in chapter 6.

Virtually all ecosystems found on Earth today contain cyanobacteria. Present-day examples of cyanobacteria resemble the fossils of the past (see figure 13.28). The geologic record shows that cyanobacteria have been photosynthesizing and making oxygen for about the past 3.5 billion years (3.5×10^9 years). They were joined in photosynthesis by land plants only somewhat recently, about 450 million years ago (450×10^6 years). At that time, the levels of oxygen in the atmosphere had finally reached levels close to those observed today.

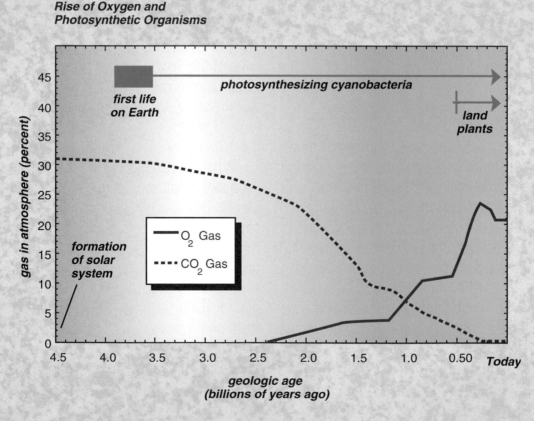

▲ **Figure 13.27** **Timelines showing geologic ages of key events on Earth.** Notice from this graph that there is no evidence yet for life in the solar system from its formation (4.6 billion years ago) through about 3.9–3.5 billion years ago. This represents the first 15–20 percent of Earth's history. About 80–85 percent of the history of life on Earth consisted only of bacteria. Only the final 10 percent of Earth's history (0.5 billion years, or 500 million years) includes more complex, multicellular plants. Look at the trends of carbon dioxide and oxygen in the atmosphere of Earth. Geologic evidence indicates that oxygen did not begin to increase in the atmosphere until about 2.4 billion years ago. This is much later than the first evidence of photosynthesizing cyanobacteria. Only recent increases in oxygen (the last 500 million years) link with the colonization of land by photosynthesizing plants.

Geologists have found fossil cyanobacteria in some of the oldest rocks on Earth. Images of fossil cyanobacteria from Australia are shown in figure 13.29. Although the rocks preserve over a dozen types of cyanobacteria, the photographs show examples of wormlike, or hairlike, cyanobacteria. Other cyanobacteria at this deposit are shaped more like globules, or tiny balls. All of the different cyanobacteria were living in shallow water and giving off oxygen through photosynthesis. Evidence for bacteria such as these is also found in rocks nearly 3.5 billion years old.

▶ **Figure 13.28 Present-day cyanobacteria.** Scientists believe that photosynthesizing bacteria such as these are responsible for the increased oxygen in the atmosphere.

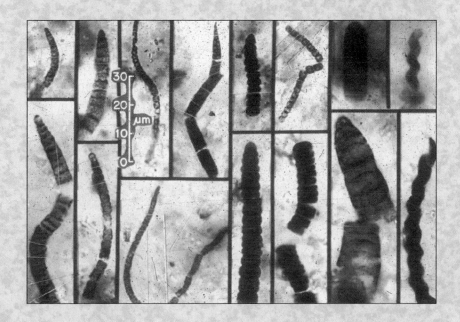

Topic: cyanobacteria
Go to: www.scilinks.org
Code: 1Inquiry653

◀ **Figure 13.29 Fossils of cyanobacteria from the Bitter Springs formation in Australia.** These bacteria are all about 850 million years old. Other types of cyanobacteria from these rocks look like globular clusters of balloons.

13. Work with your partner to develop an explanation for these 3 sentences, which were mentioned earlier. Copy each sentence in your science notebook and write your best ideas underneath.

a. Carbon dioxide and water vapor were more plentiful in early Earth's atmosphere than they are today.

b. Both carbon dioxide and water vapor have been steadily removed from the atmosphere.

c. The level of oxygen has increased to 21 percent compared with the less than 1 percent on early Earth.

14. With your partner, read Earth Zones to learn more about how cyanobacteria helped to establish the early biosphere of Earth.

READING

Earth Zones

The top layer or zone of "life" on Earth is referred to as the **biosphere.** Clearly, a bacterial biosphere that spans about 66 percent of Earth's history (two-thirds of the history of the planet) is not an idea you may be familiar with! Indeed, it is very different from the current idea of a biosphere dominated by plants and animals on land and in the oceans. However, a long history of photosynthesis by bacteria in all corners of Earth was an essential step that allowed for later forms of life, such as animals and plants. Without photosynthesis on Earth first by cyanobacteria, then much later by plants, you would not be able to take a breath of fresh air.

So what would a bacterial biosphere in early Earth have been like? Rocks show that cyanobacteria lived on the bottoms of shallow seas as dense bacterial mats—somewhat like a tangled lawn of grass. The bacterial mats slowly grew upward layer by layer. The layers are called stromatolites.

The illustration in figure 13.30 shows a stromatolite mat beginning to form on the bottom of an ancient shallow sea. The cyanobacte-ria are photosynthesizing, as shown by bacteria taking in carbon dioxide and giving off oxygen. The diagram shows four key parts of the early Earth system:

- Biosphere: cyanobacteria living as a dense mat
- Atmosphere: "air" with a lot of carbon dioxide but very little oxygen
- Hydrosphere: lakes and oceans harboring life
- Lithosphere: sediments and rocks covering the upper surface of Earth

Fortunately, scientists have modern examples of stromatolites (they do not have modern examples of some types of past life, such as dinosaurs and trilobites!). The stromatolites form mounds of cyanobacteria about 0.1–0.2 meters (m) high. Modern examples from Australia are shown in figure 13.31.

Geologists have also carefully noted many excellent examples of stromatolites from the fossil record. An example is shown in figure 13.32. The photograph shows what the mounds in figure 13.32 would look like if cut across the top. This is similar to cutting an onion across the top.

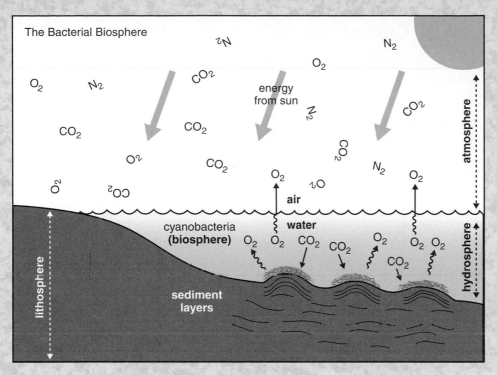

The Bacterial Biosphere

N₂ O₂ CO₂ energy from sun N₂ CO₂

O₂ N₂ CO₂ CO₂ N₂ CO₂

CO₂ CO₂ CO₂ O₂ N₂ O₂

O₂ O₂ O₂

CO₂

air

cyanobacteria **water** O₂ O₂ CO₂ CO₂ O₂ O₂ O₂
(biosphere) CO₂

lithosphere **sediment layers** **hydrosphere** **atmosphere**

◄ **Figure 13.30 Diagram of a bacterial biosphere early in Earth's history (about 3 billion years ago).** Cyanobacteria (biosphere) are a dense mat on the bottom of a primitive ocean (hydrosphere). They live within and on top of sediments and rock (lithosphere). The cyanobacteria absorb energy from the Sun and consume carbon dioxide to make oxygen in photosynthesis (shown by arrows). Some oxygen leaves the water to join carbon dioxide and nitrogen in the atmosphere.

The first life on Earth would have developed in very extreme conditions. Read the sidebar, Extremeophiles—The X-life of Earth, to find out more about organisms living in extreme conditions on Earth today.

▲ **Figure 13.31 Modern stromatolite mounds in Australia.** These mounds consist of layer upon layer of bacterial mats. Stromatolites such as these covered many floors of ancient seas.

▲ **Figure 13.32 Stromatolite mounds in the geologic record.** These are what the mounds in figure 13.31 would look like if cut across the top. They would show concentric layers, as in an onion.

Reflect and Connect

Work through the following questions in a class discussion. Write thoughts and notes from that discussion in your science notebook as you proceed.

1. Photosynthesizing organisms such as cyanobacteria produce oxygen. The gradual buildup of oxygen in our atmosphere from bacterial photosynthesis then enabled the later evolution of other organisms that require more oxygen (plants and animals). To live, plants and animals must have oxygen in the atmosphere. Is it a chicken-or-egg question? No—bacteria had to be first!

   Recall the process of respiration in plants that accompanies photosynthesis. Imagine taking plants such as *Anacharis* and placing them in freshwater on early Earth. Do you think the *Anacharis* would survive? Justify your answer.

2. Recall the items in the table of the Bare Elements handout from this explore-explain activity. Make a T-table with each item down the left side. On the right side, write whether each item represents the biosphere, lithosphere, atmosphere, or hydrosphere. Your answer may include a combination of 2 or more "spheres." The following is a list of items in the table of Bare Elements:

   - Air
   - Coal
   - Granite
   - Human bone
   - Limestone
   - Mammal tissue
   - Meteorite
   - Peach leaf
   - Whole earth

3. Use a Venn diagram to compare and contrast early Earth and Earth today. Use what you learned in all 3 parts of this explore-explain activity to develop your answers.

4. The title of this chapter is The Earth-Sun System. Look up the definition of *system* in a dictionary. Copy the definition in your science notebook. Now explain how Earth and the Sun work together as a system. You may write a paragraph, draw an illustration, or do both. If you choose to draw an illustration, include labels and descriptions that explain your illustration.

Extremeophiles—The X-life of Earth

What do you think is the most extreme environment on Earth that life could inhabit? Is it somewhere incredibly hot or places where it is very cold? Would oxygen or water be present? Answering questions such as those have helped scientists predict what the earliest organisms on Earth may have been like. It has also helped them evaluate the possibility of life elsewhere in our solar system.

Organisms that thrive in extreme conditions are called **extremeophiles.** They live in environments that are very hot or cold, that are at crushing pressures, or that are highly toxic to any other life. Extremeophiles are not animals, but rather a huge array of bacteria (single-celled organisms) that are restricted to the most inaccessible corners of Earth.

Some extremeophiles live at high temperatures that would instantly kill other organisms. They are called thermophiles. Those bacteria have recently been found living at hot springs and vents in the ocean floor at temperatures of 120–125° Celsius (C), shown in the photograph. That is much higher than the boiling temperature of water at sea level. The pressure of the overlying ocean keeps the superheated water at these vents from boiling. Similarly, some bacteria also thrive in the deepest parts of the oceans (over 11 km deep). Pressures there would crush any submarine that ventured so deep. Those organisms are called barophiles (as in barometers that measure atmospheric pressure). Barophiles have also been found in drill holes in rock that is kilometers deep.

Scientists used to think that some settings on Earth were too cold for life. Extremeophiles surprised scientists again when they were found over 1 km deep within the Antarctic ice sheet. Those parts of the glacier have been completely isolated from Earth's atmosphere for hundreds of thousands of years.

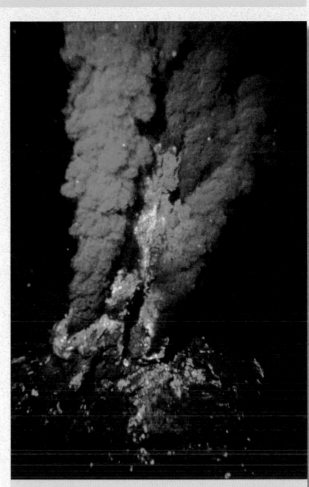

Superheated water shooting from a vent in the floor of the ocean. A vent shoots superheated water from a chimney on the floor of the ocean. Vents such as these are places where thermophiles live. The vent is called a black smoker because water leaving the chimney looks like black smoke.

Other settings on Earth were thought to be much too toxic and acidic for life. With a closer look, however, scientists found a variety of bacteria and fungi in highly acidic environs. They are called acidophiles. In fact, your stomach and intestines are a great example of an acidic setting that is highly colonized by microorganisms.

Interestingly, some extremeophiles cannot survive in environments with oxygen, and they do not photosynthesize for energy. Those bacteria derive their energy from chemical processes in complete darkness. They are called chemophiles. An example is the chemophiles that get energy by converting sulfate to hydrogen sulfide in hot springs and geysers at Yellowstone National Park. The hydrogen sulfide smell is just like rotten eggs.

By studying extremeophiles, scientists have learned much about the most basic needs and functions of life. To study extremeophiles further, however, scientists must bring the odd organisms back to their laboratories. And therein lies one of the biggest problems—without keeping the extreme conditions (temperature, pressure, or acidity), the organisms die! As scientists learn how to keep extremeophiles alive in their labs, they will be able to learn more about the history of life on Earth and possibly elsewhere in the solar system.

ELABORATE

Living It Up on Mars

In this chapter, you learned about the Earth-Sun system (see figure 13.33) and some important ways that this system changed across geologic time. From a protoplanetary disk in our solar system about 4.6 billion years ago, the Earth and Sun developed together. You saw how the Sun is closely tied to changes in the biosphere, atmosphere, and hydrosphere on Earth. Indeed, the Earth-Sun system is a work in progress!

In unit 3, you also learned that the elemental ingredients of the Earth-Sun system were created by nuclear fusion in stars. Those stars were much older than the solar system, yet located in our neighborhood of the Milky Way galaxy. So even though those earlier stars have long since blown up or burned out, their recycled remains make up our

▶ **Figure 13.33**
The Earth-Sun system.
How has this system
evolved over time?

Sun, our planets, and even all atoms in our bodies. This "stellar litter" contains all of the essential ingredients for life.

As you know, one key feature of Earth is abundant life. In this chapter, you learned how geologic processes have contributed to the characteristics of Earth today. You also learned how life is closely linked to the elemental ingredients of Earth and have studied how the Sun is part of that system. Yet it is natural to wonder about life elsewhere in our solar system—even in the universe. You can view other stars, such as the Sun, with planets, and some of those systems would have elemental ingredients and histories like our Earth-Sun system. You saw in the engage activity that scientists have evidence of planetary systems forming around distant stars. Those stars are many light-years away, so it is not possible to go to the planets to test for life.

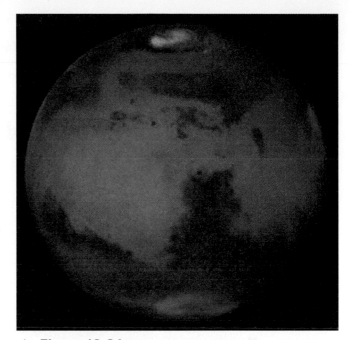

▲ **Figure 13.34** This portrait of Mars was taken by the HST. What feature do you notice at the polar cap of the planet? What does it look like? See a close-up of the polar cap in figure 13.35.

For the time being, the quest for life outside Earth (extraterrestrial life) seems to focus on the planet Mars (see figure 13.34). Why is that so? In Living It Up on Mars, you use what you have learned about changes in the Earth-Sun system to evaluate the prospects for life on Mars or in the Mars-Sun system. Scientists often use this method of analogy to solve a problem or answer a question in a different setting. It is part of the nature of science.

Topic: Mars
Go to: www.scilinks.org
Code: 1Inquiry659

In this activity, you work with a partner to evaluate prospects for life on Mars. Would you expect green Martians? Perhaps, but you need to base your conclusions on specific evidence and examples based on what you have learned about the Earth-Sun system. You will not just be presenting evidence for life on Mars.

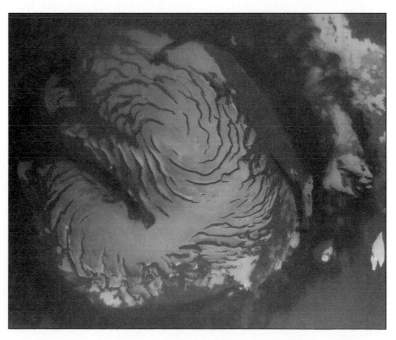

▶ **Figure 13.35 Close-up view of Mars' north polar cap.** Could this be water frozen on the surface of Mars? Look closely at the information in this activity to find out.

Materials

For each team of two students

2 copies of Conditions on Earth and Mars—What's the Score? handout

Process and Procedure

The year is 2015, and the United States prepares to launch a mission to Mars. Most prior missions used satellites for detailed images of Mars' surface and rovers to explore the surface; they returned valuable information but brought back no actual samples. On this mission to Mars, a robotic vehicle will venture across the surface of the planet, dig to depths of 1.3 m, collect samples, and then return them to Earth.

You are a mission geologist with NASA, and you have been hired to assess the prospects and evidence for life on Mars. NASA has asked if it can expect to retrieve samples of life on Mars from this mission. From your understanding of life in the Earth-Sun system, will you recognize life on Mars if you find it? From experiences on Earth, what might life on Mars look like?

Reviewing a planet's conditions is the first step for evaluating whether life might exist there. You have learned a little about the very extreme parts of Earth that support different kinds of life. Thus, to evaluate the prospects for life on Mars, you must first compare current conditions between Earth and Mars. How similar—or different—are they?

1. With your partner, read the handout, Conditions on Earth and Mars—What's the Score? It gives you information about the Earth-Sun and Mars-Sun systems. Discuss the conditions and make a note in the comment column about the similarities and differences between Earth and Mars. For each category, are they more similar or more different? Write a brief comment to justify your decision.

2. In the first column, you and your partner will answer this question for each criterion: Would this matter to life on either planet? Write a Y, N, or C in the column.

   • Y means yes, this matters to life.
   • N means no, this does not matter to life.
   • C means you cannot tell whether this matters to life.

3. As a NASA mission geologist, you must base your evidence for life on Mars on what you know about life in the Earth-Sun system. This includes recent life and early forms of life on our planet. In the far-right column, give at least 1 piece of evidence, 1 example, or 1 reason from the Earth-Sun system that explains why the condition matters to life (Y), does not matter to life (N), or you cannot tell (C). Be as specific as possible. You may cite the same example in more than 1 column.

4. In the criteria column on the handout, circle what you think the top 3 criteria are that would favor life on Mars. Also, place a large X over the 2 main criteria that you think would not favor life on Mars. You and your partner do not have to agree. If you think differently, mark your handout accordingly.

5. Listen to your teacher's instructions for how your class will share its findings and thoughts from Steps 1–4. Use your science notebook to record any observations or evidence shared by the class. This class wrap-up will help you review for the evaluate activity.

SCiLINKS
NSTA
Topic: life on other planets
Go to: www.scilinks.org
Code: 1Inquiry661

Reflect and Connect

1. Look at the description of the soils on Mars. From your experiences with iron on Earth, why is Mars known as the Red Planet?

2. Currently, scientists have been able to send robots only to explore the surface of Mars. They have not been able to bring back samples from the surface of the planet. However, scientists have collected meteorites on Earth that they determined came from Mars.
   a. What new information could scientists glean from a meteorite from Mars?
   b. Why would scientists want to go to the planet's surface if they have a meteorite from Mars here on Earth?

3. If you were to find life on Mars, would you expect it to be similar to or different from life on Earth? Justify your answer.

MOR to NASA

▶ **Figure 13.36**
NASA scientist presenting a memorandum of recommendation (MOR).
How will you write your MOR to NASA that will demonstrate what you have learned in this chapter?

An MOR is a memorandum of recommendation, and you are responsible for demonstrating what you have learned in this chapter by writing one to NASA. You have just examined data from Mars and Earth and made some inferences about life on Mars. Now you must make a decision. Do you think NASA would or would not find life on Mars?

In an MOR to NASA, you work individually as a NASA mission geologist. You have a big responsibility in preparing this MOR regarding prospects for life on Mars. Follow the steps to present NASA with your argument for why you would or would not expect to find life on Mars. Note that you are not writing just about the possibility of life on Mars; you may decide that there could not be life on Mars. Your job is to present your views and back them up with evidence and reasoning, using what you have learned from this chapter. You need to use specific examples and evidence from life in the Earth-Sun system in your reasoning about life on Mars.

Materials
For each student

your completed copy of the Conditions on Earth and Mars—What's the Score? handout

1 copy of the Scoring Rubric for MOR to NASA

Process and Procedure

1. Review the scoring rubric before you begin your work. Use it as a guide for how your teacher will evaluate your work.

2. Review your comments on the Conditions on Earth and Mars—What's the Score? handout. You will use it to formulate your MOR to NASA.

3. In your MOR to NASA, include a written section on each of the following steps:

   a. In section 1 of your MOR to NASA, provide who you are, where you live, and what the purpose of the MOR is. It would also be helpful to NASA if you summarized in 1–2 sentences the conclusion of this MOR.

   b. In section 2 of your MOR, think back to the Earth-Sun system—life here is highly varied, yet all life on Earth has several basic needs or elemental ingredients that are essential. What are those basic requirements?

      List at least 3 of the most basic requirements for life on Earth in this section of your MOR. For each requirement, show your understanding of the Earth-Sun system by stating how that basic requirement became available to life on Earth. Has this requirement stayed the same or changed over Earth's history? You may illustrate your answer.

      Would this basic requirement for life also be available as part of the Mars-Sun system? For each of your requirements, clearly give evidence stating why or why not. Would you expect that that requirement has stayed the same or changed over Mars' history?

   c. As the mission geologist, what are your predictions for finding evidence of life on Mars? In section 3 of your MOR, you need to provide NASA with 3 reasons as to why you expect or do not expect to find clear evidence of life. If life is a possibility, what might it look like and how might it function? If life is not a possibility, what are at least 3 lines of evidence that argue against finding evidence of life?

4. Review your work carefully for completeness. Make any necessary changes. Once again, refer back to the essential requirements and needs of life that you identified in Step 3b. Use your understanding of them to argue for or against prospects for life on Mars. Be sure to cite at least 3 specific examples from the Earth-Sun system to support your conclusion.

5. Participate in either a peer review or teacher review as your teacher directs. Revise your work based on that review.

CONDUCTING YOUR OWN INQUIRY

Science is a way of studying and knowing the world around you, whether you make it a career or use it to make informed decisions. In this section, you will use your understanding of inquiry as well as your skills of inquiry to conduct an investigation that interests you—one that involves more than one discipline of science. The activities throughout this program involve scientific inquiry. By now, you should have enough experience to realize that thinking scientifically is a valuable way of answering many questions.

In this special section, you investigate a scientific question of your own. You need to decide what you want to study, where you will find background information, and how you will conduct your investigation. You may work alone or in a team of two or three.

The goal of this section is for you to conceive, design, and conduct a scientific investigation of your own choosing.

One reason to study science is to learn to use the methods of science to study aspects of the natural world around you. Another reason is to understand the events that influence your life. For this activity, you will carry out a full inquiry of your own design. Remember that each of the *thinking* steps, such as asking a good question, deciding how to test it, and analyzing the meaning of the data you collect, is just as important as the hands-on step of *doing* an investigation. Your performance in this activity will demonstrate both your understanding of the particular area of science that you investigate, your understanding of the nature of science, your ability to think scientifically, and your ability to use scientific processes.

Materials
For each student

Materials will depend on the investigation you design. You will need your teacher's approval before you assemble materials.

1 copy of Scoring Rubric for Conducting Your Own Investigation handout

Cautions

You may be working with harmful chemicals.

Process and Procedure

Part I: Preparation

1. Study figure 1.13 in chapter 1, The Process of Scientific Inquiry, as you discuss the following questions with a partner. Record your best ideas in your science notebook.

   a. How has your understanding of the ideas represented in figure 1.13 changed since the beginning of the year?

   b. Identify 4–5 specific times during this program when you have used these processes.

   Looking through your science notebook may help you answer this question.

2. Obtain from your teacher a scoring rubric for this special investigation. Examine the criteria for the excellent categories on the rubric. Tell your partner what you think an excellent project would look like when it is finished.

Part II: Asking the Question

Now you will carry out your own full inquiry beginning with a question. As you proceed, you will record all your work in your science notebook.

1. Choose a problem or topic in the natural world that interests you. Think of problems or topics that involve an integrated science perspective, that is, that include more than 1 discipline of science, such as life science and physical science or physical science and earth-space science.

   If you are having difficulty thinking of an area or a problem, consider looking through your science notebook. Review the investigations that most interested you. You also might want to do some library research about a topic that interests you. The new information will provide useful background and may give you an idea for a testable question.

2. Consider some questions that you might want to investigate related to this area or problem. Record 2 or 3 good questions in your science notebook, discuss them with a partner, and select 1 question to investigate.

   a. In your science notebook, record the question in 1 or 2 sentences.

   b. Explain why your question is significant and how it is testable.

   To do this, you will need to write several sentences describing what already is known about the topic that you wish to investigate.

   c. Restate your question as a hypothesis that can be tested.

   d. Record the major concepts in the sciences to which your question and hypothesis relate and explain how they represent an integrated science perspective.

3. Show your question to your teacher for approval before you proceed.

Part III: Gathering Information and Conducting Your Investigation

1. Use the Internet, the library, local scientists, or other available resources to gather information related to your question.

Scientists use data that others collect as well as data that they gather directly through experimental investigations. You should use a similar process at this time.

2. Design an investigation to test or answer your question by doing the following.
   a. Describe your experimental design in your science notebook and include your
      - rationale, that is, how this investigation will test your question (include a description of your controls and the role that they will play);
      - hypothesis (explain what you think the answer to your question may be and why you think so);
      - procedure (include a step-by-step procedure along with a list of the materials you will need); and
      - data analysis (explain how you will analyze the data).

Your teacher may have specific suggestions about the length of time that you will have to conduct your investigation or the equipment that is available.

   b. Write in your science notebook a safety plan for your investigation. In your procedures, record the precautions that you will follow when you
      - use chemicals,
      - handle equipment, and
      - handle biological hazards such as bacteria or yeast.

Ask your teacher to explain any hazards that you do not understand and to help you identify the precautions necessary to prevent harm from an accident.

 **Caution** Review Laboratory Safety in the back of your student book and be sure that you understand all the safety considerations involved in your experimental design. Make sure that you have read and understood the hazards and precautions described on the labels and Material Safety Data Sheets for all the chemicals you plan to use in your experiment. Report all accidents, no matter how small, to your teacher.

3. Discuss your library research, experimental design, and safety plan with your teacher before you continue. If your plans are reasonable and safe, your teacher will approve further work.

4. When you have your teacher's approval, carry out the investigation you have designed to test your hypothesis.

Remember, use the proper controls to make it a valid test and record data in your journal in a way that will be most useful.

Part IV: Analyzing Your Data

1. Reorganize your data in a way that makes it easier to see patterns or understand what the data show you.
2. Decide what your data tell you and record your preliminary conclusions. Include a description of any limitations of your experimental design and any unexpected results that you may have found.

Part V: Drawing Conclusions

1. Explain what your conclusions mean at this point. Do your conclusions help you answer your question? Why or why not?
2. Describe how your results connect to the major concepts in the sciences that you selected and how they represent an integrated science perspective.

Part VI: Communicating Your Results

1. Assemble a presentation of your full inquiry that makes it possible for someone else to understand what you did, why you did it, and what you found out.

A poster, a written or verbal report, and a videotape are some examples of how you can communicate your results.

2. Be sure to identify the connections between your investigation and any of the following that are relevant:
   - The major concepts in the sciences to which your investigation relates and how the investigation represented an integrated science perspective
   - The processes of inquiry that are featured in figure 1.13 in chapter 1
   - Your understanding about inquiry and the nature of science
   - Additional questions that are generated by your findings
   - Society and technology
   - History of science
3. Present your work as your teacher directs.
4. As you listen to other students present their findings, look for evidence or examples that illustrate why the approach they took to answering their question was scientific. Consider how the findings lead to other questions.

UNIT 4

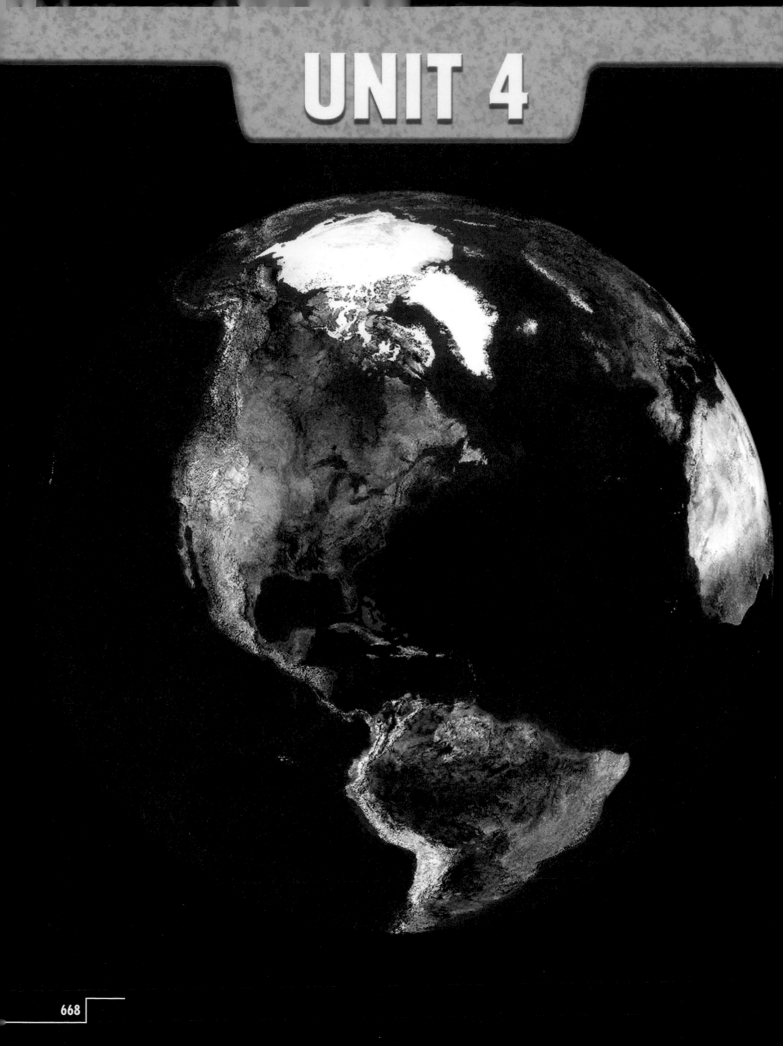

Perspectives on Science and Technology in Your World

Perspectives on Science and Technology in Your World

Science and technology contribute to your life in many ways. Science and technology also affect you on many different levels. Certain things affect you as an individual, while other things affect a community or a region. Some things people do as a society may affect the entire globe. So far this year in science, you have explored science as a way of knowing about the natural world. You also have seen ways that technology helps scientists make better observations. The Hubble Space Telescope is an obvious example. You also have noticed that technology helps scientists analyze enormous amounts of data through the use of high-speed computers.

But technology is more than using shiny, expensive instruments. Technology is a process that people use to solve problems. That includes being able to identify a problem and to suggest and test possible solutions. Which solution is the best and why? What might be some unexpected consequences?

In Perspectives on Science and Technology in Your World, you will explore different ways that science and technology affect society. As a citizen, you will use science and technology as you make decisions for yourself and for your families and communities. Some of your decisions may also have global effects.

In Crime Science, you will see how the tools and processes of technology help people solve crimes. In Risks and Hazards to Humans, you will explore the risks and hazards that people face from exposure to the environment. In Fire Ecology, you will explore how a natural disaster—wildfire—affects both ecosystems and communities. How can science and technology help? In this unit, you will learn some of the ways.

Goals for the Unit

In this unit, you will explore ways that science and technology contribute to and affect society. Specific goals for this unit include your understanding the following:

- Patterns in evidence and observations are used to develop explanations, such as in solving crimes and learning about personal risks and hazards.
- Science is a way of knowing that must meet certain standards, such as quality of evidence, use of logic and inference, and critical evaluation and confirmation of results.
- Social issues and decisions can affect the use of science and technology in society.
- Technology can change how we gather and view evidence.
- The use of science and technology affects the way society tries to solve problems.
- Science advances with new technologies, but also with the creativity and imagination of scientists.
- Humans must make choices that reduce and modify the risks from hazards to personal health or to the environment.

Unit Engage

Science and technology affect everyone in many ways. Your teacher will guide a brief activity to consider various ways that science and technology affect you, your community, and the globe.

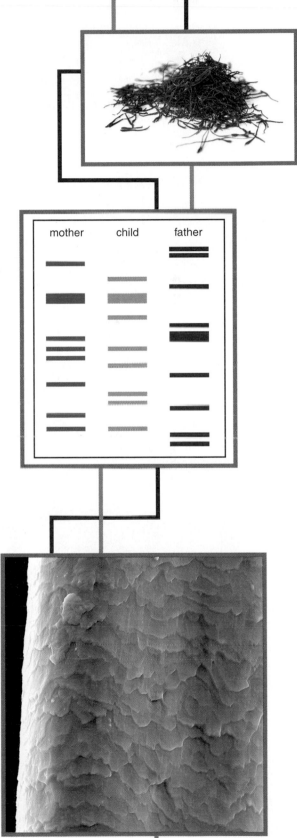

CHAPTER 14

Crime Science

Crime Science

Humans face many types of challenges. The comforts that many societies enjoy today resulted from challenges that humans met earlier in history. If humans were cold, they devised a way to stay warm. If humans were hungry, they figured out how to gather more food—and later how to grow it. Each problem presented a chance for a solution. Both science and technology have played a part in adding to human comfort, health, safety, and order.

As individuals, humans also can create new difficulties. For example, sometimes people turn to crime, thinking it will solve their problems.

Topic: forensic science
Go to: www.scilinks.org
Code: 1Inquiry674

Crime has always existed, but today committing a crime is harder to get away with. The reason is because science and technology advance, leading to new methods of crime solving. As shown in the opening photographs, solving crimes with science and technology relies on obtaining many types of evidence at crime scenes.

Forensic science includes many fields that help to bring criminals to justice. Those fields include medicine, toxicology, psychology, physics, biology, chemistry, and anthropology, to name a few. Forensic scientists specialize in drug analysis, firearms and projectile examination, chemical analysis, blood and body fluid analysis, or fingerprint identification. All forensic scientists use the process of inquiry, just as you did in the activity, Who Did It?, in chapter 1, The Process of Scientific Inquiry, of this program. In the end, forensic scientists want to test this idea: Who did it? To get to that point, they must obtain evidence, make observations, and use both of them to make logical inferences about what happened. They must also think critically to evaluate competing explanations. Importantly, forensic scientists must be open to revising an explanation based on new evidence or observations. Doing so helps them solve some very serious problems.

Goals for the Chapter

Chapter 14, Crime Science, is the first of three chapters in this unit addressing current issues linking science to society—and science to you. A key idea in forensic science is using many types of patterns. Those patterns may relate to specific individuals, such as with fingerprinting or DNA typing. Or the patterns may indicate specific substances, such as blood, that are found with chemical tests. This evidence lets you test possible explanations. Still, using science and technology for investigations will not resolve crime as a societal issue. Making good personal decisions must play a role, too.

In this chapter, your science background helps you use inquiry, analyze evidence, and solve crimes. Key goals include:

- Seeing how distinctive patterns are used as evidence
- Relating patterns to the physical and chemical properties of materials
- Using evidence to make inferences and to develop logical explanations
- Seeing how technology extends your ability to analyze evidence from a crime scene

As you study forensic science, you complete these activities:

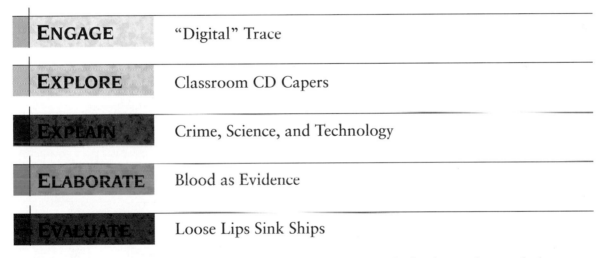

ENGAGE	"Digital" Trace
EXPLORE	Classroom CD Capers
EXPLAIN	Crime, Science, and Technology
ELABORATE	Blood as Evidence
EVALUATE	Loose Lips Sink Ships

The chapter organizer shows how the activities are linked together to help you understand key concepts in this chapter.

Linking Question

What other patterns does science reveal that help to solve a crime?

ENGAGE

"Digital" Trace

Key Idea:
Classifying patterns in fingerprints can help scientists identify criminals.

EXPLORE

Classroom CD Capers

Key Idea:
Understanding the properties of materials based on their physical and chemical characteristics can help scientists separate them into identifiable components. Scientific inquiry can help scientists use evidence to make inferences that lead to solving a crime.

Linking Question

How has using technology helped in crime investigations?

EXPLAIN

Crime, Science, and Technology

Key Idea:
New technologies help extend the analysis of evidence from a crime scene and provide additional knowledge on which to base the solution of a crime (chromatography, mass spectrometry, spectroscopy, DNA profiling).

Crime Science

Linking Question

What provides the most conclusive evidence at crime scenes?

ELABORATE

Blood as Evidence:
Part I: A Close Look at Blood

Key Idea:
The differences among cells of living organisms can help place animals (including humans) at the scene of a crime.

Loose Lips Sink Ships

Key Idea:

The process of scientific inquiry can help scientists use patterns of evidence to make inferences that lead to explanations and the solution of a crime.

CHAPTER

14 Major Concepts

▶ Classifying patterns can help scientists identify criminals.

▶ Understanding the physical and chemical properties of materials can help scientists separate substances into identifiable and traceable components.

▶ The unique differences among cells of living organisms can help place animals (including humans) at the scene of a crime. New technologies can help extend the analysis of evidence from a crime scene.

▶ Understanding basic science and technology concepts can help scientists solve a crime, but understanding alone cannot resolve crime as a societal problem.

Linking Question

Can you use your understanding of science and the tools of technology to solve a crime?

ELABORATE

Blood as Evidence: Part III: Are You My Type?

Key Idea:

Understanding the properties of materials based on their physical and chemical characteristics (blood) can help scientists separate them into identifiable and traceable components.

ELABORATE

Blood as Evidence: Part II: Is It Blood?

Key Idea:

A series of tests can be used to identify the presence of blood.

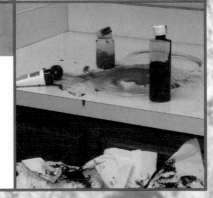

"Digital" Trace

April thought she could get away with it. She only wanted to see the questions that would be on the science final. Then she could study the right material and not waste her time cramming for the stuff that she didn't need to know. She wasn't trying to find out the answers.

April noticed her science teacher in the teachers' workroom. He had just finished copying the science final when he was called to the main office. He left the pile of 28 tests on the desk just inside the room. No one else was around, so April grabbed the top copy and took it to the bathroom. She carefully read each page, trying to memorize the questions. When she was done, she quietly slipped the test back on the pile and left school. No one would know that she had been dishonest.

Or would they? Crime scene investigators know that people always leave trace evidence behind or carry away minute particles from a crime scene. Investigators' task is to find those trace materials and preserve them in order to identify suspects and victims. April did not realize it, but she had left evidence. In the "Digital" Trace activity, work with a partner to discover how a suspicious teacher might be able to tell.

Materials
For each team of two students

2 pairs of safety goggles

1 hand lens or magnifying glass

▶ **Figure 14.1**
Can a suspicious teacher prove that April handled the test?

1–2 tsp detective powder

2 sheets of photocopy paper, carefully removed from middle of new ream

2 sheets of newspaper

3–4 pieces of transparent tape

Cautions

Do not breathe the airborne powder. Clean any powder spills by sweeping them up with a dry brush or paper towel. Avoid getting powder on your clothes or near your face. Wear your safety goggles.

Process and Procedure

1. Review with your class the scenario in the opening paragraphs. Then answer the following questions.
    a. How might April have left evidence that she looked at the science test ahead of time?
    b. How might you collect evidence to support the idea that April had done something wrong?
2. Not all evidence is easily visible. Follow these steps with your partner to reveal some invisible evidence.
    a. Lay a sheet of newspaper on your desk. Your partner will do the same with the 2nd sheet of newspaper.
    b. Carefully remove 2 sheets of photocopy paper from the middle of the ream of paper. Handle the paper only at the edges. Place 1 sheet of photocopy paper on each sheet of newspaper.
    c. Using all of your fingertips on your *right hand*, rub your forehead and the bridge of your nose.
    d. Immediately after rubbing your face, gently place your fingertips flat on your piece of photocopy paper. Don't press hard or roll your fingertips. Quickly lift your hand straight up.
3. Can you see your fingerprints on the photocopy paper? Crime scene investigators must find fingerprints in the most obscure places. Follow these steps to reveal your fingerprints on the paper.

    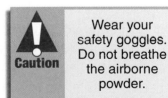

    a. Shake about 1 tsp of detective powder on your photocopy paper.
    b. Lift up the paper and gently shake the powder back and forth over the area where your fingertips touched the paper.
    c. Hold the paper up on one end over your newspaper and gently tap the back of the paper. Catch any powder that falls off the photocopy paper on the newspaper.

4. It is easy to preserve a record of your fingerprint. Practice transferring your fingerprint to a piece of clear tape. Then place the tape, sticky side down, directly into your notebook.

You may need to practice more than once to get a crisp, clear fingerprint. Can you get a good print by gently rubbing traces of powder on your finger, then lightly pressing against the sticky side of the tape? Label the print with the hand (right/left) and finger in your notebook.

   a. Cut your preserved fingerprint out of the photocopy paper and attach it with glue or tape to a page in your science notebook.
   b. Use the hand lens to look closely at your and your partner's fingerprints. What do you see? What are the similarities and differences in the patterns?
5. Complete the following reading, A Fingerprint Analysis, with your partner. You will learn about a vital type of evidence in criminal investigations.

READING

A Fingerprint Analysis

Identifying a suspect or victim is a key step in gathering evidence for a crime investigation. People have unique patterns of ridges and lines on the tips of their fingers. When people touch objects, they leave behind a record of those unique patterns as fingerprints.

Visible, or patent, fingerprints come from fingers covered by ink, blood, or other visible markers. Plastic fingerprints occur when fingers press into soft material such as soap, wax, or clay. Latent fingerprints are the hardest to see because they are made when perspiration and natural oils on the fingertips are transferred to a surface by touch. Those prints need to be exposed by some method in order to be seen clearly. In this engage activity, you exposed your fingerprints on a piece of paper by dusting them with detective powder.

To study fingerprints, forensic scientists first classify them. Each person's fingerprints are unique, but all fingerprints fall into three major categories or classifications: loops, whorls, and arches. Those patterns are shown in figure 14.2. Fingerprints can be classified further with several other features. These features include the direction of loops (toward little finger [ulnar] or toward thumb [radial]), plain whorls or double loops, and plain or tented arches.

Matching fingerprints to a person is hard work. Today the Automated Fingerprint Identification System (AFIS) can search a file of many digital fingerprints in less than a second. It is a key tool for detectives to be able to match fingerprint evidence with suspects in criminal investigations.

Topic: fingerprint
Go to: www.scilinks.org
Code: 1Inquiry680

a. loop   b. whorl   c. arch

▲ **Figure 14.2 Fingerprint types.** Fingerprints fall into one of three classifications: (a) the loop pattern, where ridge lines enter from one side and curve around to exit the same side; (b) the whorl pattern, with generally rounded or circular ridges; and (c) the arch pattern, where ridge lines enter from one side and flow out the other side.

6. Look only at the fingerprint in your science notebook from your right index finger. Determine whether that fingerprint can be classified as a loop, a whorl, or an arch. What pattern does your partner's right index fingerprint have?

Only 25 percent of the population has all loops or all arches on all ten fingers. Look at the rest of your right hand's fingerprints. Are all of your fingerprints the same classification? Do you have several fingerprint classifications on one hand?

7. In your science notebook, tally the number of people in your class who have each type of fingerprint on their right index finger. Record the class data in a table. Also, record the percent by fingerprint class (for example, 40 percent loop, 30 percent arch, and 30 percent whorl).

8. Compare your class percentages with those of the entire human population, which your teacher will reveal to you. Do they match? Why do you think this is so?

9. Create in your science notebook a simple bar graph comparing results from your class with the entire human population. On your graph, write answers to these questions: What do I see? What does it mean?

Reflect and Connect

Work individually to complete the following tasks and to answer the questions in your science notebook. Then discuss your answers with the class.

1. Explain how April's teacher could use fingerprint analysis to uncover April's dishonesty.

2. What other parts of the body might make prints or have distinctive patterns? Do you think these are unique to each individual?

3. How do crime scene investigators use scientific inquiry to solve crimes? How might an ineffective investigator be different?

You learned about the process of inquiry in the first chapter of this program. Recall the distinction between inference and evidence. You might review your notes and the activities from this lesson for examples to use in your answer.

4. How do crime scene investigators use evidence to make inferences about crimes? How do they use evidence and inference to develop explanations?

5. What fields in science may be useful for crime scene investigators to understand? Give some examples of how those different fields apply to solving a crime.

EXPLORE

Classroom CD Capers

In the last activity, you saw how a pattern such as fingerprints, might be used by forensic scientists to solve a crime. What other science concepts help investigators solve a crime? In the Classroom CD Capers activity, work with your team to explore how the physical and chemical properties of matter help forensic scientists evaluate trace evidence.

Materials
For each team of three students

3 pairs of safety goggles

1 500-mL beaker

1 petri dish cover

chromatography solvents

1 piece of filter or chromatography paper

ink samples from 4 pens

sample of ink from Crooning Carnosaurs CD

1 small metric ruler

1 pencil

1 calculator

Cautions

Ethanol, methanol, acetone, and isopropanol (isopropyl alcohol) are flammable. Keep them away from flames. Always wear your safety goggles when working with chemicals. When using acetone, have proper ventilation and do not get acetone on skin. If any solvents are spilled or splashed onto the skin or into the eyes, rinse thoroughly with water immediately and report incident to your teacher. Check with your teacher about proper disposal of solvents.

Process and Procedure

1. Read the following passage to learn about a possible crime at a high school. You will need to examine ink evidence to see who is telling the truth.

READING

The Crooning Carnosaurs CD

"Hey—that's mine! You have my new Carnosaurs CD in your backpack!" The science class had ended, but Jason Shen was clutching his backpack, and Josie Sanchez was blocking his exit at the door. They had been quite a couple while they were together. Since their breakup, however, their conflicts had disrupted several classes. Now the situation had escalated to claims of thievery. Josie had accused Jason of taking her CD by The Crooning Carnosaurs, a hot new music group. This was getting more serious.

The science teacher, Ms. Ackley, had an idea. She asked for the CD, and Jason gave it to her. The plastic cover for the Crooning Carnosaurs CD had in bold, black ink the initials "J. S." The class would be analyzing ink in their forensic science unit. They would be using paper chromatography to test the chemical properties and solubility of different inks. Investigating black pens from Jason and Josie might help to show methods in forensics—and solve a more pressing personal problem in class. First, though, Ms. Ackley had to get Josie's and Jason's stories.

Jason claimed that the CD was his and that Josie had set him up. He didn't take the CD from her. He had written his initials, "J. S.," on the CD after buying it two days ago. He was fairly

▲ Figure 14.3 Who wrote the initials "J. S." on the plastic cover of the new Crooning Carnosaurs CD? Whose CD is it?

certain that he had used one of the two black ink pens in his backpack, but he couldn't remember which one. After class, Jason was showing the new CD to a friend. That's when Josie spotted the Carnosaurs CD in his backpack.

Jason's story sounded reasonable, but Josie also asserted that the Crooning Carnosaurs CD was hers. She claimed that she had bought the CD two days ago. When they were a couple, Jason had had a bad habit of borrowing her things and keeping them, but this was going over the line. It was just this morning that she had written her initials, "J. S.," on the CD cover, and she had the black pen to prove it. Jason had taken the CD from her backpack during class, probably while she was working with her teammates on a fingerprinting activity.

Ms. Ackley asked Josie what pen she had used. Pulling two pens from her backpack, Josie said it had been a fine-point felt-tipped pen from her art class. Using one of the pens, Josie made a rapid, dark mark on the CD cover. Indeed, the pen was an identical match. But was it really? How would Ms. Ackley know who was telling the truth?

2. Discuss and answer the following questions with your team. Then share your answers in a class discussion.
   a. What evidence may be available to address the situation in question?
   b. Which evidence can be analyzed scientifically?
   c. What inferences or claims can you test with evidence from this case?
   d. How will you use evidence to develop an explanation?
3. The idea of motive sometimes helps in solving crimes, such as the case of the Crooning Carnosaurs CD. With your class, read the paragraph below on motive. Then discuss with your class the questions that follow, recording your best ideas in your notebook.
   a. How does the motive for a crime suspect differ from evidence in a case?
   b. Do you think that a motive can be used as evidence in a case?
   c. Do you think that a motive can be used to make inferences?

   In criminal cases, investigators often need to consider the possible motives of suspects. A motive is a cause or reason for a person to act in a certain way. For example, imagine that your house has a large leak in the roof. Your motive, or motivation, to fix the leak quickly might be to prevent water damage to the inside of your house during future rainstorms. In criminal cases, motives for a crime might include money, jealousy, revenge, or power. But motives for a crime may not always be clear, even when several key pieces of evidence point to a suspect. Considering various motives for all suspects can help criminal investigators search for specific types of evidence. Those new pieces of evidence can help detectives crack a case.
4. Review the reading in Step 1 with your team. Discuss these questions.
   a. How many black pens were gathered from Josie? How many were gathered from Jason?
   b. What are Jason's and Josie's stories regarding ownership of the Carnosaurs CD?
   c. What might Jason's motive have been to take Josie's CD? What might Josie's motive have been to take Jason's CD?

5. Read the following information about paper chromatography and discuss it with your team.

READING

Background Information on Paper Chromatography

Chromatography separates parts of a mixture based on their physical and chemical properties. Paper chromatography is a type of chromatography. A small spot of sample is put near the bottom of the chromatography paper. The paper is called the stationary phase because it does not move. The bottom of the paper is placed in a liquid solvent. This is the mobile phase because it moves. The upper, moving edge of the solvent is called the solvent front. These relationships are shown in figure 14.4.

As solvent travels up the paper, solvent molecules interact with sample molecules. Then solvent molecules pick up parts of the sample and move them at different rates based on the solubility of the sample in the solvent. The parts, or components, of a mixture such as ink separate out along a path on the stationary phase. If a component of a mixture is attracted more strongly to the solvent, that component travels with the solvent up the paper. If the component is attracted more strongly to the paper

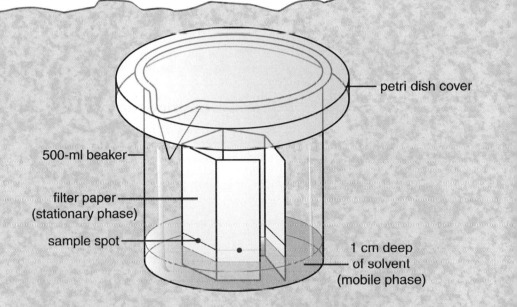

▲ **Figure 14.4 Chromatography setup.** This diagram shows the chromatography setup with sample dots on a pencil line and chromatography paper (the stationary phase) in a shallow solvent "pool" (the mobile phase).

than the solvent, it will "stick" to the paper and travel less. An insoluble component may not move at all.

These differences in attraction to the paper or solvent for a sample relate to their polarities. You learned about the polarity of atomic bonds in molecules in the Matter Is Marvelous unit,

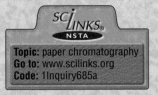

Topic: paper chromatography
Go to: www.scilinks.org
Code: 1Inquiry685a

Topic: solvent
Go to: www.scilinks.org
Code: 1Inquiry685b

and you learned that "like dissolves like." That means that polar components in a sample are attracted strongly to the polar solvents, such as water. On the other hand, nonpolar samples (not soluble in water) may require a nonpolar solvent, or mobile phase, for a clear separation on the chromatogram. Thus, different solvents can interact differently with components in a sample. You should select a solvent carefully, just as you did when considering new solvents to remove caffeine from beverages in the Matter Is Marvelous unit.

6. Read through the entire Paper Chromatography Protocol and study figure 14.4. Check your understanding with your team.

Protocol

Paper Chromatography

Materials
see materials list at start of activity

Cautions
Ethanol, methanol, acetone, and isopropanol (isopropyl alcohol) are flammable. Keep them away from flames. Always wear your safety goggles when working with chemicals. Make sure you work in an area with proper ventilation or fume hoods.

1. Determine the appropriate solvent to use for your mixture. Consider the polarity of the mixture. Is it water based and thus polar? Is it oil based and thus nonpolar? Test a sample of the mixture if you are not sure.

   Recall the saying "like dissolves like" from the Matter Is Marvelous unit. That phrase relates to the polarity of bonds in a molecule. Polar samples dissolve more easily in polar solvents. Nonpolar samples dissolve more easily in nonpolar solvents.

2. Prepare the chromatography chamber.
   a. Pour your solvents in the bottom of the 500-milliliter (mL) beaker to a depth of about 1 centimeter (cm).
   b. Cover the beaker with the petri dish cover.

3. Prepare the chromatogram by referring to the figure on the opposite page.
   a. Lightly draw a pencil line 1.5 cm above the bottom of the chromatography paper.

Caution

Wear your safety goggles when working with chemicals.

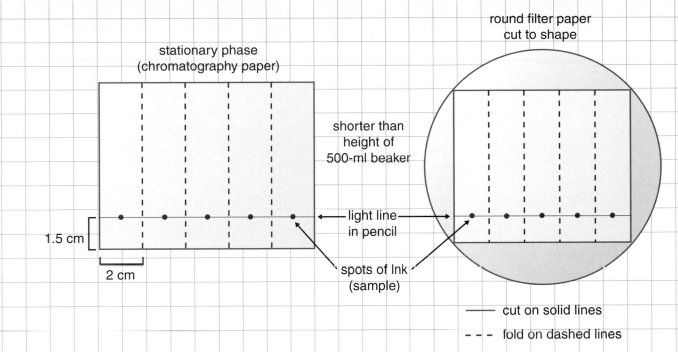

stationary phase
(chromatography paper)

round filter paper
cut to shape

shorter than
height of
500-ml beaker

← light line → in pencil

1.5 cm

2 cm

spots of Ink
(sample)

——— cut on solid lines

- - - fold on dashed lines

▲ **Paper chromato-gram.** This image shows how to prepare a rectangular paper chromatogram and where to add a light pencil line. Fold along the dashed lines. Samples are placed on the pencil line, one per vertical section. The paper is situated inside the chamber as shown in figure 14.4.

b. Place a small, neat dot of each ink sample on the pencil line, with 1 dot per section of paper. These dots should be no more than twice the width of a period at the end of a sentence. Space each sample at least 2 cm apart.

c. Label ink samples at the very top of each section. Fold the chromatography paper so that it can stand by itself inside the chamber.

d. Place the chromatography paper inside the chromatography chamber. *Make sure that the pencil line and samples are not submerged in the solvent.* The samples should rest just above the solvent. Cover the chamber with the petri dish cover.

e. During the separation, make sure that the paper does not rub or touch the beaker. Do not drape strips of chromatography paper over the side of the beaker into the solvent. During the separation, the paper will likely warp and touch the beaker wall.

4. Develop the chromatogram.

a. Observe closely as the solvent front and ink move up the paper. Note whether different components of the ink move different distances up the paper.

b. Remove the chromatogram when the solvent front is about 1.0 cm from the top of the paper, or after 15 minutes, whichever comes first. Place the chromatogram upright on your desk.

c. The solvent will continue to move up the paper for a few more minutes. When it stops, use your pencil to mark the solvent front. Do not wait until the paper is completely dry because you may not be able to see the solvent front on a dry chromatogram.

5. Analyze the chromatogram (see figure below). Each component of a sample such as ink may have unique physical and chemical properties. Those properties determine how far up the chromatogram each component moves. You can calculate a characteristic value called the **retention factor,** or R_f. R_f is defined as the ratio of the distance traveled by a spot to the distance traveled by the solvent:

$$R_f = \frac{\text{distance traveled by component (cm)}}{\text{distance traveled by solvent (cm)}}$$

a. Decide how you will arrange your observations in your notebook.

b. Unfold the dry paper chromatogram. Measure in centimeters the distance from your pencil line at the bottom of the chromatogram to the top of each color.

c. Measure in centimeters the distance from your pencil line at the bottom of the chromatogram to the pencil line you drew at the solvent front.

d. Calculate the R_f for each color.

e. Compare the differences among the values.

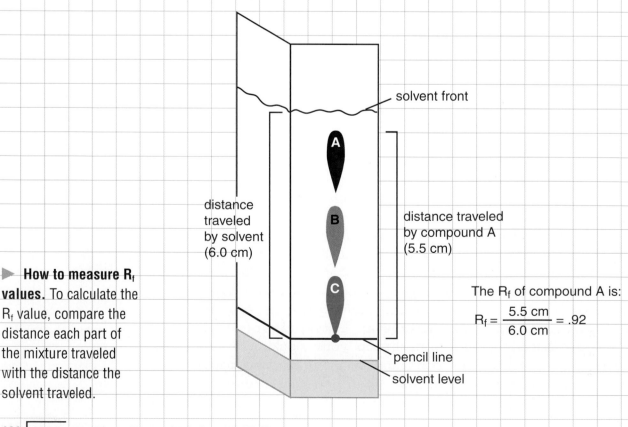

▶ **How to measure R_f values.** To calculate the R_f value, compare the distance each part of the mixture traveled with the distance the solvent traveled.

solvent front

distance traveled by solvent (6.0 cm)

distance traveled by compound A (5.5 cm)

The R_f of compound A is:

$$R_f = \frac{5.5 \text{ cm}}{6.0 \text{ cm}} = .92$$

pencil line

solvent level

7. Obtain materials for your chromatography analysis. Be sure to use a felt-tipped, wet-erase marker as an ink sample on the chromatography paper and complete the protocol as directed.

What solvent will you use to separate the components of the marker's ink? Why? What evidence will you be able to collect?

8. Record the results of your trial in your science notebook. You can tape a dried chromatogram in your notebook.
9. Discuss the following questions about Steps 7 and 8 with your team. Write your best thinking in your science notebook. Refer to figure 14.5 to help you review the concepts related to solvent polarity and dipole representations that you studied in the Matter Is Marvelous unit.
   a. What does the solvent you used in the beaker do to the ink spot on the chromatography paper? Does that tell you that the ink you tested is mostly polar or mostly nonpolar?

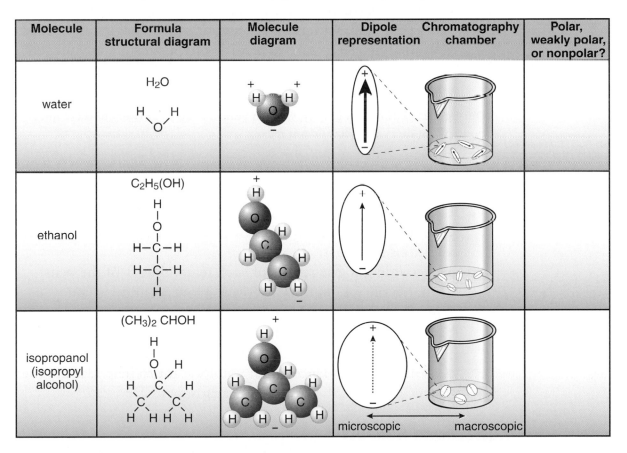

Molecule	Formula structural diagram	Molecule diagram	Dipole representation	Chromatography chamber	Polar, weakly polar, or nonpolar?
water	H_2O				
ethanol	$C_2H_5(OH)$				
isopropanol (isopropyl alcohol)	$(CH_3)_2\,CHOH$		microscopic	macroscopic	

▲ **Figure 14.5 Diagrams representing three solvents used in chromatography.** The molecule diagram represents the charge distribution on molecules, which stems largely from the electronegativity of oxygen. Dipole representation shows relative strength by the boldness of the arrow and the shape of the dipole representation (elliptical or circular). How would you complete the far right column regarding whether the solvent is polar, weakly polar, or nonpolar?

    b. The solvent carries some of the ink colors farther than others. Why do you think that happens?

    c. What are the retention factor (R_f) values for the colors in the ink? What do those values say about the colors that make up the ink?

The final steps of the protocol show how to measure the retention factor, R_f, of the spots on a chromatogram. If your initial ink spot was too large (that is, larger than about two to three times the size of a sentence period), your chromatogram may look like a long smear.

10. Obtain materials for your chromatography analysis for the Carnosaurs CD incident. Prepare your paper chromatogram and add your 4 ink spots to the paper. Obtain from your teacher the separate paper chromatogram with an ink spot from the CD cover. Refer to steps in the Paper Chromatography Protocol as needed.

11. Listen for instructions from your teacher regarding which solvents your team will use. Put on your safety goggles and begin your analysis. Keep careful records of your results in your science notebook. Different teams will use different solvents. You will be expected to share the results of your tests with the class.

During the ink chromatography, write in your notebook answers to these questions: What do I see? What does it mean?

When your chromatogram is dry, attach it to a page in your notebook. Label any key features on the chromatogram.

12. Listen to your teacher for details on when you will share your chromatography observations with the class. Then discuss these questions as a class.

    a. According to the results of each team, does 1 of the pens match the ink on the CD cover? How accurate is your evidence?

    b. From the class chromatograms, what inferences can you make about Josie's story? About Jason's story?

    c. What other evidence might you look for to help identify the true owner of the Crooning Carnosaurs CD?

Reflect and Connect

Answer the following questions individually in your science notebook.

1. The choice of solvents is crucial for proper separation in paper chromatography.

    a. What happens to a chromatogram of water-based ink when the solvent is highly polar?

b. What happens to a chromatogram of a nonpolar ink sample when the solvent is highly polar?

   c. Why can the best separation often be achieved by using a mixture of a nonpolar and a polar solvent?

   d. Which chromatography solvents in your class were mixtures? What might be the benefit of a mixed solvent?

2. The cellulose in chromatography paper is a complex molecule made up of thousands of rings of 6 atoms linked together like beads. The molecules are polar, and the attraction among adjacent cellulose molecules is what holds the fibers together in paper.

   a. What properties of paper allow it to wick up water so well?

   b. When paper is wet, it loses its strength. Use your understanding of water and cellulose molecules to explain why that happens.

3. If you calculated the R_f of a color as 0 ($R_f = 0$), how might you explain that result?

4. Can the R_f of a component be greater than 1.0? Explain your answer.

5. To learn more about evidence in crime cases, answer the following questions after reading the passage on evidence. Criminal investigators need to understand evidence as best they can.

   a. What are some similarities among forensic scientists and other kinds of scientists when they give results from their investigations?

   b. Why must scientists have integrity?

Evidence from a crime scene can be personal evidence (such as testimony or eyewitness accounts) or physical evidence (such as fingerprints or paint chips). Forensic scientists know that personal evidence is subjective. Personal evidence may depend on a person's opinions or perceptions. Physical evidence, on the other hand, consists of facts that should not depend on whom the observer is. That does not mean that physical evidence always answers scientists' questions. Inferences based on physical evidence should still be tested, even if they seem logical. Scientific integrity demands that forensic scientists be open to all possibilities. They must be willing to clear suspects as well as charge them with a crime.

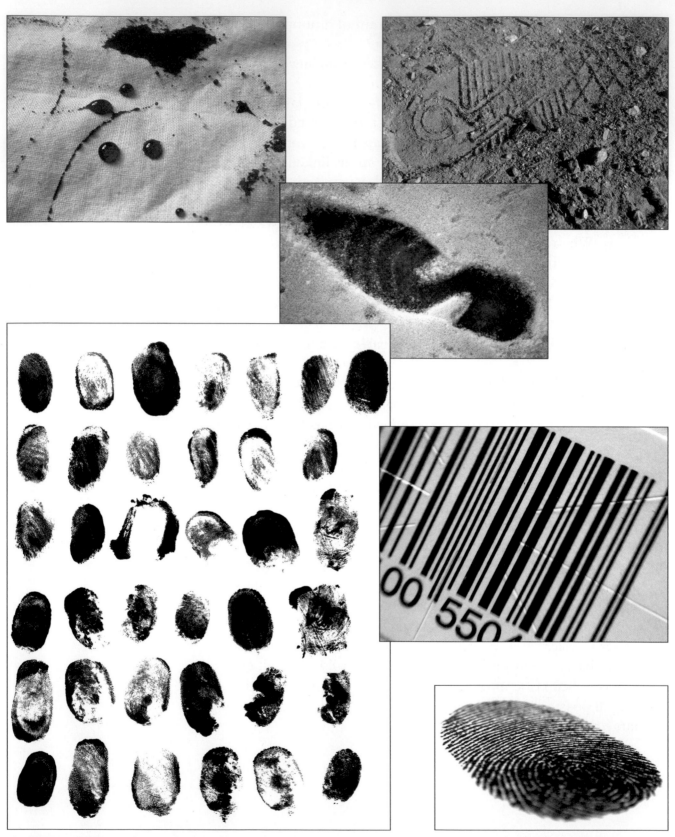

▲ **Figure 14.6** Forensic scientists can distinguish between many types of patterns that lie in evidence. Examples include fingerprints, clothing fibers, shoe prints, and elemental spectra.

Crime, Science, and Technology

Perhaps forensic scientists do not often perform paper chromatography using felt-tipped markers and beakers. However, forensic scientists do perform their chromatography tests using the same principles that you used in the last activity. Forensic scientists use sophisticated chromatography and analyze their results with computers to identify many kinds of substances.

More broadly, forensic investigators must identify distinctive patterns in their evidence. These may be patterns in chromatograms, fingerprints, hair type, prints from shoes, or fibers from clothes. In the Crime, Science, and Technology activity, you will learn how technology helps forensic scientists distinguish patterns. Forensic scientists need a general understanding of these methods to conduct most modern criminal investigations.

READING

High-Tech Tools

Crime investigators and forensic scientists owe much of their success in solving crimes to advances in technology. Technology helps them find distinctive patterns that lie in evidence. They also know how this evidence relates to the properties of matter. For example, the elements of the periodic table are the building blocks of all substances at a crime scene. At an arson scene, investigators use their understanding of what happens to substances that have burned to identify suspicious residues left after a fire.

Elements rarely occur in pure form, however, and compounds consist of combinations of elements. How then do forensic scientists identify unknown substances that are valuable evidence at a crime scene? For example, commonly abused drugs, synthetic fibers, petroleum products, chips of paint, and explosives are some of the compounds that forensic scientists must analyze in their labs. The following sections describe several technologies that help them do that.

Chromatography

Chromatography helps forensic scientists identify unknown substances that consist of mixtures. For example, in the last activity, you explored how paper chromatography can be used to test the components of ink. Another kind of chromatography is called **thin-layer chromatography (TLC).** The stationary phase in TLC is a glass plate covered with a thin layer of very fine grains or particles. They coat the plate like a layer of very fine sand on sandpaper.

A small spot of sample is placed at the bottom of the glass plate. The plate is placed into a chamber just above a liquid solvent. As in paper chromatography, the solvent slowly rises up the plate (see figure 14.7). A component of the sample that is more attracted to the solvent and more soluble in it will move up the TLC plate near the solvent front. A component more attracted to particles on the glass plate will not rise as far.

► Figure 14.7 **Thin-layer chromatography (TLC) setup.** The TLC setup is similar to your setup for paper chromatography. Rather than a paper stationary phase, the solvent and sample can move up a glass plate coated with fine particles.

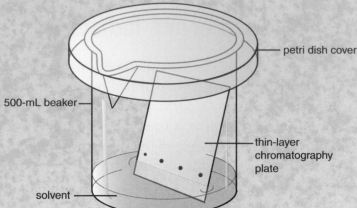

petri dish cover

500-mL beaker

thin-layer chromatography plate

solvent

This process can separate an original sample spot into several distinctive spots.

Sometimes the components of a sample are colorless during a separation. These cannot be seen by eye. Forensic scientists can detect the spots by placing the TLC plate under ultraviolet (UV) light or by spraying the plate with a reacting chemical. You can use a UV light in paper chromatography, too. Once the spots are detected, scientists measure an R_f value for each spot in a sample. That value is then compared with R_f values of known substances to test for a match.

Stop & THINK

1. A TLC was performed on spinach leaves and carrots. The resulting spots on the chromatograms look like those in figure 14.8.

   a. What are the R_f values of each spot on both chromatograms? Remember to measure the distance from the line to the *center* of the spot. Record your work in your notebook.

   b. Use the chart of standard pigments in figure 14.9 to identify the pigments in spinach and carrots.

   c. How can you explain the difference in color between spinach and carrots?

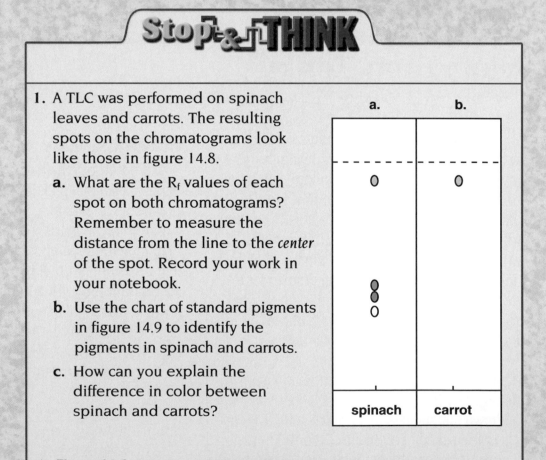

a.   b.

spinach   carrot

▲ Figure 14.8 **Carrot and spinach TLC chromatograms.** With the right solvent, TLC separates the components of a sample into spots. When scientists get patterns like those shown here, they measure to the *center* of each spot for an R_f value. (a) Chromatogram of pigments in spinach leaves. (b) Chromatogram for carrots.

Pigment	Color of Spot	R_f value
Carotene	Yellow-orange	0.93
Chlorophyll *a*	Blue-green	0.46
Chlorophyll *b*	Green	0.42
Xanthophyll	Yellow	0.35

▲ **Figure 14.9** **Table of pigments and R_f values.** When known pigments are tested under the same conditions in TLC, their R_f values become a known against which unknown pigments are matched.

Other types of chromatography move a sample through a hollow column or tube that is very narrow. This method works as if air or liquid were being blown through a long, narrow straw. The hollow column, represented by the straw, is the stationary phase. The mobile phase in the column can be a gas (gas chromatography) or a liquid (high-performance liquid chromatography [HPLC]).

After a sample is added to the column, some components of the sample may move easily with the mobile phase. That is a good example of "like dissolves like" from the Matter Is Marvelous unit. Those components pass quickly through the column and exit first at the other end. In contrast, other components move slowly through the column and take longer to exit. The results are shown in a chromatography plot. The plot shows the amount of a component as it exits the column (on the vertical axis) as a function of time (on the horizontal axis). As shown in figure 14.10, each peak on the chromatogram shows one component of the sample mixture.

Gas and liquid chromatography lets forensic chemists analyze a sample in minutes. Those methods also tell the purity of a sample, or the

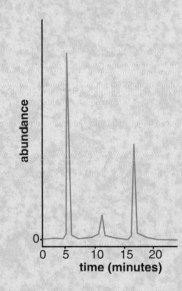

▲ **Figure 14.10** **Chromatogram substance with time.** Each sample component is recorded by a peak when it exits the column. The first component exits at about 6 minutes. Components that are less attracted to the mobile phase exit at about 11 and 17 minutes. Peak size tells the amount of the component in the sample (see figure 14.11).

amount of a component in a sample. That is shown by the height of a peak. The greater the amount of a substance, the larger the peak in the chromatogram (see figure 14.11). A small peak indicates only traces of a substance.

But how do forensic scientists know what the peaks are on a chromatogram? They must compare their results with chromatograms of known samples in the same testing situations. For example, imagine a known sample with peaks at 4 and 11 minutes. If a substance recovered as evidence has peaks at those two times, it can be tentatively identified as the known substance. The key here is matching results from evidence at a crime scene with chromatogram patterns for a set of known substances.

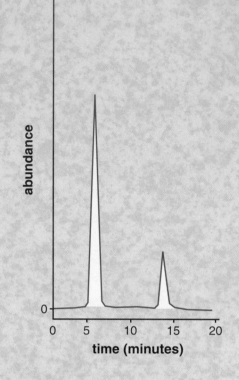

▶ Figure Figure 14.11 **Chromatogram with two peaks**. Some peaks are higher or wider than other peaks. The peak size tells the amount of the substance in a forensics sample. Here, the peak to the left (about 6 minutes) indicates more of that substance than the peak to the right (about 14 minutes).

Stop & THINK
continued

2. Figure 14.12 shows the chromatogram of a known mixture of acetaminophen and codeine in addition to a chromatogram of an unknown drug mixture found at a crime scene.

   a. Compare the 2 chromatograms. What substance is in the unknown mixture in figure 14.12?

▶ **Figure 14.12**
What can you learn from comparing a chromatogram from (a) a known mixture of acetaminophen and codeine with (b) an unknown mixture?

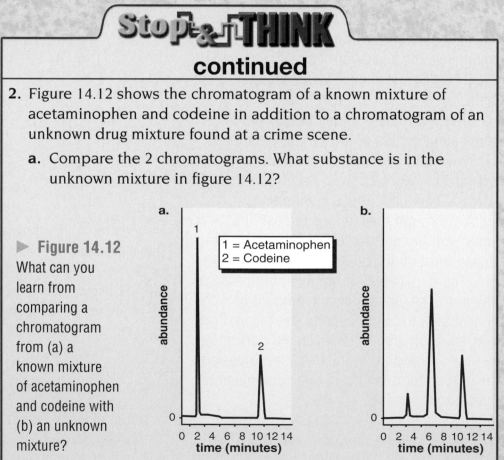

b. What are the exit times of the peaks that do not match the known peaks in figure 14.12?

c. What is not contained in the unknown drug mixture?

3. The chromatography plot of some soft drink additives looks like the one in figure 14.13.

a. What additives might be added to soft drinks? Make a T-table listing the additive and the time when its peak appears on the chromatogram plot.

b. The solvent in this chromatogram is methanol, a polar molecule. If the last additive to exit the column is benzoic acid, what does that suggest about its polarity relative to methanol?

c. How does the polarity of caffeine compare with that of aspartame?

d. A popular soft drink contains 4 additives. In decreasing order of abundance, the additives are aspartame, ascorbic acid, caffeine, and benzoic acid. In your notebook, draw an example of what the chromatography plot for this soda might look like.

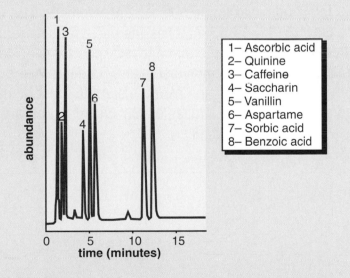

▲ **Figure 14.13 Soft drinks contain a mixture of additives.**
Certain types of chromatography (such as HPLC) separate the additives in soda.

Mass Spectrometry

Sometimes substances at crime scenes are easy to identify with chromatography. At other times, a substance can be a complex mixture or a little-studied chemical. Chromatography may not give positive identification. For example, you may have seen a blurring or stretching of components with your ink chromatography. In cases such as that, forensic scientists need another tool to get a clear answer.

Mass spectrometry is a particularly sensitive tool for identifying evidence from crime scenes. A **mass spectrometer** identifies substances by measuring their atomic weight. Many samples have distinctive patterns of peaks that allow for identification. For example, mass spectrometry is used to test athletes for illegal drugs such as anabolic steroids.

To see how this works, imagine analyzing molecules of water, H_2O. A source of energy in the mass spectrometer strips one electron and breaks bonds in the H_2O molecules. This gives four kinds of fragments: H_2O^{+1}, OH^{+1}, O^{+1}, and H^{+1}. Each of them has the same charge, +1, but different masses. Using a periodic table, their masses are 18, 17, 16, and 1, respectively. These fragments show up as four peaks on a mass spectrum (see figure 14.14).

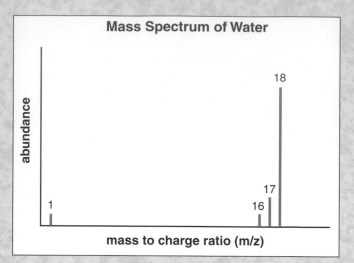

▲ **Figure 14.14 Mass spectrum for water.** This mass spectrum shows the abundance of fragments from water, H_2O, as a function of their mass (*x*-axis). Low-abundance fragments are H^+, O^+, and OH^+, with H_2O^+ the most abundant.

No two substances give the same mass spectrum. This lets forensic scientists identify with certainty the substance in question. For example, a mass spectrum such as figure 14.15 matches the pattern for heroin. A key point is that a mass spectrometer does not identify substances. Rather, a mass spectrum from an unknown sample must be matched with a mass spectrum from a library of known substance.

▶ **Figure 14.15**
Mass spectrum of heroin. When an unidentified drug was found at a crime scene, it gave this mass spectrum. Because this mass spectrum matches heroin's, forensic chemists can identify the drug as heroin. No other drug has the same spectrum.

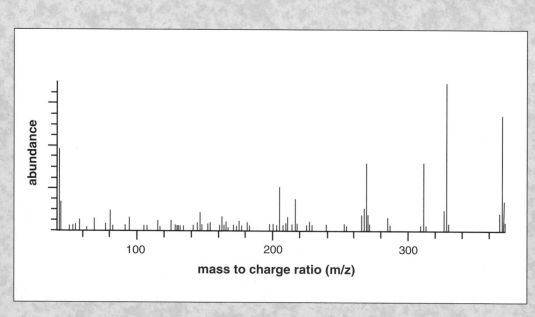

Experienced forensic chemists can use patterns of substances to identify by eye those that they encounter frequently. You use this approach in the evaluate activity. Computers also can be used to store the mass spectra of many substances, forming a library of known substances. Using such databases, computers help forensic scientists quickly find matches for substances from crime scenes. Similar types of databases in computers are used to catalog fingerprints and test for matches between evidence and suspects at crime scenes.

Stop & THINK
continued

4. For each of the following molecules, draw a simple diagram of what its mass spectrum might look like. Refer to figure 14.16. Label possible peaks with mass and the atoms and assume that all fragments have a charge of +1. Bonds between atoms can only be broken, not formed, in the mass spectrometer.

   a. CO_2 (carbon dioxide)

   b. CH_4 (methane)

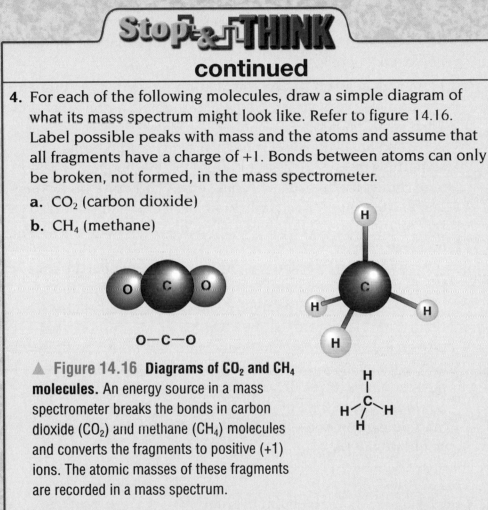

O—C—O

H—C—H with H above and H below

▲ **Figure 14.16 Diagrams of CO_2 and CH_4 molecules.** An energy source in a mass spectrometer breaks the bonds in carbon dioxide (CO_2) and methane (CH_4) molecules and converts the fragments to positive (+1) ions. The atomic masses of these fragments are recorded in a mass spectrum.

5. Other technologies also give spectral patterns. For example, X-ray spectroscopy can tell investigators what elements are in a sample. You learned in the last unit that such methods allow astronomers to determine the elements in stars and the molecules in nebulae. Answer the following based on figure 14.17 and the investigation of jewelry chemistry that follows. Is the ring a fake?

   a. Refer to figure 14.17 and compare the X-ray emission spectrum for the graduation ring in with the X-ray emission spectra for the metals. Is the ring pure platinum? Explain why or why not.

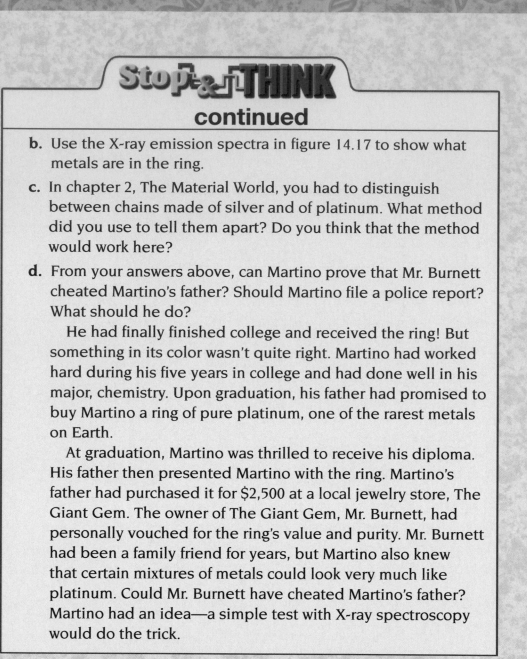

Stop & THINK
continued

b. Use the X-ray emission spectra in figure 14.17 to show what metals are in the ring.

c. In chapter 2, The Material World, you had to distinguish between chains made of silver and of platinum. What method did you use to tell them apart? Do you think that the method would work here?

d. From your answers above, can Martino prove that Mr. Burnett cheated Martino's father? Should Martino file a police report? What should he do?

He had finally finished college and received the ring! But something in its color wasn't quite right. Martino had worked hard during his five years in college and had done well in his major, chemistry. Upon graduation, his father had promised to buy Martino a ring of pure platinum, one of the rarest metals on Earth.

At graduation, Martino was thrilled to receive his diploma. His father then presented Martino with the ring. Martino's father had purchased it for $2,500 at a local jewelry store, The Giant Gem. The owner of The Giant Gem, Mr. Burnett, had personally vouched for the ring's value and purity. Mr. Burnett had been a family friend for years, but Martino also knew that certain mixtures of metals could look very much like platinum. Could Mr. Burnett have cheated Martino's father? Martino had an idea—a simple test with X-ray spectroscopy would do the trick.

DNA Typing—A New Tool in Criminal Investigations

Evidence at crime scenes certainly is not always a strange powder or a metal. Very often, evidence is a biological material. When solving crimes, forensic scientists need ways to determine, without a doubt, from whom those biological materials originated. That evidence often leads forensic scientists to the perpetrator of a crime.

You may have heard the term *DNA*. You will study much more about DNA in the next grade level of this program. **DNA** is short for **deoxyribonucleic acid.** The DNA in animal cells has a code to determine eye or hair color or the pattern of fingerprints. In 1985, scientists in England found that humans have widely different DNA patterns. In fact, each person (except for identical twins) has his or her own unique DNA pattern. This lets investigators use DNA from a crime scene as evidence, just like fingerprints.

Topic: DNA
Go to: www.scilinks.org
Code: 1Inquiry700

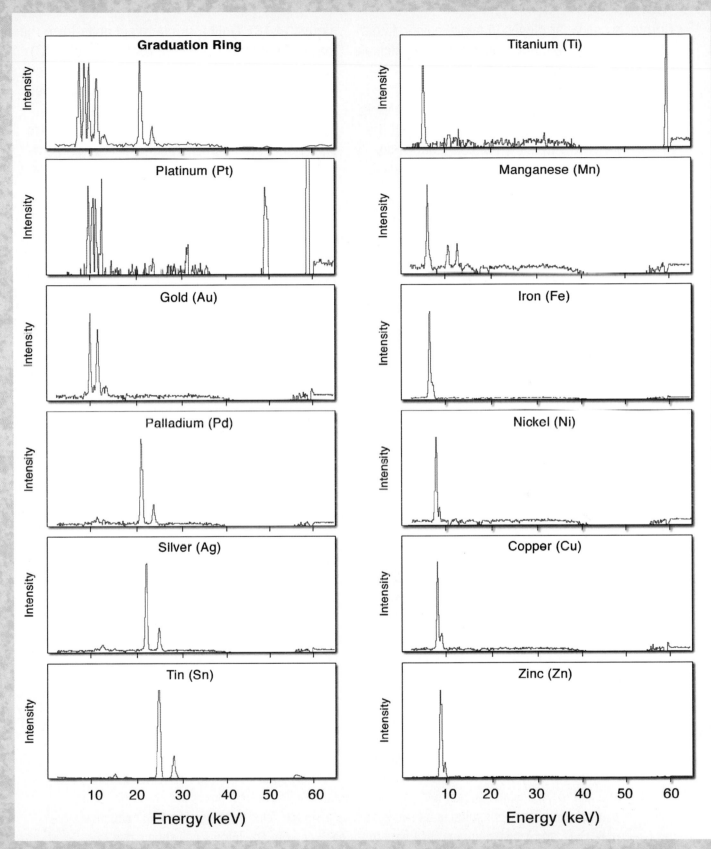

▲ **Figure 14.17** Should Martino's father have paid $2,500 for the graduation ring, supposedly made of pure platinum? Compare the X-ray emission spectrum of the graduation ring with the X-ray emission spectra for metals to evaluate this.

Criminals can wear gloves to avoid leaving fingerprints, but they frequently leave evidence such as blood, hair, or saliva. Those traces contain DNA.

Where is DNA found? You learn later that most DNA is found in the nuclei of cells. DNA is a large molecule twisted into a spiral called the double helix, sort of like a twisted ladder (see figure 14.18). Only four chemical units form the **bases** found in DNA: adenine (A), cytosine (C), guanine (G), and thymine (T). The exact pattern of A, C, G, and T in DNA is unique for each person. This is how DNA stores hereditary data, regardless of the tissue. Just think—you share some similarities in DNA pattern with all mem-

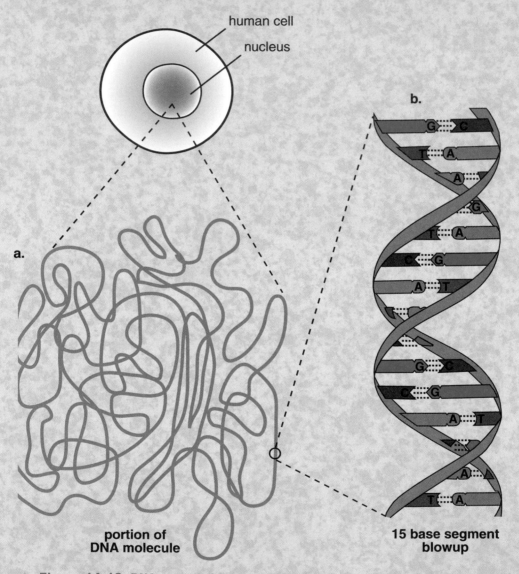

human cell

nucleus

a.

b.

portion of
DNA molecule

15 base segment
blowup

▲ **Figure 14.18 DNA strand with a close-up of a double helix.** The DNA strand in (a) is part of a single, long molecule. DNA consists entirely of sequences of the four chemical units: adenine (A), cytosine (C), guanine (G), and thymine (T). These DNA bases are shown in (b) as pairs of molecules that spiral in a form known as a double helix. Specific repeating sequences of A, C, G, and T give a unique DNA pattern for each person. The human cell shows that this DNA comes from a cell nucleus.

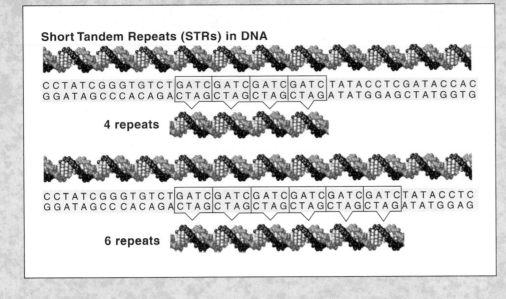

Short Tandem Repeats (STRs) in DNA

```
CCTATCGGGTGTCT GATC GATC GATC GATC TATACCTCGATACCAC
GGATAGCCCACAGA CTAG CTAG CTAG CTAG ATATGGAGCTATGGTG
```

4 repeats

```
CCTATCGGGTGTCT GATC GATC GATC GATC GATC GATC TATACCTC
GGATAGCC CACAGA CTAG CTAG CTAG CTAG CTAG CTAG ATATGGAG
```

6 repeats

◀ **Figure 14.19 DNA showing 4 and 6 repeats for a key DNA segment.** The repeating base pattern GATC is located in a specific segment of the DNA molecule. For this DNA segment, the individual has patterns of both 4 repeats in the segment and 6 repeats in the same segment. They are called a 4,6 repeat. This repeat pattern leads to a unique DNA fingerprint.

bers of your immediate family, but nobody else on Earth has your exact pattern of DNA! The only exception is if you have an identical twin.

Forensic investigators now use specific segments of DNA for identification. Those segments have an order of the four bases, such as GATC, that repeats. The key is measuring how many times that sequence is repeated in a given DNA segment. This is called **DNA typing.** The method gives a distinctive DNA fingerprint when many genetic markers are analyzed.

A person has two features in each DNA segment—one inherited from his or her mother and a second from his or her father. For example, an individual with 4 repeats and 6 repeats (GATC) in a DNA segment is shown in figure 14.19. The pattern of these repeats is called **tandem repeats** ("tandem" because the repeats lie next to each other). In figure 14.19, the individual's DNA pattern for this segment is called a 4,6 repeat. Looking at this pattern for several key DNA segments is called **short tandem repeat (STR) analysis.** STR testing is the most common method used by the FBI and criminal investigators today.

STR results are shown as bands that reveal a person's repeat pattern (see figure 14.20). The position of each band must be compared with STR positions in a known sample. These are

shown in the "lanes" next to the sample. Counting up from the bottom reveals the repeat pattern, such as the 4,6 STR pattern in figure 14.20.

DNA typing is an important part of testing biological materials in crime laboratories. Reexamining such DNA evidence at a later time has also led to the acquittal of innocent people. Similarly, DNA typing provides key evidence to convict suspects who are guilty. And with the forensic needs in disasters such as the World Trade Center terrorist attacks, new approaches to DNA typing have reduced the time and cost of analysis (see the sidebar, Somber Solutions).

▶ **Figure 14.20 Short tandem repeat (STR) results for a 4,6 repeat.** The STR pattern is shown by positions of gel bands. These are compared with known band positions to the left. The results show a person with a 4,6 repeat DNA fingerprint.

4,6 STR Gel Bands

L

6
5
4
3
2
1

Number of repeats

Somber Solutions

In the face of new challenges, scientists must refine and develop strategies for answering complex questions. Solutions that use new technologies often emerge because of a new problem that needs to be solved. Forensic scientists working in the wake of the World Trade Center attacks found themselves in that situation. They needed to match 14,249 body parts recovered from the wreckage of the Twin Towers to the 2,795 people thought to have perished at the site. Their technological innovations and solutions to the challenge placed them at the forefront of DNA typing.

As little as ten years ago, DNA fingerprinting required long, intact sequences of DNA for analysis. These were typically longer than about 5,000 bases. However, human remains from mass disasters, burial sites, and many forensic cases may contain very little undamaged DNA in cell nuclei. In the case of the World Trade Center attacks, some of the recovered pieces of bone and tissue were decomposed so badly that they contained only short intact DNA sequences. Forensic scientists needed a new approach to be able to work accurately with the many degraded samples.

As a solution, forensic scientists used a newer method of DNA fingerprinting that uses much shorter sequences of DNA—the length was only about 100 bases long. Scientists found that other valuable DNA segments consisted of just 50 DNA bases. The trick was not using the DNA in cell nuclei, but extracting DNA from cell mitochondria, or **mtDNA**. Cells can have hundreds of mitochondria, compared with having a single nucleus. After the World Trade Center attacks, forensic scientists collected samples from victims' family members and genetic samples left behind by victims. Many of these DNA samples were from toothbrushes, hairbrushes, and combs. After analyzing the samples, the measurements were used to develop an identification database. That set of "known" DNA profiles was used to make matches against DNA profiles from human remains recovered from the site.

In total, tens of thousands of DNA analyses would be required for the enormous number of remains and the large number of reference samples collected for the database. This presented two very serious practical challenges. First, the scientists needed to process mtDNA profiles quickly and inexpensively. Second, they needed to sift through the database quickly and efficiently to make matches. Those actions would give families of the victims certain closure about their loved ones.

Fortunately, recent research had reduced the time for DNA and mtDNA analysis from days to minutes. Only a tiny sample was needed, and the cost had been reduced to about $10 per sample (older methods cost up to $2,500 per sample). By using computers to rapidly

World Trade Center twin towers in New York City.

Wooly mammoths and horses on tundra. Wooly mammoths, bison, and horses have not roamed the Arctic tundra for thousands of years. However, traces of these animals still remain in the soil. Their DNA fingerprints have been recovered and identified from Arctic soils. This evidence is consistent with fossil evidence from the same ecosystem.

sift through sample analyses and the database, the new methods quickly answered the question, Does it match? New technologies such as these have significantly reduced the amount of time, sample size, and cost needed for DNA profiling.

Eventually, the hope is that new forensic tools will be integrated into forensic laboratories and become part of the investigator's "toolbox." If so, scientists and investigators will be able to use the technologies to evaluate evidence from crime scenes and disaster sites around the world and to apply them to war zones in places such as Iraq, Bosnia, or Rwanda. Such methods have also been applied in other fields, such as identifying the remains of extinct animals in ecosystems. For example, distinctive mtDNA fingerprints of wooly mammoths, horses, and bison have been retrieved from the soils of the Arctic tundra, even though those animals have not inhabited the region for thousands of years.

Reflect and Connect

1. For each item on the list of crime scene evidence, do the following:
   - Describe what analytical method could tell the identity or source of the evidence.
   - Describe what the results of the test might tell you.
   - Determine whether you would be certain of the results or would need to conduct further tests.

   Crime Scene Evidence
   a. White powder found in the house of a teenager accused of dealing drugs
   b. Skin cells under an assault victim's fingernails
   c. Ink from a pen found on a man suspected of writing a ransom note

2. DNA typing can resolve whether people are genetically related because an STR pattern comes from a person's biological parents. Use the DNA bands in figure 14.21 to evaluate whether the mother and father are biological parents for the child. Does each band in the child's DNA fingerprint match one from the mother or father? Explain how you can tell.

3. Results of DNA typing in an assault investigation are in figure 14.22. Lanes 1, 2, and 3 show STR results from the victim and

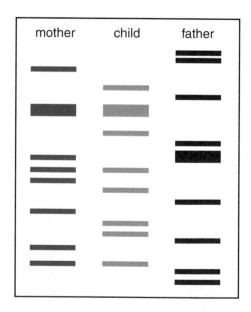

▲ **Figure 14.21 DNA STR bands of a child and parents.** Are the mother and father the actual biological parents of the child? DNA fingerprints such as these tell whether the three people are genetically related. Such DNA comparisons are made when paternity or maternity is in question, as in the case of kidnapping.

2 suspects. Lane 4 shows gel band positions for a standard sample. Lane 5 is DNA evidence from blood in the victim's car, where the alleged assault took place. Lane 6 is DNA evidence from another blood sample retrieved from the victim's car.

a. Does the DNA evidence support the victim's claim that she was bleeding in her car? Explain your evidence.

b. Which suspect is the source of the blood in the car? How do you know?

c. The victim came to police with bloodstains on her shirt and shoes. She claimed to have been assaulted in her car by her boyfriend. Her boyfriend (suspect A) denied the claim and pointed out that he was not the only man she was seeing. The other man (suspect B) also denied assaulting the woman. Does the DNA evidence prove who is telling the truth? Explain your answer.

4. Today new technologies are used to analyze crime scene evidence more completely than in the past. People imprisoned on death row are requesting that their cases be reopened so that evidence can be analyzed using new technologies. As a result, thousands of inmates are now waiting for their cases to be reevaluated. Do you think this is a good use of new forensic technologies? Why or why not?

5. DNA typing helps couples establish their rights as parents of a child by proving their biological relationship. In addition, DNA typing helps people conduct searches to find long-lost relatives. DNA typing can also reveal relationships among people that may be surprising and potentially hurtful. Would you want your DNA profile to be part of a large database so that it was available for anyone to search? Why or why not?

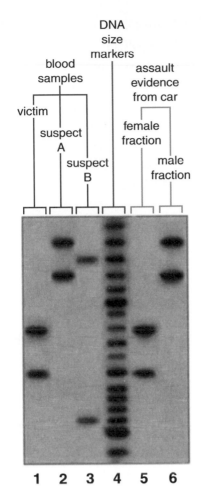

▲ **Figure 14.22 DNA evidence in an assault case.** DNA typing for blood samples from an assault victim and two suspects can be compared with blood evidence recovered at the scene of the crime.

Blood as Evidence

ELABORATE

In the last activity, you saw that DNA typing can be used when cells are obtained as evidence. This can establish who was at a crime scene. Besides hair, skin, or saliva at crime scenes, another source of biological evidence is blood. The nucleated white cells in blood samples can be used for DNA typing. As with the other methods you studied, blood can provide distinctive evidence for solving a criminal investigation.

But how do forensic scientists know whether a substance is blood? Depending on factors such as the surface that the substance falls on or how old the substance is, it may be difficult to distinguish blood from

► **Figure 14.23**
High-magnification photographs of fibers. Trace evidence such as these fibers can provide key evidence to establish who was at a crime scene. The fibers are from a red carpet.

other stains. In the Blood as Evidence activity, you use inquiry to test and figure out whether certain stains at a high school could be blood.

Part I: A Close Look at Blood

Materials
For each team of three students

1 microscope

1 set of slides

Cautions

Wear gloves while handling any biological materials thought to contain blood.

Always handle chemicals carefully. Wear safety goggles and protective gloves when you are conducting tests with chemicals. Use paper plates to hold the unknown samples as you test them so that you don't handle the samples once you apply chemicals to them. If you get chemicals on your skin, wash thoroughly with water and report the incident to your teacher.

Process and Procedure

1. Think back to your studies and investigations with cells in unit 2, The Machinery of Life. Then write the answers to these questions in your science notebook.
   a. What differences are there among cells in plants and animals?
   b. How are red blood cells different from other body cells?

◀ Figure 14.24
Using microscopes.
Blood cells can be iden-
tified with microscopes.

2. Use a microscope to look at the slides your teacher prepared.
As you look at the slides, do these things.
   a. Make a table in your science notebook with headings for the
   slide number, a written description of observations, a drawing of what you see through the microscope, and your prediction about the identity of the substance on the slide.
   b. Study each slide and fill in your table.
   c. Discuss your observations and predictions with your team.
3. Check your predictions with your teacher. How many slides did
you correctly identify?

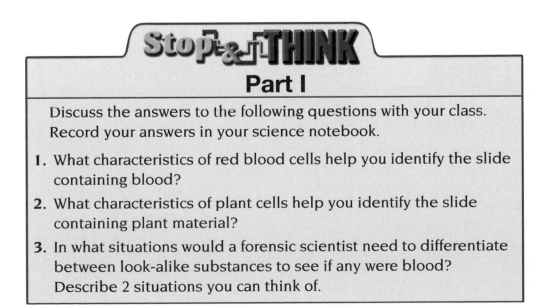

Stop & THINK

Part I

Discuss the answers to the following questions with your class.
Record your answers in your science notebook.

1. What characteristics of red blood cells help you identify the slide
containing blood?

2. What characteristics of plant cells help you identify the slide
containing plant material?

3. In what situations would a forensic scientist need to differentiate
between look-alike substances to see if any were blood?
Describe 2 situations you can think of.

Part II: Is It Blood?

Microscopes help forensic scientists distinguish between a stain that looks like blood and one that is real blood. But this analysis might not be definitive, and getting a microscope to a crime scene may be difficult. Therefore, forensic scientists need other methods to distinguish blood from similar-looking substances. In this part of the investigation, work with your team to determine whether any samples in a set of stains are real blood.

Materials
For each team of three students

3 pairs of safety goggles

3 pairs of safety gloves

1 set of suspected bloodstains on filter paper

1 sample of known blood on filter paper

access to testing stations

access to the Internet

2 paper plates

1 pair of scissors

Process and Procedure

1. Before coming to the science lab to analyze stains, search the Internet for tests that forensic scientists use to identify blood. Take notes in your science notebook about the tests you find and come to class prepared to try some of those tests on stains that look like blood.

2. Read about the following bloody situation for a high school drama teacher. Your teacher may assign this short reading as homework.

READING

Just Playing Around?

The inspector burst into the bedroom, but it was too late. She lay motionless in bed, with a small, fresh bite on the side of her neck. Blood trickled down to her chest, soaking into her white nightgown and the pillow beneath her pale face. The bedroom curtains rustled in a gentle breeze next to an open window. The perpetrator could not be far.

The horrifying scene was in the school's spring production of *Dracula*. Students in the drama club were prohibited from using real blood in theater productions. They were

▲ **Figure 14.25 Spattered stage blood.** What is the difference between stage blood and real blood? The drama teacher, Ms. Jones, needed to find out.

supposed to use a synthetic, safe "stage blood." Still, the effect of the blood in the opening night performance was vivid and shocking. The audience had gasped.

Ms. Jones, the new drama teacher, began to wonder. Could the blood have been real? She had a talented troupe, and the show had gone very well, particularly the scene in the bedroom. But rarely in theater do things go *that* well on opening night! Depending on the source, animal or human blood could be a significant health risk, so breaking that rule was no laughing matter. Ms. Jones also knew that the star senior playing Dracula, Matt Sparks, was a practical joker and that he had an uncle who owned a

large steak house in town. Might Matt have obtained animal blood at the steak house? Had he taken a joke too far?

After the audience and actors had gone home for the evening, Ms. Jones returned to the now-quiet men's dressing room. Indeed, on a shelf in a back closet, she found several containers with dried, bloodlike mixtures (figure 14.25). The containers held different reddish-brown substances of various consistencies. Some paper towels in the garbage had apparently been used to wipe up the spatters. How could she tell whether one of the mixtures might be real blood? Some lab work was in order.

3. With your team, discuss the tests you researched. Find out from your teacher what chemicals and tests are available for you to use.

Make note of all tests but be prepared to try only those that use chemicals provided by your teacher. Not all chemicals that you read about will be available to you. Some chemicals are expensive and not safe to use in a classroom setting.

4. Obtain from your teacher a bag of labeled stains from the shelf in the men's dressing room. With your team, plan how you will determine whether the stains are blood. The appearance of the stain may give you a clue about its identity, and microscopes may still be available to you. But you need more evidence than that. What specific tests can you conduct, and what evidence will you be looking for? Write your plan in your science notebook and confirm it with your teacher.

Many tests rely on a chemical reaction that changes the properties of the stain, making it unusable in further tests. How can you make sure that you maintain samples of each stain to use for another test or to repeat your test? Keep in mind that a forensic scientist will want to preserve as much stain as possible for tests such as DNA. Those tests can identify the donor of the biological substance. If you decide that a stain is blood, you should be able to justify your decision with observations from multiple tests.

Caution

Wear safety goggles when conducting tests with chemicals.

5. Move to lab stations to conduct your tests, sharing materials with other teams. Record the results of your tests in a data table in your science notebook.

6. Share the results of your investigation with the class. Did other teams reach the same conclusion? What evidence did they have that was different from yours?

7. If real blood was used in the drama production, what action should Ms. Jones take next?

Part II

Answer the following questions in a class discussion. Record your answers in your science notebook. Your initial research from Step 1 of this activity will help you.

1. Explain why the tests you used to identify blood caused a reaction with blood and not with most other substances. Were there some exceptions?

2. How does the process of inquiry support your conclusion that blood is present in a sample?

Part III: Are You My Type?

Once forensic scientists find blood at a crime scene, they must examine it further. First, they record the shape and pattern of the bloodstain. The bloodstain might tell, for example, whether a bleeding person was standing or moving, was wounded at the head or the leg, or was hit by a bullet or a blunt object. Blood that falls a short distance often makes a round drop. Blood dripping from higher up can make a splash pattern, with tiny droplets surrounding the central drop. Blood hitting at an angle makes an oblong drop that tells the direction of movement. Analyzing the patterns of blood spatters is serious science. Next, forensic scientists determine whether the blood is from a human or another animal.

Finally, forensic scientists analyze the stain for its genetic patterns using DNA/STR technology. The scientists can compare the DNA types of victims and suspects with blood evidence recovered at a crime scene to see if there is a match. In Part III, you learn how blood types can help identify guilty suspects.

Topic: blood type
Go to: www.scilinks.org
Code: 1Inquiry713

Materials
For the entire class

1 blood-typing tray

3 toothpicks

1 sample of simulated blood

1 vial of anti-A serum

1 vial of anti-B serum

1 vial of anti-Rh serum

1 overhead projector

Process and Procedure

1. How does blood-typing work? To answer that question, read Eight Types of Blood. Blood-typing is one of the most important methods in criminal investigations. Discuss your understanding of the reading with the class.

Blood consists of cells and other substances suspended in plasma. **Plasma** is a clear, straw-colored liquid that is about 90 percent water. The other 10 percent of plasma includes proteins, essential elements, food molecules, oxygen, carbon dioxide, and cellular waste.

Red blood cells are a critical part of blood (figure 14.26). As a red blood cell matures, it loses its nucleus and other cell structures and fills with hemoglobin. **Hemoglobin** is a protein in red blood cells that moves oxygen from the lungs to body tissues during cellular respiration. You studied this process in The Machinery of Life unit. Hemoglobin contains iron, which also combines with oxygen to give red blood cells their color. Dried or dirty blood at a crime scene can vary in color and is not as easy to identify as fresh blood.

White blood cells contain nuclei. They are colorless because they lack hemoglobin. They move from the bloodstream by slipping through the walls of capillaries and migrating among the cells of body tissues. They play a major role in defending the body against sicknesses caused by pathogens that invade the body. A **pathogen** is any foreign particle or organism, such as a bacterium, fungus, or virus, that has the potential to cause a disease.

The surfaces of red blood cells host millions of structures called **antigens**. In the ABO system, antigens determine the blood type of a person. For example, if red blood cells have A antigens on their surfaces, the person is type A. Type B individuals have B antigens on their red blood cells. Type AB individuals have both A and B antigens on their red blood cells. Type O individuals have neither A nor B antigens. This results in four blood types: A, B, O, and AB.

One more factor is essential in blood-typing—determining whether the red blood cells also have an Rh antigen. That antigen was first discovered in rhesus monkeys. About 85 percent of the U.S. population has an Rh antigen, making them Rh positive. People lacking this antigen are Rh negative. Combining ABO blood type (O, A, B, AB) with the Rh antigen (+, −) gives eight distinctive types of blood: O^+, O^-, A^+, A^-, B^+, B^-, AB^+, and AB^-. Figure 14.27 shows estimates of the frequency in the U.S. population of these eight blood types.

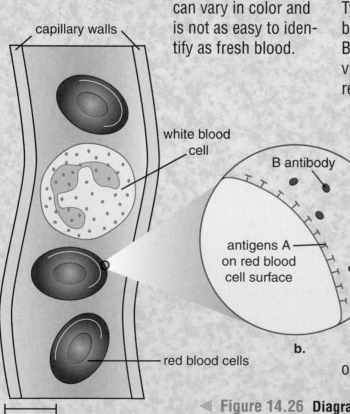

capillary walls

white blood cell

B antibody

antigens A on red blood cell surface

b.

red blood cells

~5 μm

a.

◀ **Figure 14.26 Diagram of blood and red blood cells with antigens.** Blood consists largely of (a) red and white blood cells in plasma. (b) The close-up shows antigens on the surface of red blood cells and antibodies in the plasma.

Blood type	Frequency (percent)
O⁺	38%
O⁻	7%
A⁺	34%
A⁻	6%
B⁺	9%
B⁻	2%
AB⁺	3%
AB⁻	1%

▲ **Figure 14.27 Table showing frequencies of eight blood types in the U.S. population.** ABO blood type is shown in left column with + or − for Rh antigen. Type O⁺ is most common, and AB⁻ is least common. Frequencies may vary depending on ethnic group. Do you know your blood type?

Sometimes a person can lose a lot of blood, such as during surgery or uncontrollable bleeding. Part of his or her treatment would include getting more blood, but not any human blood will do. Careful attention must be paid to blood type. The reason is because blood also contains proteins called **antibodies**. Antibodies are molecules that are activated in response to foreign antigens. Antibodies circulate freely in your bloodstream and will not react with the antigens on your red blood cells. But mixing the antigens of an ABO blood with the same type of antibodies can lead to serious consequences. The antibodies will attach to antigens on those blood cells. For example, antibody A (called anti-A) links to the A antigen and antibody B (anti-B) links to the B antigen. When more and more red blood cells are linked together with the same antigens, dangerous clots of red blood cells may form.

Agglutination is the process where antibodies link red blood cells together and cause clumps in the bloodstream. It is a reaction between antigens and antibodies. Agglutination can be fatal during medical procedures such as blood transfusions (see figure 14.28). At the same time, a simple visual test for agglutination can be used to determine the ABO type for a blood sample. That test is a key tool for forensic scientists.

The agglutination test for blood-typing is simple. Scientists add a test solution to a blood sample and see if it clumps, or agglutinates. The test solution is called serum, and two key serums contain antibody A (anti-A serum) or antibody B (anti-B serum). If the blood agglutinates only in reaction to anti-A serum, scientists know the blood is type A. If the blood agglutinates only with anti-B serum, they know it is type B. If agglutination occurs with both anti-A and anti-B serums, the blood type is AB. If no agglutination occurs with either serum, it is type O blood (that is, no A antigens or B antigens on red blood cells).

Another agglutination test determines whether the blood is Rh positive or negative. As with blood antibodies, scientists use an anti-Rh serum that causes agglutination with Rh-positive blood. If the blood does not clump, it is Rh negative.

Blood type	Frequency in U.S. population	Antigens on red blood cells	Antibodies in plasma	Can give blood to these types	Can receive blood from these types
A	40%	A antigens	anti-B	A, AB	O, A
B	10%	B antigens	anti-A	B, AB	O, B
AB	4%	A and B antigens	neither anti-A nor anti-B	AB	O, A, B, AB
O	46%	Neither A nor B antigens	both anti-A and anti-B	O, A, B, AB	O

▲ **Figure 14.28 Table of blood types, blood donors, and blood receivers.** Donor blood contains only red blood cells with antigens in saline, but no plasma. Therefore, donor blood does not contain antibodies.

2. Answer the following questions based on the reading in Step 1.
   a. What are the components of blood?
   b. What feature on the surface of red blood cells can make them different from person to person?
   c. How do antibodies cause agglutination? What is happening physically in the blood that is harmful and that may even be fatal?
3. How do scientists determine a blood type? To answer that question, copy the table in figure 14.29 in your science notebook. Write 1 of the ABO blood types in each of the 4 empty cells depending on whether a blood sample agglutinates when the anti-A (top) serum or the anti-B serum (side) is added. Explain your 4 entries in the table in your notebook using the words *antibody* and *antigen*.

ABO blood type table		Agglutinates with anti-A serum	
		Yes	No
Agglutinates with anti-B serum?	Yes		
	No		

▲ **Figure 14.29 Table of blood types with serum.** Two serums, anti-A and anti-B, are used to test a blood sample for agglutination. The results provide information as to which of the four ABO blood types is present in the sample.

4. Can a person with type A blood receive a transfusion with type B blood? Discuss that question with your partner and explain your answer in your notebook using the words *antigen* and *antibody.*
5. Watch as your teacher demonstrates the blood testing procedure. In which wells do the blood samples agglutinate? Use your table from Step 3 to identify blood types.
6. Blood samples are recovered from a broken store window at a crime scene, and 5 employees are questioned as suspects in the case. Blood-typing results from the recovered blood and the 5 suspects are shown in figure 14.30.
   a. Copy a sketch of these results in your notebook and label the blood type beneath each agglutination test. Use the ABO system, with +/– for the Rh antigen. Include the frequency in the population for each blood type.

	crime scene	suspect #1	suspect #2	suspect #3	suspect #4	suspect #5
anti-A serum	●	●	●	●	●	●
anti-B serum	●	●	●	●	●	●
anti-Rh serum	●	●	●	●	●	●
blood type (ABO, +/−)						
frequency in population (percent)						

▲ **Figure 14.30 Agglutination tests for blood from a crime scene and five suspects.** Is there a match between crime scene and suspect blood? What types of blood are shown?

b. Is there a match between the crime scene and 1 of the suspects? If so, what is the blood type and the estimated frequency in the population for that blood type?

c. What is the least common blood type shown? What is the most common blood type shown?

7. To test the guilt of a suspect, an investigator may need to know the likelihood that another suspect has the same ABO$^{+/-}$ blood type. That information is also vital for prosecutors in criminal cases who need to present a case of guilt "beyond a reasonable doubt." The following reading will help you see how such evidence is evaluated. Following the reading, complete the questions in Step 8.

Beyond a Reasonable Doubt

When forensic scientists identify a suspect using evidence only from a crime scene, how certain are they? Often, they are very sure because they have calculated the odds that they are wrong as being very low. But how do they know that their odds of being wrong are so low?

The way that forensic scientists "take a chance" when they interpret evidence is just like figuring odds in gambling. Both rely on probability. **Probability** is the frequency of an event in a larger set of occurrences. For example, how often would a person flip a coin and have it land heads up? This happens very close to half, or 50 percent, of the time (50 out of 100 flips, or 1 time in every 2 flips). Another way to write that is that the probability, or "odds," are $P = \frac{1}{2} = 0.5$.

But what if you were only 50 percent sure ($P = 0.50$) that you could identify a suspect? Those odds would not satisfy a forensic scientist. Forensic scientists increase their odds of not being wrong (lower values of P) by including other factors to identify a suspect. These are called **independent events** or factors. For example, if event A were independent, it would not affect whether event B would also occur. With coin flipping, a person getting a heads while standing on one side of the room is independent of a person's flipping result on the other side of the room. There is no way that the second person can increase or decrease the odds of the first person getting a heads. Alternatively, two sequential flips by the same person are also independent events.

When two events are independent, you can find the probability that they will both occur. You do this by taking the probability of each event and multiplying those probabilities. Therefore, the chance of tails on a coin flip is 50 percent ($P = \frac{1}{2} = 0.5$). What is the probability that you would flip a coin twice and get tails both times? To find the answer, multiply the probabilities for the two flips:

$$P_{total} = P_{flip\#1} \times P_{flip\#2}$$
$$= \frac{1}{2} \times \frac{1}{2} = \frac{1}{4} \text{ or}$$
$$= 0.5 \times 0.5 = 0.25 \text{ (or 25\%)}$$

The probability for two tails is 25 times out of 100, less than the 50 percent probability for either of the initial events. How many times out of 100 would you likely flip heads, heads, and then tails ($P = 0.125$)? Can you show that the probability of rolling a 1 on a die (which has six sides) and then flipping heads on a coin is about 8 percent ($P = 0.083$)?

a.

b.

Imagine that you have three dice and two pennies. (a) Can you show that the odds of rolling three 1s together are P = 0.0046, or about 0.5 percent? How many times do you "win" per 1,000 tries? (b) What are the odds of rolling three 1s, then flipping two heads?

Blood feature (type, enzymes, proteins)	Frequency in population	Probability (P) of each feature	Accumulating probability (P_{total}) per next feature
Adenosine Deaminase, Type 1	90%	0.90	0.90
Type O	46%	0.46	0.41
Adenylate Kinase, Type 1	91%	0.91	0.38
Erythrocyte Acid Phosphatase, Type BA	43%	0.43	0.16
Esterase D, Type 1	79%	0.79	0.13
Phosphoglucomutase, Type 1+ 1+	41%	0.41	0.05

Six independent blood ingredients and their frequency in the population. Forensic scientists look at the combination of genetic markers in a bloodstain to evaluate from whom the blood came. The frequency of occurrence of people with this makeup is calculated by multiplying the frequencies for each marker.

Forensic scientists use probability to test matches in their evidence. They often need to calculate the probability that a suspect whose blood matches that from a crime scene is actually the person who left the blood there. If blood at a crime scene is type O, a type O suspect could be guilty. However, 46 percent of the population also has type O blood (see figure 14.27). Using the Rh antigen as an independent factor, the odds decrease a few percent when the person is O+ (38 percent). The odds decrease much further (to about 7 percent) when the blood is type O‾. Other special ingredients, or genetic markers, in the blood can be used as additional independent factors. These include the varieties of blood enzymes and proteins. As more blood ingredients are included in the analysis, the number of people with that same combination of ingredients keeps decreasing.

It is easy to show the effect of combining several independent ingredients when analyzing blood. The figure above shows the probability of occurrence for six independent characteristics of blood. Individually, only three of the probabilities are just under 50 percent. But if blood with all six ingredients, or genetic markers, were recovered at a crime scene, what would the probability be that a suspect would have that same blood? To find out, multiply the frequency of occurrence of all of the ingredients:

$$P_{total} = P_1 \times P_2 \times P_3 \times P_4 \times P_5 \times P_6$$
$$= 0.90 \times 0.46 \times 0.91 \times 0.43 \times 0.79 \times 0.41$$
$$= 0.05$$

The result suggests that only 5 percent of the population (5 out of 100) would have blood with the ingredients in this figure. So only 1 person out of 20 (P = $\frac{1}{20}$ = 0.05) would match the crime scene blood sample. It is not likely that each suspect in a case would have that exact mixture. The probability graph shows how adding each additional genetic marker, up to six total, sequentially reduces the probability. If any one genetic marker of a suspect does not match, then investigation of that person might be suspended in the case. If the suspect's blood matches the crime scene sample, the forensic scientist would have reason to continue investigating that suspect. The investigation would continue based on the odds against such a match occurring if the suspect were innocent.

Forensic scientists need to be certain about identification. As the list of blood ingredients grows, the probability decreases for finding another person with the same kind of blood.

Probability is also used in DNA typing. Recall that to get a DNA profile or fingerprint, the number of Short Tandem Repeats (STRs) are counted for a specific segment of the DNA molecule. With STRs, identification can be convincing. But there is still a slight possibility that another individual will have the same STR pattern. However, by including more STR segments from the same DNA, scientists greatly increase their certainty. This is just like adding blood ingredients. If scientists look at three STRs, 1 person in 5,000 might have the same

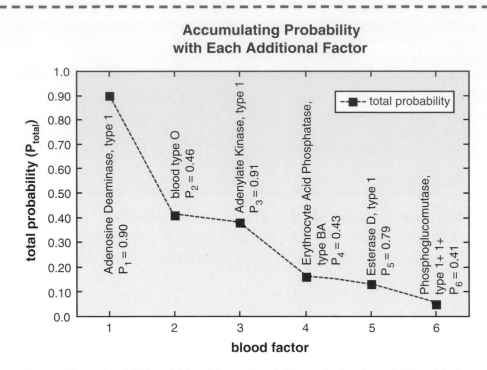

Accumulating Probability with Each Additional Factor

total probability (P_{total})

blood factor

- Adenosine Deaminase, type 1 $P_1 = 0.90$
- blood type O $P_2 = 0.46$
- Adenylate Kinase, type 1 $P_3 = 0.91$
- Erythrocyte Acid Phosphatase, type BA $P_4 = 0.43$
- Esterase D, type 1 $P_5 = 0.79$
- Phosphoglucomutase, type 1+ 1+ $P_6 = 0.41$

-■- total probability

P_{total} with each additional blood ingredient. By analyzing for additional independent genetic markers in blood, the probability of a given person having the same profile decreases.

pattern (P = 0.0002 = 2 × 10^{-4}). If they look at six STRs, 1 person in 2 million might have the pattern (P = 0.0000005 = 5 × 10^{-7}). If scientists look at 13 or more STRs, the odds that another person would have the same pattern fall to 1 in trillions (P < 1 × 10^{-12}) or less.

Odds in the trillions with 13 STRs are significant and compelling evidence. Odds at this level are hundreds of times more than the number of people on the planet. Consequently, this is why you can say that each person has a unique DNA fingerprint (except for identical twins). With odds such as these, forensic scientists have a great chance of accurately identifying and convicting suspects by DNA typing.

8. Answer the questions below based on the reading, FYI—Beyond a Reasonable Doubt.
   a. Why might a forensic scientist use DNA fingerprints rather than blood-typing?
   b. What are the limitations of blood-typing?
   c. What is the probability of flipping 4 heads in a row? Five in a row?
   d. What is the probability of flipping 2 heads, then 2 tails?
   e. Using 2 dice, what are the odds of rolling 2 6s? A 3 and a 4?
   f. Imagine that 100,000 lottery tickets are printed and 4 of them are winning tickets. If 20,000 people each buy a single ticket, what are their odds of winning? If 1 person buys 10 tickets, what are his or her odds of winning?

So You Want to Be a Forensic Scientist?

Are you a good thinker? Do you like to solve puzzles? Are you good with details and record keeping? Most importantly, are you curious about science and do you abide by the rules of evidence when you explore science? If so, you may have what it takes to be a forensic scientist.

Above all, forensic experts are scientists. They apply scientific knowledge to many aspects of criminal cases to resolve specific questions about evidence. Their expert opinion in criminal cases is based on carefully collecting evidence, performing tests on evidence and interpreting results, remaining unbiased and objective, and having a strong scientific background. Forensic scientists must work ethically, and their primary goal must be to uncover the truth of a matter. They must also be able to defend their work in the courtroom as expert witnesses so that jurors can understand them.

How do you become a forensic scientist? First, you need at least a bachelor's degree in a scientific discipline such as biology, chemistry, or physics. Many forensic science fields require advanced degrees. For example, a medical examiner is a doctor with a medical degree. A forensic engineer who analyzes accidents, fires, and wrongful injury cases often needs an advanced degree in electrical engineering, mechanical engineering, or civil engineering.

If you want to specialize in DNA testing, you need a background in biology with an emphasis on genetics and biochemistry. If you are interested in examining trace evidence, you should pursue a chemistry degree, also taking courses in botany, microbiology, mineralogy, textiles, and instrumental analysis. To determine the time of death of victims in criminal investigations, you need to study the insects that inhabit decaying bodies. A degree in entomology is required for that specialty area.

Regardless of the natural or physical science field you choose to study in college, you need to understand and to be able to apply the process of inquiry. You need to be experienced in the logic of evidence and know how to use evidence to support your conclusions. You need to be able to write well so that people outside your scientific field can understand your conclusions. You need to know how to apply probability and statistics to your work, similar to what you did in considering probabilities (the Beyond a Reasonable Doubt reading). You need to understand technology and to be able to use it to enhance your inquiry. And you need to be a person of integrity whom others can trust to provide scientific facts in the fascinating world of crime science.

Reflect and Connect

Work individually to answer these questions in your science notebook.

1. Forensic scientists often ask 1 simple question: Does it match? For example, does the footprint in the mud match any of the suspect's shoes? How does that simple question apply to the study of blood at a crime scene?

2. Develop a probability question of your own with independent factors or events and write the answer (solution) in your science notebook.

3. What chemical reactions take place in the following tests?
   a. Hydrogen peroxide presumptive test for blood
   b. Phenolphthalein presumptive test for blood
   c. Antiserum blood-typing

4. When college guidance counselors help students who are interested in forensic science, they suggest that the students choose a course of study in a particular science, such as biology, chemistry, or physics (see the sidebar, So You Want to Be a Forensic Scientist?). When did you use knowledge from a particular field of science in this activity? List in your notebook as many examples as you can.

5. Can the use of new technologies to identify criminals solve society's crime problem? Why or why not?

EVALUATE

Loose Lips Sink Ships

What a mess! The captain of the cruise ship was suitably mortified—Captain Nelson had run the luxury liner aground and slammed into the pier. The docking was just supposed to be a brief port call in Miami, Florida, as part of a cruise from the Dominican Republic. But besides ruining the pier, he had damaged three tugboats and broken two propellers by hitting bottom in shallow water. In the chaos of the crash and the screeches of scraping metal, two male stowaways had jumped from a low balcony in the stern (rear) to the pier. They had scrambled through the waiting crowd and eluded the customs officials stationed at the exit plank on the bow (front).

Police officers were quickly called to the scene. The peculiar accident and the rapid entry of two men into the United States were suspicious. The police had been tracking several cases of illegal entry and drug smuggling by freight liners from the Caribbean region. Such activities were a federal offense, so was this yet a new ploy in a drug smuggling game of cat and mouse? Or was it a case of illegal entry into the country, perhaps with more stowaways hidden on board? This violated procedures of the U.S. Citizenship and Immigration Services department. The officers needed to find out if the luxury liner fiasco was truly an accident or if it resulted from criminal intent.

One of the police officers asked Captain Nelson how the accident happened. Docking the liner was supposedly a routine maneuver. Captain Nelson was embarrassed to reveal that he had been distracted by reading a note from a secret admirer (see figure 14.31). First Mate Cindy Douglas had passed the note to him just as he was making his final approach to the dock. She claimed to have found the note taped to the captain's door. The note so unnerved the captain that he momentarily lost his focus at a time when he could least afford to do so.

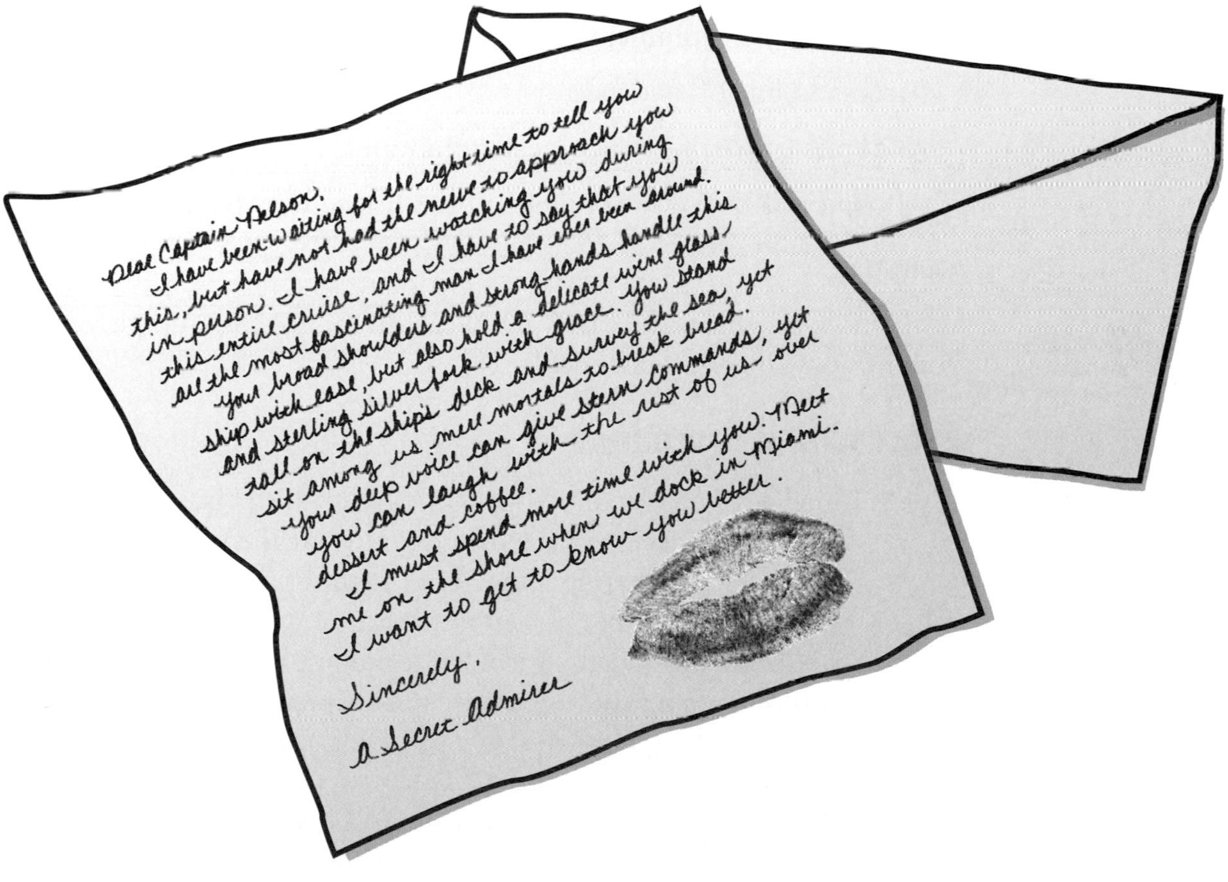
Dear Captain Nelson,
I have been waiting for the right time to tell you this, but have not had the nerve to approach you in person. I have been watching you during this entire cruise, and I have to say that you are the most fascinating man I have ever been around. Your broad shoulders and strong hands handle this ship with ease, but also hold a delicate wine glass and sterling silver fork with grace. You stand tall on the ship's deck and survey the sea, yet sit among us mere mortals to break bread. Your deep voice can give stern commands, yet you can laugh with the rest of us over dessert and coffee.
I must spend more time with you. Meet me on the shore when we dock in Miami. I want to get to know you better.
Sincerely,
A Secret Admirer

▲ **Figure 14.31 Letter to Captain Nelson, sealed with a kiss.** Captain Nelson received this note from a secret admirer. Is there really a secret admirer? Who could that person be?

But who really put the note on Captain Nelson's door, and who is the secret admirer? Was the note a fake to cover complicity in drug smuggling? Or did an intentional distraction in a secret note provide a cover for a scheme of illegal entry or drug smuggling? Might there be other explanations?

In the Loose Lips Sink Ships activity, you and your team work as forensic scientists to study various types of evidence collected from the ship and several passengers. You write a short summary of "who did it" and why. You use inquiry and your knowledge of science and technology in crime investigations. Examine the evidence collected and explain your case.

Materials
For each team of three students

3 pairs of safety goggles

3 pairs of safety gloves

access to lab equipment for tests

access to bag of evidence

3 copies of Miami Police Report handout

3 copies of Evaluate Scoring Rubric: Loose Lips handout

Cautions

Handle all chemicals carefully. Wear safety goggles and gloves when you are working with chemicals.

Process and Procedure

1. Imagine that you and your team are criminal investigators in Miami. Your team is the first to arrive at the scene and will be the lead investigating team. Your team boards quickly. Where would you go first on the luxury liner? Whom would you need to talk to, and what sort of evidence might you need to secure from him or her to investigate the suspicious events?

    Your team needs to think quickly about evidence that could link a person to the case. Make a T-table showing whom you need to speak to and what evidence might link him or her to the suspicious events. Your team might not be able to pursue each of your ideas, but they will get you thinking about key evidence.

2. Review with your team exhibit E, the note to Captain Nelson from an alleged secret admirer (see figure 14.31). Discuss what types of clues and evidence could be obtained from the note. At this point, also read through and review with your teacher each of the steps in this investigation.

4 fingerprints from note

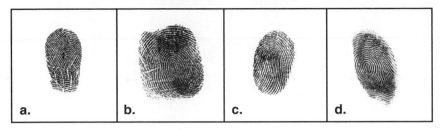

a.   b.   c.   d.

8 fingerprints from suspects

Stowaway #1   Stowaway #2   Captain Nelson   Cindy Douglas

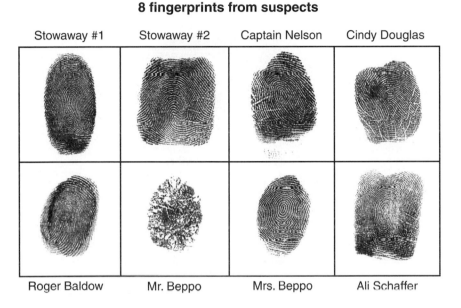

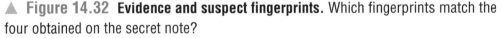

Roger Baldow   Mr. Beppo   Mrs. Beppo   Ali Schaffer

▲ **Figure 14.32 Evidence and suspect fingerprints.** Which fingerprints match the four obtained on the secret note?

3. Study the bag of evidence for your team and read the Miami Police Report. Note additional evidence shown in your text as figures. Answer the following questions with your team. Record your ideas in a T-table in your science notebook.
   a. What kinds of evidence are listed for this case?
   b. What tests can your team use to analyze the evidence?
   c. What can the results of the tests tell you about the case?
4. Decide which of the tests that you listed in Step 3b you think will be most valuable. With your team, prioritize the tests and determine a schedule for completing them. For each station at which you wish to work, make a table in your notebook, listing what exhibit will be analyzed at that station and what the evidence is. Show this list to your teacher before beginning work at the station.

a. Ali Schaffer (female, younger)

b. Mrs. Beppo (female, older)

c. Mr. Beppo (male, older)

▲ **Figure 14.33** **Lip prints.** Do lip prints from (a) Ali Schaffer, (b) Mrs. Beppo, or (c) Mr. Beppo match the seal on the secret note? Why might investigators want Mr. Beppo's lip print?

Because this is an evaluate activity, your teacher is looking to see that you can apply the techniques and thought processes that you learned earlier in this chapter to this new forensic case.

Caution | Wear safety goggles and gloves when working with chemicals.

5. Work as a team to carefully conduct the tests. Collect data and record your results. Keep a record of your results in the "Findings" column of the police report. If you need to record additional data and results, use your science notebook.

6. Discuss the results of the tests with your team. To do this, do the following.

  a. What statements about the case can you make with certainty, based on your tests of the evidence?

  b. Make a T-table listing key suspects in the case and possible motives.

7. You will investigate the case for 2–3 class periods. In the final class period, you will complete 2 tasks.

   a. Participate in a class discussion of the evidence analyzed by each team. Discuss the most important pieces of evidence and their significance for the case. A T-table might help you organize this information.

   You may decide to use a T-table to organize your data, but other methods to organize the evidence could include bubble diagrams, Venn diagrams, outlines, or multicolumned tables. Use your best note taking to make this table, recording it in your science notebook. You will use it in the timed writing in Part B.

   b. In the final 20–25 minutes of class, you complete a short, individual in-class writing assignment. You can use your notes from the previous class discussion, but all writing that you turn in must be your own. You will use your best writing and use complete sentences to describe key points from the four sections below:

Part A: Findings

- What 3 pieces of evidence were most valuable in the case? Explain your answer in writing.
- What are at least 2 pieces of evidence that were not valuable? Explain your answer in writing.

Part B: Inferences

- What inferences can you make from the most important pieces of evidence?

Part C: Explanations

- What is your explanation for what happened in the case and why? Be sure to address the following:
  - Who might have written the note? What evidence supports your conclusion?
  - Is there a link between the drug smuggling and the secret note? Explain your answer using evidence from the case.

Part D: Alternative Explanations

- Compared with your best explanation, what other explanations did you consider? What pieces of evidence led your team to refute those explanations?

   This is an individual short-writing assignment. You will be evaluated not on "getting" the correct answer, but on using evidence and inference to back up and support each conclusion that you make. This should be your best writing. If your teacher cannot read your writing, he or she will return your summary to you.

Mass spectra.
Scientists provided the following laboratory results: (a) the mass spectrum of exhibit D, (b) the mass spectrum of exhibit K, (c) the mass spectrum of a known sample of heroin, and (d) the mass spectrum of a known sample of cocaine.

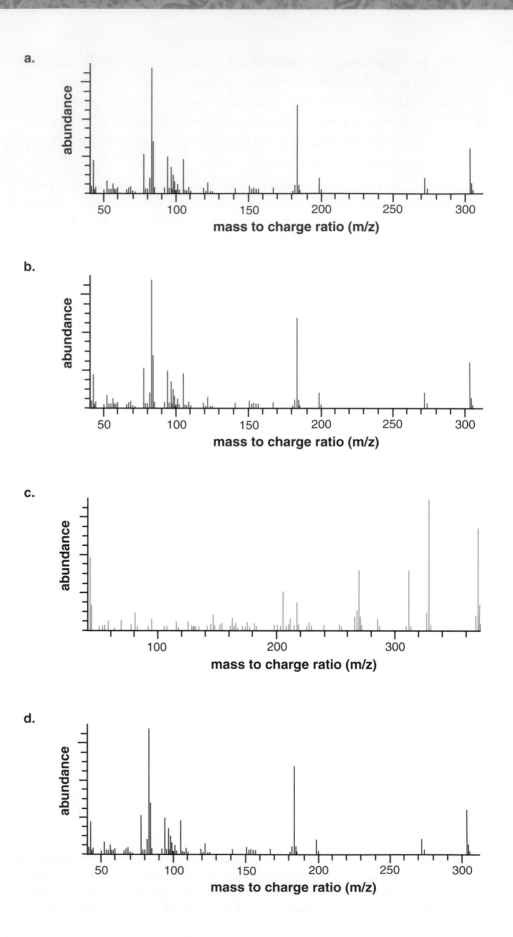

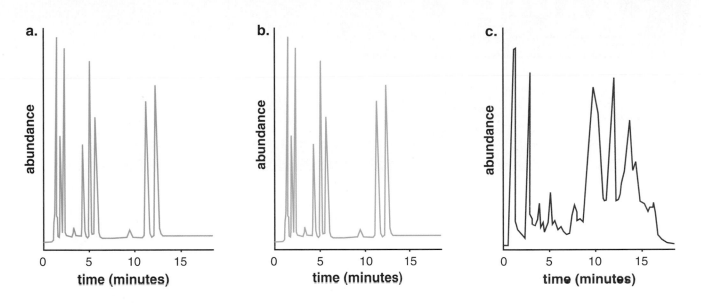

▲ **Figure 14.35 HPLC spectra.** Scientists provided the following HPLC chromatogram results: (a) a stain on exhibit T, (b) soft drink additives, and (c) a food stain (chicken meat).

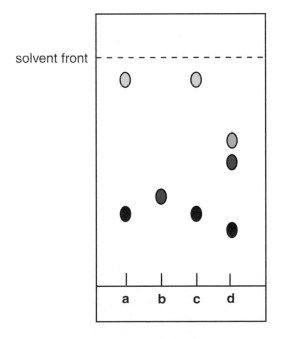

▲ **Figure 14.36 TLC chromatogram.**
Scientists provided a TLC chromatogram of the following lipstick samples:(a) exhibit I, (b) Cindy Douglas's lipstick, (c) Mrs. Beppo's lipstick, and (d) Ali Schaffer's lipstick.

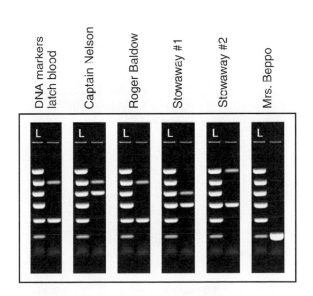

▲ **Figure 14.37 DNA blood-typing results.** Scientists analyzed the blood found on the latch and the blood of their key suspects. The results are the DNA profiles pictured here.

CHAPTER 15

Risks and Hazards to Humans

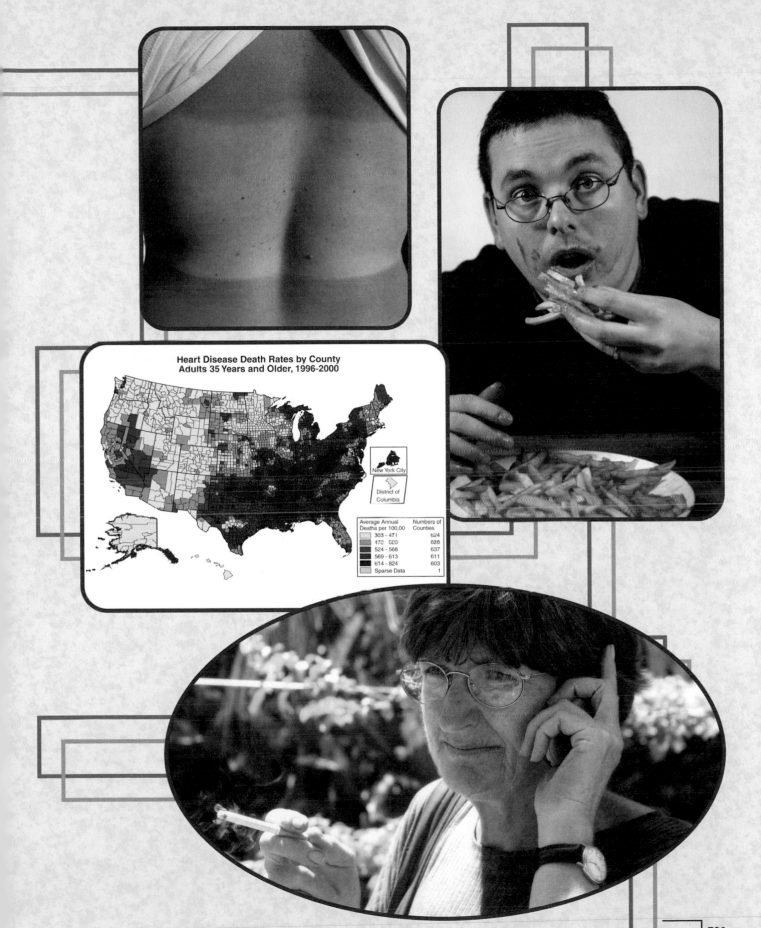

Heart Disease Death Rates by County
Adults 35 Years and Older, 1996-2000

New York City

District of
Columbia

Average Annual Deaths per 100,00	Numbers of Counties
303 - 471	624
472 - 500	028
524 - 568	637
569 - 613	611
614 - 824	603
Sparse Data	1

Risks and Hazards to Humans

In chapter 14, Crime Science, you considered new ways to use evidence to explain and answer questions at crime scenes. You pieced together evidence, often using patterns and technology, to build a case against a person who committed a crime. You saw that forensic science involves many fields of science and math. It may not always be easy to determine who is guilty of a crime. Still, you learned that you can infer and test a "story" from evidence recovered at a crime scene.

In chapter 15, Risks and Hazards to Humans, you consider other ways that scientists study risks and hazards to human health. Those risks and hazards are a simple result of living on Earth. In many cases, technology can help reduce their impact. In other cases, the effects of hazards are closely related to human behavior and decisions. Those hazards include health risks that form gradually, over long periods of time. Sometimes hazards may strike suddenly, such as earthquakes. In the opening images, which photos do you think show slow risks and which photos show rapid hazards? Are any of those part of your community?

One hazard you may think of is overexposure to the Sun. You have been learning this year that life relies on the Sun in many ways. Ironically, the intense energy from the Sun can also be too much of a good thing for people on Earth, especially when they get sunburned. The cause for concern is not always sudden or fast, like a tornado or a flash flood. Health risks from sunburns accumulate over a lifetime. In fact, overexposure to the Sun is a prime example of a risk that grows slowly. In this chapter, you will think more about those types of gradually occurring risks, as well as rapidly occurring hazards.

Goals for the Chapter

In chapter 15, you consider hazards and risks by answering questions such as these:

- How can living on Earth be hazardous to people's health? What is the major health risk or hazard that affects you, your family, or your community?
- Why is exposure to the Sun a health risk? How much sunlight is too much, and how can you tell?
- How do personal decisions affect risk level?

SCiLINKS®
NSTA

Topic: health hazards
Go to: www.scilinks.org
Code: 1Inquiry732

- What is a key difference between health risks that accumulate slowly and hazards that occur suddenly?
- How can technology reduce the impact of a risk or hazard?

Using technology to reduce risks and hazards is the work of many scientists and engineers. Still, the hazards affecting people in various regions may be unique. You begin this chapter by learning more about a risk that affects everyone—overexposure to radiation from the Sun. The chapter ends as you investigate a key health risk or hazard that affects you, your family, or your community. You will complete these activities:

ENGAGE	Beguiling Beads
EXPLORE	The Sun's Invisible Radiation
EXPLAIN	Risky Business and UV Radiation
ELABORATE	Volcanic Hazards at Vesuvius
EVALUATE	Risks, Hazards, and Your Community

The chapter organizer shows how the activities are linked together to help you understand key concepts in this chapter. Refer to the chapter organizer to follow the flow of concepts in the chapter.

Linking Question

Why do the beads change color with some types of radiation or light, but not with others?

ENGAGE

Beguiling Beads

Key Idea:

Simple tools can be used to detect risks or hazards, such as natural radiation.

EXPLORE

The Sun's Invisible Radiation
Part 1: Splitting Sunlight

Key Idea:

You can separate EM radiation with a prism to determine the type of radiation that makes the plastic beads change color. The experiment is just like a historic experiment done hundreds of years ago (Sir Isaac Newton).

Part 2: The UV Part of Sunshine

Key Idea:

The intensity of UV radiation from the Sun depends on several factors, such as position of the Sun in the sky (e.g., time of day, season), presence of clouds, and elevation.

Part 3: The SPF Test

Key Idea:

You can use plastic beads as a tool to test different ways to reduce or block completely your exposure to harmful UV radiation from the Sun.

Risks and Hazards to Humans

Linking Question

Why should I care about exposure to radiation from the Sun?

Risks, Hazards, and Your Community

Key Idea:

Your family or your community has a unique set of health risks and hazards. These have patterns that can be shown geographically and as a function of time. Understanding the causes of the risk or hazard can help you develop creative solutions for reducing level of risk.

Linking Question

What health risks or hazards have been important for you, your family, or your community? How can you reduce the level of risk from that health issue or natural hazard?

ELABORATE

Volcanic Hazards at Vesuvius

Key Idea:

Hazards that occur rapidly with many deaths often relate to natural events in our environment (volcanoes, hurricanes, earthquakes). People living in areas with natural hazards must decide the level of risk that they are willing to accept.

CHAPTER 15 Major Concepts

▶ Living on Earth has various risks and hazards. Some illnesses related to health and fitness develop over tens of years. Other types of hazards are rapid.

▶ Levels of risk for a hazard (i.e., probability, odds) may increase or decrease based on decisions made by you, your family, or your community.

▶ Science and tools can be used to detect and measure risks and hazards, and technology can be used to reduce levels of risk.

▶ Explanations for the cause of a risk or hazard must be carefully tested. Scientists strive to understand such causes for risks and hazards, beyond just noting how factors and symptoms are correlated.

EXPLAIN

Risky Business and UV Radiation

Key Ideas:
- Levels of risk for an illness, such as skin cancer, are different for each person. The risk levels depend upon sets of factors, some of which relate to personal decisions that will increase or decrease your odds of getting a disease.
- Physicians and scientists test possible explanations and causes for illnesses and hazards. Maps are a useful way to depict where illnesses and hazards occur.

Linking Question

If some serious diseases can take tens of years to develop (skin or lung cancer, diabetes, heart disease), what causes hazards that occur rapidly?

Beguiling Beads

You are very lucky to have radiation sensors as part of your body. In fact, you have two radiation sensors on your head! Those sensors tell you what colors you see, what words you read, whether it's light or dark outside, and even whether people are in front of you. What are those radiation sensors? They are your eyes!

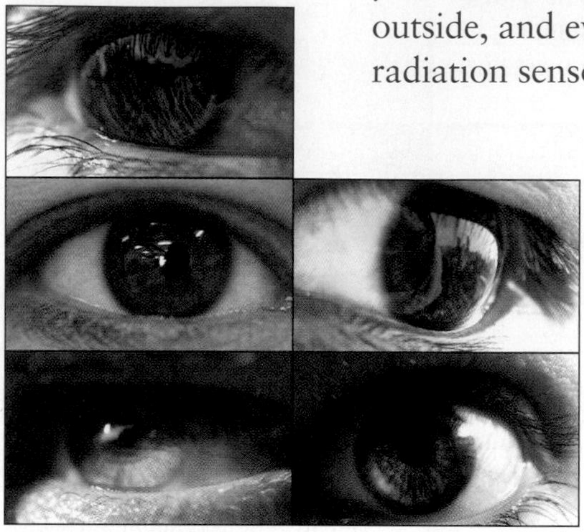

Your eyes detect electromagnetic (EM) radiation that you know as "light." You learned a lot about EM radiation and types of light in The Earth and Beyond unit. Light may come from the Sun, stars, lightbulbs, lightning, fire, or colored lasers. Your eyes are very effective at detecting light, yet your eyes do have some limits. You can see colors of the spectrum ranging from red to violet, the **visible spectrum.** Beyond that narrow range of radiation, your eyes are useless. You need different types of sensors to detect radiation beyond the visible spectrum.

But what if you had another detector that could tell you when other types of radiation were around you? Might you be able to tell the source of that other radiation? In Beguiling Beads, you use a detection system analogous to eyes, but made of a simple material. It will help you understand the types of radiation around you in addition to visible light.

▲ **Figure 15.1**

Radiation sensors. These specialized radiation sensors are well adapted to detect "light." How can you detect other types of radiation?

Materials

For each team of three students

1 set of beads

light sources indicated by teacher

Cautions

Wear sunblock if the class is outside for extended periods. Do not look directly at artificial sources of light or at the Sun.

Process and Procedure

1. Obtain 1 set of plastic beads that you and your two partners will use.
2. According to your teacher's directions, visit each radiation station, taking your beads with you. Maintain the beads at their original color (white) before beginning at each station.

You can keep the beads white by closing your hand around them until you are at the station.

3. At each station, use a table in your science notebook to keep track of the following information.
   a. Can you detect radiation from the source with your eyes?
   b. What color are your plastic beads before you expose them to the radiation source? Place the beads several inches in front of the radiation.
   c. What happens when you expose the beads to the radiation for 10–15 seconds? If the beads change, describe how fast the change occurs.
   d. What happens when you remove the beads from the radiation? How quickly do they respond?
   e. Protect the beads from radiation by tightly closing your hand around them for 30 seconds. Open your hand slightly and peek in. What color are the beads?
4. Consider each station you visited in Step 3. How might you explain the beads' response for each station? Write your explanation in your notebook.

▲ **Figure 15.2**
Rays of sunshine. You know this source of radiation. How do the beads react in sunlight? How can you explain this?

Reflect and Connect

Participate in a class discussion of what you have observed.

1. Discuss with your classmates these items and record your best ideas in your notebook.
   a. What do you think caused the beads to change color?
   b. How could you test whether your answer to Question 1a is correct?
2. When exploring with the beads, you saw that they could detect a type of radiation that your eyes could not. How could you design a scientific experiment to determine whether that type of radiation is harmful or is a hazard to you? Discuss your idea with your class and explain it in your science notebook.

EXPLORE

The Sun's Invisible Radiation

In Beguiling Beads, you experimented with beads to see how they responded to different types of radiation. In some types of radiation, the beads changed color; in other types of radiation, they did not. In this chapter, you will see that too much radiation from the Sun can be a serious health risk. It can lead to skin damage and cancer. If not treated properly, those cancers can result in death. In The Sun's Invisible Radiation, you work with a team to figure out what type of radiation makes the beads change color and what type of radiation relates to possible health risks.

► **Figure 15.3**
Rainbow. Rainbows show only the visible part of the Sun's EM spectrum. But other kinds of radiation that you cannot see may be health risks. How can you detect those kinds of radiation?

Part I: Splitting Sunlight

Materials
For each team of three students

1 plastic strip or 1 set of beads	1 pair of scissors
1 glass prism (not acrylic)	1 towel or cloth
1 ring stand with rotating clamp to grasp prism	several strips of masking tape, 15 cm long
2 sheets of white paper	1 box
several pieces of clear tape	1 ruler

► **Figure 15.4**

Prism-box setup. For this activity, set up your box and ring stand with the prism as shown. First, get a well-defined color spectrum without the box. Then position the prism in the gap such that a bright spectrum shines onto the paper at the bottom of the box. View the spectrum through the gap in the box top or through the hole cut in the side.

Box Setup for Splitting Sunlight

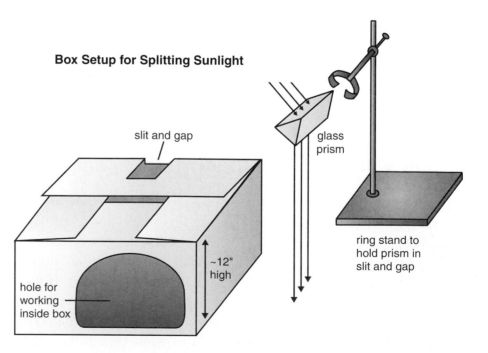

slit and gap

glass prism

~12" high

hole for working inside box

ring stand to hold prism in slit and gap

Cautions

Use appropriate protection from the Sun for outdoor activities. Glass prisms are fragile and can break.

Process and Procedure

1. Listen to your teacher for special instructions regarding the setup and equipment that you will use. Then gather your materials with your team.

2. Study figures 15.4 to 15.8 to see what the correct prism-box setup looks like and to see how to get a good spectrum. The goal is to rotate the prism (around its long axis), projecting a rainbow, or spectrum of the colors, onto the paper on the bottom of the box. Use the Sun's radiation for the experiments.

    a. Set up a ring stand on a table (see figure 15.4) with the prism held firmly in the ring stand clamp (see figure 15.5). The height of the prism should be about the same height as the box.

    b. First, practice getting a good color spectrum without the box. Rotate the prism back and forth in the sunlight until you project the visible spectrum onto the paper. You can see the colors best by taping a piece of white paper on the table.

    Align the prism face toward the Sun. For a clean spectrum, rotate the prism back and forth so that the rainbow on the paper has no white between red and blue. You should see a smooth change of colors from red on one end to violet on the other end. Strips in the middle should show orange, yellow, green, and blue. Your spectrum is not quite focused if you see a white strip in the middle or if the edges of red and violet are not clear.

    c. Once you have a good color spectrum, move your box assembly beneath the prism as shown in figure 15.6. Place a piece of white paper in the bottom of the box. Check that the spectrum of colors shines to the paper on the bottom of the box.

    d. Experiment with the opening in the side of the box. The hole should be large enough to allow you to write on the white paper, see your color spectrum from the side, and manipulate your beads or strip.

    Check that the prism is far enough in the box so that the box does not block the red or blue colors.

    e. Note that after about 10 minutes outside, you may need to rotate and readjust the "focus" on your prism and color spectrum. Write in your notebook why you may need to do that.

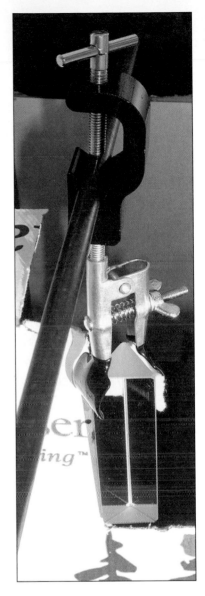

▲ **Figure 15.5**
Clasp around prism.
You can use several layers of masking tape or cloth around the ring stand clamps to help hold the prism firmly.

Figure 15.6

Prism-box cross section.
This cross section of figure 15.4 shows the prism positioned at the box top. Sunlight enters the prism and is redirected to the white piece of paper on the floor of the box. The hole in the side of the box enables you to record observations on the white paper and to change the positions of the beads in the box. *It is important to position the prism in the gap so that the box does not block the red or blue colors.*

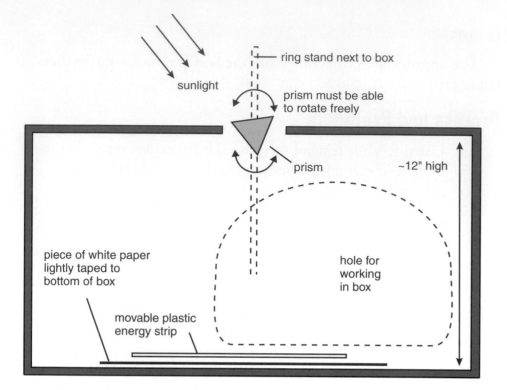

cross-section of prism-box setup

3. Obtain your best spectrum of colors on the bottom of the box. Place your plastic strip or beads across the color spectrum. Make sure the strip is about 3 times longer than the width of the spectrum (see figure 15.7). If you cannot see a position where the strip or beads change color, readjust your prism.

4. Think again about your own radiation sensors, your eyes. You learned in The Earth and Beyond unit that colors of the visible spectrum relate to the wavelength of light detected by your eyes. Figure 15.8 shows those wavelengths in nanometers (nm) for colors of the visible spectrum, in addition to the adjacent infrared (IR) and ultraviolet (UV) radiation.

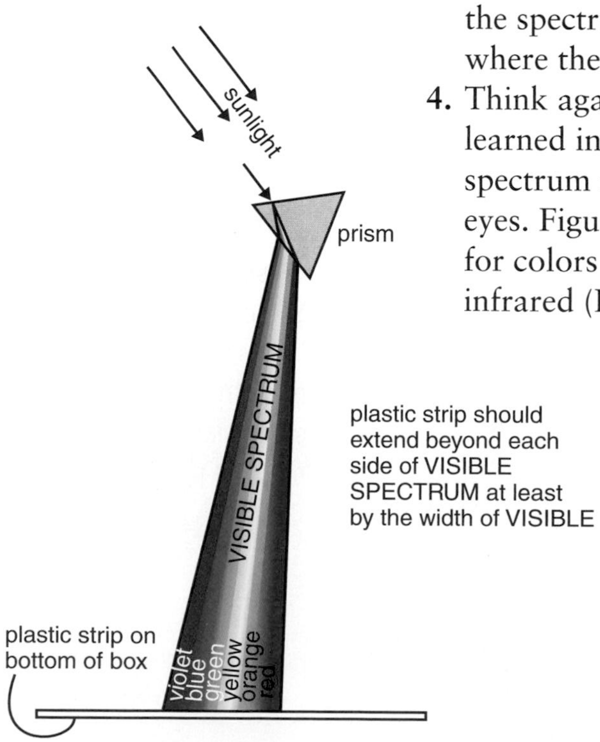

◀ **Figure 15.7 EM radiation through prism.** The plastic strip or beads should extend beyond the ends of the red and violet colors of the visible spectrum. You should see an isolated segment in the strip (or a region for several beads) where the strip changes color. Is the color change easier to see looking down from the top of the box or looking in from the hole in the side?

Draw a sketch like figure 15.8 in your notebook. Mark the region on your sketch where you observed the strip or beads change color.

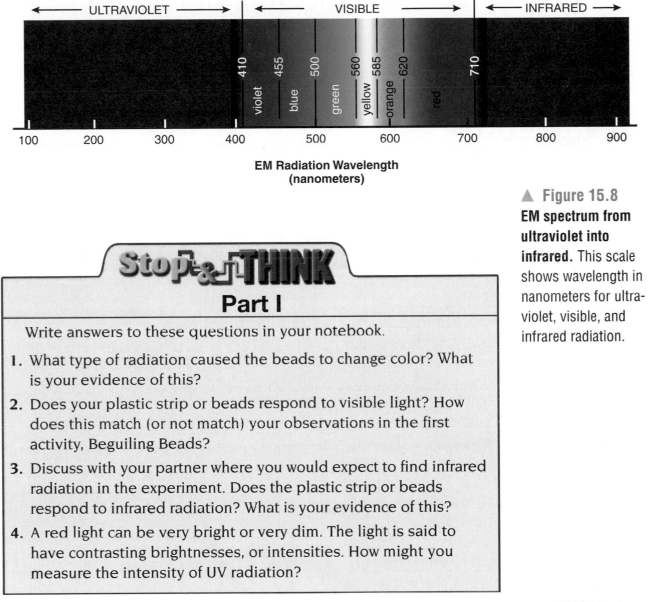

**EM Radiation Wavelength
(nanometers)**

▲ **Figure 15.8**
**EM spectrum from
ultraviolet into
infrared.** This scale
shows wavelength in
nanometers for ultra-
violet, visible, and
infrared radiation.

Stop & THINK

Part I

Write answers to these questions in your notebook.

1. What type of radiation caused the beads to change color? What is your evidence of this?

2. Does your plastic strip or beads respond to visible light? How does this match (or not match) your observations in the first activity, Beguiling Beads?

3. Discuss with your partner where you would expect to find infrared radiation in the experiment. Does the plastic strip or beads respond to infrared radiation? What is your evidence of this?

4. A red light can be very bright or very dim. The light is said to have contrasting brightnesses, or intensities. How might you measure the intensity of UV radiation?

Part II: The UV Part of Sunshine

When you look at the Sun, you probably think of the energy coming from the Sun as just sunshine. In Part I, you used a prism to separate sunshine into distinctive parts of radiation with different wavelengths. That demonstrates that UV radiation is a part of sunshine. Your eyes are well adapted to detect radiation in the form of visible light, but you have to use something else, such as the beads, to detect or "see" radiation that is not visible. How can you tell how intense, or strong, that nonvisible radiation is? High intensities of radiation can be a serious health risk.

Topic: ultraviolet radiation
Go to: www.scilinks.org
Code: 1Inquiry741

Materials

For each team of three students

access to maps of the United States and the world, showing elevation

Process and Procedure

1. Complete the short reading, The UV Index.

READING

The UV Index

Have you ever noticed that sunshine sometimes feels very warm to your skin? The sunshine may feel especially intense during the summer. In contrast, the Sun shines in the winter, but the intensity of its radiation is not as strong. Health risks from the Sun's radiation, such as skin cancer, are related to the amount of radiation that a person receives. A simple tool can tell you how much UV radiation you might be exposing yourself to. It's the UV Index.

The **UV Index** gives the intensity of UV radiation from the Sun at about noon, which is when the Sun is at its highest point in the sky. The scale of the UV Index goes from 0 to 12+. At 0, there is no danger of overexposure to UV radiation; 12 or higher (12+) are the highest levels of UV exposure. UV Indexes higher than 12 are possible at some places on the globe. Without protection, the risk of rapid sunburn is very high.

A number of factors are used to calculate the UV Index. The main factors are time of day, closeness to the equator (latitude), angle of the Sun from the horizon (time of year), elevation, and cloud cover. For example, figure 15.9 represents how the intensity of the Sun's radiation varies with time of day and latitude. The plot is only representative because other factors such as cloud cover and elevation are not included. Those factors also need to be considered as part of the actual UV Index.

The UV Index is a guide for your risk to overexposure from the Sun. For a UV Index greater than 10, if you are unprotected from the Sun, you can be sunburned within 15–20 minutes. Even if you do not become sunburned, you are absorbing UV radiation.

Topic: UV Index
Go to: www.scilinks.org
Code: 1Inquiry742

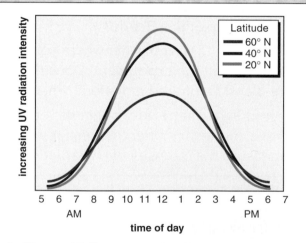

▲ Figure 15.9 **Diurnal UV radiation with latitude.** The three curves show how UV radiation intensity varies with time of day at three different latitudes. San Francisco, California; Denver, Colorado; and New York City, New York, are about latitude 40° north. A geographic change from 40° north to 60° north results in a larger decrease in UV intensity than a change from 20° north to 40° north.

2. Study figure 15.10 with your partner. It may help to make a labeled sketch of the maps in your science notebook.

A useful strategy would be to work with your partner to answer these questions about the maps: What do I see? What does it mean?

3. Answer these questions with your partner about figure 15.10.
   a. What overall patterns do you note on the July 25 and January 11 UV Index?
   b. What are the maximum and minimum values of the UV Index for January 11 and for July 25?
   c. Determine the location of your town on each map. What was the UV Index for your town on each day?
   d. Do you see a difference in your town between July 25 and January 11? If so, write in your notebook a possible reason for this difference.
   e. Look carefully at the patterns on each map. What factors do you think might be important in calculating the UV Index? What is your evidence from the maps? List those factors in your notebook.
   f. Find the location of Denver, Colorado, on July 25, 2003. What was the UV Index?

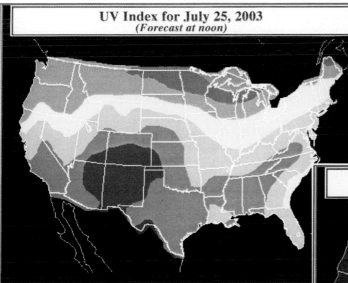

UV Index for July 25, 2003
(Forecast at noon)

UV Scale

0 1 2 3 4 5 6 7 8 9 10 11 12

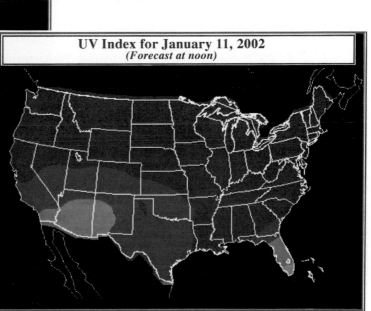

UV Index for January 11, 2002
(Forecast at noon)

▲ **Figure 15.10** **UV Index maps.** The maps show the estimated UV Index for the United States for one day in the summer (July 25, 2003) and one day in the winter (January 11, 2002). Note that colors on the scale indicate UV Index. Study patterns in the maps. How do you think the patterns relate to factors affecting the UV Index?

g. Figure 15.11 shows a record for the UV Index for Denver, Colorado, on each day of 2001. How are the values recorded here similar to and different from the values recorded on January 11, 2002, and July 25, 2003?

► **Figure 15.11**
UV Index map for Denver. This graph shows the UV Index in Denver, Colorado, for each day in 2001.

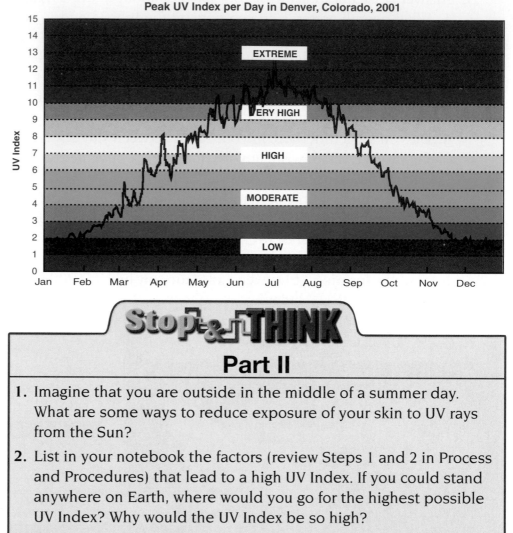

Peak UV Index per Day in Denver, Colorado, 2001

EXTREME

VERY HIGH

HIGH

MODERATE

LOW

Stop & THINK

Part II

1. Imagine that you are outside in the middle of a summer day. What are some ways to reduce exposure of your skin to UV rays from the Sun?

2. List in your notebook the factors (review Steps 1 and 2 in Process and Procedures) that lead to a high UV Index. If you could stand anywhere on Earth, where would you go for the highest possible UV Index? Why would the UV Index be so high?

3. Where would you expect the lowest possible values to be on Earth at about noon? Explain why.

4. Imagine that you have an opportunity to travel to Australia. Much of the country is very sunny, and you anticipate being outside a lot. During what months of the year would you have the highest possibility of overexposure to the Sun?

Part III: The SPF Test

In Part I, you used a prism to separate types of radiation that come from the Sun. You were able to see the visible part of the spectrum, and you used beads to detect UV radiation. You could not "see" the UV radiation. Maybe you have learned that overexposure to UV radiation leads to sunburn and to skin cancers. Those conditions are serious health risks if not treated properly.

In this part, you investigate ways to reduce your exposure to UV radiation from the Sun. You test a variety of common materials to see how effective they are at reducing or even completely blocking UV radiation. What is the best way to reduce UV exposure while you are outside? To tell, you need to do an SPF test—a Sun protection factor test.

Materials
For each team of three students

1 set of beads

1 small mirror

1 steady source of radiation, such as the Sun

1 shallow pan and water

1 set of radiation test materials

Process and Procedure

1. According to your teacher's directions, your team will get 1 test material or a group of test materials to determine how well they block UV radiation. Which material blocks UV rays the best?
2. Design a setup to test how well your material blocks UV radiation.
   a. Discuss with your teammates your ideas for a design.
   b. Write in your notebook the procedure that you will use. Describe how you will use a control in the experiment to tell how effectively a material blocks UV radiation.
   c. Develop a data table on which to record your results and observations.

Sometimes individual beads will turn different brightnesses in the same intensity of light. Thus, before starting your experiment, check your two beads in sunlight to see whether they are comparable.

3. Conduct your investigation and record your results in your science notebook.
4. Do you think that reflected sunlight also has a component of UV radiation? Using your beads and a mirror, design an investigation to answer that question.
   a. Discuss your ideas with your teammates.
   b. Record your procedures and experimental setup in your notebook.

If your prism-box setup is still available, you can use it to test for UV reflection off a mirror. Your teacher also might ask whether you think UV radiation can reflect off water. What do you think?

▲ **Figure 15.12**
Sun protection. You can protect yourself from the Sun in a number of ways. But how effective is this method?

    c. Draw a sketch in your notebook for the setup of your experiment. Write in your notebook what you predict will happen.

5. Conduct your investigation and record your results. Were your results different from your prediction?

6. How often do you go swimming in either pools, lakes, oceans, or rivers? Do you know whether UV radiation goes through the water to your skin? To find out, design an experiment with control beads, a pan, and water at different depths. Follow the stages in Steps 4 and 5 to design and then conduct this experiment.

7. Be prepared to share your results with your classmates and to give evidence for your ideas.

Reflect and Connect

Work individually to answer the following in your notebook.

1. Imagine that you are outside in the middle of a summer day. Based on your investigations, list some behaviors and decisions you think would best protect you from UV radiation. Write in your notebook why you think they would offer protection.

2. Do the results from investigations in your class support this solution? Write in your notebook why or why not.

3. Which of these may be most effective at reducing the amount of UV radiation that enters your eyes: a wide-brimmed hat or UV-blocking sunglasses? Use observations from your investigation to explain why.

4. Write down ideas you might have about how UV radiation causes a sunburn.

EXPLAIN   # Risky Business and UV Radiation

You have learned that you cannot see UV radiation with your eyes. In the last activity, therefore, you used a prism to isolate UV rays and a strip (or beads) to determine their wavelength. This showed that ultraviolet radiation is a part of sunshine. You then experimented with ways to reduce UV intensity and even block UV radiation.

But why is UV radiation a health risk? Why should you consider limiting your exposure to UV rays? After all, you learned in The Machinery of Life and The Earth and Beyond units why you need the Sun. How does UV radiation damage your skin, possibly leading to cancer? In the Risky Business and UV Radiation activity, you learn more about UV radiation, level of risk, risk factors, and damage to skin cells from UV radiation.

Risky Business

Learning about the dangers of too much UV radiation and skin cancer depends on understanding health risks. Each risk can contribute separately to the likelihood of having an illness. A number of risks together tell your overall level of risk. For example, if you are regularly exposed to UV radiation from the Sun, you increase your risk (chances) of getting skin cancer. But this does not mean that you will get cancer. Rather, you increase the odds that you will get skin cancer. Likewise, skin cancer can occur in people who are not very often exposed to UV radiation.

Levels of risk are related to **risk factors.** A risk factor is a condition that changes the odds that you might get an illness. A single factor can increase or decrease your odds. Some risk factors are inherited, but other risk factors are from decisions that you make. For example, imagine that you protect your skin from sunburn until you are 18 years old. Physicians estimate that this will reduce your risk of skin cancer by at least 50 percent. Compared with overall odds of 1 in 5 for skin cancer (20 percent), you might reduce your risk level from 20 percent to 10 percent.

A key concept in understanding health risks is seeing how risk factors combine. When they are combined, a group of risk factors indicates how your overall odds compare with the average. For example, a low-fat diet is one factor that can decrease your odds of heart disease. Regular exercise is a different factor that also can decrease your risk of heart disease. Yet another factor is whether heart disease is a part of your recent family history.

When those factors are combined, your odds of having heart disease later in life will probably differ from the average. Depending on the risk factors, each person will probably have a different level of risk for a given illness. For example, figure 15.13 shows how many deaths result from

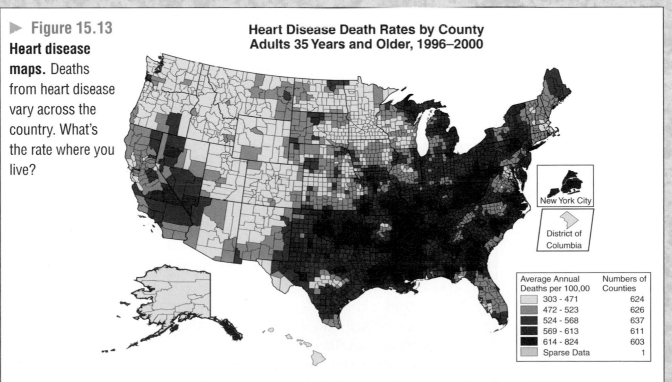

▶ **Figure 15.13**
Heart disease maps. Deaths from heart disease vary across the country. What's the rate where you live?

Heart Disease Death Rates by County
Adults 35 Years and Older, 1996–2000

New York City

District of Columbia

Average Annual Deaths per 100,00	Numbers of Counties
303 - 471	624
472 - 523	626
524 - 568	637
569 - 613	611
614 - 824	603
Sparse Data	1

heart disease each year in different states. Some states are higher than the average; other states are lower than the average. More work would be needed to understand the many factors and reasons for the differences on the map.

Here is another example. When trying to determine what causes illnesses such as skin cancer, physicians need to study risk factors. Factors that lead to an increased risk of skin cancer include sunburning easily, having blond or red hair, having green or blue eyes, having many moles, and having a family history of skin cancer. Another factor is having been exposed to artificial forms of UV radiation, such as having used tanning beds. If you have more than one of the risk factors, you are at a higher-than-average risk level for skin cancer, particularly if you get sunburned. If your skin is of a darker complexion and you minimize UV exposure, you are likely at a lower risk for skin cancer.

What is another example? Smoking is a factor that greatly increases the risk level for lung cancer. It is hard to say when lung cancer might strike, but smoking greatly increases the chances that an individual will die from lung cancer. At the same time, not everyone who smokes gets lung cancer. A person might die first from another cause, such as a car accident. Nonsmokers are at a low risk for lung cancer, but they still can get lung cancer from other causes.

For years, physicians had shown that certain behaviors (such as getting sunburns and tans) were linked with skin cancer later in life. They saw a clear correlation between the behavior and the illness. A **correlation** means that two things increase or decrease together. For example, more sunburns correlates with increased risk for skin cancer. But even when two things correlate, one factor does not necessarily cause the other. When one factor causes another, it is a **cause-and-effect** relationship. Showing that one factor causes something else requires a deeper understanding of evidence. Scientists need to study and investigate why correlations exist before two observations can be linked by cause and effect.

A health risk means that physicians have shown a clear link between a behavior or a factor and the resulting illness. With skin and lung cancer or heart disease, certain decisions and behaviors can increase the level of risk. The results can be deadly. To really understand causes, a disease such as skin cancer must be studied at the level of cells in the skin. You consider this in the next reading.

Get together with 2 other students. Discuss the following questions. Then record your answers in your notebook.

1. Consider the following situations. Decide whether each one is a correlation or a cause-and-effect relationship. Give evidence of your decision.
   a. You notice every September that birds begin to migrate south at the same time that the leaves on trees start to change color.
   b. You notice that each year when it gets colder in the fall, the grass changes color from green to brown.
   c. Your teacher tells you that of all of the students in your class, those with wider arm spans are also taller.

   d. You read in the newspaper that people who drink alcohol and then drive a car are involved in more accidents than other drivers.

2. The maps in figure 15.14 show cancer mortality rates by state for skin cancers, melanoma (the most dangerous type of skin cancer), lung cancer, and all cancers. (The most complete data available for each state are for white males and females, so you will use this data.) Use those maps and the reading, FYI—Mortality Rates, to answer the following.

   a. Use the map to determine the mortality rate for skin cancers and melanoma for men and for women in your state. Write those rates in your notebook.

   b. What are the overall mortality rates for all cancers for men and women in the United States?

   c. Calculate about how many deaths from skin cancer occur for men and for women in your state each year.

Your teacher will give you figures for the number of men and women in your state.

   d. In 2003, the United States had about 103 million white men. Using the mortality rate for all cancers (Step 2b), calculate how many deaths resulted from cancer from 1990 to 1994 (5 years).

3. Discuss with your team the maps in figure 15.14 and answer the questions below.

   a. For skin cancers and melanoma, write in your notebook the general geographic patterns that you see for high mortality rates and low mortality rates.

   b. Consider a pattern that is based on geography. For skin cancers and melanoma, for example, Arizona, New Mexico, and Louisiana might not completely match with the trends noted in Question 3a. List in your notebook some factors that might explain why those states appear to stand out.

   c. Consider a pattern related to gender (male or female). With skin cancers and melanoma, what is the pattern in Wyoming? How might you explain this?

Key industries in Wyoming are ranching, oil, coal, and natural gas.

   d. Consider the geographic patterns for lung cancers. What differences and similarities do you note between men and women? Are lung cancers more typical for men or women?

   e. Consider the map for all cancers. What geographic patterns do you note? How might you explain those patterns?

Cancer Mortality Maps

*Mortality rates are for Caucasians, all ages, for the 25-year period from 1970 to 1994

Skin Cancer (nonmelanoma)

Males

Mortality Rate per 100,000 Persons per Year

0.6–0.9 0.9–1.1 1.1–1.2 1.2–1.4 1.4–1.8

Total Number of Deaths: 28,187

Females

Mortality Rate per 100,000 Persons per Year

0.20–0.37 0.37–0.40 0.40–0.43 0.43–0.50 0.50–0.70 Sparse Data

Total Number of Deaths: 15,611

Melanoma

Males

Mortality Rate per 100,000 Persons per Year

1.7–2.7 2.7–2.8 2.8–3.1 3.1–3.3 3.3–4.3

Total Number of Deaths : 73,365

Females

Mortality Rate per 100,000 Persons per Year

1.1–1.5 1.5–1.6 1.6–1.7 1.7–1.8 1.8–2.1

Total Number of Deaths: 49,846

◄ ▼ Figure 15.14 Mortality rate maps. These maps show mortality rates for white men and women from skin cancer, melanoma, lung cancer, and all cancers. Mortality rates are shown as deaths per 100,000 persons per year.

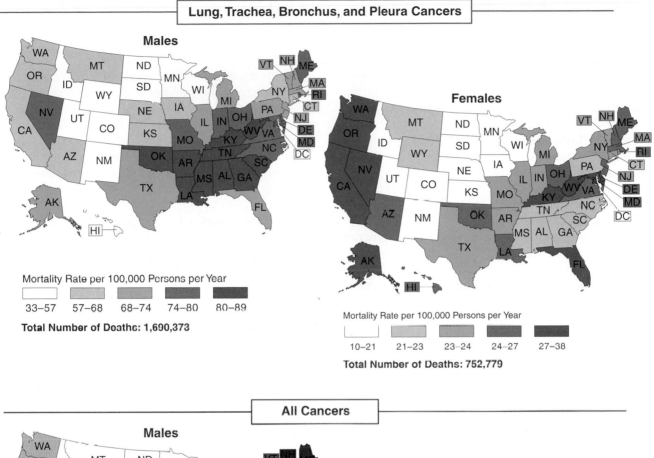

Lung, Trachea, Bronchus, and Pleura Cancers

Males

Mortality Rate per 100,000 Persons per Year

33–57   57–68   68–74   74–80   80–89

Total Number of Deaths: 1,690,373

Females

Mortality Rate per 100,000 Persons per Year

10–21   21–23   23–24   24–27   27–38

Total Number of Deaths: 752,779

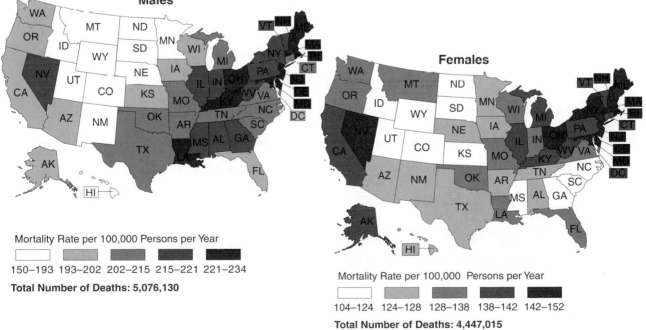

All Cancers

Males

Mortality Rate per 100,000 Persons per Year

150–193 193–202 202–215 215–221 221–234

Total Number of Deaths: 5,076,130

Females

Mortality Rate per 100,000 Persons per Year

104–124 124–128 128–138 138–142 142–152

Total Number of Deaths: 4,447,015

Mortality Rates

A consequence of risks and hazards may very well be death. Scientists need a way to measure how often those deaths occur. **Mortality rates** tell how often a risk or hazard results in human deaths. These are typically done each year, or on an annual basis. Mortality rates are determined relative to a certain number of people. For many reporting agencies, the number is 100,000 (10^5) people. Mortality rates are then easily shown with shading or colors on maps.

Consider the maps of mortality rate for cancers in figure 15.14. The shading links to the key to show the number of deaths each year per 100,000 people in the state. The time period is at the top of each map for skin cancers, melanoma, lung cancer, and all cancers. Imagine that a state has 2 million white males (2×10^6 men). Those men have a mortality rate from lung cancer of 88 per 100,000 from 1970 to 1994 (25 years). The following calculation shows that about 44,000 men died from lung cancer in this 25-year period.

$$\left(2{,}000{,}000 \text{ men} \times \left(\frac{88 \text{ deaths}}{100{,}000 \text{ men} \times \text{year}} \right) \right.$$
$$\times (25 \text{ years}) = 44{,}000 \text{ deaths}$$

Here is another example. Figure 15.13 shows an average mortality rate per year for heart disease in men over 35 years of age. That mortality rate is about 675 deaths per 100,000 men, which is nearly 10 times the rate for lung cancer cited above. In 2003, about 52 million men were in this category (52×10^6 men). Here is how many die each year due to heart disease:

$$\left(52{,}000{,}000 \text{ men} \times \left(\frac{675 \text{ deaths}}{100{,}000 \text{ men} \times \text{year}} \right) \right)$$

$$= (52 \times 10^6 \text{ men}) \times \left(\frac{675 \text{ deaths}}{10^5 \text{ men} \times \text{year}} \right)$$

$$= 351 \times 10^3 \frac{\text{deaths}}{\text{year}} = 351{,}000 \frac{\text{deaths}}{\text{year}}$$

Data is available online from the U.S. Census Bureau regarding the number of people in the United States and where they live. Those population data can be combined with risk or hazard data to tell how many people actually die.

READING

Health Risks from UV Radiation

"Fun in the Sun" might be what you think of in the summer for relaxation or exercise. Or you may work outside in the summer, perhaps on a farm or in the yard. In any case, summer is when you spend a lot of time outdoors. And being outside means that your skin (face, shoulders, and legs) is exposed to UV radiation. Evidence of too much UV radiation is a sunburn.

Why is too much radiation from the Sun a problem? Most people know that UV overexposure can cause skin cancer (figure 15.15). This is a serious health issue. For example, each year nearly 1.4 million people are diagnosed with skin cancer in the United States. Of those cases, one person dies each hour due to skin cancer. The chances are about 20 percent (1 in 5) that you

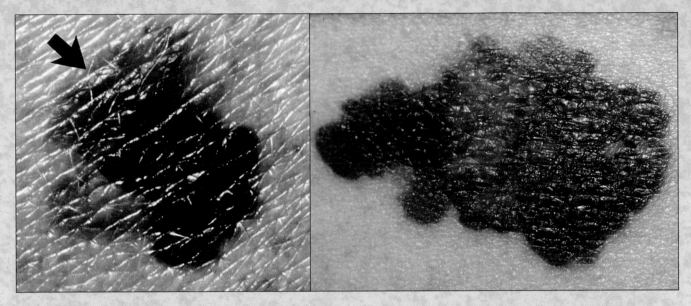

▲ **Figure 15.15 Photos of skin cancer.** These photos show various cancers of the skin.

will have skin cancer in your lifetime. So if your class has 30 students, about six of you will likely get skin cancer.

The most dangerous skin cancer is **melanoma**. Each year it results in nearly 8,000 deaths in the United States. Many physicians think that there is a link between sunburns as a child and melanoma later in life. If not treated early, cells from skin cancer can move to other organs. This spread of cancer is called **metastasis** (figure 15.16). Thus, the tumor in the skin does not directly cause death. The danger is when cells spread to other organs (such as the lungs, liver, lymph nodes, skeleton, and brain) and shut down their vital functions.

Physicians are trying to understand exactly how UV radiation damages skin cells.

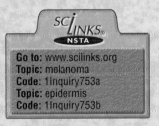

Go to: www.scilinks.org
Topic: melanoma
Code: 1Inquiry753a
Topic: epidermis
Code: 1Inquiry753b

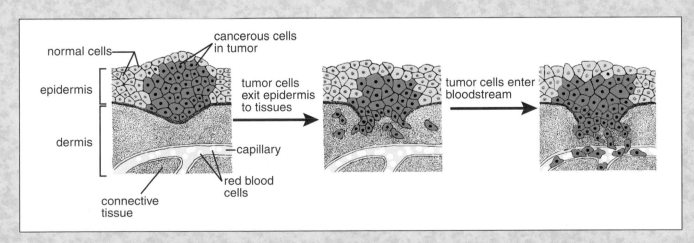

▲ **Figure 15.16 Skin cancer and metastasis.** Cancer is caused by unregulated growth of cells. The spread of cancer cells from a localized tumor to other parts of the body is called metastasis. Metastasis is dangerous because cancer cells get transported to other organs in the body.

Differences in skin type, amount of skin pigment, hair color, and history of UV exposure are factors that vary from person to person. The outer layer of the skin, the **epidermis,** is mostly skin cells with special cells called **melanocytes.** Those cells produce the pigment **melanin,** which gives skin its color. The melanin absorbs UV radiation, protecting skin from the Sun. People with darker skin produce more melanin than people with lighter skin. However, UV radiation also triggers some **melanin** production. This is a protective mechanism to absorb UV radiation. Melanin production gives some people darker skin—a tan.

Skin cells not only change color, but they may be damaged by UV radiation. In some cases, the genetic material (DNA) in cells becomes damaged. When a cell's DNA is damaged, the cell may lose its ability to regulate its growth and division into new cells. Uncontrolled cell growth can lead to a tumor in the skin. Figure 15.17 shows photographs of cancerous skin cells in the epidermis and dermis. Overexposure to the Sun also leads to premature aging of the skin, making the skin appear thick, wrinkled, and leathery (see figure 15.18).

Ultraviolet radiation leads to other health risks, too. Even though you cannot see UV radiation, it still enters your eyes. Research shows that UV radiation is linked with cataracts. This condition is a clouding of the lens of the eye. Cataracts make vision hazy and blurry. UV radiation entering the eyes also degrades the **retina,** the back part of your eyes needed to sense light so that you can see.

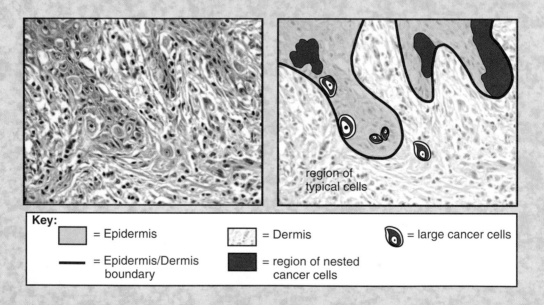

▲ Figure 15.17 **Photomicrograph and illustration of melanoma in the epidermis.** The photograph to the left is represented in the diagram to the right. The epidermis contains large, individual cancer cells; clusters of nested cancer cells; and smaller, normal epidermal cells. The dermis contains mostly normal cells in addition to the large cancer cell in the center. It has likely migrated from the epidermis into the dermis. This is a stage in metastasis.

▲ **Figure 15.18 Aging of skin.** Two relatives showing aging of skin possibly from overexposure to the Sun.

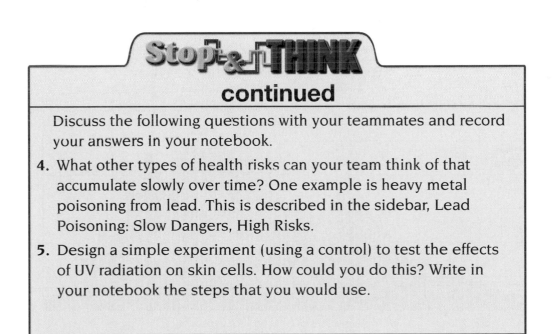

continued

Discuss the following questions with your teammates and record your answers in your notebook.

4. What other types of health risks can your team think of that accumulate slowly over time? One example is heavy metal poisoning from lead. This is described in the sidebar, Lead Poisoning: Slow Dangers, High Risks.

5. Design a simple experiment (using a control) to test the effects of UV radiation on skin cells. How could you do this? Write in your notebook the steps that you would use.

Lead Poisoning: Slow Dangers, High Risks

Lead has been a part of societies for thousands of years. Even 2,000 years ago, citizens of the Roman Empire used lead in a variety ways. The Romans used lead as a food seasoning, birth control, makeup, a paint pigment, and a wine preservative. They also made common items such as coins, cups, plates, pots, pans, and pipes with lead. The Romans knew that eating a large amount of lead was toxic, but it had become a part of their lives, even though some Romans suffered from lead poisoning. Some historians and scientists have even argued that lead poisoning led to the downfall of the Roman civilization.

Lead is still found today in things such as car batteries, solder, paint, bullets, and fishing weights. Until the mid-1980s, lead was added to gasoline to reduce engine knocking. In the 1960s and 1970s, lead pollution from gas totaled about 250,000 metric tons per year (see the graph of lead added to gasoline). All of that lead was expelled as car exhaust.

The lead gathered in soils in cities, where most cars were found. Lead is not currently used in paints, but many people live in houses with flaking, old layers of paint. Those paint chips release lead into the houses and neighborhoods, posing a very serious health risk.

So what are the dangers of lead poisoning? Indeed, the Romans knew the perils of lead toxicity and eating too much lead. Ingestion led to sudden, or *acute*, lead poisoning. But the Romans did not understand the dangers of slow, continual exposure to lead during their lives. Lead poisoning occurs even in small amounts. Continuous exposure to small amounts of lead results in *chronic* lead poisoning. Just like overexposure to UV radiation, the symptoms build up slowly over long periods of time. When people realize they are stricken, it is often too late.

The health dangers of low-level lead poisoning have been well documented in the last 20–25 years. Research stemmed from physicians who were

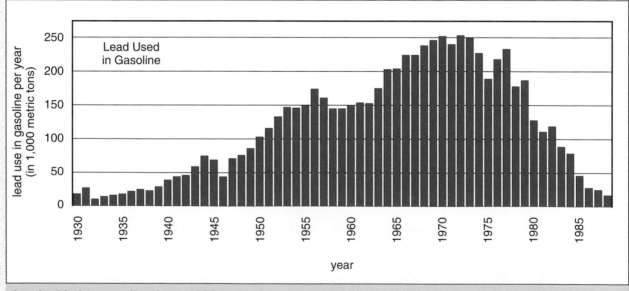

Lead added to gasoline from 1930 to 1988 in the United States in thousands of metric tons. Most of this lead became part of air pollution in cities, especially in years of heavy lead emissions—the 1960s and 1970s. In about 1988, the Unites States eliminated lead from use in car gasoline.

concerned about the lead from gasoline in air pollution. The symptoms include damage to the nervous system (such as seizures, headaches, tiredness, and difficulty concentrating or remembering), reproductive system (decreased fertility, miscarriage, reduced sperm count, and abnormal sperm), and kidneys. Moreover, chronic lead poisoning can also result in reduced learning ability, mental retardation, anemia (decreased number of red blood cells), and high blood pressure. In young children, learning ability is strongly affected. Studies show that affected children remain impaired in learning ability later in life. Recently, scientists have shown that chronic lead exposure results in behavioral problems, increased aggression, and criminal behavior.

Fortunately, new technologies enable chemists to eliminate lead from products such as gasoline and paint. In the mid-1970s, auto manufacturers in the United States started equipping car engines with parts that ran on unleaded fuel (catalytic converters). That new technology allowed gasoline refineries to remove lead from gas. Such changes are gradually reducing the amount of lead in the environment. In many areas, the risk of lead poisoning will gradually reduce.

READING

EM Radiation from the Sun

So how does UV radiation relate to processes in the Sun? Why do tans and sunburns indicate too much UV radiation and damage to the skin? You can better understand answers to those questions by considering EM radiation from the Sun.

You have been learning that EM radiation comes to Earth from the Sun. The radiation curve in figure 15.19 shows how much UV radiation comes from stars—such as the Sun—with different temperatures. You studied curves like this in chapter 10, The Stars. The red star (which is cool) emits little UV radiation. In contrast, much of the blue (hot) star curve is in the UV part of the spectrum. The UV part of the spectrum is about 20–25 percent of the total radiation of the star. The star also emits IR radiation, but that is much less than the visible and ultraviolet radiation. A star such as the Sun is between the red and blue stars.

The curves in figure 15.19 are for radiation leaving a star. The Sun's radiation at Earth's surface is reduced for two reasons. First, about 23 percent of the radiation is reflected back to outer space at the top of the atmosphere. Second, another 20 percent of the radiation is absorbed by gases in the atmosphere. Thus, about 43 percent of the initial radiation does not reach Earth's surface. Starting with about 342 watts per meter squared ($342 W/m^2$) directed toward Earth, only $195 W/m^2$ actually reach Earth.

Reflection and absorption by the atmosphere are easy to see on the Sun's radiation curve. In figure 15.20, the upper curve shows EM radiation arriving at Earth. The lower curve is reduced at all wavelengths due to reflection. In addition, the sharp "valleys" in this curve are from absorption of radiation by the atmosphere. This occurs at specific wavelengths. For example, two water absorption peaks are shown at 940 and 1,130 nm. Water in the atmosphere is absorbing the Sun's radiation at those wavelengths. The curve also shows an intensity peak at wavelengths of about 500 nm. This intensity peak, which is in the middle of the visible spectrum, is what gives the Sun its whitish color to your eyes. You also used an absorption valley like this in The Earth and Beyond unit to distinguish between stars.

Physicians now know that UV radiation enters the skin and damages DNA in skin cells. This could explain a link between UV radiation and skin cancer. Medical evidence also indicates that artificial UV radiation, such as tanning beds, poses the same health risks as the Sun's UV radiation. This also supports a cause-and-effect link between UV radiation and skin cancer. Fortunately, there is a natural block for UV radiation with wavelengths shorter than about 300 nm. The natural block is the molecule ozone (O_3). Ozone absorbs UV radiation in the atmosphere and explains the sharp drop in the radiation curve at 300 nm (see figure 15.20). This gas molecule protects against harmful radiation with wavelengths shorter than 300 nm.

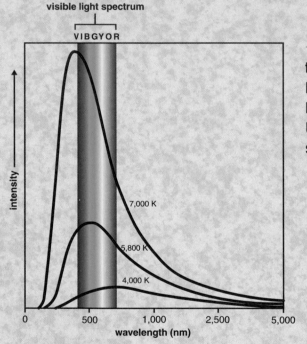

◀ **Figure 15.19 Radiation curves for three stars from UV to IR parts of the spectrum (100–2,000 nm).** The stars are a blue star, a yellow-white star such as the Sun, and a red star. Each star emits UV radiation. However, the red star emits little UV radiation, while much of the radiation given off by a blue star is in the UV part of the spectrum.

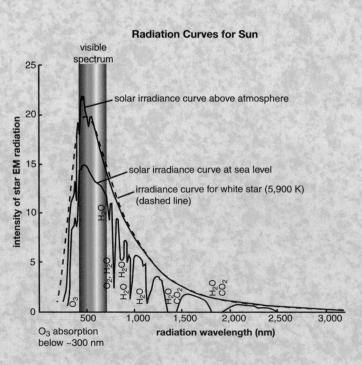

▶ **Figure 15.20 Radiation curve for Sun.** The upper curve shows solar radiation arriving at Earth. The lower curve shows the radiation that actually arrives at Earth's surface after passing through the atmosphere. The curve is lower overall due to reflection at the top of the atmosphere. It also shows "valleys" at specific wavelengths from absorption by atmospheric gases. The dashed line shows the radiation curve for a star at a temperature of 5,900 Kelvin (K).

UV Radiation—for Bones and for the Birds

Some health risks are double-edged swords. They may be helpful in small amounts, but harmful in large doses. For example, you obviously need food to sustain your body. But too much of the wrong foods, along with little physical activity, can put you at increased risk for heart disease, diabetes, and other health problems. The same is true of UV radiation.

You have learned about the health risks of overexposure to UV radiation. At the same time, your body needs a small amount of UV radiation to produce vitamin D. Vitamin D is used to regulate calcium and phosphorus. Those elements are used in bone growth and maintenance. In growing children, rickets is a serious disease that results from a lack of vitamin D.

Vitamin D is made when UV radiation interacts with a special molecule in your skin. Vitamin D is also found in foods such as animal products, oily fish, artificially fortified foods (for example, margarine,

butter, and cereals), and supplements. You need only 10–15 minutes of sunlight on the face and wrists each day to get the daily requirement of Vitamin D. Vitamin D deficiency is most likely to occur during the winter in cold northern climates. The days may be short and cold, the UV radiation is much less intense, people wear more clothes, and more time is spent indoors.

Other animals besides humans use UV radiation in entirely different ways. For example, many birds can "see" UV radiation between 320 and 400 nm. Birds have special light receptors in their eyes that humans do not. As you have learned, humans are blind in that range. You had to use plastic beads to "see" radiation in that range!

For example, a small falcon, the kestrel, uses UV reflections from the dried urine of voles on grass to help find its prey. A vole is a small mammal similar to a mouse. Other birds use UV vision to find camouflaged insects. Still other

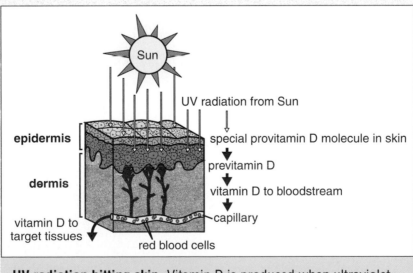

UV radiation hitting skin. Vitamin D is produced when ultraviolet light reacts with a special molecule in the epidermis. The vitamin D is then transported in your bloodstream to tissues such as muscle, tendons, and bone.

birds, such as the starling, use UV reflections from inside the mouths of their chicks to feed them. Nestlings with the strongest UV reflections in their mouths have also been shown to have the best resistance to certain bird diseases. That may be an excellent example of natural selection for the fittest starling chicks.

Blue tits and Zebra finches also use UV reflections in selecting a mate. The female blue tit, for example, selects a male with blue crest feathers that have bright UV reflections.

So if you are ever wondering whether you've been out in the Sun too long, just ask a falcon or finch what it thinks!

Vole

Kestrel. The kestrel is a small falcon that hunts insects and rodents. It uses the UV reflections from the dried urine of voles on grass to help find its prey. A vole is a small mammal similar to a mouse.

Blue tit. The female blue tit uses UV reflections off feathers to select a mate. She selects a male showing the brightest UV reflection off his crest feathers.

Reflect and Connect

1. Red stars often have an intensity peak in the IR part of the spectrum. Does that also mean that they emit more IR radiation than a blue star? Use figure 15.19 to explain why or why not.

2. Copy figure 15.20 into your notebook. Draw as accurately as you can the boundary of where atmospheric ozone absorbs UV radiation.

3. Would a UV Index from the Sun be higher in space or at the surface of Earth? Explain why in your notebook. Refer to figures.

4. In chapter 10, you considered the radiation spectra of stars in our galaxy that were different temperatures. The temperatures of stars were related to the stars' colors. This was shown on a Hertzsprung-Russell (H-R) diagram.

   Imagine that your team is able to fly a mission to orbit 3 supergiant stars: β Centauri, Rigel, and Betelgeuse. You orbit all 3 stars at the same distance. Use an H-R diagram (which shows that they are all the same luminosity) to indicate which of those stars might have the highest UV Index for your team while in orbit. Write your evidence in your notebook. Be prepared to share your evidence with your classmates.

Volcanic Hazards at Vesuvius

ELABORATE

So far in this chapter, you have explored health risks that grow slowly over time. The risks grow over the course of years or decades. You may find it difficult to imagine that such risks are worth the worry. However, it is important to learn how the environment and the decisions that you make relate to increased or decreased risks to your health.

Other types of health risks occur more rapidly. When those events result in many deaths in a brief period of time, they are often called **hazards** or **disasters**. Hazards can be related to typical, yet forceful, weather or geologic events. In Volcanic Hazards at Vesuvius, you return to ancient Italy to study an example of a natural hazard that occurs in many places: volcanic eruptions. Complete the readings and questions to learn about the history of volcanic eruptions of one dangerous volcano—Vesuvius.

Topic: natural disaster
Go to: www.scilinks.org
Code: 1Inquiry761

Vesuvius: One of the World's Most Dangerous Volcanoes

Imagine a warm August day in the year AD 79 in southern Italy. Roman villagers are beginning the grape harvest and going about their daily business. The location is the Bay of Naples, which is on the sunny flank of a dangerous volcano, Vesuvius (see figure 15.21). Residents in the area had felt some earthquakes, but nothing could prepare them for what was about to happen. The sleeping giant, Vesuvius, would awaken violently that day just after noon.

Volcanoes may be active over millions of years. When they are not active, they are called dormant. Volcanoes can lie dormant for thousands of years before surging back to life. Such was the case at Vesuvius. Plenty of geologic evidence shows that Vesuvius was active before AD 79. However, the cycle of eruptions that began on that August 24 grew in intensity for nearly 2,000 years. Vesuvius' last major eruption was in 1944. Since then, it has remained in a largely dormant state.

Pompeii and Vesuvius—August 24, AD 79

The first few hours of the eruption were unlike anything that residents had seen. Pliny the Younger wrote about the initial explosions from the town of Misenum, which was across the Bay of Naples (see figure 15.21). He described an initial column of gas and ash that rose rapidly to 25,000–30,000 feet. Massive columns of ash and steam such as this are now called Plinian eruptions. The term is in recognition of Pliny's detailed notes and descriptions. **Plinian eruptions** spread thick blankets of ash for hundreds of miles downwind. An example is shown in the opening image of this chapter.

Topic: Plinian eruption
Go to: www.scilinks.org
Code: 1Inquiry762

To the southeast and downwind of Vesuvius, residents of Pompeii had a very different experience of the eruption than Pliny the

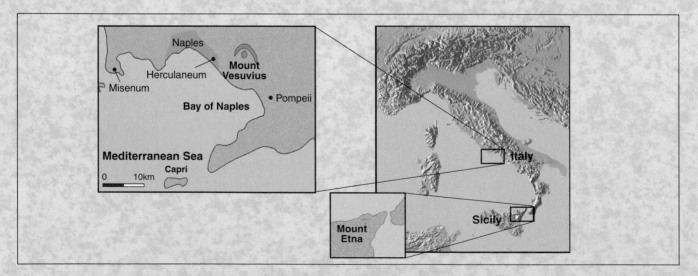

▲ **Figure 15.21 Map of Italy with inset of Vesuvius on the Bay of Naples.** Surrounding towns include Pompeii and Herculaneum. Pliny the Younger wrote his famous descriptions of the AD 79 eruption from the town of Misenum. How might he have responded to these questions: What do you see? What does it mean?

Younger did (see figure 15.21). Within hours, the sky probably went dark as the thick volcanic ash blocked all sunlight. Ash fell at a rate of about 15 centimeters (cm) per hour. Residents were bombarded by falling volcanic rocks nearly the size of baseballs. With the darkness, the thick ash and falling volcanic rocks made escape dangerous or impossible. By midnight, volcanic ash and rocks had accumulated to depths of 1.5 meters (m), or nearly 5 feet. Structures began to collapse under the weight of the volcanic debris. Many people were trapped inside.

Thousands of people died in that first eruption. Graphic evidence of their plight is natural casts in volcanic ash of people and pets at the time of death (see figure 15.22). The hazard must have struck quickly. For years, it was thought that the massive ash- and rockfall were fatal to the residents of Pompeii, burying them alive. Alternatively, other workers suggested that the residents had died from breathing poisonous gases given off by Vesuvius.

Surviving such an event is difficult to imagine. The falling rocks would have led to many injuries and perhaps some deaths. You can think of Pompeii as a crime scene similar to those you considered in the last chapter. Does the evidence at Pompeii support residents dying by heavy ashfall, by poisonous gases, or perhaps by both?

In fact, geologists have not found those explanations entirely satisfying. Closer study of the geologic evidence has led to new inferences about the cause of deaths. For example, geologists have few other examples of people getting buried alive in ash. So that explanation is not supported with modern examples. Moreover, massive deaths by poisonous gas at volcanoes are extremely rare. Such events are not associated with Plinian eruptions. Another piece of evidence was that some residents of Pompeii perished on roofs and structures above the ash layer. They could not have been buried alive in only several feet of ash. Other people beneath the ash layer were inside of collapsed structures.

Recent geologic work at Pompeii and another town, Herculaneum, is thought to tell a different story. That explanation might tell how thousands of people died during the AD 79 eruption of Vesuvius. It also fits with many other deaths that have occurred at other volcanoes around the world in the past 200 years. What was the cause in this geologic crime scene? What happened on the sunny flanks of Vesuvius?

▲ Figure 15.22 **Casts in volcanic ash.** These photos show casts of people who perished in Pompeii in the AD 79 eruption of Vesuvius. These remains have been preserved for nearly 2,000 years. They serve as key evidence of how people died. It's a geologic crime scene.

Discuss with 2 other classmates the following questions and record answers in your notebook.

1. The photograph in figure 15.23 shows an erupting volcano in Hawaii. Streams of orange molten lava run like a thick river to the ocean.
   a. Using a T-table, compare what you see in this eruption with what you have read about the AD 79 eruption at Vesuvius. What key features can you infer for each volcanic eruption?
   b. Would you call this type of eruption a volcanic hazard (or natural disaster)? Explain why or why not.

   Think of how you might define a natural hazard (or natural disaster).

▶ **Figure 15.23**
Molten river. This photograph shows a vent and lava river running from a volcano in Hawaii. Would you call this eruption a natural disaster?

2. In May 1980, Mount St. Helens in Washington State exploded in a massive Plinian-style eruption. The eruption blanketed parts of the western United States in ash and killed 57 people. In early October 2004, a dome of rocks at the summit of Mount St. Helens inflated by at least 300 feet. Also, earthquakes occurred every minute, in addition to small but violent ash and steam explosions.

   Were those signs of an impending eruption? Did the volcano blow? Research what has been happening at Mount St. Helens from October 2004 to today.

▲ **Figure 15.24** Plinian-style eruption from Mount St. Helens in May 1980.

Herculaneum: Another Volcanic Crime Scene

Herculaneum was a Roman sea town about 5 kilometers (km) west of Vesuvius (see figure 15.21). Herculaneum was rediscovered in the 1700s. The town is a valuable archaeological site due to recovered statues and art depicting many facets of Roman society. Moreover, findings at Herculaneum provided key evidence about deaths in the AD 79 Vesuvius eruption.

On the first day, August 24, residents of Herculaneum probably had some ash falling on them. They were close to the volcano. But as geologists now know, they were too close. At some point during the night or perhaps early the next day, Herculaneum was covered by a rushing wall of volcanic material. It destroyed buildings and buried residents alive. So what types of volcanic material were responsible for all of that death and destruction?

For years, archaeologists and geologists thought that Herculaneum had been buried by a massive **volcanic mudflow** (or **lahar**). These rapid flows consist of muddy volcanic ash and rock. They are one of the most dangerous volcanic hazards. Figure 15.25 shows an image of a modern volcanic mudflow.

At other times, volcanic rocks tumble and crash down the steep flank of a volcano. They are called **volcanic avalanches.** Both volcanic avalanches and mudflows are highly dangerous. When ash becomes wet and breaks loose from the steep slopes of tall volcanoes, conditions become even more hazardous. Volcanic mudflows can strike without warning, sometimes even days after the main eruption. Scientists need to know exactly how the residents of Herculaneum and Pompeii died so they can better understand current volcanic hazards.

From the evidence found at Pompeii and Herculaneum, geologists and archaeologists have another explanation for the AD 79 eruption. The new explanation matches evidence that has been unearthed at each town. Fieldwork

▲ **Figure 15.25 Volcanic mudflow.** Volcanic mudflow as a result of the Mount St. Helens eruption. Mudflows are one of the most serious volcanic hazards.

and comparisons with active volcanoes have helped geologists recognize that volcanic hazard—a pyroclastic flow.

The word pyroclastic comes from the Greek words *pyro* for "fire" and *klastos* for "broken" or "pieces." A **pyroclastic flow** is a glowing, hot cloud of volcanic gases, droplets of liquid rock, and rock fragments ripped from inside the volcano. This deadly, dense, scorching cloud is hundreds of degrees Celsius and races as a glowing cloud down the flanks of a volcano. Reaching speeds of over 120 kilometers per hour, these clouds are also called **glowing avalanches.** In fact, Pliny the Younger described one such glowing avalanche that surged down Vesuvius. The glowing cloud nearly made it across the Bay of Naples to Pliny at Misenum.

Pyroclastic flows eventually slow down and settle to the ground. When they settle, the volcanic material compacts. It becomes fused and welded as a hard, glasslike volcanic rock. Due to

Topic: pyroclastic flow
Go to: www.scilinks.org
Code: 1Inquiry765

▲ **Figure 15.26 Pyroclastic flow.** Pyroclastic flows are one of the most dangerous volcanic hazards. This photograph shows the front of a small pyroclastic flow (lower left) surging down the flank of Mount St. Helens.

the intense heat, it is nearly impossible for organisms to breathe in pyroclastic flows. Deposits like this are found throughout the world. In some cases, they extend hundreds of kilometers from the volcano where the pyroclastic flow started.

Geologists now believe that pyroclastic flows were an immediate cause of death at Herculaneum and Pompeii. Geologists have been able to identify clear evidence of those pyroclastic flows as distinct layers within the ash. Geologists have observed several pyroclastic flows at other volcanoes in modern times, helping the geologists understand them better. For example, in 1902, pyroclastic flows from Mount Pelée (on Martinique in the Caribbean Sea) killed about 28,000 people, leaving only two survivors. In 1999, 40 photographers and scientists were killed by a pyroclastic flow at Unzen Volcano in Japan.

But volcanic mudflows are also very dangerous. In 1985, volcanic mudflows from the Nevado del Ruiz (in Colombia, South America) killed 23,000 residents in several towns in its path. Those volcanic mudflows were very different from the welded deposits that buried Pompeii and Herculaneum.

Massive volcanic mudflows were also part of the 1980 Mount St. Helens eruption and the 1991 Plinian eruption of Mount Pinatubo in the Philippines. Geologists are now able to distinguish between deposits from volcanic mudflows and pyroclastic flows.

Reflect and Connect

The eruptions of Vesuvius have the most detailed written record of any volcano on Earth. The history of those eruptions is shown in figure 15.27a. The following graph, figure 15.27b, shows estimates for the number of deaths in volcanic eruptions and the way they happened. Work in a team of 3 to answer these questions in your notebook.

1. Answer these questions in reference to figure 15.27a.
   a. How many total eruptions are represented?

   You will need to add the number of eruptions for each calendar year interval.

   b. When was the last time Vesuvius erupted? How many years ago was that?
   c. In the last 2,000 years, how many times has Vesuvius been quiet for at least 50 years?

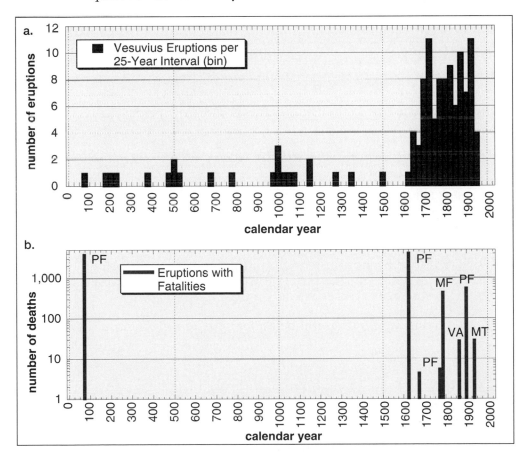

▲ **Figure 15.27 Two records of volcanic eruptions at Vesuvius, Italy.** (a) The record of eruptions from the calendar years 0 to 2000; eruptions are grouped by number in 25-year intervals. (b) Number of deaths related to various eruptive phases at Vesuvius; the log scale is used to show both large and small numbers of deaths. Symbols indicate how most deaths occurred: PF, pyroclastic flow; MF, volcanic mud-flow; VA, volcanic avalanche; and MT, massive tephra, or volcanic, fallout.

d. When did the most active period of Vesuvius eruptions start, and when did it end?

e. For the most active period of Vesuvius eruptions, how many eruptions are shown on the graph? How does that number compare with the total number before then?

2. Figure 15.27b shows the record of deaths from volcanic hazards at Vesuvius. Write answers to the following in your notebook.

a. Note eruptions where deaths were recorded. Complete a T-table in your notebook with 2 columns showing (1) the year of eruption and (2) the estimated number of deaths.

b. In what years did a large number of deaths from volcanic hazards occur? About how many deaths were there?

Note that a log scale is used to show large numbers and small numbers together on the *y*-axis.

c. Use the graph to estimate the total number of recorded deaths from volcanic eruptions at Vesuvius during the past 2,000 years.

d. What type of volcanic hazard appears responsible for most deaths at Vesuvius in the last 2,000 years? List your evidence. Symbols are shown for pyroclastic flow (PF), volcanic mudflow (MF), volcanic avalanche (VA), and massive tephra fallout (MT).

A tephra fallout is volcanic matter falling from the air.

e. From your analysis of those data, how hazardous are volcanic eruptions from Vesuvius? List your evidence.

f. For the eruptions shown in figure 15.27a, what percentage of the time over the past 2,000 years have people been killed in volcanic eruptions?

3. Currently, several million residents live in the vicinity of Vesuvius, including the populous city of Naples, Italy. A modern eruption of Vesuvius could be devastating.

a. What ways can you think of to reduce the risk of volcanic hazards in that area?

b. What things are you aware of that are used to reduce the risks of volcanic hazards in the United States today?

4. The Cascade Volcanic Arc in the Pacific Northwest is a region of active volcanoes. Figure 15.28 shows the history of activity for the main Cascade volcanoes over the last 4,000 years. The positions of the ash puffs show major eruptions per volcano.

a. Do any of the volcanoes appear dormant? If so, list them in your notebook.

b. Which volcano appears to have been the most active in the last 4,000 years?

c. Have any of these volcanoes recently been in the news? The Cascades Volcano Observatory has up-to-the-minute information on each volcano and its eruptive history.

d. Using figure 15.28, consider the 4,000-year volcanic history for the Cascades. Make a table with columns showing (1) the volcano name, (2) the number of eruptions in the last 4,000 years, and (3) the average number of eruptions per thousand years.

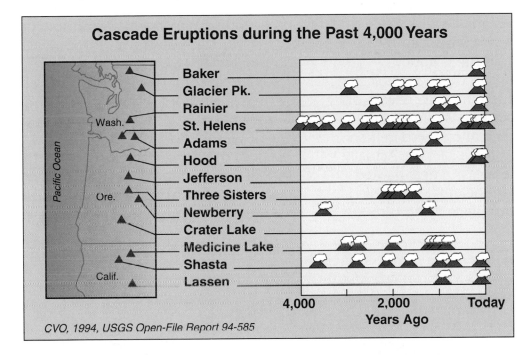

▲ **Figure 15.28 Map showing frequency of eruption of volcanoes in the Cascades in the past 4,000 years.** Have you ever seen one of these active or dormant volcanoes?

Volcanic Eruptions and All That Gas

Making models of eruptions is a fun way to learn about volcanoes. In another class, perhaps you added vinegar to baking soda to imitate a volcanic reaction. However, that is not a realistic model of a volcanic eruption. In fact, it's a really bad model.

The chemical reaction between an acid (vinegar) and a base (baking soda) produces water (H_2O) and some fizzing carbon dioxide (CO_2). Sure, volcanoes emit CO_2 and H_2O during eruptions. But those gases are already part of the magma. They are not produced by a chemical reaction in the eruption.

It is more realistic to think of a volcanic eruption as a sudden, massive release of pressure—an explosion. When molten rock is inside the volcano, it also gets shot into the air during the *explosion*. Actually, anything atop the volcano gets blasted into the air. Molten rock that is expelled cools to a solid rock while flying through the air. Those rocks are called **volcanic bombs.** They are often found in volcanic fields around the flanks of volcanoes.

Volcanic explosions also have a massive **blast wave**, or shock wave. A blast wave is a pulse of pressure that moves rapidly through the air outward from the volcanic explosion. Blast waves do not contain volcanic material, but they are highly destructive. They push over most anything in their path. Squeezing a balloon and hearing a pop is a mini-example of a blast wave. The pop travels through air and is detected by your eardrums. Massive tracts of forest were flattened by the blast wave from the May 1980 volcanic eruption at Mount St. Helens in the state of Washington (see photograph).

Besides the rock, what about all of the gas that comes out of volcanoes? Where does it come from? Well, you can find a good model in your house or grocery

volcanic bombs

Volcanic bomb. Volcanic rocks like these are thrown into the air during volcanic eruptions. They are called volcanic bombs.

store—a bottle of soda or seltzer water. It represents gas leaving volcanic rock during an eruption. Before you open the bottle, the carbonated drink is under pressure—just like the magma inside a volcano. Just before eruption, the gas is still *dissolved* in the liquid and not present as bubbles. You learned about dissolved substances earlier this year.

When you open the bottle, you hear a quick "ffsst" and hiss as you release the pressure. The gas is being released from the liquid as gas molecules join to form bubbles. You see the bubbles form right before your eyes. This is the opposite of when gas dissolves into liquid. The release of pressure from the bottle is like lava being shot out of a volcano. Besides liquid rock being shot out of the volcano, a lot of gas is also released from the liquid as the lava exits the volcano. The gas was dissolved in the lava inside the volcano. The gas rapidly and violently leaves the lava as the volcano explodes.

Trees toppled by volcanic blast wave. This photo shows massive trees that were stripped of branches and blown flat by a volcanic blast wave. It occurred in May 1980 at Mount St. Helens, Washington. The blast wave moved across the picture from left to right. For scale, two geologists can be seen in the red circle at the lower right. This shows that the diameters of tree trunks are 1.8–2.1 m.

Risks, Hazards, and Your Community

In this chapter, you have studied risks and hazards that affect humans. Some risks are slow, growing over years. Those risks stem from behaviors such as overexposure to UV radiation, smoking, poor eating habits, and lack of regular exercise. Small risk factors that spread through a population can affect large numbers of people. Many high-risk events can be rapid. They may occur in minutes, hours, or days. Hazards with a rapid impact include earthquakes, hurricanes, tsunamis, floods, tornadoes, and drought.

In Risk, Hazards, and Your Community, you show what you have learned about risks and hazards and their effect on humans. You do this by researching a significant risk or hazard that affects you, your family, or your community. You show your understanding by using a graph and a map related to the risk or hazard. Other concepts you may want to include are cause and effect, probability, risk level, risk factors, and mortality rates. You also get to design a creative solution to the problem. Follow the steps to research the risk or hazard.

Materials

For each student

access to library and Internet

1 map of the world, North America, or the lower 48 states

1 Evaluate Rubric handout

Process and Procedure

Often, the outcomes of risks and natural hazards are detrimental for individuals and communities. At some level, decisions that people make relate to the final effects. In this activity, you research and learn more about a hazard or risk that relates directly to you. Read all of the steps of the Process and Procedure before starting Step 1.

1. Choose a risk factor or hazard that affects you, your family, or your community.
2. Make a T-table in your notebook. On 1 side, write 3 things that you know about the risk or hazard. On the other side, write 3 things that you do not know about the risk or hazard but that you would like to learn more about.
3. Begin researching your risk or hazard. Use a combination of books and Internet resources. Keep an accurate list of all resources, which you will use to cite in your reference list. You may do your research individually, or your teacher may ask you to complete your research with a partner who has the same topic. When conducting your research, use the following questions as guidelines for the type of information to gather about your hazard or risk.

    - What is the physical, biological, or geologic cause?
    - How can scientists measure the effects on humans or ecosystems?
    - What geographical area or region is affected?
    - How does the risk or hazard vary with time?
    - Is the risk natural or humanmade?
    - What is the result of the hazard or risk factor on humans?
    - How many humans are typically affected each year?
    - What groups of people are most likely to be affected, and least likely to be affected?
    - How can the level of risk be reduced?

4. In Step 5, you will write a short report on your hazard or risk. Three parts of this report are summarized here. Be sure to note these points as you do your research.

    - *Map.* Learn about the regional or global extent of your chosen risk or hazard and represent that information on a map. Obtain from your teacher a blank map of the world, North

America, the lower 48 states, or your state (you draw that one!). Consider the effectiveness of using a color scale in a key or legend to indicate gradations from high risk to low risk across your map. Review examples from chapter activities

- *Graph of data.* Develop at least 1 graph that demonstrates a key feature or pattern of the risk or hazard. If no predictable pattern exists, use a graph as evidence to show that there is no predictable pattern. Typically, this graph shows the hazard as a function of time. Review examples of graphs from chapter activities.

- *Creative solutions.* Sometimes people think carefully and creatively about a risk or hazard. When they do, they may be able to suggest or invent a new solution to lessen the impact of the risk or hazard. What are the top 3 things that you could do to lessen the impact of the risk or hazard on humans or on the ecosystem? Do your suggestions involve technology? Why or why not?

5. Work individually to complete a short, written summary of your risk or hazard. Use 5 short sections:

- *Section 1: summary of research findings.* What did you find in your Step 3 research?

- *Section 2: map.* Describe the map that you developed in Step 4. Combining your written words with the map, describe the geographic extent of your risk or hazard.

- *Section 3: graph.* Write about the graph(s) that you developed in Step 4. Describe how frequently the risk or hazard occurs or how frequently it affects humans or ecosystems.

- *Section 4: creative solutions.* Use your imagination to develop a creative solution that you thought of in Step 4. Think about the risk or hazard in a different way—one that will help humans or the ecosystem respond to its impact. Is your solution realistic? Describe whether it uses technology and why it does or does not use technology.

- *Section 5: reference list.* Include a full reference list of every source of information that you used.

Use headings with titles for each of the sections listed. Also, use complete sentences and paragraphs, proper grammar, and correct spelling.

Your teacher will review with you how to cite the research of other people in your report. Refer to the summary on your SRCD, How to Cite References. You will see that you must use the results of scientists in your summary. Just make sure to cite that work in your reference list. In contrast, using the creative work, data, or ideas of others *without* citing them in your reference list is a form of stealing. That form of stealing is called plagiarism. To write a good report, accurately cite all materials that you use.

CHAPTER 16

Fire Ecology

Fire Ecology

So far in the Perspectives on Science and Technology in Your World unit, you have learned about some of the problems of living in modern society. Those problems include crime that arises out of human interactions. Humans also face risks from living on Earth. Some hazards are catastrophic, such as pyroclastic flows during a volcanic eruption. Other hazards are harder to recognize, and the gradual health effects accumulate over periods of years. One example that you studied was overexposure of skin to the Sun's ultraviolet rays.

This unit, however, is not about only humans. Humans are but one part of Earth's ecosystems. Human activities can affect basic natural processes such as water flow, animal migration, and forest growth. Changes to natural processes also can create new risks to the ecosystems—risks that affect all organisms, including humans. For example, look at the opening images for this chapter. How has technology changed an ecosystem in one of the photographs? Are humans protected from a natural hazard? Is there an impact to the ecosystem?

Science can help people understand the risks of living on Earth, and technology can play a role in protecting people from harm. Ultimately, however, humans must think carefully about risks and benefits. Humans must make decisions to determine the best course of action in the face of natural and societal hazards.

Goals for the Chapter

In chapter 16, Fire Ecology, you examine one way that humans have affected an ecosystem. You investigate the policy of wildfire suppression, study data about forests over the last century, and confront common ideas about forests. By the end of the chapter, you will be able to answer the following questions:

- What was the purpose of fire suppression policies?
- What is an ecosystem, and how does fire suppression affect a forest ecosystem?
- What are the risks posed to ecosystems by fire suppression? What are the risks to humans as part of the ecosystem?

- How do scientists study forests? How do they determine the impact humans have had on a forest ecosystem?
- How can humans use science and technology to evaluate policies for forest management?

You will gain a better understanding of forests and fire ecology in the following activities:

ENGAGE	Questioning Smokey
EXPLORE	To Build a Fire
EXPLAIN	Fire Suppression and the Fire Triangle
EXPLORE	A Quick Fix?
EXPLAIN	More Than Meets the Eye
ELABORATE	Fire in Other Ecosystems
EVALUATE	Burning Issues

Even though this chapter deals with the human impact on forest ecosystems, you can use the understanding and abilities that you gain to study many other interactions between humans and their environment. For example, mining produces valuable resources for society (natural gas, coal, oil, valuable metals, and salts). But how do different types of mining affect ecosystems? How do possible impacts in the ecosystem then affect the health and lives of humans?

From the opening image and activity titles, you might guess that this chapter is about wildfires. As an integrating chapter, though, you use concepts from many disciplines that you have studied this year. Concepts range from physical sciences (atoms and elements, chemical reactions such as combustion, and energy) to the life sciences (food chains, food webs, ecosystems, and photosynthesis) to many other issues of science, technology, and society. You continue using inquiry through evidence and inference, as well as writing, graphing, and analyzing. Solving complex problems in science, such as fire suppression, relies on using many fields together.

The important concepts in this chapter are included in the activities. Use the chapter organizer to help you see the organization of concepts.

WHY?

remember—
only you can **PREVENT FOREST FIRES!**

What is fire and how is it a natural process in forests?

ENGAGE

Questioning Smokey

Key Idea:

What do you know about the pros and cons of fire suppression?

EXPLORE

To Build a Fire

Key Idea:

Fire requires three major components to burn.

EXPLAIN

Fire Suppression and the Fire Triangle

Key Ideas:

• Forest fires are started by a heat source, such as a lightning strike.

• When fuel builds up due to fire suppression, larger, dangerous, and more destructive fires result.

Fire Ecology

Linking Question

What can we do to lower the risk of large, dangerous fires?

EXPLORE

A Quick Fix?

Key Idea:

One way to reverse the impact of fire suppression is to thin forests of their excess fuel.

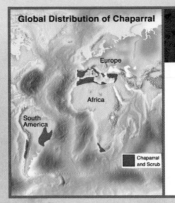

Europe

Africa

South
America

Chaparral
and Scrub

Burning Issues

Key Idea:

Science can inform public debate about forest management, but decisions made by humans reflect social issues, opinions, and personal beliefs.

Linking Question

As humans work together to manage forests, what competing interest must their management strategies take into account?

ELABORATE

Fire in Other Ecosystems

Key Idea:

The chaparral ecosystem in California remains largely unchanged even with massive fire suppression efforts.

CHAPTER

16 Major Concepts

▶ **Forests are ecosystems with complex interrelationships and interdependencies of organisms.**

▶ **Forest fires are a part of this ecosystem.**

▶ **Our decisions about how to manage forest fires has a big impact on the balance and stability of this ecosystem.**

▶ **The process of scientific inquiry and technological design can help policy makers and communities make well-informed decisions.**

EXPLAIN

More Than Meets the Eye

Key Idea:

Forests are complex ecosystems made up of living and nonliving components. Every management strategy has an effect on this ecosystem.

Linking Question

What other ecosystems are affected by fire and by humans' decisions about how to manage them?

Questioning Smokey

In the history of public service messages, never has an icon been more popular than that of Smokey Bear. Since 1944, Smokey Bear has welcomed visitors to national forests with his proud stewardship and the cautionary words, "Only you can prevent forest fires."

Today other messages are emerging. What are those messages, and how do they affect Smokey's campaign? In Questioning Smokey, you work with a partner to answer those questions.

Materials

Process and Procedure

1. Study the image in figure 16.1 and answer the following questions in your science notebook.
   a. What is the message?
   b. How does the image get the message across?
   c. What emotions does the message appeal to?

   Use the strategy that you have been using this year: What do I see? and What does it mean?

▶ **Figure 16.1 1960 Smokey Bear poster.** Smokey Bear presents his message in an early poster from 1960. What do you think his message is and why?

Smokey Bear message in 2003. This image was taken by a fire-fighter in 2003 near Magdalena, New Mexico. What do you think the message is?

2. Study the image in figure 16.2 and answer the following questions in your science notebook.
   a. What is the message that the photo gives about forest fires?
   b. How is the message different from the one presented in figure 16.1?
   c. What do you think about the message?
3. Look carefully at the 2001 poster for Smokey Bear in figure 16.3. How is the message similar to the one in the 1960 poster in figure 16.1? How is it different? Pay particular attention to the "Only You" slogan at the bottom.

Use the strategy that you have been using this year: What do I see? and What does it mean?

◀ Figure 16.3
Smokey Bear message in 2001. This 2001 poster is a recent version of the Smokey Bear campaigns. How do you think its message is similar to or different from the message in figure 16.1?

Reflect and Connect

Discuss the following questions with your partner. Record the answers in your science notebook.

1. Are forest fires good or bad? Refer to figures 16.1, 16.2, and 16.3 in your answer.
2. What do the 3 figures say about the change in perception of fires between 1960 and 2003?
3. According to figure 16.1, when humans carelessly start forest fires, how do the fires affect the natural system of the forest? Does figure 16.3 give the same message?
4. According to figure 16.2, when humans allow naturally occurring wildfires to burn, how do the fires affect the forest?

SIDEBAR

Smokey's Story

How did Smokey Bear become a national symbol? During World War II, many people who regularly worked on firefighting crews were overseas. The U.S. Department of Agriculture's Forest Service needed to caution people about starting fires that it could not put out. The Forest Service licensed the Bambi character from the Walt Disney Company to appeal to people's desire to protect animals in forest fires. When the license to use Bambi ran out after one year, the Forest Service looked to another animal to continue the message. In 1944, Smokey Bear became the symbol for fire prevention.

Smokey Bear soon got a real-life counterpart. In 1950, a human-caused forest fire swept through the Capitan Mountains of New Mexico. Forest rangers, members of the military, employees of the State Game Department, and civilian volunteers fought the fire. Eventually, the fire burned 6,800 hectares. During the fire, a bear cub was stranded in a tree, badly burned on the paws and hind legs. He was rescued by one of the fire crews and flown to a veterinary hospital in Santa Fe, New Mexico. He was named Smokey after the fire-prevention bear created just a few years earlier.

When Smokey healed, he was flown to the National Zoo in Washington, D.C. He rapidly became a celebrity. Schoolchildren wrote him so many letters that he was given his own zip code. When he died in 1976, his body was returned to his birthplace in New Mexico. He is buried at the Smokey Bear Historical Park in downtown Capitan, New Mexico.

To Build a Fire

When someone says "fire," the image that comes to mind may be that of cozy candlelight or of a raging force that burns a neighborhood building to the ground. What is this thing called fire? And how do people control fire so that it is useful rather than destructive? Why would Smokey Bear be so concerned with preventing wildfires?

In this activity, To Build a Fire, you work in a team to explore fire. Your laboratory experiences will help you understand the science behind starting, sustaining, and putting out fires.

Materials
For each team of three students

3 pairs of safety goggles

1 metal fire tray

1 small beaker

1 spray bottle filled with water

1 box of wooden matches

supplies for tests

Cautions

Follow directions carefully so that your explorations of fire are safe. You are responsible for following the safety rules for fire as well as the general laboratory safety rules.

- Always wear your safety goggles. Tie back long hair and loose clothing.
- Always use the metal fire tray under your burning experiments (see figure 16.4).
- Keep the box of matches away from flames.
- Assign one person from your team to handle the spray bottle of water and to watch that all of the burning fuels stay on the fire tray. If any fire becomes too big or escapes the fire tray, extinguish it immediately with a spray of water.
- When you have completed your burning experiments, extinguish all smoldering

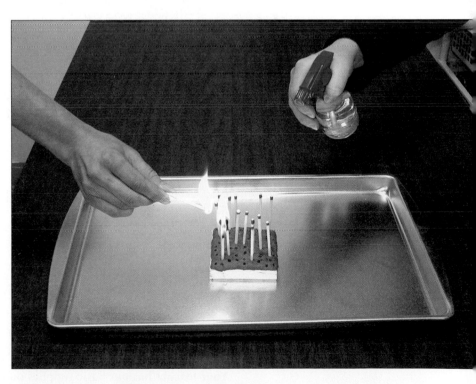

▲ **Figure 16.4 Metal tray under matches.** Use the metal fire tray under all fire experiments to protect your desk from fire.

fuel, using the spray bottle, before placing the remains in the metal trash can.

- Let your teacher know if you have asthma or respiratory problems. You can wear a dust mask to avoid breathing the smoke generated by your experiments.

Process and Procedure

Use safety goggles.

Caution

1. Put on your safety goggles. Cover your work area with the metal fire tray. Assign 1 person to hold the spray bottle and to watch for unsafe fires.
2. Distribute the matches (1 for each team member). Do not light the matches yet. Instead, observe the matches and discuss the following questions as a team. Record your answers in your science notebook.
   a. What is the match made of? Are all matches made of the same material as this one?
   b. What will you do to light the match? Why do you do this?
   c. If the match is a system, what do you need to add to the system for it to burn? In other words, why is it not burning now?

It may be helpful to include a careful sketch of the match with labels and a scale.

3. Strike the matches on the matchbox. Observe the burning matches. Blow them out when the fire gets too close to your fingers.

Listen to your teacher's instructions for disposing of the match.

4. What happens when a fire starts on the tip of a match? What keeps the match burning? Work with your team to complete the following tasks to help you answer those 2 questions.
   a. Three things are needed to produce fire. Together they make up the **fire triangle.** Draw a triangle in your science notebook. Next to the triangle, list the things that you think are needed to produce a fire.

SCiLINKS®
NSTA
Topic: fire triangle
Go to: www.scilinks.org
Code: 1Inquiry784

You may list more than three ideas.

   b. What can you do to test your ideas? How do you know which of your ideas really affect fire? Design 3 simple tests to determine the 3 things needed to produce fire. Record your design ideas in your science notebook. Then check your ideas with your teacher to make sure they are safe.

Your teacher has put basic supplies on the supply table for you to use in your tests. If you want to use something that has not been provided, ask your teacher.

5. Perform your tests, being sure to follow all of the safety rules. Record your results in your science notebook. When you are finished, carefully extinguish all fire materials. Make sure matches are completely extinguished by spraying them with water. Place burned materials in the designated metal trash can. Return supplies to the supply table for other classes to use.

6. Draw a new fire triangle in your science notebook. Based on the results of your tests in Step 5, label each of the 3 sides of the triangle with a component needed to produce fire. Beside each label, describe how you know it is essential for fire.

To decide on the three labels for your fire triangle, think about which of your tests resulted in the best fire. Why do you think that happened? What caused a fire to burn well? What caused a fire to go out?

7. Share your fire triangle with the class. Is each team's triangle the same or different? How can you use your tests to convince other teams that your labels are correct? Come to a consensus as a class about which components make up the fire triangle.

Activity adapted with permission from Smith, J. K., & McMurray, N. E. 2000. *FireWorks curriculum featuring ponderosa, lodgepole, and whitebark pine forests.* (General Technical Report RMRS GTR 65). Fort Collins, CO: U.S. Department of Agriculture, Forest Service, Rocky Mountain Research Station.

Reflect and Connect

Work individually to answer the following questions in your science notebook.

1. Fire is a chemical reaction much like cellular respiration, which you studied in chapter 7, Cells Are Busy Places. The formula for cellular respiration is as follows:

$$C_6H_{12}O_6 + 6\ O_2 \longrightarrow 6\ CO_2 + 6\ H_2O + energy$$
$$\text{(glucose)} \quad \text{(oxygen)} \qquad \text{(carbon dioxide)} \quad \text{(water)}$$

Use that information to complete the following sentences.
   a. Three factors needed for fire are _____.
   b. Three things produced by a fire are _____.
   c. Use the things in Steps 1a and 1b to represent combustion (fire) as a chemical formula like the above formula for cellular respiration.

2. If combustion is a chemical reaction that requires the combination of the 3 components of the fire triangle, how could you prevent combustion?

3. You are surrounded by burnable things and by oxygen. Why aren't they on fire?

4. Imagine that you are standing on the moon with matches and a candle. Do you think you would be able to light the candle?

Think back to chapter 13, The Earth-Sun System. How is oxygen produced for Earth's atmosphere?

5. Which part of the fire triangle does each of the following fire-fighting techniques address?
   a. Smoke jumpers fight forest fires by starting a backfire outside of the fire. The backfire then burns back into the fire.
   b. If your clothing catches on fire, you should "stop, drop, and roll."
   c. Firefighters spray a foamy fire retardant directly on the fire's flames.
   d. City firefighters rely on water from fire hydrants. They spray water on buildings to stop the fire.
   e. When people build houses in fire-prone areas, they are directed to clear the land of trees and shrubs 30 meters (m) out from all sides of the house.

EXPLAIN · Fire Suppression and the Fire Triangle

READING

Changing Forests

As you saw in To Build a Fire, fire is a chemical reaction that produces heat and light. Small fires, such as campfires that roast your marshmallows, are nonthreatening. However, fires that consume thousands of hectares (ha) of forest and that approach buildings and people can be life threatening. Those fires create billowing smoke, intense heat, and glowing skylines. Such fires have long-lasting effects on forests, humans, and the economy. It is no wonder that Smokey Bear has campaigned successfully to stop, or suppress, forest fires. Efforts to stop forest fires are called **fire suppression.**

But a new story has emerged after nearly a century of fire suppression. People are used to thinking that they are preserving forests when they put out forest fires. That way of thinking is largely in response to Smokey's warnings. One type of scientist looks at forest fires in a different way. That scientist is called an ecologist.

An **ecologist** is a kind of biologist who studies the living and nonliving parts of the environment and the ways that they interact. Ecologists look at how all plants and animals interact. They see much evidence that fire is a natural process in forests. Ecologists now see that when people suppress natural fires, they are changing forests rather than preserving them. Many types of

▲ **Figure 16.5** **Ponderosa grove in 1909.** This photograph shows an open ponderosa pine stand that had been subjected to frequent ground fires every seven years on average from 1600 to 1900. Few shrubs are evident beneath the mature ponderosa pines. Instead, a local wildflower called lupine thrived.

▲ **Figure 16.6** **The same ponderosa grove in 1979.** This photograph was taken from the same position in September 1979, 70 years after the photograph in figure 16.5. The large ponderosa pine in the center foreground in the 1909 view (see figure 16.5) as well as other trees were cut during timber harvests in 1952 and 1962.

forests are very different today than they were 100 years ago.

How have forests changed because of fire suppression? To find out one way in which they have changed, compare figures 16.5 and 16.6. The photographs were taken 70 years apart in the same location. They date from 1909 and 1979.

Do you notice more trees in the photograph from 1979—(see figure 16.6)? In fact, the old saying rings true here—"You can't see the forest for the trees." You cannot see as far into the distance as you can in the 1909 photo. Too many tree seedlings clutter and block the view. The **canopy** of the forest consists of the tall trees that shade the ground. The canopy has not changed much except that some trees have been logged.

In contrast, compare the understory between figures 16.5 and 16.6. The **understory** consists of shorter trees, grasses, and shrubs that grow under the canopy. The understory has grown into a dense layer that did not exist in 1909. The types of trees have also changed. Rather than separated clumps of ponderosa pines, many of

the more shade-tolerant Douglas firs are filling in the spaces.

The dense tangle in figure 16.6 is a result of fire suppression. When fires burned through this forest hundreds of years ago, those fires burned with a low intensity. The fires were low to the ground with only moderate heat. Such fires regularly burned the seedlings but left larger trees relatively unscathed. The open, parklike structure of the early forest canopy allowed sunlight to reach the ground, encouraging the growth of wildflowers such as lupine.

Fire suppression changed how these forests looked. When people stopped forest fires, even those started by lightning strikes, they stopped a natural thinning and clearing of the understory by low-intensity fires at ground level. Virtually all seedlings continued growing, unstopped. The seedlings grew so thick that sunlight no longer penetrated the trees' branches. Shade-tolerant

Go to: www.scilinks.org
Topic: canopy
Code: 1Inquiry787a
Topic: understory
Code: 1Inquiry787b
Topic: ponderosa pine
Code: 1Inquiry787c

▲ **Figure 16.7 Douglas fir close-up of a bough.**
Douglas firs are common in mixed-conifer forests in the western United States at low to medium elevations. They are a moderately shade-tolerant conifer that has replaced ponderosa pines in some ranges due to fire suppression policies.

trees such as Douglas firs (figure 16.7) were then able to take over. Douglas firs survived better than the original species, such as ponderosa pines, which need more sunlight. The result is a very dense forest. It is much denser than the forest that grew naturally for thousands of years.

So what's wrong with a dense Douglas-fir forest? The structure of a fir forest makes the forest prone to large, severe fires. That was not true of the original ponderosa forest, which had a modest understory. The understory in figure 16.6 consists of accumulating live and dead trees (fuel) and little open space to slow the spread of a fire. During hot, windy periods in late summer and early fall, these dense fir forests often experience lightning strikes. Even natural fires in dense fir forests burn longer and more completely than the low-intensity fires of 100 years ago. Figure 16.8 shows marked changes in forests in the Pacific Northwest that have occurred with fire suppression. Note the decrease in ponderosa.

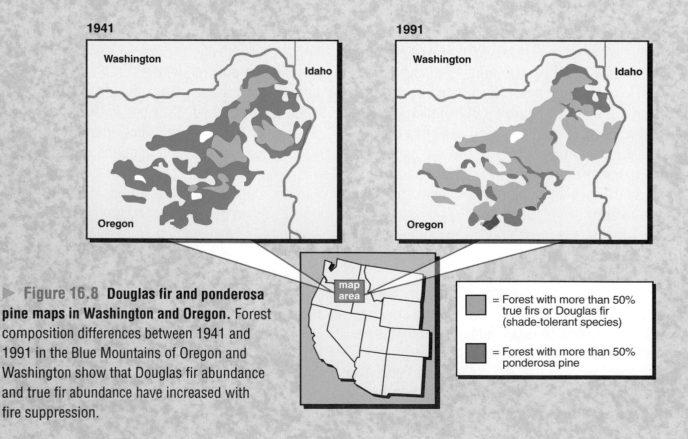

▶ **Figure 16.8 Douglas fir and ponderosa pine maps in Washington and Oregon.** Forest composition differences between 1941 and 1991 in the Blue Mountains of Oregon and Washington show that Douglas fir abundance and true fir abundance have increased with fire suppression.

= Forest with more than 50% true firs or Douglas fir (shade-tolerant species)

= Forest with more than 50% ponderosa pine

▲ **Figure 16.9 Conifers killed by beetles.** The photograph of a mountainside in Colorado shows patches of dead trees mixed with live trees. The trees were killed by beetles that infest weakened trees during low rainfall years. The dead and dying trees provide more fuel than would typically exist on the forest floor.

But small seedlings are not the only plants burned in the forest. Today's fires gain momentum and turn into **crown fires.** Those fires move through the canopy of a forest and destroy entire stands of mature trees. Fuels on the ground ignite the dense understory, which results in the fire spreading up the branches of saplings. The flames climb to the tops of full-grown trees until the entire forest is on fire. The fire spreads through the tightly packed layers of fuel as though it were climbing a ladder. Crown fires are natural in some types of pine forests that consist of species such as lodgepole pine or jack pine. Crown fires can be very damaging in forests of mature ponderosa pine.

In fact, forests that are susceptible to crown fires are full of connecting layers of **ladder fuels.**

Crown fires are difficult and dangerous to fight. The result of these large, catastrophic fires is much higher plant and animal mortality, in addition to loss of human lives and buildings. After such a fire, it will take a decade or more for a forest to reestablish itself.

Combined with fire suppression, several other factors make wildfires even more devastating. For example, strong winds move flames rapidly from mountain to mountain. Or climate patterns of low rainfall leave trees in a weakened condition. In that state, they can be infested with various types of pine beetles. Sometimes 30 percent or more of trees will die. As the trees die, they provide more fuel than normal. Such patterns contributed to devastating fires in Southern California in fall 2003.

Check your understanding of the reading by answering the following questions in your science notebook.

1. Study the graph in figure 16.10 and answer the following.
   a. Describe the trends that you see illustrated in the graph.
   b. For the 20-year period from 1950 to 1970, approximately how many million acres burned?
   c. For the 20-year period from 1980 to 2000, approximately how many million acres burned?
   d. Compare the acres per year burned from 1950 to 1970 with the acres per year burned from 1980 to 2000.
   e. Even though better fire suppression technologies are available and more money is spent fighting fires today than half a century ago, the trend over the last 2 decades is upward. Based on your reading of Changing Forests, how can you explain the trend from 1980 to 2000?

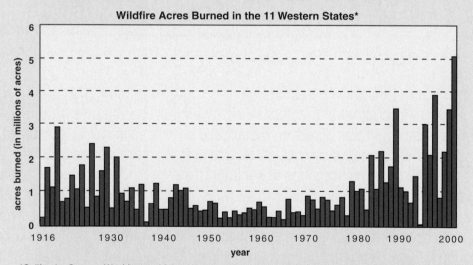

Wildfire Acres Burned in the 11 Western States*

*California, Oregon, Washington, Idaho, Nevada, Arizona, Utah, New Mexico, Wyoming, Montana, Colorado
Source: USDA Forest Service, Rocky Mountain Research Station

▲ **Figure 16.10 Acres burned in 11 western states.** What pattern do you see in this graph? What inferences might you draw from this graph?

2. Ponderosa pines typically shed their lower branches as they mature. In contrast, Douglas fir branches are well distributed over the height of the tree. The Douglas fir also has more leaf mass in its crown, which provides the shade necessary for many of the smaller seedlings to thrive at its base. How does the difference in structure between the 2 trees affect the incidence of crown fires in each type of forest?

Fuel for the Fire Triangle

You saw in your experiments that the fire triangle represents the three components of fire: fuel, heat, and oxygen. Those components are needed in the right combination to produce a fire. If you take away any one of the components, the fire stops. But what happens when one of the three components is in abundant supply? How does that change the nature of the fire?

Fire needs air that is at least 16 percent oxygen. Because Earth's atmosphere is 21 percent oxygen, oxygen is usually in plentiful supply for fire. When heat is applied to fuel in the presence of oxygen, a fire starts. Fuel and heat are critical to sustaining a fire once it starts.

When the amount of fuel is small, the fire burns out quickly. You saw this in your experiment with matches. When there is an abundance of fuel, however, the fire can burn for a long time. With more fuel to feed the fire, the temperature of the fire rises. And the more heat there is, the faster the fire spreads. The high temperatures dry and heat the fuel in the fire's path. That "preheating" prepares the fuel to burn more readily.

With plenty of fuel creating high local temperatures, large fires take on a life of their own. Smoke and heat billow upward, drawing in more air and oxygen from the sides. In that sense, wildfires can create their own wind. In large fires, each component of the fire triangle is in abundant supply. There is increased oxygen, high heat, and a lot of fuel. When fires reach this stage, they are difficult to control. If enough firefighters and bulldozers are available, they can clear a **firebreak** around the fire

▲ **Figure 16.11 Bulldozer clearing firebreak.** An important strategy for controlling wildfires is to clear a firebreak. This removes a wildfire's access to new fuel on the other side of the break.

(see figure 16.11). This is an area cleared of all vegetation. The break takes away the fire's access to fuel. Building firebreaks may seem to be destructive to the forest. But the amount of damage is small compared with a catastrophic wildfire.

Sometimes firefighters are helped by nature. With a weather change, rain or snow falls and cools down the fire's heat. With decreased heat, the rate of the reaction decreases, and the fire becomes more manageable. Firefighters then use other techniques to cut off the supply of heat, fuel, or oxygen to put out the fire.

Critics of the policy of fire suppression recognize that forests in which there have been no fires contain too much fuel. Those people understand the fire triangle and see that the unnatural increase in the density of trees and shrubs in forests can only fuel larger, hotter fires in the future. As a result, policies about forest management are changing. Instead of putting out all fires, even those that are caused naturally by lightning, forest managers are letting fires burn as long as they do not threaten human lives or buildings. The fires help restore forests to a more natural state, with less buildup of dangerous fuels.

Critics of the "let it burn" policy say that the forests are out of balance—that they already contain too much fuel. If managers let many forests burn, the fires may burn out of control as crown fires that completely destroy, rather than rejuvenate, the forests. Scientists are now devel-oping tests to thin the forests before natural fires start. If managers can return the forests to the structure they had when ground fires burned every decade or so, new fires will not have enough fuel to become catastrophic.

Did fires burn often, or did they burn infre-quently? Can scientists tell how often forest fires burned in the past? Yes, ecologists can do that in considerable detail. To see how, read the side-bar, Fire: A Natural Disturbance.

Reflect and Connect

Answer the following questions in your science notebook.

1. How do humans interact with forests? Which of those interactions change the forests? Which ones do not change the forests?

2. Imagine that you are a forest manager addressing a citizen group that wants to leave a forest as it is. The citizens do not want loggers with chain saws and large trucks going into the local forest and clearing any trees. How will you use the fire triangle to convince the citizens that thinning the forest is a useful management strategy that may pre-vent catastrophic fires?

3. Many policies regarding forests were developed with eco-nomic goals in mind. One economic goal that drove fire suppression policies was to preserve trees for a profitable building materials industry, rather than allow the trees to burn. The poster in figure 16.12 illustrates that sentiment.
   a. How would you propose that trees thinned from over-crowded forests be used by people where you live? Would you thin big trees or small trees? How would size affect the use of trees for profit?
   b. Can a management strategy that helps restore forests also be profitable? Is managing for profitability impor-tant? Why or why not?
   c. Aside from lumber, for what other uses are forests managed?

4. Scientists formulate and revise scientific explanations and mod-els using logic and evidence. Explain how science has helped forest managers and ecologists understand that they need to revise the model for managing forests.

▲ Figure 16.12
Smokey Bear poster, 1952. This 1952 poster depicts the forests and their lumber as natural resources that can be harvested or logged to enhance the economy.

Fire: A Natural Disturbance

When scientists noticed the changes in western forests during the last century of fire suppression, they needed to know fire's role in past forest ecosystems. To study the history of wildfires in western states, they turned to two types of records: tree rings and fire-related deposits in river sediments.

Fire Scars on Tree Rings

Tree rings are used to study the growth history of a tree. A **tree ring** is a growth band that represents one season of a tree's growth. Under normal conditions, early in the growing season, the ring is white. Near the end of the growing season, the ring is dark. The change in color from dark to light and back to dark makes it easy to distinguish and count the rings. The image shows about 19 tree rings. Variations in growing conditions from year to year produce a sequence of wide, narrow, and average ring widths.

Tree rings. The color change of the ring from spring to fall helps distinguish the tree rings—and each year of growth. This image shows about 19 years of growth.

In a year when a fire burns near the base of a tree, the tree ring is quite different. It typically is black, with a rolled-in and burnt appearance. **Ground fires** often scar trees around the base but do not kill them. As a scarred tree continues to grow, new wood encloses the fire wound. Scientists date fire scars to calendar years. In that way, scars provide a clear record of the frequency, extent, and intensity of fires across time. Thus, tree ring data provide centuries of fire history.

By studying tree rings, scientists have learned that in the past, fire was common in forests. Forests burned as often as every five to 10 years. The image shows scars about every 20 years. Most of the fires were low-intensity surface or ground fires. Those small fires burned small tree seedlings and the fine grass and pine needle fuels on the ground. The ground fires scarred mature trees but rarely killed them. When large, catastrophic fires replaced whole stands of trees, tree ring data were affected. Thus, scientists pieced together a history of forest fire and rejuvenation.

Tree ring data also suggest a correlation between climate change and forest fires. Fire intensities are not constant through time. They fluctuate with the climate change—from cool and wet to warm and dry. Fire occurrence is influenced strongly by drought conditions on a seasonal scale and major climate changes on a century scale. Tree ring data gathered from long-lived sequoia trees indicate that maximum fire frequencies occurred from about AD 1000 to AD 1300 during the Medieval Warm Period. Fewer fires broke out during the Little Ice Age, a period of cool temperatures across the globe. However, although fire frequency was lower, more severe fires burned during this period because fuel had accumulated between fires.

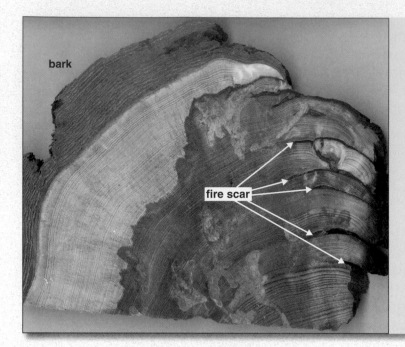

bark

fire scar

Tree rings with fire scars. Events such as fires have a recognizable effect on tree ring growth. Scars are formed that extend partly along tree rings.

Charcoal in River Sediments

Tree ring studies help scientists piece together fire histories that go back hundreds of years. But how do scientists get records of forest fires going back thousands of years?

Geologists usually do that work. They study deposits of charcoal washed from mountains into river sediments. Those river sediments form **fire-related deposits.** The charcoal and river sediments are carried downstream from the mountains. They then begin to accumulate in low-lying areas next to the mountains. When fires were common in the mountains, numerous layers contain charcoal. When fires were severe, the amount of charcoal in layers can be large.

In parts of the western United States, geologists are finding telltale deposits of gravel, rock, and charcoal in river sediments. The abundance of charcoal downstream from both lodgepole and ponderosa pine forests shows that fires

Debris and charcoal flow downhill from regions of unstable slopes where severe fires have removed virtually all vegetation. The river carries pieces of charcoal down the river and deposits the charcoal as sediments in lowlands next to the mountains.

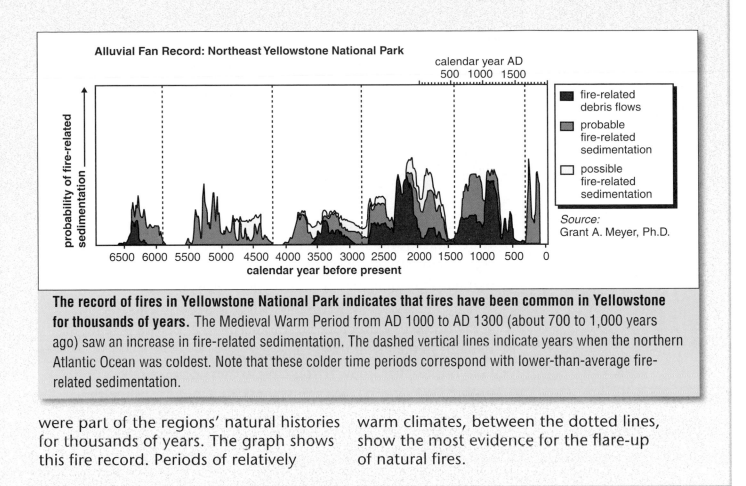

Alluvial Fan Record: Northeast Yellowstone National Park

calendar year AD
500 1000 1500

probability of fire-related sedimentation

■ fire-related debris flows

▨ probable fire-related sedimentation

□ possible fire-related sedimentation

Source: Grant A. Meyer, Ph.D.

6500 6000 5500 5000 4500 4000 3500 3000 2500 2000 1500 1000 500 0
calendar year before present

The record of fires in Yellowstone National Park indicates that fires have been common in Yellowstone for thousands of years. The Medieval Warm Period from AD 1000 to AD 1300 (about 700 to 1,000 years ago) saw an increase in fire-related sedimentation. The dashed vertical lines indicate years when the northern Atlantic Ocean was coldest. Note that these colder time periods correspond with lower-than-average fire-related sedimentation.

were part of the regions' natural histories for thousands of years. The graph shows this fire record. Periods of relatively warm climates, between the dotted lines, show the most evidence for the flare-up of natural fires.

A Quick Fix?

A large amount of fuel in a forest creates the potential for a catastrophic fire. What can be done about it? How do forest managers know which management strategy is most effective in eliminating crown fires and preserving stands of trees? Can forests be managed to encourage regular, low-intensity fires?

In this activity, A Quick Fix?, you work with your team to develop models that answer those questions. Based on your investigations, you make recommendations about how to manage a forest that is dense with fuel due to the suppression of fire.

Materials
For each team of four students

4 pairs of safety goggles

1 metal fire tray

1 spray bottle filled with water

1 matchstick model base

1 ball of clay (nonflammable)

1 box of wooden matches

Cautions

In this activity, you light many matches at a time. The flames and the heat will be greater than those in the investigation To Build a Fire. Follow all of the rules for working with fire.

- Always wear your safety goggles. Tie back long hair and loose clothing.
- Always use the metal fire tray under your burning experiments.
- Keep the box of matches away from flames.
- Assign one person from your team to handle the spray bottle of water and to watch that all of the burning fuels stay on the fire tray. If any fire becomes too big or escapes the fire tray, extinguish it immediately with a spray of water.
- When you have completed your burning experiments, use the spray bottle to extinguish all smoldering fuel before placing the remains in the metal trash can.
- Let your teacher know if you have asthma or respiratory problems. You can wear a dust mask to avoid breathing the smoke generated by your experiments.

Process and Procedure

1. Read the memo in figure 16.13. Discuss the assignment with your class.

▶ **Figure 16.13**

Forest thinning memo. This memo is from the National Forest Advisory Board to forest management teams. It requests that the teams develop and describe new thinning strategies to safeguard forests from wildfires. Teams must also test their approaches with scientific models.

MEMORANDUM

TO: Forest Management Teams
FROM: National Forest Advisory Board
REGARDING: Thinning strategies to reduce the probability of widespread fire

The Forest Management Advisory Board will be meeting in two days. The members of the board would like to hear your recommendations for a forest thinning program that would help the forest survive a fire. Our goal is to preserve as many trees as possible, but to cut down and remove the extra fuel that could lead to a catastrophic fire.

As you know, we are mandated by our national charter to vote on a particular strategy only after we study the data from your investigations. Your team does not have enough time to conduct investigations using real trees in a real forest, so we suggest that you create models of forests using matchsticks to represent trees.

Over the next two days, please conduct as many investigations as you can using the forest models. Prepare a statement that describes your observations and recommends a particular thinning pattern and technique that preserves the most trees if a fire breaks out.

---

2. Put on your safety goggles. Make sure a class member is ready to use the spray bottle to put out any unsafe fires. Watch as your teacher demonstrates a fire using a model forest.

   a. What happens to the trees when lightning strikes the forest?
   b. When the fire has finished burning, count the number of unburned trees. Record that number in your science notebook.

3. Meet with your team of 4 students. Gather your team's materials. Cover your work area with the metal fire tray. Assign 1 person to hold the spray bottle and to watch for unsafe fires.

4. Make a model forest by doing the following.
   a. Place the square board on your desk.
   b. Press the clay across the top of the board so you cover the entire top of the board with clay about a centimeter thick.
   c. Use 50 matchsticks to construct a forest after 100 years of fire suppression, similar to the one your teacher constructed for the demonstration. As you do that, consider the following:

   • Each match represents a tree. The tip of the match represents the flammable crown of the tree. The base of the match can be "planted" into the layer of clay on the forest board.

   • Some trees are taller than others. Break matches so they are various heights.

   • Some trees grow in the shade of bigger trees. Arrange your trees in a way that resembles a forest with large trees and a crowded understory.

   • Some trees have died but are still part of the forest. Lay some trees on the ground under other trees. Or lean some trees against live trees, like dead snags.

Do not light this forest yet. First you will "manage" the forest in Step 5.

5. What density and arrangement of trees will result in more unburned trees if lightning strikes your model forest?
   a. Thin the forest in a way that you think will stop a forest fire. Will you remove the thinned trees or leave them in the forest in piles? How will you know which way works best?
   b. Test to see how well your design works by lighting 1 edge of the forest as your teacher did in the demonstration. Let the fire burn. In the end, how many trees are left unburned? Record the results of your trial in your science notebook.
   c. If necessary, make adjustments to your design and test it again. How many trees are unburned this time? Record the results in your science notebook.

d. As a team, decide on the density, arrangement, and removal strategies that you will recommend to the National Forest Advisory Board. Remember, you must have data to support your recommendations.

Your strategy will be judged on the number of trees in your model before the burn and the number that remained after the burn. The higher the two numbers, the more seriously the National Forest Advisory Board will take your suggestions.

e. Write your team's strategy in 1 statement to present to the board.

6. Present your strategy to the board. Your class will role-play a board meeting. Discuss the results of your tests. Listen as others present their strategies. Are the strategies similar in some ways? Are they different in some ways?

Activity adapted with permission from Smith, J. K., & McMurray, N. E. 2000. *FireWorks curriculum featuring ponderosa, lodgepole, and whitebark pine forests.* (General Technical Report RMRS-GTR-65). Fort Collins, CO: U.S. Department of Agriculture, Forest Service, Rocky Mountain Research Station.

Reflect and Connect

Answer the following questions individually. Record your answers in your science notebook.

1. If you were a member of the National Forest Advisory Board, what strategy would you recommend that the board choose? Why?

2. One hundred years ago the characteristics of forests were the result of natural processes of fire, drought, flood, seed germination, and insects. Of the 3 types of forests in figure 16.14, which do you think would be susceptible to crown fires that destroy most of the trees? Which would survive a forest fire? How do you know?

▼ **Figure 16.14**

Presettlement conifer densities. Forests in presettlement times had these structures and densities.

Type of forest	Number of trees in 1/15 of an acre (area 50 ft × 50 ft)	Arrangement of trees
Lodgepole pine/subalpine fir	49	Trees are dense and quite evenly spaced.
Ponderosa pine	5	Trees occur singly, occasionally in pairs.
Whitebark pine/subalpine fir	13	Trees occur in clusters of 2 to 5.

Source: From Smith, J. K., & McMurray, N. E. 2000. *FireWorks curriculum featuring ponderosa, lodgepole, and whitebark pine forests.* (General Technical Report RMRS-GTR-65). Fort Collins, CO: U.S. Department of Agriculture, Forest Service, Rocky Mountain Research Station.

3. How could public opinion affect the final plan for forest thinning?

4. You worked as a scientist during this activity. Describe the process of inquiry that you used.

A Fiery California Matchstick Study—for Real

When the experimental forest at Blacks Mountain near Susanville, California, burned in September 2003, it became part of scientists' study of forest management. The Cone Fire ravaged most of the forest's trees, turning them into charcoal. The dense underbrush and thick tree growth led to a spectacular wildfire—but the fire did not burn everything.

One patch of forest was an experimental plot. Researchers had thinned the trees and burned its underbrush. Their goal was to see how management techniques affect forest ecosystems. The unintended result was the creation of a natural fire wall. The fire did not destroy that part of the forest.

Other patches of the forest had undergone different management techniques. Some patches are shown in the figure.

Some were selectively logged by taking out the large trees so that stand diversity was low (called **low-diversity** plots). Others were burned without thinning. Still others were thinned by taking out a variety of trees, leaving stands of high diversity (called **high-diversity** plots). Researchers kept an eye on all of the plots to note changes in plant growth, tree growth, and wildlife populations. But they did not imagine that their work would become an experiment on how forest management protects a forest during fire.

The Cone Fire started in a thickly forested area. It quickly grew into a crown fire that consumed all of the trees in its path. This is shown in the image. When the fire reached the experimental plots, its behavior changed. It did not keep moving as a crown fire.

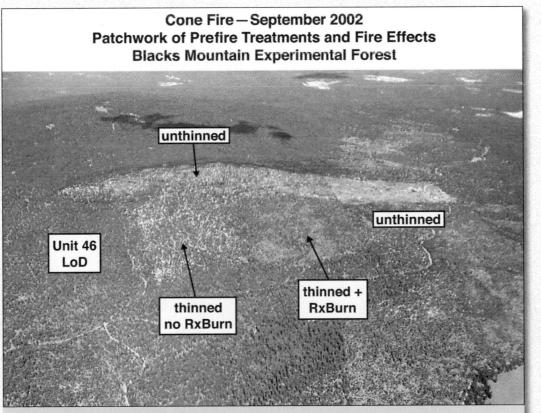

An aerial view of the 2003 Cone Fire. This view shows the effect on plots that were treated with various management techniques. All of the plots pictured here are low-diversity plots.

Cone Fire as crown fire in unthinned forest.
The photograph is a view of the results of a forest fire in an unthinned forest.

Where plots had been thinned, leaving scattered trees, the fire dropped to the ground and burned as a ground fire. Some trees died as this fire moved along the soil and pine needle bed, but enough survived for the stand to regenerate.

Other plots had been purposefully treated in past years with low-intensity ground fires. These are called **prescribed burns.** In those plots, the fire also dropped to the ground. They are shown in the images. Because neither plot contained ladder fuels, the fire could not climb back into the crowns of the trees.

The Cone Fire points to the importance of reducing surface fuels by using prescribed burns. When low-level fuels are reduced in prescribed burns, fires are less able to jump to the crown level. Similarly, thinning also appeared to inhibit significantly the movement of fires through middle to upper levels of trees.

Managing forests is not simple. The trees that fuel fires also offer shelter for wildlife. Removing or burning all trees in a forest can negatively affect some types of wildlife. Scientists continue to study the Blacks Mountain Experimental Forest for clues that will help them understand management techniques.

The unplanned Cone Fire turned several forest plots in California into an experiment like your experiments with matchsticks. Ecologists were able to test several types of management strategies. The two pictured here are after the Cone Fire in (a) a thinned forest with no prescribed burn and (b) a thinned forest with a prescribed burn.

5. By using inquiry, you worked to solve a problem and you practiced the abilities of technological design.
   a. What problem did you solve?
   b. What solutions did you propose?
   c. How did you implement your solutions?
   d. How did you evaluate your solutions? How well did they work?
   e. How did you communicate your best solution to the class?

More Than Meets the Eye

In A Quick Fix?, you did experiments to select a thinning strategy to reduce the chances of crown fires. Those are the most damaging and hazardous types of wildfires. Imagine that the National Forest Advisory Board were to follow your recommendations to protect forests from catastrophic fires. The board could manage a forest so that fire would not destroy it.

But what if the advisory board wanted to manage the forest for a different purpose? One use might be to manage the forest for cost-effective timber sales. Or what about managing for wildlife habitat? Or for recreational use? Or for all of those uses? Would the management strategies be different? How many factors do forest managers need to juggle, and how difficult is the task?

In More Than Meets the Eye, you look at a forest as more than just a collection of trees. You work in a team to describe several key parts of a forest ecosystem and the way they interact. You read about research that tries to achieve a sustainable forest ecosystem. A goal of the study is to make recommendations for forest management that are based on sound science.

Materials
For each team of three students

3 sheets of graph paper   1 calculator

Process and Procedure

In a team of 3 students, complete the following steps.
1. In the activity, Sun Worship, in chapter 7, you learned how energy flows through an ecosystem from producers and then to herbivores, carnivores, and decomposers. The following reading, The Web of Life, describes those concepts further. Complete the reading and discuss your understanding with your team.

The Web of Life

The study of the living and nonliving parts of the environment and the way they affect organisms is called **ecology.** The living part of the environment is called the **biotic** environment. Organisms from the smallest bacterium to the largest mammal are part of the biotic environment. The nonliving part is called the **abiotic** environment. Temperature, water, and rocks are examples of abiotic parts of the environment. Soils are a vital combination of abiotic (weathered rock) and biotic (microorganisms and vegetation) parts of an environment.

The biotic and abiotic components of a forest are interdependent. The environment affects organisms, and organisms interact with one another. Some interactions are favorable, such as between sunlight and a growing tree. Other interactions are harmful, such as a beetle infestation that causes most or all of the pines in a forest to die. The community of organisms and its physical environment make up an **ecosystem.**

One of the most basic interactions in a community of organisms is the consumption of food. Food gives organisms the energy to function. Feeding relationships are a major part of interactions in an ecosystem. Those relationships define the cycle of matter from organism to organism. Feeding relationships show the flow of energy through the organisms of an ecosystem.

Green plants anchor feeding relationships by absorbing energy from the Sun and converting the light energy into the chemical energy found in sugars. This process, called photosynthesis, makes it possible for plants to produce their own food. You started learning about photosynthesis in unit 2, The Machinery of Life. Because the Sun's energy is converted to matter in organisms, plants are called **producers.** Photosynthesizing organisms are called primary producers because they are at the first level of converting, or "fixing," the Sun's energy in the ecosystem.

Animals cannot make their own food by photosynthesis. Animals must get their energy from plants or other animals. Organisms that are unable to make their own food are called **consumers.** Consumers eat plants or other animals. Consumers use the chemical energy that they get from their food to grow and stay alive.

▲ Figure 16.15 **Fox food chain.** A food chain describes the feeding relationships among organisms.

The conversion of chemical energy to the energy used by living organisms is not efficient. Whenever an organism breaks down its food, some of the energy escapes as heat. Even during the process of decay, consumers called **decomposers** break down the bodies of dead plants and animals and give off heat. That is why you can put a thermometer in the center of a compost pile and measure a higher temperature than that of the air around the pile. Bacteria and fungi such as mushrooms are examples of decomposers.

The feeding relationships among organisms are represented as a **food chain**. A food chain diagram illustrates what animals prefer to eat. For example, in figure 16.15, the rabbit eats the raspberry bushes. The fox then eats the rabbit. Food chains are vital in all ecosystems.

Ecosystems contain more organisms than a single food chain, however. Those organisms interact in many different ways. For example, foxes eat rabbits, yet foxes also prey on birds or mice that eat grass seed. Foxes also might eat the birds that consume insects. When food chains become interconnected, they form a **food web**. Figure 16.16 shows a food web with relationships among primary producers, consumers, and decomposers. Food webs can be very complex, and this one shows only several main players.

Matter cycles through the food web from the nonliving environment to the living environment, then back to the nonliving. When an animal eats a plant as food, both energy and matter are passed from the plant to the animal. You considered this energy transfer in unit 2. When one animal eats another animal, the energy and matter are again passed on through another link in the food web. Eventually, energy leaves the ecosystem in the form of heat. But matter continues to cycle.

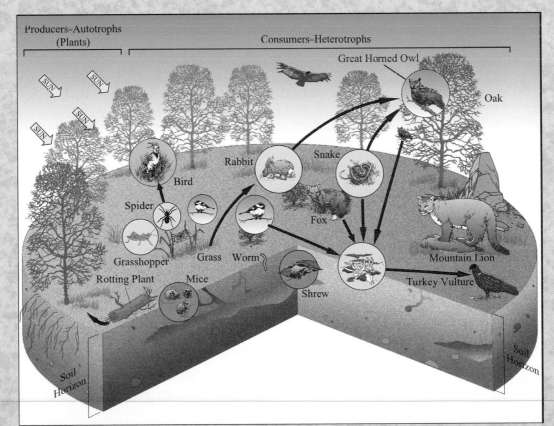

▲ **Figure 16.16 Oak-grassland food web.** Food webs are more complex than the food chain shown in figure 16.15. How many additional interactions are shown here? What are key parts of the food web in an ecosystem where you live?

F. E. Clements, a pioneer in ecology, recognized three types of interactions within an ecosystem. If one or more of these interactions changes, the ecosystem changes.

1. *The physical environment has an effect on organisms in an ecosystem.* For example, water resources, temperature, type of geology, and necessary nutrients in the soil affect tree growth.
2. *Organisms have an effect on their environment.* For example, new trees that provide shade where none existed before create cooler temperatures near those trees.
3. *Organisms have an effect on other organisms.* For example, new plants crowd out the plants that were food sources for squirrels, leaving less for squirrels to eat.

An ecosystem has many factors that affect organisms in either beneficial or adverse ways. Those factors may slow an organism's growth, kill an organism, or stimulate an organism's growth and reproduction. An example is how wet or dry conditions and climate patterns affect the growth of plants. This is fundamental because plants are the primary producers.

The web of life depends on many interactions among abiotic and biotic components of an ecosystem. Those interactions connect all organisms to one another, including humans. Often, people are reminded of the impact of their actions on the complex dynamics of life only when they see visible changes, such as decreased ponderosa pine stands in a fire-suppressed forest.

2. Recall from chapter 7 your use of the terms *autotroph* and *heterotroph*. Complete the following 2 sentences and then complete the table for Step 2c.
   a. An autotroph is _____.
   b. A heterotroph is _____.
   c. Refer to figure 16.16. Make a T-table listing each organism on the left. On the right, indicate whether the organism is an autotroph or a heterotroph.
3. Imagine a forest ecosystem and answer the following questions with your team. Record your answers in your science notebook.
   a. What nonliving things make it possible for trees to grow in the forest ecosystem?
   b. What living things (besides other trees) interact with the trees? What are the interactions?
   c. What might happen to the trees if any of those living or nonliving things disappeared? Which of those things are limiting factors for trees?
   d. Fire is a natural abiotic part of a forest ecosystem. How does fire suppression affect the forest ecosystem?
4. Think back to your forest model. Then answer the following questions with your team. Record your answers in your science notebook.
   a. What variables in the forest ecosystem were you changing when you conducted your fire tests?

b. What variables in the forest ecosystem did you not consider?

c. What are the limits of your matchstick forest model as a model for forest management?

5. Key interactions occur among organisms in mixed-conifer forests of the western United States. Those forests are also important for lumber and recreation. Wildfires can have many ecologic and economic impacts. Managing forests is one way to reduce the chances of wildfires. But how does forest management affect animals? How would you be able to tell?

With your team, read Thinning Strategies and Ecosystem Health. After completing the reading, you will examine some data for predators and prey to decide for yourself whether thinning is effective.

READING

Thinning Strategies and Ecosystem Health

Using your matchstick model, you found a thinning strategy that would reduce fire damage to forests. Thinning can also benefit companies that sell the lumber. Everyone uses this wood in buildings, furniture, fences, and paper products.

However, cutting down trees for management purposes is controversial. Some people are opposed to thinning and prescribed burns. They worry that such management alters the forest ecosystem and reduces habitat for wildlife. They are also concerned that the economic interests of logging companies are driving decisions to thin forests. They want to be sure that forest managers have the best interests of the forest ecosystem in mind.

But due to fire suppression, many forests today are not in a natural state. Many people assume that a dense, green forest is a healthy forest. This buildup of fuel is not natural, however. It can lead to catastrophic wildfires. So what is the most effective low-impact strategy for managing forests?

Scientists working to answer that question must use data to address people's concerns. Researchers need to know how parts of forest ecosystems interact. Their work results in data about wildlife populations, nutrient cycling, plant diversity, insect abundance, and past fire frequencies. Regarding forest management, this work can help ensure that policy makers consider the whole ecosystem.

Consider again the mixed-conifer forests in the southwestern United States. One study taking place on the Kaibab Plateau in northern Arizona is informing forest management in this region (see the images from the Kaibab Plateau, figure 16.17). These forests range from ponderosa to mixed-conifer to spruce and fir forests. Catastrophic fires on the Kaibab Plateau are a major concern. Thus, USDA Forest Service scientists from Fort Collins, Colorado, have been studying how two thinning methods affect the forest ecosystem. The first method harvests single trees, leaving an open, more "natural" state of the forest. A thinned forest remains.

▷ **Figure 16.17**
Kaibab Plateau, Arizona. The Kaibab Plateau in Arizona is shown as a shaded relief map and by conifer type. The organisms are part of the ponderosa ecosystem at the Kaibab Plateau. How would you organize them in a food web?

Stellar's jay

Kaibab squirrel

ponderosa pinecone

beetle

Kaibab National Forest

Grand Canyon
National Park

northern goshawk

northern flicker

red squirrel

ants

The second method is a more widespread removal of trees. The mature trees that are left are rich in cones and seeds to enhance rapid reforestation. These are called seed trees.

Researchers need to know how the two thinning methods affect wildlife. Do thinned forests or scattered seed trees better support wildlife? The researchers are looking at several levels of the food chain: birthrates of a carnivore, the northern goshawk; the density of goshawk prey; and cone and seed production in ponderosa pines. Goshawks at the Kaibab Plateau hunt several kinds of prey; the prey rely on the trees and cones for food. Scientists hope to see which management strategy best preserves the integrity of the forest ecosystem.

6. Figure 16.17 shows organisms of the ponderosa and mixed-conifer ecosystem of the Kaibab Plateau. With your team, arrange these organisms in your notebook to represent a food web at the Kaibab Plateau.

Discuss with your teammates what you think the organisms might eat. Place primary producers near the bottom of your food web and carnivores at the top.

▼ **Figure 16.18**

Goshawk fecundity table. This table shows fecundity in the northern goshawk on the Kaibab Plateau and the abundance of several key species of prey for goshawks.

7. Study with your team the data from the Kaibab Plateau in figure 16.18. Discuss as a team what questions you think the researchers are trying to answer. How are they trying to answer them?

Fecundity is a key indicator for a forest ecologist. It tells, for example, the number of female goshawk chicks per year that successfully mature to leave the nest. The overall fecundity tells whether goshawks were successful in nesting. Success is a function of food availability.

Year	Goshawk fecundity*	Red squirrel density**	Kaibab squirrel density	Northern flicker density	Stellar's jay density	All prey species density
1994	0.1338	0.3685	0.0844	0.3277	0.2233	1.0039
1995	0.3377	0.4955	0.1931	0.4163	0.2787	1.3836
1996	0.2529	0.5317	0.1083	0.4158	0.3163	1.3721
1997	0.2258	0.4739	0.0993	0.3153	0.3245	1.2130
1998	0.5585	0.9713	0.1671	0.4305	0.3682	1.9371
1999	0.4536	1.0529	0.1263	0.6299	0.4671	2.2762
2000	0.6173	1.3779	0.2607	0.7668	0.3159	2.7213
2001	0.1553	0.3126	0.0657	0.4021	0.2863	1.0667
2002	0.0680	0.3770	0.0377	0.2178	0.2156	0.8481

* Fecundity = number of female chicks produced per reproductive adult female
** Density = prey density per hectare; a hectare is an area of 100 m × 100 m

Data Source: Reynolds, R. T. and Salafsky, S. R. USDA Forest Service, Rocky Mountain Research Station, Fort Collins, Colorado.

8. The data in figure 16.18 can be graphed in several ways. The graphs can be used to test for interactions between predator and prey. You can use values for goshawk fecundity to test for 1 of several relationships with other data.

   a. Discuss your ideas with your teammates as to what data you can graph.

   b. Write in your notebook the idea that you will test with the graph.

For example, if you plotted Stellar's jays (*y*-axis) versus year (*x*-axis), the graphs would tell you how much the population of Stellar's jays varied from year to year.

   c. Obtain graph paper and make the graph with your teammates.

   d. Use the "What I see" and "What it means" strategies with the graph. Discuss whether your graph shows a *correlation*.

Recall from chapter 15, Risks and Hazards to Humans, that a *correlation* shows that two factors vary together. A correlation does not demonstrate that one factor causes the other to change. Other types of evidence may be needed to test whether two factors are causally related.

   e. Discuss with your team whether your data might indicate a *causal* relationship. If so, write the reasons in your notebook.

9. How do the populations of goshawk prey compare between the forest plots managed 2 different ways? Do you think that the birds or squirrels prefer one type of forest plot over the other? Where might goshawks find the most food for their young? Figure 16.19 helps you answer those questions. Recall the 2 forest management strategies; then complete the following steps:

   • *Thinned plots.* Single trees are removed, leaving an open forest.

   • *Seedtree plots.* There is a widespread removal of trees, leaving mature trees rich in cones and seeds.

   a. Figure 16.19 has 3 variables: density of goshawk prey, year, and management method. Reduce the number of variables from 3 to 2 by combining the management method into a ratio, as follows:

$$R\left(\frac{\text{thinned}}{\text{seedtree}}\right) = \frac{\text{prey density in thinned plots}}{\text{prey density in seedtree plots}}$$

Make a table in your science notebook with 5 columns for prey (4 prey species plus all of them) and 4 rows for the years. Use a calculator to fill in the table with 18 values for $R(\frac{\text{thinned}}{\text{seedtree}})$.

You have used ratios a number of times in this program. Examples of ratios are star luminosity relative to the Sun (L_{star}/L_{Sun}), probability and odds, density of materials, and even any time that you use a percent.

b. At the bottom of each column, determine an average value for $R(\frac{\text{thinned}}{\text{seedtree}})$ per prey species. Make a separate T-table showing goshawk prey species and the average value of $R(\frac{\text{thinned}}{\text{seedtree}})$.

10. Complete these sentences in your notebook about the meaning of the ratio $R(\frac{\text{thinned}}{\text{seedtree}})$.

    a. A value of $R(\frac{\text{thinned}}{\text{seedtree}})$ greater than 1 indicates that the prey prefers _____ forest plots.

    b. A value of $R(\frac{\text{thinned}}{\text{seedtree}})$ less than 1 indicates that the prey prefers _____ forest plots.

    c. The highest value of $R(\frac{\text{thinned}}{\text{seedtree}})$ is _____ for the _____ (insert prey).

    d. The lowest value of $R(\frac{\text{thinned}}{\text{seedtree}})$ is _____ for the _____ (insert prey).

    e. The average value of $R(\frac{\text{thinned}}{\text{seedtree}})$ for all prey species is _____. This indicates that the overall prey density is greater in _____ forest plots.

11. Make a bar graph showing values of $R(\frac{\text{thinned}}{\text{seedtree}})$ for goshawk prey species and all species (on the vertical axis) as a function of year (on the horizontal axis). Use 5 colors or patterns per bar for each category per year.

Year	Red squirrel density*		Kaibab squirrel density		Northern flicker density		Stellar's jay density		All prey species density	
	Thinned	Seedtree	Thinned	Seedtree	Thinned	Seedtree	Thinned	Seedtree	Thinned	Seedtree
1999	0.8386	0.3184	0.0418		0.1554	0.2127	0.1079	0.1264	1.1438	0.6575
2000	1.0210	0.3434	0.0980	0.0281	0.2190	0.3424	0.1014	0.0718	1.4394	0.7857
2001	0.0798	0.0177	0.0292		0.1599	0.2185	0.0862	0.1177	0.3551	0.3539
2002	0.2021	0.0458	0.0187	0.0278	0.0937	0.0794	0.0844	0.1167	0.3990	0.2696

▲ **Figure 16.19**

Goshawk prey in seedtree and thinned management plots. This table shows the density of goshawk prey in forest plots with two management strategies. Where should goshawks go to find their favorite food?

■ = too few observations to accurately determine density

*Density = prey density per hectare; a hectare is an area of 100 m × 100 m

Data Source: Reynolds, R. T. and Salafsky, S. R. USDA Forest Service, Rocky Mountain Research Station, Fort Collins, Colorado.

12. Answer the following questions regarding your analysis in Step 9.

    a. In which forest plots are the squirrel species most common, seedtree or thinned plots? What is a possible explanation for this?

b. In which forest plots are the 2 birds (Stellar's jay and northern flicker) most common, seedtree or thinned plots? What is a possible explanation for this?

c. Either thinning strategy would be effective at reducing catastrophic fires in mixed-conifer and ponderosa forests. Which management strategy appears to provide the most prey for nesting goshawks?

13. Be prepared to share your team's recommendation with the class. Discuss similarities and differences among all of the teams' recommendations. Are overall prey densities higher across the Kaibab Plateau (see figure 16.18) or in the 2 types of managed forest plots (see figure 16.19)?

Reflect and Connect

Answer the following in your science notebook. Be prepared to share your ideas in a class discussion.

1. Consider your previous data. What limiting factors affect the northern goshawk? How do you know?

2. Complete the following steps based on an ecosystem around your school.

   a. Decide with your team what ecosystem you will consider. Describe that ecosystem in 2–3 sentences in your notebook. Where is the ecosystem? What animals live there?

   b. Identify with your team about 15 organisms that live in that ecosystem. Write the names of the organisms in your notebook, along with whether each is an autotroph or a heterotroph.

   c. Turn to a new page in your science notebook. Draw a food web diagram similar to figure 16.16 to represent feeding interactions for the organisms.

To help you develop a food web, complete these two sentences: Several producers at the bottom of the food web include _____. A consumer at the top of the food web (a carnivore) is a(n) _____.

3. Fire suppression is 1 way humans have affected the forest ecosystem. Describe 3 other ways humans affect ecosystems around the world.

4. Is it possible for people to make different decisions about forest management even when they are using the same data? Explain your answer using data from the Kaibab Plateau. Describe the role science plays in society's decision making.

5. If human activity affects ecosystems, do those activities pose a risk to humans? Explain your answer.

6. What does the title of the previous explore activity, A Quick Fix?, refer to? In light of what you have learned in this explain activity, is there a quick fix? Explain your answer.

Fire in Other Ecosystems

Suppression of fire is changing many of the basic processes of the ponderosa and mixed-conifer ecosystems. Does fire suppression affect other ecosystems in a similar way? In Fire in Other Ecosystems, you work with a team to explore the role of fire in the California chaparral ecosystem. The chaparral borders many growing communities in Southern California. You also assess the risks of letting fires burn in this ecosystem.

▲ **Figure 16.20 California chaparral.** Fire is a key part of chaparral ecosystems, such as the one here in coastal California. Fire in the chaparral is essential for seed germination and replenishing nutrients in soils. Have you ever seen an ecosystem like the chaparral?

Part I: Cone Responses to Fire

Materials
For each team of three students

3 pairs of safety goggles

1 metal fire tray lined with aluminum foil

1 spray bottle filled with water

1 Bunsen burner

1 pair of tongs

matches

aluminum foil

6–10 pinecones

Cautions

You use a Bunsen burner in this activity. The flame of a Bunsen burner is very hot. Remember to follow all of the rules for working with flames:

- Always wear your safety goggles. Tie back long hair and loose clothing.
- Always use the metal fire tray under your burning experiments.
- Keep the box of matches away from flames.
- Assign one person from your team to handle the spray bottle of water and to watch that all of the burning fuels stay on the fire tray. If any fire becomes too big or escapes the fire tray, extinguish it immediately with a spray of water.

- When you have completed your burning experiments, extinguish all smoldering fuel, using the spray bottle, before placing the remains in the metal trash can.

- Hot resin may drip from the pinecones and burn your skin. Handle the pinecones with the tongs at all times.

- Let your teacher know if you have asthma or respiratory problems. You can wear a dust mask to avoid breathing the smoke generated by your experiments.

Process and Procedure

Gather with your team of 3 students for the following pinecone activity.

1. Different kinds of plants may respond in very different ways to a fire. For example, some pinecones show an intriguing response. With your team, observe several pinecones provided by your teacher.
   a. What role does a pinecone play in the life of a tree?
   b. Would you describe the pinecone as open or closed?

2. Imagine that you are an animal that eats seeds from pinecones. How would you get into a cone? Use the materials your teacher provides to try to get to the seeds in 1 of your cones. How successful are you?

3. What happens when you heat your pinecones? Do high temperatures affect the cones? How much heat do you need? Design an experiment to answer those questions. Plan to heat cones, which you wrap in aluminum foil, in an oven. Record the results of your investigation in your science notebook.

Discuss with your partners how long and how hot you want to heat your pinecones. What other factors should you consider?

4. Based on the results of your investigation in Step 3, what do you think happens when you burn a cone?
   a. Set up a safe burning area by placing the Bunsen burner on the metal fire tray.
   b. Assign 1 person to observe the experiment and to be aware of unsafe fires.
   c. Put on your safety goggles.
   d. Light the Bunsen burner.
   e. Hold the pinecone with the tongs and place the cone in the Bunsen burner flame.
   f. Observe what happens over the next 10 minutes.
   g. Discuss your observations with the class.

Caution — Use safety goggles.

Part I

Discuss the following questions with your class. Record your answers in your science notebook.

1. Fire is often viewed as a destructive event in ecosystems. What do the results of your pinecone experiment tell you about the role of fire with regard to pine trees with this type of cone?

Pinecones that respond to fire are sometimes called serotinous cones. They are found in chaparral as well as other types of pine forests in North America.

2. In a forest with frequent fires, what do you think happens to these types of pine trees?
3. In a forest in which fires are suppressed, what do you think happens to these types of pine trees?

Part II: The Chaparral

Materials
For each team of three students

1 copy of Census Tract Data for Hillsdale handout

Process and Procedure

1. In addition to forest ecosystems, other ecosystems also require fire for growth. Read the following description of the California chaparral ecosystem.

READING

California Chaparral

Topic: chaparral
Go to: www.scilinks.org
Code: 1Inquiry814

The native plant community covering many California hills is called the **chaparral.** This ecosystem is known around the world as Mediterranean scrub and can be found in Chile, the cape of South Africa, southwestern Australia, and the Mediterranean (where it gets its name). Those regions are located between 30° and 45° north or south in latitude (see figure 16.21).They have mild, rainy winters followed by hot, dry summers. In winter, dense vegetation thrives. In summer, the vegetation dries dramatically.

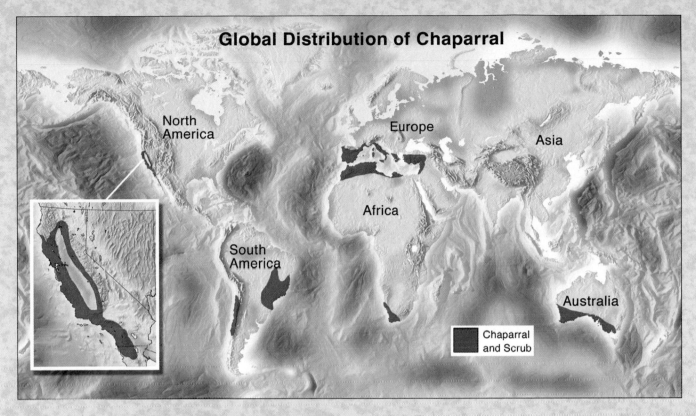

Global Distribution of Chaparral

North America

Europe

Asia

Africa

South America

Australia

Chaparral and Scrub

▲ **Figure 16.21 Global and California distribution of chaparral.** The chaparral ecosystem is found in several parts of the world characterized by wet winters and hot, dry summers. The box shows the distribution of the chaparral in California.

Plants that live in the chaparral are well adapted to the drought conditions that characterize half of their growing season. They retain their leaves year-round. New leaves in winter are soft. But by summer, those same leaves have become hardened by waxes and oils to prepare them for a long, dry summer. The tough, waxy coatings reduce water loss and give some protection from intense summer radiation. In chapter 15, you considered other ways to block the Sun's radiation. Those were more practical than developing a hard, waxy coating!

Chaparral consists of many small, woody plants that are full of oils and that are extremely flammable. Because of that fact, many areas of chaparral burn each year. The plants are adapted to burn periodically, about every 25–30 years. This eliminates old growth and begins the regenerative process. Where the chaparral burns regu-

larly, the ashes replenish soil nutrients for the next growing season. Wildflowers not present in dense, old-growth chaparral thrive on newly burned hillsides.

Common plants of the chaparral ecosystem include toyon, sugar bush, yucca, coffeeberry, California buckwheat, scrub oak, mountain mahogany, and chamise (greasewood). Higher-elevation chaparral is dominated by manzanita and ceanothus, with intermixed patches of conifers. Examples are shown in figure 16.22.

A variety of animals live among the chaparral plants (see figure 16.23). Decomposers such as fungi, bacteria, and worms live off decaying material and waste. They return organic compounds to the soil and provide nutrients for plants. Multitudes of mice, rabbits, small birds (sparrows, towhees, quail), and insects rely on plants for food in this ecosystem. Lizards and

a.

b.

▶ Figure 16.22 **Photographs of chaparral.**
Chaparral dominates parts of the foothills of
the Sierra Nevada of California. The ecosystem
includes plants such as (a) chamise,
(b) manzanita, and (c) *Ceanothus cordulatus*
at high-elevation mixed with conifer.

c.

▲ **Figure 16.23 Chaparral plants and animals.** Plants and animals in the chaparral are very different from those in ponderosa forests. Most animals, both predators and prey, need to be able to move quickly through dense plant growth.

birds prey on insects and insect larvae. All of those animals are hunted by key carnivores such as snakes, coyotes, gray foxes, roadrunners (at low elevations), and small hawks. With short wings and long tails, the small hawks are able to hunt in the chaparral by moving rapidly along the top of and through the dense growth.

Threats to the chaparral ecosystem include the use of off-road vehicles on trails, causing erosion and sediment displacement. Human development also threatens the chaparral as more people clear the chaparral to build homes. Building isolates the chaparral patches, disrupting wildlife corridors through the chaparral.

2. How do fires in the chaparral affect it as an ecosystem? Make a T-table in your science notebook. In one column, list the positive effects of fire in the chaparral. In the other column, list the negative effects of fire. When you have completed your T-table, discuss your ideas with the rest of the class. Add to your table based on the class discussion.

3. Look at figure 16.24 with your team. The table shows how fire-related conditions in the chaparral relate to seed germination. Analyze the data by answering the following questions in your science notebook.

   a. What is *germination*? How do you usually germinate seeds?

   b. What questions are the researchers trying to answer?

   c. How many tests did the seeds of each species undergo? Number them in your science notebook and describe each test according to information from the table.

   d. Based on the germination rate of the control seeds, what can you infer about the fire adaptation of the 5 plants in this study?

   e. Heat often helps germinate the seeds of fire-adapted plants. Which plant germinates in response to heat? What can you infer about the other plants?

   f. Scientists have wondered if reactions involving the chemicals in burned wood or smoke play a role in the germination of seeds from fire-adapted plants. What do the data tell you about that idea? Use specific examples from the data table.

   g. Chaparral plants often have seeds with thick seed coats. A little water might not be enough for germination. What do the data tell you about the effect of scarification of the seeds during fire episodes? Why do you think this is so?

Scarification is where the coat of a seed is scratched, abraded, or cracked somewhat.

   h. Using the data from these tests, describe a chaparral ecosystem 1 year after a fire. What would be growing?

   i. Using the results from these tests, describe a chaparral ecosystem 30 years after a fire.

4. Fire is natural and essential in chaparral ecosystems. Scientists have found evidence that natural wildfires were frequent in chaparral country because of the quick buildup of fuel during the wet season. Fire suppression has not changed the frequency or intensity of chaparral fires: fires burn nearly as often and burn as many acres as they did before fire suppression. After each fire, the chaparral plants and animals reestablish themselves in a flourishing ecosystem.

Effects of Fire on Seed Germination in California Chaparral

A. Hoaryleaf ceanothus

B. Whispering bells

C. Large-flowered phacelia

D. Tree poppy

E. Golden eardrops

Seed Germination (percent)

Plant	A	B	C	D	E
Test 1: Control (no treatment)	0	0	1	0	0
Test 2: Heat 0°C 1 hour	50	0	0	0	0
Test 3: Heat 105°C 5 min	87	0	0	0	0
Test 4: Heat 115°C 5 min	47	0	0	0	0
Test 5: Charred Wood[1]	0	80	44	46	0
Test 6: Smoke 5 min[2]	0	100	59	74	0
Test 7: Smoke 15 min	0	15	66	99	0
Test 8: Scar[3]	98	100	99	19	0

[1] Treated with water that has had charred wood soaking in it.
[2] Placed in soil that has been exposed to smoke.
[3] The seed coat has been broken; scarification.

▲ **Figure 16.24 Seed germination table for chaparral flowers.** Scientists conducted different tests on seeds from the chaparral to see how fire-related conditions affect seed germination.

Then what makes chaparral fires a problem today? Discuss your answer to that question with your team as you study figure 16.25. Record your ideas in your science notebook.

5. Who is most affected by chaparral wildfires? What are the costs to citizens in a community? To address those questions, work with your team to study a map (see figure 16.26) and census data for a fictional town located partly in the chaparral. Then answer the following questions in your science notebook.

To make decisions and to answer the questions, use specific observations from the map and the **Census Tract Data for Hillsdale** handout.

▲ **Figure 16.25**
Firefighting in the chaparral. Chaparral fires can be extremely difficult to battle. Many of the chaparral plants have leaves containing highly flammable oils and waxes.

a. Figure 16.26 is a map of neighborhoods in what fictional city?

b. South of Hillside Boulevard are neighborhoods in the chaparral hillsides. North of Hillside Boulevard are neighborhoods in the flat land below the hillsides. How would you characterize the economic differences between people who live north and south of Hillside Boulevard?

Once again, use the map and the handout to give specific examples.

c. What benefits might people perceive that they have by building south of Hillside Boulevard?

d. What risks do people have when they build south of Hillside Boulevard?

e. If people voluntarily build in the chaparral, who should pay to fight fires in the chaparral? Why do you think so?

f. Chaparral fires present social and economic challenges to policy makers in cities. Can the science behind chaparral fires inform the debate about those challenges? Can science solve the challenges? Explain your answers.

6. Participate in a class discussion, sharing your answers to Step 5.

▶ **Figure 16.26**
Hillsdale. Map of census tracts for the fictional town of Hillsdale. The locations of two fire stations are shown. Shading shows per capita income per tract.

Stations A and B, Hillside Shores

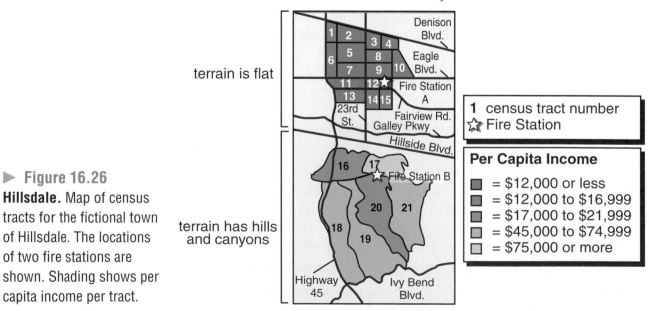

Reflect and Connect

Work individually to answer the following in your science notebook.

1. Describe the ways that some seeds are adapted to fire in mixed-conifer and chaparral ecosystems.

2. Draw a diagram that shows a possible food web in the California chaparral. For ideas, refer to the animals in figure 16.23 and the readings around that figure.

You might get additional ideas from figure 16.16.

3. With more people building houses in California's chaparral, fires are being suppressed to protect lives and property. How will this fire suppression affect the chaparral ecosystem?

4. Read the following statement and answer the questions below: A natural event becomes a natural hazard or disaster only when society is exposed to the forces it unleashes.
   a. How are chaparral fires an example of a natural event becoming a natural hazard?
   b. Describe 3 additional natural events that can become natural hazards or disasters.
   c. Are all segments of society exposed equally to natural hazards? Explain your answer.

5. Some human activities increase society's risk of natural hazards. They also increase the rate of change of ecosystems and affect the physical and chemical cycles of Earth. Are those changes to ecosystems also natural hazards? Explain your thinking.

Burning Issues

EVALUATE

It is not always easy to make decisions about fires and forests. The number of factors that must be considered makes the task complex. Many different stakeholders are part of the decision-making process. **Stakeholders** are the people who have a vested interest in the decisions being made. Stakeholders can have very different opinions based on their understanding of the issue.

In Burning Issues, you work with your team to develop one stakeholder's proposal for management of a local forest. Your team needs to base its position and arguments on the science-based strategies that you have studied in this chapter—and during the school year. For example, how would your matchstick experiments inform the position you take regarding forest management at Weston? What would be the risks and benefits of a management strategy to you? How do you know?

The process is community-based. Therefore, you need to evaluate other teams' proposals using what you learned about fires and forest ecology in this chapter as evidence. You present your proposal and ideas at a town meeting. The final task is working as stakeholders in the community to reach a consensus on how to address the issue.

Materials
For each team of six students

1 blank transparency

1 copy of Stakeholder handout

transparency markers

6 copies of Burning Issues Scoring Rubric handout

access to an overhead projector

Process and Procedure

1. Meet in a team of 6 students and read the following 3 documents. Discuss each document with your team.
   - Notice about the Weston town meeting (see figure 16.27)
   - Map of Weston (see figure 16.28)
   - Summary report from USDA Forest Service about forests bordering Weston (see figure 16.29)

Weston Town Meeting at Town Hall
7:00 p.m., May 15

The Fire Program Advisory Group will hold a special meeting at the Town Hall. The group will discuss science-based strategies to manage better the forests that surround Weston and reduce the risk of catastrophic fires that could threaten the town. As a town at the wildland-urban interface, Weston is in a positon to develop a state-of-the-art fire program in conjunction with the U.S. Department of the Interior and the U.S. Department of Agriculture (USDA) Forest Service.

The Fire Program Advisory Group seeks to gather and analyze information, collect public comments, and make recommendations on priorities and strategies for managing our forests. The advisory group wishes to hear a variety of viewpoints and perspectives from the community. This will help the advisory group develop scientific tools and policies that will be used by federal forest fire managers.

Please attend the Town Meeting. Speakers will have four minutes and should present a graphic to display efficiently their data and position. The meeting will adjourn only after all stakeholders have been heard.

To prepare for the Town Meeting, please take time to review the attached information about Weston and forest service strategies.

▶ **Figure 16.27**
Weston town meeting notice. This bulletin notifies citizens of Weston about a town meeting being held to consider forest management policies and wildfire reduction efforts.

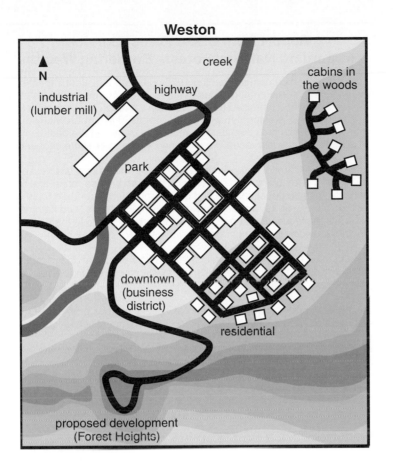

Weston

industrial (lumber mill) · highway · creek · cabins in the woods · park · downtown (business district) · residential · proposed development (Forest Heights)

▲ **Figure 16.28 Weston map.** The map of Weston shows industrial, business, residential, and proposed residential development. Weston is built at the edge of a national forest. It is home to retired people seeking a quiet place to live, vacationers pursuing outdoor recreation and nature, and employers and employees of local lumber and recreation businesses.

2. Who are the stakeholders who would be concerned about this issue? Work with your team to develop a list of the stakeholders who would likely attend the town meeting. Come up with at least 5 stakeholders.

3. Divide a piece of paper into 6 small pieces of paper, each with a different number, 1 to 6. Fold the pieces of paper and place them in a hat or another small container.

4. Have each team member draw 1 piece of paper. The number you draw is the stakeholder position you will assume.

5. Obtain from your teacher a set of Stakeholder descriptions. With your team, compare the number you picked with the description of the stakeholder. Discuss the interests of the stakeholders. Are the stakeholders similar to your list from Step 2?

► Figure 16.29
USDA Forest Service
summary report. This
report from the USDA
Forest Service outlines
several key issues in
forest management for
the area around
Weston.

**Report from USDA Forest Service
Regarding National Forests Bordering Weston**

The national fire prevention campaign from the 1920s has had a distinct impact on the forests bordering Weston. Fire exclusion has resulted in the buildup of large quantities of brush, understory, and small- to medium-sized trees in Weston's forests. These forests also include many dead and dying trees interspersed with dense stands of live trees. Many of the dead trees have been infested with pine beetles as a result of low rainfall the past 3–4 years. The unnatural fuel accumulation could result in a large and intense forest fire should one occur.

In addition, urban and residential development has placed homes and businesses in the forest. These structures run a particularly high risk of damage in an intense forest fire. Not only will wildland fuels burn, such as trees, shrubs, and other vegetation, but urban fuels will burn as well. These include shingle roofs, wooden decks, landscaping plants, and flammable household materials. Moreover, some private structures reside outside the boundary for fire-protection services provided to citizens residing within the Weston city limits.

To help alleviate the fuel problem in the forests, the USDA Forest Service recommends reducing fuels and changing the types of fuels that exist in the Weston forests. Options to accomplish this include

- mechanical treatment in which crews physically remove brush, trees, and debris;
- biological treatment in which crews introduce animals such as goats, sheep, cattle, or insects to feed on plants in the forest; and
- fire treatment in which crews schedule and control prescribed burns, letting a succession forest replace the existing forest.

Each of these methods has its advantages and its disadvantages. A combination of the methods may be used to treat a large area like the forests surrounding Weston. In addition, home- and business-owners are asked to protect their buildings by limiting fuels at their locations.

6. Convene as a class and regroup according to your stakeholder number. For example, all of the stakeholder 1 representatives gather into one group, all of the stakeholder 2 representatives gather into another group, and so on. There will be 6 groups in all.

If you have more than three or four students in your stakeholder group, your teacher may divide the group. If so, make sure that you have several people to work with in your new team.

7. Review your stakeholder description with your new group. Discuss your position and key issues with your stakeholder team. Based on your position, how should fire reduction be treated?

8. Use the Burning Issues Scoring Rubric to identify your teacher's expectations for the work you will do in the next steps.

9. Prepare a 4-minute presentation for the town meeting. In your presentation, complete the following.
   a. Describe who you are. What is your stake in this issue?
   b. What would your team like to see happen and why? Explain how your position and strategy is solving a problem. How will your strategy affect the forest ecosystem?

   c. How will you test to see if your strategy works? What do you predict the outcome of your test will be?

   d. Be prepared to answer questions of the other stakeholders at the town meeting.

It is essential that your stakeholder team use evidence and specific examples from the chapter and from what you learned during the school year to show your understanding of the science and the issues.

10. When another stakeholder group is presenting, record what it says. To organize the notes that you take during the town meeting, create a chart in your science notebook with the column headings below. Fill in the chart as each group makes its presentation.
- Stakeholder Number (1–6)
- Stakeholder Position
- Stakeholder Strategy
- My Views of Stakeholder's Position
- Questions and Discussion

Note that one of the rows will be your presentation. Be sure to leave space in the boxes so you can write your ideas and record points from the other stakeholders' presentations.

11. Attend the town meeting where all stakeholder teams present their positions and strategies. Your teacher will represent the Fire Program Advisory Group and facilitate the meeting.

12. Your final task is to participate in a discussion to evaluate the different strategies. What suggestions have significant merit and why? What suggestions do you find lacking, and why is that? The goal of the discussion is to reach a community consensus on forest management and fire reduction strategies.

Note that you do not need to decide on just one of the strategies. Your solution may include elements from several proposals. Use as much science and as many examples from the chapter as possible in your deliberations.

Laboratory Safety

The science laboratory has the potential to be either a safe place or a dangerous place. The difference depends on how well you know and follow safe laboratory practices. It is important that you read the information here and learn how to recognize and avoid potentially hazardous situations. Basic rules for working safely in the laboratory include the following.

Basic Safety

1. Be prepared. Study the assigned activity before you come to class. Resolve any questions about the procedures before you begin to work.

2. Be organized. Arrange the materials you need for the activity in an orderly way.

3. Maintain a clean, open work area, free of anything except those materials you need for the assigned activity. Store books, backpacks, and purses out of the way. Keep laboratory materials away from the edge of the work surface.

4. Tie back long hair and remove dangling jewelry. Roll up long sleeves and tuck in long clothing. Do not wear loose-fitting sleeves or open-toed shoes in the laboratory.

5. Wear safety goggles and a lab apron whenever you work with chemicals, hot liquids, lab burners, hot plates, or apparatuses that could break or shatter. Wear protective gloves when working with preserved specimens, toxic and corrosive chemicals, or when otherwise directed to do so.

6. Never wear contact lenses while conducting any experiment involving chemicals. If you must wear them (by a physician's order), inform your teacher *before* conducting any experiment involving chemicals.

7. Never use direct or reflected sunlight to illuminate your microscope or any other optical device. Direct or reflected sunlight can cause serious damage to your retinas.

8. Keep your hands away from the sharp or pointed ends of equipment, such as scalpels, dissecting needles, or scissors.

9. Observe all cautions in the procedural steps of the activities. **Caution** is a signal word used in the text and on labeled chemicals or reagents that tell you about the potential for harm and injury. It reminds you to observe specific safety practices. *Always read and follow this statement.* It is meant to help keep you and your fellow students safe.

   Caution statements advise you that the material or procedure has *some potential risk* of harm or injury if directions are not followed.

10. Become familiar with the caution items and precautions identified in the following table.

Cautions

The caution symbol alerts you to procedures or materials that may be harmful if directions are not followed properly. You may encounter the following common hazards during this course:

Caution items	Precautions
Sharp object	Sharp objects can cause injury, either a cut or puncture. Handle all sharp objects with caution and use them only as your teacher instructs you. Do not use them for any purpose other than the intended one. If you do get a cut or puncture wound, call your teacher and get first aid.
Irritant	An irritant is any substance that, on contact, can cause reddening of living tissue. Wear safety goggles, a lab apron, and protective gloves when handling any irritating chemical. In case of contact, flush the affected area with soap and water for at least 15 minutes and call your teacher. Remove contaminated clothing.
Reactive	These chemicals are capable of reacting with any other substance, including water, and can cause a violent reaction. **Do not** mix a reactive chemical with any other substance, including water, unless directed to do so by your teacher. Wear your safety goggles, a lab apron, and protective gloves.
Corrosive	A corrosive substance injures or destroys body tissue on contact by direct chemical action. When handling any corrosive substance, wear safety goggles, a lab apron, and protective gloves. In case of contact with a corrosive material, immediately flush the affected area with water and call your teacher.
Biohazard	Any biological substance that can cause infection through exposure is a biohazard. Before handling any material so labeled, review your teacher's specific instructions. **Do not** handle in any manner other than as instructed. Wear safety goggles, a lab apron, and protective gloves. Any contact with a biohazard should be reported to your teacher immediately.
Safety goggles	Safety goggles are for eye protection. Wear goggles whenever you see this symbol. If you wear glasses, be sure the goggles fit comfortably over them. In case of splashes in your eyes, flush your eyes (including under the lid) at an eyewash station for 15–20 minutes. If you wear contact lenses, remove them **immediately** and flush your eyes as directed. Call your teacher.
Lab apron	A lab apron is intended to protect your clothing. Whenever you see this symbol, put on your apron and tie it securely behind you. If you spill any substance on your clothing, call your teacher.
Gloves	Wear gloves when you see this symbol or whenever your teacher directs you to do so. Wear them when using **any** chemical or reagent solution. Do not wear your gloves for an extended period of time.
Flammable	A flammable substance is any material capable of igniting under certain conditions. **Do not** bring flammable materials into contact with open flames or near heat sources unless instructed to do so by your teacher. Remember that flammable liquids give off vapors that can be ignited by a nearby heat source. Should a fire occur, **do not** attempt to extinguish it yourself. Call your teacher. Wear safety goggles, a lab apron, and protective gloves whenever you handle a flammable substance.
Poison	Poisons can cause injury by direct action within a body system through direct contact with skin, inhalation, ingestion, or penetration. Always wear safety goggles, a lab apron, and protective gloves when handling any material with this label. If you have any preexisting injuries to your skin, inform your teacher before you handle any poison. In case of contact, call your teacher immediately.

11. Never put anything in your mouth and never touch or taste substances in the laboratory unless your teacher specifically instructs you to do so.

12. Never smell substances in the laboratory without specific instructions from your teacher. Even then, do not inhale fumes directly; wave the air above the substance toward your nose and sniff carefully.

13. Never eat, drink, chew gum, or apply cosmetics in the laboratory. Do not store food or beverages in the lab area.

14. Know the location of all safety equipment and learn how to use each piece of equipment.

15. If you witness an unsafe incident, an accident, or a chemical spill, report it to your teacher immediately.

16. Use materials only from containers labeled with the name of the chemical and the precautions to be used. Become familiar with the safety precautions for each chemical by reading the label before use.

17. To dilute acid with water, *always add the acid to the water.*

18. Never return unused chemicals to the stock bottles. Do not put any object into a chemical bottle, except the dropper with which it may be equipped.

19. Clean up thoroughly. Dispose of chemicals and wash used glassware and instruments according to your teacher's instructions. Clean tables and sinks. Put away all equipment and supplies. Make sure all water, gas jets, burners, and electrical appliances are turned off. Return all laboratory materials and equipment to their proper places.

20. Wash your hands thoroughly after handling any living organisms or hazardous materials and before leaving the laboratory.

21. Never perform unauthorized experiments. Do only those experiments your teacher approves.

22. Never work alone in the laboratory and never work without your teacher's supervision.

23. Approach laboratory work with maturity. Never run, push, or engage in horseplay or practical jokes of any type in the laboratory. Use laboratory materials and equipment only as directed.

24. Use the smallest amount of material necessary to conduct an experiment successfully.

In addition to observing these general safety precautions, you need to know about some specific categories of safety. Before you do any laboratory work, familiarize yourself with the following precautions.

Heat

1. Use only the heat source specified in the activity.

2. Never allow flammable materials such as alcohol near a flame or any other source of ignition.

3. When heating a substance in a test tube, point the mouth of the tube away from other students and you.

4. Never leave a lighted lab burner, hot plate, or any other hot objects unattended.
5. Never reach over an exposed flame or other heat source.
6. Use tongs, test-tube clamps, insulated gloves, or pot holders to handle hot equipment.
7. Shut off all sources of natural gas after use.
8. Never touch equipment such as glassware or iron rings that have been heated. They can be very hot, even though they may not look hot.

Glassware

1. Never use cracked or chipped glassware.
2. Use caution and proper equipment when handling hot glassware; remember that hot glass looks the same as cool glass.
3. Make sure glassware is clean before you use it and when you store it.
4. To put glass tubing into a rubber stopper, moisten the tubing and the stopper. Protect your hands with a heavy cloth when you insert or remove glass tubing from a rubber stopper. Never force or twist the tubing.
5. Immediately sweep up broken glassware and discard it in a special, labeled container for broken glass. ***Never pick up broken glass with your fingers***.

Electrical Equipment and Other Apparatuses

1. Before you begin any work, learn how to use each piece of apparatus safely and correctly in order to obtain accurate scientific information.
2. Never use equipment with frayed insulation or loose or broken wires.
3. Make sure the area in and around the electrical equipment is dry and free of flammable materials. Never touch electrical equipment with wet hands.
4. Turn off all power switches before plugging an appliance into an outlet. Never jerk wires from outlets or pull appliance plugs out by the wire.
5. Assemble lab apparatuses so that the setup does not tip easily.

Living and Preserved Specimens

1. Be sure that specimens for dissection are properly mounted and supported. Do not cut a specimen while holding it in your hand.
2. Wash your work surface with a disinfectant solution both before and after using live microorganisms.
3. Always wash your hands with soap and water after working with live or preserved specimens.
4. Care for animals humanely. General rules for their care are listed below.
   a. Always follow carefully your teacher's instructions about the care of laboratory animals.
   b. Keep the animals in a suitable, escape-proof container in a location where they will not be disturbed constantly.

c. Keep the containers clean. Clean cages of small birds and mammals daily. Provide proper ventilation, light, and temperature.

d. Provide water at all times.

e. Feed regularly, depending on the animals' needs.

f. Treat laboratory animals gently and with kindness in all situations.

g. If you are responsible for the regular care of any animals, be sure to make arrangements for their care during weekends, holidays, and vacations.

h. Your teacher will provide a suitable method to dispose of or release animals, if it becomes necessary.

5. Many plants or plant parts are poisonous. Work only with the plants your teacher specifies. Never put any plant or plant parts in your mouth.

6. Handle plants carefully and gently. Most plants must have light, soil, and water, although the specific requirements differ.

7. Wear the following personal protective equipment when handling or dissecting preserved specimens: safety goggles, a lab apron, and protective gloves.

Accident Procedures

1. Report *all* accidents, incidents, and injuries, and all breakage and spills, no matter how minor, to your teacher.

2. If a chemical spills on your skin or clothing, wash it off immediately with plenty of water and have a classmate notify your teacher immediately.

3. If a chemical gets in your eyes or on your face, wash immediately at the eyewash fountain with plenty of water. Flush your eyes for at least 15 minutes, including under each eyelid. Have a classmate notify your teacher immediately.

4. If a chemical spills on the floor or work surface, do not clean it up yourself. Notify your teacher immediately.

5. If a thermometer breaks, do not touch the broken pieces with your bare hands. Notify your teacher immediately.

6. In case of a lab table fire, notify your teacher immediately. In case of a clothing fire, drop to the floor and roll. Use a fire blanket if one is available. Have a classmate notify your teacher immediately.

7. Report to your teacher all cuts and abrasions received in the laboratory, no matter how small.

Chemical Safety

All chemicals are hazardous in some way. A hazardous chemical is defined as a substance that is likely to cause injury. Chemicals can be placed in four hazard categories: flammable, toxic, corrosive, and reactive.

In the laboratory investigations for this course, every effort is made to minimize the use of dangerous materials. However, many "less hazardous" chemicals can cause injury if not handled properly. The following information will help you become aware of the types of chemical hazards that exist and of how you can reduce the risk of injury when using chemicals. Before you work with any chemical, be sure to review safety rules 1 through 10 described at the beginning of the Laboratory Safety.

Flammable Substances

Flammable substances are solids, liquids, or gases that will burn. The process of burning involves three interrelated components—fuel (any substance capable of burning), oxidizer (often air or a specific chemical), and ignition source (a spark, flame, or heat). To control fire hazard, one must remove, or otherwise make inaccessible, at least one side of the fire triangle.

Flammable chemicals should not be used in the presence of ignition sources, such as lab burners, hot plates, and sparks from electrical equipment or static electricity. Containers of flammables should be closed when not in use. Sufficient ventilation in the laboratory will help to keep the concentration of flammable vapors to a minimum.

Toxic Substances

Most of the chemicals you encounter in a laboratory are toxic, or poisonous to life. The degree of toxicity depends on the properties of the specific substance, its concentration, the type of exposure, and other variables. The effects of exposure to a toxic substance can range from minor discomfort to serious illness or death. Exposure to toxic substances can occur through ingestion, skin contact, or inhalation of toxic vapors. Wearing a lab apron, safety goggles, and protective gloves is an important precautionary measure when using toxic chemicals. A clean work area, prompt spill cleanup, and good ventilation also are important.

Corrosive Substances

Corrosive chemicals are solids, liquids, or gases that by direct chemical action either destroy living tissue or cause permanent changes in the tissue. Corrosive substances can destroy eye and respiratory tract tissues. The consequences of mishandling a corrosive substance can be impaired sight or permanent blindness, severe disfigurement, permanent severe breathing difficulties, and even death. As with toxic substances, wear a lab apron, safety goggles, and protective gloves when handling corrosive chemicals to help prevent contact with your skin or eyes. Immediately wash off splashes on your skin or eyes with water, while a classmate notifies the teacher.

Reactive Substances

Under certain conditions, reactive chemicals promote violent reactions. A chemical may explode spontaneously or when it is mechanically disturbed. Reactive chemicals also include those that react rapidly when mixed with another chemical, releasing a large amount of energy. Keep chemicals separate from each other unless they are being combined according to specific instructions in an activity. Heed any other cautions your teacher may give you.

Glossary

A

abiotic (abiótico): Abiotic refers to not living. An abiotic factor is a nonliving part of an ecosystem.

absorption spectra (espectros de absorción): Absorption spectra contain absorption lines, which are produced as matter absorbs electromagnetic radiation.

action potential (potencial de acción): An action potential is a brief change in the electrical potential across the membrane of a neuron. Action potentials are electrical signals that travel along a neuron as a nerve impulse.

aerobic respiration (respiración aeróbica): Aerobic respiration is cellular respiration that requires the presence of oxygen.

amplitude (amplitud): In a single wave, amplitude is the size of the displacement of a particular portion of the wave from the rest position of the medium.

anaerobic respiration (respiración anaeróbica): Anaerobic respiration is cellular respiration that does not require oxygen.

antibody (anticuerpo): Antibodies are proteins in the blood that either disable or weaken antigens. This process allows white blood cells to destroy the antigens. Antibodies are made by the body's immune system.

antigen (antígeno): An antigen is any material, usually a protein that is recognized as foreign in the body. Antigens trigger the production of antibodies by the body's immune system.

apparent brightness (brillo aparente): Apparent brightness refers to the amount of light reaching us per unit area from a luminous object.

artifacts (artefactos): Artifacts are material remains made by humans, such as pieces of pottery, tools, and textiles that are cultural evidence.

astronomical unit (AU) (unidad astronómica): An astronomical unit is equal to the average distance of Earth from the Sun, which is about 150 million kilometers. These units are used to measure distances within the solar system.

atmosphere (atmósfera): The gaseous layer that surrounds an astronomical body, such as a planet or a star is known as an atmosphere.

atom (átomo): An atom is the smallest unit of an element that maintains the properties of that element.

axon (axón): An axon is a structure that extends out from a neuron and conducts impulses *away* from the cell body.

B

behavior (comportamiento): Behaviors are responses to external and internal stimuli. The actions or reactions any organism exhibits are its behaviors.

big bang (big bang): The big bang is the term used to describe the event that gave birth to the universe.

biomechanist (biomecánico): Biomechanists study the mechanics of living organisms (biomechanics).

biosphere (biosfera): Biosphere refers to the "layer" of life on Earth.

biotic (biótico): Biotic refers to living or recently living. A biotic factor is an organism or its remains in an ecosystem.

blast wave (onda de choque): This kind of wave is a powerful, compressive wave that travels rapidly through the atmosphere. Blast waves are produced by sudden events, such as explosions, volcanic eruptions, or even large rock slides.

blueshift (desplazamiento hacia el azul): A blueshift is a Doppler shift in which spectral features are shifted to shorter wavelengths. This happens when the relative motion of the observer and the object is toward each other.

C

canopy (bóveda forestal): A forest's is the typically dense, upper portions of trees and other tall vegetation that shades the forest floor.

carbohydrates (carbohidratos): A carbohydrate is an organic compound made of carbon, hydrogen, and oxygen. The hydrogen and oxygen atoms are in a 21 ratio. Examples of carbohydrates include sugars, starch, and cellulose.

carbon-based molecules (moléculas de carbono): Also called organic molecules, these molecules are built of carbon combined with other elements.

cardiac muscle (músculo cardíaco): Cardiac muscle is a specialized type of muscle tissue found only in the heart.

catalyze (catalizar): An increase in the rate of a chemical or biochemical reaction caused by a catalyst. A catalyst is a substance that increases the rate of a chemical or biochemical reaction. A catalyst takes part in a reaction but is not changed during the reaction and emerges in its original form.

cathode rays (rayos catódicos): These are rays of high-speed electrons emitted from a cathode in an evacuated tube in which an electric current has been applied.

cause-and-effect (causa y efecto): Cause-and-effect describes the relationship between an event or action and the related outcome (effect) of that action. Cause-and-effect indicates a closer relationship than two things that are correlated.

cell (célula): A cell is the basic living unit.

cell cycle (ciclo celular): The cell cycle describes an ordered sequence of events in the life of a dividing cell, composed of mitosis (M) interphase growth, and DNA synthesis phases (G_1, S, and G_2).

cellular respiration (respiración celular): Cellular respiration is the series of chemical reactions by which a living cell breaks down carbohydrates or other organic compounds to release energy.

center of mass (centro de la masa): Center of mass is the point at which a system of masses would balance if placed on a pivot. In a binary star system, the center of mass would lie nearer to the more massive component. In the case of a single mass, it is the point at which it can be assumed all the mass is concentrated.

Cepheid variable star (estrella variable cefeida): This type of star is a particularly luminous type of pulsating variable star that follows a period-luminosity relationship and thus is very useful for measuring cosmic distances.

chain reaction (reacción en cadena): A chain reaction is a self-sustaining reaction that, once started, steadily provides the energy and matter necessary to continue the reaction.

chaparral (chaparral): A chaparral is a biome consisting of dense shrubs and bushes, and scattered trees. A chaparral is specially adapted for hot, dry summers, mild, rainy winters, and regeneration by fires each 25–30 years.

characteristic property (propiedad característica): This type of property is one that can be used to help identify the material. It is not dependent on the amount of material.

chemical property (propiedad química): A chemical property is one that describes the ability of a substance to undergo a change, involving breaking or forming chemical bonds, that transforms it into a different substance.

chromatography (cromatografía): Chromatography describes techniques for separating the components of a mixture based on their affinity for a stationary and mobile phase.

comets (cometas): A relatively small, icy object that orbits a star is known as a comet.

compound (compuesto): A compound is a substance that is made from the atoms of two or more elements that are chemically bonded.

compressional wave (onda de compresión): See longitudinal wave.

concentration gradient (gradiente de concentración): A concentration gradient is a difference in the concentration of certain molecules over a distance.

conceptual model (modelo conceptual): A conceptual model describes a system through the use of symbolic representations.

conductivity meter (medidor de conductividad): A conductivity meter measures the ability of an electric current to pass through a material.

conductor (conductor): A conductor is a material in which heat, electric charge, or both can flow readily. Good conductors of heat are usually good conductors of electric charge.

constellation (constelación): A constellation is a region of the sky. There are 88 official constellations that cover the celestial sphere.

consumers (consumidores): Consumers are organisms that are not capable of making their own food and depend on the producers for nourishment.

control (control): In an experiment, the control is the individual, thing, or group designated to receive no treatment (the unchanged group). All other groups are compared against the control.

correlation (correlación): Correlation indicates an association between variables or sets of observations. It measures how strongly the variables may be related to each other. After noting a correlation, an observer must collect additional data to test for a cause-and-effect relationship.

cosmology (cosmología): Cosmology is the branch of astronomy concerned with the origin, structure, and evolution of the universe.

covalent molecule (molécula covalente): A covalent molecule is one in which the atoms are held together by covalent bonds. Covalent bonds form when electrons are shared somewhat equally between nuclei in a compound.

crest (cresta positiva): The highest (positive) displacement from the rest condition of the medium carrying the wave is called a crest.

critical mass (masa crítica): Critical mass is the minimum mass of fissionable material in a nuclear reactor or nuclear bomb that will sustain a chain reaction.

crown fire (incendio de copa o aéreo): A crown fire is a type of forest fire that engulfs trees from mid levels to their tops. Crown fires can spread rapidly from treetop to treetop.

crystal lattice (red cristalina): A crystal lattice is a three-dimensional arrangement of particles (atoms, ions, or molecules) that repeats throughout a solid.

cyanobacteria (cianobacteria): Cyanobacteria are the blue-green bacteria that carry on oxygen-producing photosynthesis much like plants, but without a membrane.

D

decomposer (descompositor): Decomposers are organisms that feed on dead plants and animals or their wastes. These consumers break down organic matter to a form that can be re-used by plants in the ecosystem. Decomposers are a key step in nutrient cycling.

dendrite (dentrita): A dendrite is a structure that extends out from a neuron and transmits impulses *toward* the cell body.

density (densidad): This characteristic physical property of a substance is equal to the mass divided by the volume.

deoxyribonucleic acid (DNA) (ácido desoxirribonucleico): DNA is the hereditary material of most organisms. DNA makes up genes and contains deoxyribose, a phosphate group, and one of four DNA bases.

depolarization (despolarización): Depolarization refers to a change in electrical potential of the neuron where the inside of the cell is more positive than the outside of the cell compared to a resting neuron.

differentiation (diferenciación): Differentiation is a form of specialization, such as when developing cells become ordered into certain tissues and organs.

diffusion (difusión): The movement of a substance down its concentration gradient from a more concentrated area to a less concentrated area is called diffusion.

dipole (dipolo): A dipole consists of equal but opposite charges that are separated by a short distance.

dissociation (disociación): Dissociation describes the process where ions are separated, as when an ionic compound dissolves.

distillate (destilado): The distillate is the product of distillation.

distillation (destilación): Distillation is a process used to separate two or more components in a liquid mixture.

diuretic (diurético): A diuretic is any substance or agent that promotes the increased formation and excretion of urine.

DNA bases (bases del ADN): DNA bases consist of four nitrogen-containing bases. These bases are adenine, thymine, guanine, and cytosine.

DNA typing (examen del ADN): DNA typing is a method of forensic investigation that relies on the unique DNA profile, or "fingerprint" of each individual. Forensic scientists use DNA typing to compare DNA profiles among suspects and DNA samples recovered at a crime scene.

Doppler effect (efecto Doppler): The apparent change in frequency, wavelength, or both when there is relative motion between a source and an observer is called the Doppler effect.

E

echolocation (localización por ecos): Echolocation describes the process used by bats, dolphins, and other animals to detect objects. Using this sonarlike process, the animal emits high-pitched sounds that reflect off an object and return to the ears or other sensory receptors.

ecology (ecología): Ecology is a field in biology that studies organisms and their relationship to their environment.

ectothermic (ectotérmico): An organism that is ectothermic has a body temperature that varies with the environment. These organisms obtain their body heat from outside of their body, that is, from the sun.

electric current (corriente eléctrica): An electric current is the flow of electric charge.

electrical conductivity (conductividad eléctrica): Electrical conductivity describes the ability of a substance to conduct electric charge.

electrical potential (potencial eléctrico): The energy created by a difference in charge distribution is called the electric potential. In a neuron, the difference in charge is across the membrane.

electrolyte (electrólito): An electrolyte is a substance that when dissolved in water will conduct an electric current. Electrolytes in your blood and other body fluids are important for regulating body functions, such as nerve impulses and muscle contraction. Some examples of electrolytes in your body include sodium (Na^+), potassium (K^+), and calcium (Ca^{2+}).

electromagnetic spectrum (EM spectrum) (espectro electromagnético): The EM spectrum is the complete spectrum of light, including radio waves, infrared, visible light, ultraviolet light, X-rays, and gamma rays.

electromagnetic radiation (EM radiation) (radiación electromagnética): EM radiation is radiation consisting of EM waves, which move at the speed of light (300,000 kilometers per second in a vacuum).

electromagnetic waves (EM waves) (ondas electromagnéticas): The term EM waves is a synonym for light, which consists of all waves in the EM spectrum.

electronegativity (electronegatividad): Electronegativity is the measure of the ability of an atom in a chemical compound to attract electrons.

electron (electrón): An electron is an extremely small negatively charged particle in an atom or ion.

electroscope (electroscopio): An electroscope is a device used to detect electric charges.

electrostatic force (fuerza electrostática): This is a force that one electric charge exerts on another. When the charges are alike (both negative or both positive), the force is repulsive; when the charges are opposite (one negative and one positive), the force is attractive.

element (elemento): An element is a pure substance made of only one kind of atom.

element tube (tubo de elementos o tubo de gases): This type of tube is filled with elements such as hydrogen, nitrogen, or neon. When electricity is applied to the tube, a distinctive color of light is emitted. The color of light is characteristic of the element or elements in the tube.

endothermic (endotérmico): An organism that is endothermic keeps its body temperature constant through internal mechanisms.

enzyme (enzima): A protein or part-protein molecule made by an organism and used as a catalyst in a specific biochemical reaction.

energy (energía): Energy is described as the ability to do work.

epidermis (epidermis): The epidermis is the outermost layer of skin.

ethogram (etograma): An ethogram is a description of a set of related patterns of behavior.

evidence (evidencia): Evidence is information gathered through investigations, such as data and observations. Evidence is free of opinion and can be gathered by others with similar results.

excitatory neurotransmitter (neurotransmisor excitador): An excitatory neurotransmitter makes it more likely for a neuron to initiate an action potential (nerve impulse).

extensive property (propiedad extensive): This type of property depends on the amount of matter that is present. Mass is an example of an extensive property.

extremeophiles (extremofilos): Organisms that thrive in what, for most terrestrial life-forms, are intolerably hostile environments are called extremeophiles.

F

fact (hecho): A piece of information that is currently proven to be true is called a fact.

family (familia): A vertical column on the periodic table is called a family. These columns are also known as groups.

fire triangle (triángulo del fuego): The fire triangle represents the three things needed to create or sustain a fire: oxygen, fuel, and heat. Lacking any one of these, a fire will go out.

firebreak (línea de contención de incendios): A firebreak is any natural or artificial barrier against the spread of fire. Firebreaks can take many forms, including an area cleared of vegetation; an area of green, slow-burning fuel; or a body of water.

fire-related deposits (depósitos originados por incendios): Fire-related deposits refers to river sediments (sand, gravel) that include the remains from forest fires such as charcoal. Rains wash these deposits down from mountains. Geologists study these deposits to measure the frequency and severity of fires from the surrounding area.

fire suppression (supresión del fuego): Fire suppression relates to policies and decisions where all fires are put out when discovered. The practice of fire suppression can result in the dangerous build-up of fuels in forests.

fission (fisión): Nuclear fission is the splitting of an atomic nucleus, particularly that of a heavy element, into two main parts accompanied by the release of much energy.

fluorescent tube (tubo fluorescente): This type of light fixture consists of a glass tube filled with mercury vapor and coated on the inside with a fluorescent powder. When electricity is applied to the tube, electrons bombard the mercury, causing it to emit ultraviolet light. The ultraviolet light causes the fluorescent powder to glow—giving off visible light.

flux (flujo): The rate of flow of a measurable quantity through a reference surface is known as flux.

food chain (cadena alimenticia): A food chain describes the transfer of food from one feeding level to another, beginning with producers.

food web (red alimenticia): A food web represents the network of feeding relationships and food chains in an ecosystem. Food webs also show where competition might exist for the same source of food.

forensic science (ciencia forense): Forensic science is a professional field of examining evidence and often identifying the perpetrators of crime. Forensic science relies on an understanding of inquiry methods, technology, and physical properties of matter.

frame of reference (marco referencial): A fixed orientation in space from which all observations are made. There is no absolute frame of reference.

frequency (frecuencia): Frequency describes the rate at which peaks of a wave pass by a point. Frequency is measured in units of 1 per second; 1/s is equivalent to 1 hertz (Hz).

fulcrum (fulcro): A fulcrum is the object on which a lever pivots.

fusion (fusión): Nuclear fusion is the combining of nuclei of light atoms, such as hydrogen, into heavier nuclei accompanied by the release of much energy.

G

galaxy (galaxia): A galaxy is a huge collection of anywhere from a few hundred million to more than a trillion stars, all bound together by gravity.

gravitational equilibrium (equilibrio gravitacional): This particular type of equilibrium describes a state of balance in which the force of gravity pulling inward is precisely counteracted by the outward force due to pressure.

gravity (gravedad): Gravity is the force by which every object in the universe (that has mass) attracts every other object.

ground fire (incendio superficial): A ground fire burns fuel only along the forest floor. It burns such things as litter, grasses and other non-woody plants. Ground fires typically have minimal impact on taller trees.

group (grupo): A vertical column on the periodic table is called a group. Groups are numbered 1–18 on modern periodic tables. These columns are also known as families.

H

half-life (periodo de semidesintegración): The time required for half the atoms of a radioactive isotope of an element to decay is called half-life.

hazards (peligros): Hazards are events that may expose people to injury or death. Natural hazards also damage or destroy public or private property.

health risks (peligros para la salud): A health risk is any factor or variable that has a negative impact on an organism. Independent risk factors can combine to create higher total levels of risk.

hemoglobin (hemoglobina): Hemoglobin is an iron-containing protein in red blood cells that transports oxygen from lungs to the body's tissues. Hemoglobin gives blood its red color.

hertz (Hz) (hertz): The unit used to represent the frequency of a wave equivalent to 1 per second (1/s) is called a hertz (Hz).

homeostasis (homeostasis): Homeostasis is a fundamental characteristic of living systems. In a social context, this refers to maintaining a stable number of individuals within a population. In the physiological sense, it is the tendency of an organism to maintain a stable, constant internal environment.

Hubble's law (Ley de Hubble): This law, discovered by Edwin Hubble, mathematically expresses the idea that more-distant galaxies move away from us faster than galaxies that are closer to us.

hydrosphere (hidrosfera): The hydrosphere is often called the "water sphere" as it includes all Earth's water that is found in streams, lakes, the soil, groundwater, and air.

hypertonic (hipertónica): A hypertonic solution is one where the concentration of solutes outside a cell is *greater* than the concentration inside.

hypothesis (hipótesis): A statement that suggests an explanation of an observation or an answer to a scientific problem is called a hypothesis.

hypotonic (hipotónica): A hypotonic solution is one where the concentration of solutes outside a cell is *less* than the concentration inside.

I

incandescent lightbulbs (lámparas incandescentes): Lightbulbs that produce light from very hot metal are called incandescent lightbulbs. The metal in these bulbs is usually tungsten, and the bulb is evacuated and filled with an inert gas such as argon.

inference (deducción): An inference is a logical assumptions based on evidence, but one that you have not directly observed.

inhibitory neurotransmitter (neurotransmisor inhibidor): An inhibitory neurotransmitter makes it more difficult for a neuron to initiate an action potential (nerve impulse).

innate behavior (comportamiento innato): Innate behavior is behavior that is genetically determined, as in the organization of an ant society. Another word for innate behavior is instinctive behavior.

instinct (instinto): Instinct describes the capacity of an animal to complete a fairly complex, stereotyped response to a key stimulus without having prior experience.

insulator (aislante): An insulator is a material that is a poor conductor of heat, electric charge, or both.

intensive property (propiedad intensiva): This type of property is one that does not depend on the amount of matter present. Density is an example of an intensive property.

interneurons (interneuronas): An interneuron is an associative neuron, that is, a neuron located between a sensory neuron and a motor neuron.

inverse square law (ley de la inversa de los cuadrados): Any quantity that decreases with the increased square of the distance between two objects is said to follow an inverse square law.

ion (ión): An ion is a charged particle.

ionic compounds (compuestos iónicos): Ionic compounds are neutral compounds made from combinations of positive and negative ions.

ionization (ionización): Ionization describes any process that results in the formation of an ion. An example is the formation of ions from solute molecules by the action of the solvent.

ionization energy (energía de ionización): Ionization energy is the energy required to remove one electron from a neutral atom of an element.

isotonic (isotónica): An isotonic solution is one where the concentration of solutes outside a cell equals the concentration inside.

isotope (isótopo): An isotope is a form of an element having a particular number of neutrons in the nuclei of its atom. Different isotopes of a particular element have the same atomic number (number of protons) but different mass numbers because of the different number of neutrons.

L

ladder fuels (combustibles en continuidad vertical): Ladder fuels are vegetation (living or dead) of different heights that transfer fire from the forest floor to the canopy.

lambda (λ) (lambda): Lambda (λ) is the Greek letter used to represent wavelength.

law (ley): A law is a universally accepted explanation for something in the natural world that always holds true under specific conditions.

law of conservation of matter (ley de conservación de la materia): This law states that matter is neither created nor destroyed during ordinary chemical or physical reactions.

learned behavior (comportamiento aprendido): A behavior that is developed as a result of experience is called a learned behavior.

lepton (lepton): A lepton is one of the elementary particles. An electron is an example of a lepton.

level of risk (nivel de riesgo): The level of risk indicates the odds or probability that an undesirable event or sickness might occur. The level of risk can be increased when several risk factors combine (see risk factor).

lever (palanca): A simple machine that consists of a bar that pivots about a fulcrum.

light-year (ly) (año-luz): A light-year is the distance that light can travel in one year, which is 9.46 trillion kilometers.

lipid (lípido): A lipid is a fat, oil, or fatlike compound that usually has fatty acids in its molecular structure. These are important components of the plasma membrane.

lithosphere (litosfera): The relatively rigid outer layer of a planet is known as the lithosphere. It generally includes the crust and the uppermost portion of the mantle.

longitudinal wave (onda longitudinal): This type of wave travels through a medium in which the particles of that medium move back and forth in the same direction as the wave. A sound wave travels this way.

luminosity (luminosidad): The total power output of an object is known as its luminosity and is usually measured in watts or in units of solar luminosities ($L_{Sun} = 3.8 \times 10^{26}$ watts).

M

macromolecule (macromolécula): A macromolecule is a large molecule made up of hundreds or thousands of atoms. Proteins, carbohydrates, and nucleic acids are examples of macromolecules.

main sequence stars (estrellas de secuencia principal): Main sequence stars are those that plot along the prominent line of points running from the upper left to the lower right on a Hertzsprung-Russell (H-R) diagram. Main sequence stars shine by fusing hydrogen into helium in their cores.

mechanical advantage (MA) (rendimiento mecánico): Mechanical advantage is the ratio of output force to input force for a machine.

medium (medio): The medium is the matter through which a wave travels.

melanin (melanina): Melanin is a brown pigment found in skin and produced in melanocytes.

melanoma (melanoma): Melanoma is a skin cancer that begins in melanocytes. It is prone to metastasis, and is the most serious form of skin cancer.

metabolism (metabolismo): Metabolism is the sum of all the chemical changes taking place in an organism.

metastasis (metástasis): Metastasis is the spread of cancer cells from one part of the body to another.

meteorite (meteorito): A meteorite is a rock from space that lands on Earth.

mitosis (mitosis): Mitosis is the replication of the chromosomes and the production of two nuclei in one cell; it is usually followed by the division of the cytoplasm of the cell.

mixture (mezcla): A mixture is a blend of two or more kinds of matter, each of which retains its own identity. A mixture can be separated by physical means.

molecule (molécula): A molecule is a neutral group of atoms that are held together by covalent bonds.

monosaccharide (monosacárido): A monosaccharide is a simple sugar with three to seven carbon atoms in its carbon skeleton.

mortality rates (tasa de mortalidad): The number and frequency of deaths in a group of organisms over a particular period of time is referred to as the group's mortality rate.

motive (motivo): A motive is a cause or reason for a person to act in a certain way.

motor neurons (neuronas motrices): These are specialized neurons that receive impulses from the central nervous system and transmit them to a muscle or gland.

multicellular (multicelular): Multicellular organisms are composed of many cells.

N

nebula (nebulosa): A nebula is a cloud of gas in space and is usually glowing.

nerve impulse (impulso nervioso): A nerve impulse is a wave of chemical and electrical changes (action potential) that pass along a neuron in response to a stimulus.

neuron (neurona): A neuron is a unique type of cell found in the brain and body that is specialized to process and transmit information. Another name for a nerve cell is a neuron.

neurotransmission (neurotransmisión): Neurotransmission is the process that occurs when a neuron releases neurotransmitters to communicate with another neuron across the synapse.

neurotransmitter (neurotransmisor): A neurotransmitter is a chemical messenger, often similar to or identical with a hormone, that diffuses across the synapse and transmits a nerve impulse from one neuron to another.

neutron (neutrón): A neutron is an electrically neutral particle that is contained in the nucleus of an atom.

nuclear reaction (reacción nuclear): A reaction that involves the nucleus of an atom is a nuclear reaction. Examples of these types of reactions are fission and fusion reactions.

nucleic acid (ácido nucleico): The term nucleic acid describes DNA or RNA. These are organic compounds composed of nucleotides and are important in coding instructions for cell processes.

nucleus (núcleo): 1. In atoms, the nucleus is the central core, containing positively charged protons and usually electrically neutral neutrons. 2. In eukaryotic cells, the nucleus is the membranous organelle that houses the chromosomal DNA.

O

operational definition (definición operacional): Agreeing on criteria that will define a targeted action or behavior during an investigation is referred to as an operational definition.

orbit (órbita): An orbit describes the path that one body takes as it moves around another, usually circular or elliptical.

organelle (orgánulo): An organelle is an organized structure within a cell with a specific function. A chloroplast and a mitochondrion are examples of organelles.

organic molecules (moléculas de carbono): Also called carbon-based molecules, organic molecules are built of carbon combined with other elements.

osmosis (osmosis): The movement of water across a selectively permeable membrane is called osmosis.

outgassing (desgaseamiento): Outgassing describes the process of releasing gases from a planetary interior, usually through volcanic eruptions.

P

parallax (paralaje): Parallax refers to the apparent shift of an object when viewed at different angles.

parallax angle (ángulo de paralaje): The parallax angle is half of a star's annual back and forth shift due to stellar parallax.

pathogen (patógeno): A pathogen is an agent such as a virus, bacteria, or poison in the body that can lead to disease or death.

period (periodo): 1. A period is the time required to complete on full cycle or action of a repetitive event. 2. The horizontal rows on the periodic table are called periods.

periodic table of the elements (tabla periódica de los elementos): The periodic table of the elements is an arrangement of the elements in order of their atomic numbers so that elements with similar properties fall in the same column, or group.

permeability (permeabilidad): Permeability describes the ability of a membrane or other material to permit a substance to pass through it.

photosynthesis (fotosíntesis): Photosynthesis is the process by which living cells that contain chlorophyll use light energy to make organic compounds from inorganic materials.

physical model (modelo físico): A physical representation of an object or idea is called a physical model. Often these models are bigger or smaller than the original so that a person can manipulate them.

pitch (tono): Pitch is the highness or lowness of sound related to the frequency of the sound.

plasma (plasma): Plasma is the clear, straw-colored liquid of blood that is about 90 percent water. Plasma also includes proteins, essential elements, food molecules, oxygen, carbon dioxide, and cellular waste.

plasma membrane (membrana plasmática): This membrane is also called the cell membrane and is at the boundary of every cell. The plasma membrane serves as a selective barrier to the passage of ions and molecules.

plinian eruptions (erupciones plinianas): Plinian eruptions are massive volcanic explosions that eject gas, ash, and rock high into the atmosphere (>10–15 km). Such eruptions are named for Pliny the Younger, who carefully described the eruption of Vesuvius in 79 AD.

polar (polar): Particles that are polar have an unequal distribution of charge.

prescribed burns (incendios controlados): Prescribed burns are a method of subjecting portions of a forest to low-intensity burns. Prescribed burns reduce fuel on the forest floor and reduce the chances for catastrophic wildfires.

probability (probabilidad): Probability is the measure of the odds or chances of an event occurring.

producers (productores): Producers are organisms that make their own food (autotrophs). All consumers (and decomposers) in the food web rely on producers.

proplyd (proplyd): The term proplyd is short for protoplanetary disk.

protein (proteína): A protein is an organic compound composed of one or more polypeptide chains of amino acids. Most structural materials and enzymes in a cell are proteins.

proton (protón): The proton is the positive particle in the nucleus of the atom or ion. The number of protons of a particular atom is equal to the atomic number of that atom.

protoplanetary disk (disco protoplanetario): A protoplanetary disk is a disk of material surrounding a young star. This material may eventually form planets.

protoplanets (protoplanetas): Newly forming planets are called protoplanets.

pure substances (sustancias puras): These are substances that have a fixed composition and differ from mixtures in that every sample of a given pure substance has exactly the same characteristic properties and composition.

pyroclastic flow (flujo piroclástico): A pyroclastic flow is a rapidly moving cloud of hot volcanic gas, ash, and rock fragments resulting from large volcanic eruptions. They are often associated with Plinian eruptions such as the 79 AD eruption of Vesuvius. Pyroclastic flows can spread from volcanoes at velocities of 100 km/hour or more and kill virtually all life in their path.

Q

quantum (quantum): A quantum of energy is the minimum quantity of energy that can be gained or lost by an atom.

quark (quark): A quark is one of the elementary particles of which all protons and neutrons are made.

R

radioactive decay (desintegración radioactiva): Radioactive decay is the spontaneous disintegration of a nucleus into a slightly lighter and more stable nucleus, accompanied by the emission of particles, electromagnetic radiation, or both.

red blood cells (glóbulos rojos): Red blood cells contain the iron-bearing protein hemoglobin. Red blood cells carry oxygen from the lungs to tissues of the body.

redshift (desplazamiento hacia el rojo): A redshift is a Doppler shift in which spectral features are shifted to longer wavelengths. This shift is caused when the relative motion of the observer and the object is away from each other.

reflex (reflejo): A reflex is an involuntary reaction or response to a stimulus.

repolarization (repolarización): Repolarization is a change back to the electrical potential of a resting neuron after depolarization. After repolarization, the inside of the neuron is more negatively charged than the outside of the neuron.

retention factor (factor de retención): The retention factor, R_f, is the ratio of the distance traveled by the compound divided by the distance traveled by the solvent. This factor is used in chromatography.

retina (retina): The retina is the light-sensitive layer of tissue that lines the back of the eyeball. The retina transfers a signal through the optic nerve to the brain.

risk factors (factores de riesgo): Risk factors are sets of conditions that determine the odds for disease for an organism.

S

salt (sal): A salt is a type compound made from positive and negative ions. Salts vary widely in their solubility.

sarcomeres (sarcómeros): Sarcomeres are the basic units of contraction in skeletal and cardiac muscles.

selectively permeable (permeabilidad selectiva): Selectively permeable refers to a property of biological membranes that allows some substances to cross and prevents others from crossing.

sensory neurons (neuronas sensoriales): This type of neuron is one that receives impulses from a sensory organ or receptor and transmits them toward the central nervous system.

sensory receptor (receptor sensorial): A sensory receptor is a specialized sensory structure or an organ that detects stimuli.

single celled (unicelular): Single-celled organisms are composed of only one cell.

skeletal muscle (músculo esquelético): Skeletal muscle is a type of muscle tissue that is attached to skeletal parts and responsible for voluntary muscle movement.

smooth muscle (músculo liso): Smooth muscle is the type of muscle found in the walls of hollow internal organs. Contraction of smooth muscle is under involuntary control.

solvation (solvatación): Solvation is the process whereby a solute particle is surrounded by solvent molecules.

solvent (solvente): A solvent is a liquid substance that is used to dissolve another substance. For example, water dissolves most substances and is considered the "universal solvent."

spectra (espectros): Spectra produced by elements are the bands of light at a particular wavelength that are either absorbed or emitted due to the changing energy states of their electrons. White light produces a continuous spectrum (singular) and is seen as a rainbow.

stakeholders (partes interesadas): Stakeholders are the people with a vested interest in the decisions being made.

stellar parallax (paralaje estelar): Stellar parallax is the apparent shift in the position of a nearby star against a distant object that occurs as we view the star from different positions in Earth's orbit of the Sun.

stimulus (estímulo): Stimulus is a change or signal in the internal or external environment that causes an adjustment or reaction by an organism.

strong nuclear force (fuerza nuclear fuerte): This force is what holds particles within the nucleus together. This force is strongest at very close distances.

sublimation (sublimación): Sublimation describes the change of state from a solid directly to a gas.

superclusters (supercúmulos): Superclusters consist of many clusters of galaxies, groups of galaxies, and individual galaxies and are the largest known structures in the universe.

surface tension (tensión superficial): Surface tension describes the force needed to overcome intermolecular attractions and break through the surface of a liquid or spread out the liquid.

synapse (sinapsis): The synapse is the site where the end of an axon and the end of a dendrite communicate with each other.

synaptic space (espacio sináptico): The space between the axon of one neuron and the dendrite of another neuron at the end of a neuron's synapse is called the synaptic space (and is also commonly known as the synaptic cleft). Neurotransmitters are released into the synaptic space.

synthetic (sintético): The term synthetic is used to describe substances that are human made.

T

tandem repeats (repeticiones en tandem): In DNA, tandem repeats are characterized by the occurrence of multiple nucleotides (usually four or more) in a pattern that are directly adjacent to each other.

theory (teoría): A theory is a well-tested hypothesis that organizes knowledge, fits existing data, explains how events or processes are thought to occur, and successfully predicts future observations.

thermal pressure (presión termal): Thermal pressure is the ordinary pressure in a gas arising from motions of particles that are due to the object's temperature.

transverse wave (onda transversal): A transverse wave is a type of wave moving through a material in which the motion of the material moves at right angles to the direction the wave is traveling.

tree rings (anillos de árboles): A tree ring is a growth band that represents one season of a tree's growth. Each ring is composed of the lighter-colored, thinner cells created during the earlier part of the tree's annual growth cycle (also known as earlywood) and the darker, thicker cells created during the later part of the cycle (also known as latewood).

trough (cresta negativa): A trough is the position in a repeating wave with the greatest negative (lowest) displacement from the rest condition of the medium.

turgor pressure (presión de turgencia): Turgor pressure is the pressure within a cell resulting from the influx of water due to osmosis.

U

understory (sotobosque): A forest's understory is the layer of foliage beneath the forest canopy. *See* canopy.

unicellular (unicelular): Unicellular refers to organisms that are single celled.

UV Index (Índice UV): The UV Index indicates the intensity of ultraviolet radiation. The UV Index varies from about 1 (low intensity) to 12 or higher (high intensity) depending on factors such as time of day, cloud cover, elevation, and seasonal angle of the sun.

V

valence electron (electrón de Valencia): Valence electrons are electrons that are available to be lost, gained, or shared in the formation of chemical compounds. These electrons are located in the outermost energy level of an atom.

variable (variable): A variable is a quantity that can change or be manipulated during the course of a scientific investigation.

variable star (estrella variable): A star that changes in brightness is called a variable star.

visible spectrum (espectro visible): The visible spectrum refers to the portion of the entire electromagnetic spectrum to which our eyes are sensitive, usually considered in the range from about 410–710 nanometers.

volcanic avalanche (avalancha volcánica): A volcanic avalanche is a rapidly moving slide of debris composed of rock, soil, or mud on the steep flanks of an active volcano. Volcanic avalanches destroy virtually anything and can travel several kilometers before coming to rest.

volcanic bombs (bombas volcánicas): Volcanic bombs are lava and other ejecta in a molten or partially molten state that are hurled from erupting volcanoes. Some initially molten bombs acquire a rounded shape as they cool in flight.

volcanic mudflow (flujo de lodo volcánico): Volcanic mudflows typically form by subjecting the loose volcanic deposits on the flanks of volcanoes with voluminous water from rain or melting snow. They can be catastrophic and strike areas around volcanoes well after the main sequence of eruptions.

W

watt (vatio): A watt is the basic unit of power equivalent to 1 joule of work per second (1 J/s).

wavelength (longitud de onda): Wavelength is the distance between adjacent waves, usually measured from crest to crest or trough to trough. The symbol for wavelength is the Greek letter lambda (λ).

white blood cells (glóbulos blancos): White blood cells are blood cells in the body's immune system that help to fight infection from viruses, bacteria, and fungi.

Glosario

A

abiótico (abiotic): Abiótico se refiere a lo no viviente. Un factor abiótico es una parte no viviente de un ecosistema.

ácido desoxirribonucleico (ADN) (deoxyribonucleic acid [DNA]): El ADN es el material hereditario de la mayoría de los organismos. Produce genes y contiene desoxirribosa, un grupo de fosfatos y una de las cuatro bases del ADN.

ácido nucleico (nucleic acid): El término ácido nucleico se refiere al ADN o al ARN. Estos son compuestos orgánicos formados por nucleótidos, y son importantes en la codificación de instrucciones para los procesos celulares.

aislante (insulator): Un aislante es un material que casi no conduce calor o cargas eléctricas.

amplitud (amplitude): En una onda simple, la amplitud es el tamaño del desplazamiento de una determinada porción de la onda desde la posición de reposo del medio.

ángulo de paralaje (parallax angle): El ángulo de paralaje es la mitad del desplazamiento anual oscilante de una estrella debido al paralaje estelar.

anillos de árboles (tree rings): Un anillo de un árbol es una banda que representa una etapa en el crecimiento del árbol. Cada anillo está compuesto por las células delgadas y de color claro formadas durante el principio del ciclo de crecimiento anual del árbol (también se conoce como madera de primavera o temprana) y las células más gruesas y de color más oscuro formadas durante el periodo posterior del ciclo (también se conoce como madera de otoño o tardía).

anticuerpo (antibody): Los anticuerpos son proteínas presentes en la sangre, que inhiben o debilitan la acción de los antígenos. Dicho proceso permite que los glóbulos blancos destruyan los antígenos. Los anticuerpos son producidos por el sistema inmunológico del cuerpo.

antígeno (antigen): Un antígeno es cualquier sustancia —generalmente una proteína— que el cuerpo reconoce como extraña. Los antígenos hacen que el sistema inmunológico del cuerpo produzca anticuerpos.

año-luz (light-year [ly]): Un año-luz es la distancia que recorre la luz en un año, la cual es de 9.46 trillones de kilómetros.

artefactos (artifacts): Artefactos son restos materiales de objetos hechos por los seres humanos, como trozos de alfarería, herramientas y productos textiles que son evidencia de cultura.

atmósfera (atmosphere): Se conoce como atmósfera a la capa gaseosa que rodea un cuerpo astral como un planeta o una estrella.

átomo (atom): Un átomo es la unidad más pequeña de un elemento que mantiene las propiedades de dicho elemento.

avalancha volcánica (volcanic avalanche): Una avalancha volcánica son fragmentos de roca, suelo o barro en rápido desplazamiento por los lados empinados de un volcán activo. Las avalanchas volcánicas destruyen virtualmente cualquier cosa y pueden avanzar por varios kilómetros antes de detenerse.

axón (axon): Un axón es una prolongación de una neurona que transmite impulsos hacia *afuera* del cuerpo celular.

B

bases del ADN (DNA bases): Las bases del ADN son cuatro bases que contienen nitrógeno. Son la adenina, tiamina, guanina y citosina.

big bang (*Big bang*): Es el término inglés que se usa para describir el suceso que dio comienzo al universo.

biomecánico (biomechanist): Los biomecánicos estudian el mecanismo de los organismos vivos (biomecánica).

biosfera (biosphere): Biosfera se refiere a la "capa" de vida sobre la Tierra.

biótico (biotic): Biótico se refiere a lo viviente o lo que estuvo vivo recientemente. Un factor biótico es un organismo de un ecosistema o sus restos.

bombas volcánicas (volcanic bombs): Las bombas volcánicas son una mezcla de lava y otras materias en estado fundido o parcialmente fundido que son lanzadas por las erupciones volcánicas. Algunas bombas que salen en estado fundido adquieren una forma redondeada al enfriarse en su trayecto por el aire.

bóveda forestal (canopy): La bóveda forestal es la parte superior de los árboles y otra vegetación alta, típicamente densa, que provee sombra al suelo de los bosques.

brillo aparente (apparent brightness): El brillo aparente se refiere a la cantidad de luz que nos llega por área unitaria desde un objeto luminoso.

C

cadena alimenticia (food chain): Una cadena alimenticia describe la transferencia de alimento de un nivel de alimentación a otro, comenzando con los productores.

carbohidratos (carbohydrates): Un carbohidrato es un compuesto orgánico hecho de carbono, hidrógeno y oxígeno. Los átomos de hidrógeno y de oxígeno se hallan en una proporción de 2 a 1. Entre los carbohidratos se encuentran los azúcares, el almidón y la celulosa.

catalizar (catalyze): Un aumento en la velocidad de una reacción química o bioquímica causado por un catalizador. Un catalizador es una sustancia que aumenta la velocidad de una reacción química o bioquímica. Un catalizador actúa en una reacción pero no sufre cambios durante la reacción y retiene su forma original.

causa y efecto (cause-and-effect): El término causa y efecto se aplica a la relación entre un suceso o acción y el resultado (efecto) de esa acción. Causa y efecto indica una relación más estrecha que la que existe entre dos cosas que están correlacionadas.

célula (cell): La célula es la unidad básica dotada de vida propia.

centro de la masa (center of mass): El centro de la masa es el punto en el cual un sistema de masas se equilibraría si se colocara sobre un pivote. En un sistema estelar binario, el centro de la masa estaría más cerca del componente con mayor cantidad de masa. En el caso de una masa simple, se trata del punto en el cual se puede suponer que está concentrada toda la masa.

chaparral (chaparral): Un chaparral es un bioma poblado de densos arbustos y matas y árboles dispersos. Un chaparral está especialmente adaptado para veranos calurosos y secos, inviernos templados y lluviosos y la regeneración por incendios cada 25 a 30 años.

cianobacteria (cyanobacteria): Las cianobacterias son las bacterias de color azul verdoso que producen oxígeno mediante un sistema de fotosíntesis muy parecido al de las plantas, pero sin membrana.

ciclo celular (cell cycle): El ciclo celular describe una secuencia ordenada de sucesos en la vida de una célula en estado de división, la cual consta de las fases de mitosis (M), crecimiento interfaz y síntesis del ADN (G_1, S y G_2).

ciencia forense (forensic science): La ciencia forense es el sector profesional dedicado al examen de evidencia y a menudo identifica a los perpetradores de un crimen. La ciencia forense se basa en el entendimiento de métodos de investigación, en la tecnología y en las propiedades físicas de la materia.

combustibles en continuidad vertical (ladder fuels): Los combustibles en continuidad vertical son vegetación (viva o muerta) de diferentes alturas que propaga el fuego desde el suelo del bosque a la bóveda forestal.

cometas (comets): Se denomina cometa a un objeto helado, relativamente pequeño, que describe una órbita alrededor de una estrella.

comportamiento (behavior): Comportamiento es la respuesta a estímulos externos e internos. Las acciones o reacciones que manifiesta un organismo son su comportamiento.

comportamiento aprendido (learned behavior): Se denomina comportamiento aprendido a aquel que se desarrolla como resultado de la experiencia.

comportamiento innato (innate behavior): El comportamiento innato está determinado por los genes, como en el caso de la organización de una sociedad de hormigas. Otro término para comportamiento innato es comportamiento instintivo.

compuesto (compound): Un compuesto es una sustancia formada por los átomos de dos o más elementos que están ligados por características químicas.

compuestos iónicos (ionic compounds): Los compuestos iónicos son compuestos neutros formados por combinaciones de iones positivos y negativos.

conductividad eléctrica (electrical conductivity): La conductividad eléctrica se refiere a la capacidad de una sustancia para transportar una carga eléctrica.

conductor (conductor): Un conductor es un material en el cual el calor, una carga eléctrica o ambas pueden fluir con facilidad. Los buenos conductores de calor generalmente son buenos conductores de electricidad.

constelación (constellation): Una constelación es una región del cielo. Existen 88 constelaciones oficiales en la aparente esfera celeste.

consumidores (consumers): Los consumidores son organismos que no son capaces de producir su propio alimento y dependen de los productores para su nutrición.

control (control): En un experimento, el control es el individuo, objeto o grupo que no recibe tratamiento (el grupo inalterado). Todos los otros grupos se comparan con el control.

correlación (correlation): La correlación indica una asociación entre variables o conjuntos de observaciones. Mide hasta qué grado las variables están relacionadas entre sí. Luego de notar una correlación, el observador debe reunir más datos para una prueba de relación causa-efecto.

corriente eléctrica (electrical current): Una corriente eléctrica es el flujo de una carga eléctrica.

cosmología (cosmology): La cosmología es la rama de la astronomía referente al origen, estructura y evolución del universo.

cresta negativa (trough): Cresta negativa es la posición en una onda repetitiva con el mayor desplazamiento negativo (más bajo) desde la condición de reposo del medio.

cresta positiva (crest): Se denomina cresta positiva al desplazamiento más alto (positivo) desde la condición de reposo del medio que transporta la onda.

cromatografía (chromatography): La cromatografía describe las técnicas utilizadas para separar los componentes de una mezcla según su afinidad por una fase estacionaria o móvil.

D

deducción (inference): Una deducción es una suposición lógica basada en evidencia, pero que no se ha observado directamente.

definición operacional (operational definition): Se habla de definición operacional cuando se llega a un acuerdo en los criterios que definen una acción o comportamiento objeto de una investigación.

densidad (density): Esta propiedad física característica de una sustancia es equivalente a la masa dividida por el volumen.

dentrita (dendrite): Una dentrita es una prolongación de una neurona que transmite impulsos *hacia* el cuerpo celular.

depósitos originados por incendios (fire-related deposits): Estos son sedimentos de ríos (arena, grava) que incluyen los restos de incendios forestales, como carbón. Las lluvias arrastran estos depósitos por las montañas. Los geólogos estudian dichos depósitos para medir la frecuencia y severidad de los incendios de las zonas circundantes.

descompositor (decomposer): Los descompositores son organismos que se alimentan de plantas y animales muertos o sus desechos. Descomponen la materia orgánica transformándola a un estado en que puede ser reutilizada por las plantas en el ecosistema. Los descompositores son un paso clave en el ciclo de nutrientes.

desgaseamiento (outgassing): Desgaseamiento se refiere al proceso por el cual se liberan gases desde el interior planetario, generalmente a través de erupciones volcánicas.

desintegración radioactiva (radioactive decay): La desintegración radioactiva es la desintegración espontánea de un núcleo, volviéndose éste más ligero y estable. Tal desintegración se caracteriza por la emisión de partículas, radiación electromagnética o ambas.

desplazamiento hacia el azul (blueshift): Este es un desplazamiento Doppler en el cual las líneas espectrales se desplazan disminuyendo la longitud de onda. Esto sucede cuando el movimiento relativo del observador y el objeto es el uno hacia el otro.

desplazamiento hacia el rojo (redshift): Este es un desplazamiento Doppler en el cual las líneas espectrales se desplazan incrementando la longitud de onda. Este desplazamiento se produce cuando el movimiento relativo del observador y el objeto es en dirección contraria el uno al otro.

despolarización (depolarization): La despolarización se refiere a un cambio en la potencia eléctrica de la neurona cuando el interior de la célula es más positivo que su exterior en comparación con una neurona en reposo.

destilación (distillation): La destilación es un proceso utilizado para separar dos o más componentes de una mezcla líquida.

destilado (distillate): El destilado es el producto de la destilación.

diferenciación (differentiation): Diferenciación es una forma de especialización, como la de las células en desarrollo que se agrupan para formar ciertos tejidos y órganos.

difusión (diffusion): Se denomina difusión al desplazamiento de una sustancia hacia su gradiente de concentración; desde una zona más concentrada a una menos concentrada.

dipolo (dipole): Un dipolo consta de cargas iguales pero opuestas separadas por una distancia pequeña.

disco protoplanetario (protoplanetary disk): Un disco protoplanetario es un disco de material que rodea a una estrella joven. Con el tiempo, dicho material puede formar planetas.

disociación (dissociation): Disociación se refiere al proceso en el cual los iones se separan, como cuando un compuesto iónico se disuelve.

diurético (diuretic): Un diurético es toda sustancia o agente que aumenta la formación y excreción de orina.

E

ecología (ecology): La ecología es un campo de la biología que estudia los organismos y su relación con su entorno.

ectotérmico (ectothermic): Un organismo ectotérmico tiene una temperatura corporal que varía según el ambiente. Dichos organismos obtienen su calor corporal del exterior, es decir, del sol.

efecto Doppler (Doppler effect): Se denomina efecto Doppler al cambio aparente en la frecuencia, longitud de onda o ambas cuando existe un movimiento relativo entre una fuente y un observador.

electrólito (electrolyte): Un electrólito es una sustancia que cuando se disuelve en agua actúa como conductor de corriente eléctrica. Los electrólitos de la sangre y otros fluidos corporales son importantes en la regulación de las funciones corporales, como los impulsos nerviosos y la contracción muscular. Algunos electrólitos del cuerpo son el sodio (Na^+), el potasio (K^+) y el calcio ($Ca2^+$).

electrón (electron): Un electrón es una partícula con carga negativa extremadamente pequeña de un átomo o ión.

electrón de valencia (valence electron): Los electrones de valencia son aquellos que se pueden perder, ganar o compartir en la formación de compuestos químicos. Dichos electrones están situados en el nivel de energía más externo de un átomo.

electronegatividad (electronegativity): La electronegatividad es la medida de la capacidad de un átomo de un compuesto químico para atraer electrones.

electroscopio (electroscope): Un electroscopio es un dispositivo utilizado para detectar cargas eléctricas.

elemento (element): Un elemento es una sustancia pura constituida por un solo tipo de átomo.

endotérmico (endothermic): Un organismo endotérmico mantiene una temperatura corporal constante mediante mecanismos internos.

energía (energy): Energía se refiere a la capacidad de efectuar trabajo.

energía de ionización (ionization energy): La energía de ionización es la energía necesaria para quitar un electrón de un átomo neutro de un elemento.

enzima (enzyme): Sustancia proteínica producida por un organismo y que actúa como catalizador en una reacción bioquímica específica.

epidermis (epidermis): La epidermis es la capa más exterior de la piel.

equilibrio gravitacional (gravitational equilibrium): Este tipo particular de equilibrio se refiere al estado de equilibrio que se produce cuando la fuerza de gravedad que impulsa un objeto hacia adentro es contrarrestada por una fuerza equivalente hacia fuera debido a la presión.

erupciones plinianas (plinian eruptions): Las erupciones plinianas son grandes explosiones volcánicas que arrojan gas, cenizas y rocas hacia la atmósfera (>10–15 km). Tales erupciones se conocen como plinianas en honor a Plinio el Joven, quien describió detalladamente la erupción del Vesuvio en el año 79 dC.

espacio sináptico (synaptic space): Se denomina espacio sináptico al espacio entre el axón de una neurona y la dentrita de otra al final de la sinapsis de una neurona. Los neurotransmisores son liberados en el espacio sináptico.

espectro electromagnético (electromagnetic spectrum [EM spectrum]): El espectro electromagnético es el espectro total de luz, incluidas las ondas de radio, los rayos infrarrojos, la luz visible, la luz ultravioleta, los rayos X y los rayos gama.

espectro visible (visible spectrum): El espectro visible se refiere a la porción del espectro electromagnético total al cual son sensibles nuestros ojos, por lo general considerado entre unos 410 a 710 nanómetros.

espectros (spectra): Los espectros producidos por elementos son las bandas de luz a una longitud de onda determinada que son absorbidas o emitidas debido al estado cambiante de energía de sus electrones. La luz blanca produce un espectro (singular) continuo y se ve como un arco iris.

espectros de absorción (absorption spectra): Los espectros de absorción contienen líneas de absorción, las cuales se producen a medida que la materia absorbe la radiación electromagnética.

estímulo (stimulus): Un estímulo es un cambio o señal en el ambiente interno o externo por el cual se produce un ajuste o una reacción en un organismo.

estrella variable (variable star): Se denomina estrella variable a la que experimenta cambios en su luminosidad.

estrella variable cefeida (Cepheid variable star): Este es un tipo de estrella variable púlsar particularmente luminosa que sigue una relación periodo-luminosidad, y por eso es muy útil para medir distancias cósmicas.

estrellas de secuencia principal (main sequence stars): Las estrellas de secuencia principal son aquellas que se encuentran a lo largo de la línea de puntos prominente que va desde la posición superior izquierda a la inferior derecha en el diagrama de Hertzsprung-Russell (H-R). Las estrellas de secuencia principal brillan al fusionar hidrógeno en helio en su núcleo.

etograma (ethogram): Un etograma es una descripción de un conjunto de patrones de comportamiento relacionados.

evidencia (evidence): Evidencia es información recopilada a través de investigaciones, como datos y observaciones. La evidencia es carente de opinión, y otros pueden reunir la información obteniendo resultados similares.

examen de ADN (DNA typing): El examen de ADN es un método forense de investigación que se sustenta en el perfil único del ADN o "huella digital" de cada individuo. Los científicos forenses utilizan este método para comparar el ADN de los sospechosos con muestras de ADN obtenidas en la escena de un crimen.

extremofilos (extremeophiles): Se denomina extremofilos a los organismos que medran en ambientes que son intolerablemente hostiles para la mayoría de las formas de vida terrestre.

F

factor de retención (retention factor): El factor de retención, R_f, es la relación de la distancia recorrida por un compuesto dividida por la distancia recorrida por el solvente. Este factor se utiliza en la cromatografía.

factores de riesgo (risk factors): Los factores de riesgo son conjuntos de condiciones que determinan las posibilidades de que un organismo enferme.

familia (family): Una columna vertical de la tabla periódica es una familia. Estas columnas también se conocen como grupos.

fisión (fission): La fisión nuclear es la división de un núcleo atómico, particularmente el de un elemento pesado, en dos partes, lo cual libera una gran cantidad de energía.

flujo (flux): Se denomina flujo a la proporción de movimiento de una cantidad mensurable a través de una superficie de referencia.

flujo de lodo volcánico (volcanic mudflow): El flujo de lodo volcánico, o lahar, generalmente se produce cuando depósitos volcánicos acumulados sobre las laderas de los volcanes son arrastrados por torrentes de agua de lluvia o de nieve derretida. Puede tener resultados catastróficos y afectar las zonas circundantes a los volcanes mucho después de la principal secuencia de erupciones.

flujo piroclástico (pyroclastic flow): Flujo piroclástico es una nube de gas volcánico, cenizas y fragmentos de roca a muy alta temperatura que se mueve rápidamente como resultado de fuertes erupciones volcánicas. A menudo se las relaciona con las erupciones plinianas, como la erupción del Vesuvio en 79 dC. Al salir del volcán, el flujo piroclástico puede desplazarse a velocidades de 100 km por hora o más y virtualmente acabar con todo tipo de vida a su paso.

fotosíntesis (photosynthesis): La fotosíntesis es el proceso por el cual las células vivas que contienen clorofila utilizan la energía solar para producir compuestos orgánicos a partir de materiales inorgánicos.

frecuencia (frequency): La frecuencia se refiere a la velocidad a la cual picos de una onda pasan por un punto. La frecuencia se mide en unidades de 1 por segundo; 1/s es equivalente a 1 hertz (Hz).

fuerza electrostática (electrostatic force): Esta es la fuerza que una carga eléctrica ejerce sobre otra. Cuando las cargas son iguales (ambas negativas o positivas), la fuerza es repulsiva; cuando las cargas son opuestas (una negativa y otra positiva), la fuerza es atractiva.

fuerza nuclear fuerte (strong nuclear force): Esta fuerza es la que mantiene unidas las partículas dentro del núcleo. Es una fuerza que alcanza su potencia máxima a distancias muy cercanas.

fulcro (fulcrum): Un fulcro es el objeto que sirve de punto de apoyo a una palanca.

fusión (fusion): La fusión nuclear se produce al combinar núcleos de átomos livianos, como el hidrógeno, con núcleos más pesados, con lo cual se libera gran cantidad de energía.

G

galaxia (galaxy): Una galaxia es un enorme conjunto de estrellas en cantidades que varían desde unos pocos cientos de millones a más de un trillón, todas ellas agrupadas por la fuerza de la gravedad.

glóbulos blancos (white blood cells): Se denominan glóbulos blancos a aquellas células del sistema inmunológico que ayudan a combatir las infecciones provocadas por virus, bacterias y hongos.

glóbulos rojos (red blood cells): Los glóbulos rojos contienen la proteína hemoglobina que aporta hierro a la sangre. Los glóbulos rojos transportan oxígeno desde los pulmones a los tejidos del cuerpo.

gradiente de concentración (concentration gradient): Un gradiente de concentración es una diferencia en la concentración de ciertas moléculas a lo largo de cierta distancia.

gravedad (gravity): La gravedad es la fuerza por la cual todo objeto del universo (que tiene masa) atrae a todo otro objeto.

grupo (group): Se llama grupo a cada una de las columnas verticales de la tabla periódica. Los grupos están numerados del 1 al 18 en las tablas periódicas modernas. Estas columnas también se conocen como familias.

H

hecho (fact): Se conoce como hecho a toda información cuya veracidad ha sido probada.

hemoglobina (hemoglobin): La hemoglobina es una proteína con contenido de hierro presente en los glóbulos rojos que transportan oxígeno desde los pulmones a los tejidos del cuerpo. La hemoglobina da a la sangre su característico color rojo.

hertz (Hz) (hertz [Hz]): Se denomina hertz (Hz) a la unidad utilizada para representar la frecuencia de un onda equivalente a 1 por segundo (1/s).

hidrosfera (hydrosphere): La hidrosfera se llama a veces "esfera de agua", ya que incluye toda el agua de la Tierra que se halla en los ríos, los lagos, el suelo, el subsuelo y el aire.

hipertónica (hypertonic): Una solución hipertónica es aquella en la cual la concentración de solutos en el exterior de la célula es mayor que la concentración en el interior.

hipótesis (hypothesis): Se denomina hipótesis a una declaración que sugiere una explicación de una observación o una respuesta a un problema científico.

hipotónica (hypotonic): Una solución hipotónica es aquella en la que la concentración de solutos en el exterior de la célula es *menor* que la concentración en el interior.

homeostasis (homeostasis): La homeostasis es una característica fundamental de los sistemas vivientes. En un contexto social, se refiere a mantener un número estable de individuos en una población. En el sentido fisiológico es la tendencia de un organismo a mantener un ambiente interno constante y estable.

I

impulso nervioso (nerve impulse): Un impulso nervioso es una onda de cambios químicos y eléctricos (potencial de acción) que pasan por una neurona en respuesta a un estímulo.

incendio de copa o aéreo (crown fire): Un incendio de copa o aéreo es un tipo de incendio forestal que envuelve a los árboles desde la mitad hasta las copas. Este tipo de incendio se puede propagar rápidamente de la copa de un árbol a la de otro.

incendio superficial (ground fire): Un incendio superficial quema solo el combustible existente a lo largo del suelo del bosque. Se queman cosas como residuos, hierbas y otras plantas no leñosas. Un incendio superficial tiene un efecto mínimo en los árboles más altos.

incendios controlados (prescribed burns): Los incendios controlados son un método mediante el cual se realizan incendios de baja intensidad en algunas partes de un bosque. Los incendios controlados reducen el combustible del suelo forestal y disminuyen las probabilidades de incendios catastróficos.

Índice UV (UV Index): El índice UV indica la intensidad de la radiación ultravioleta. El índice UV varía desde aproximadamente 1 (baja intensidad) hasta 12 o más (alta intensidad) dependiendo de factores como la hora del día, la cantidad de nubes presentes, la altitud y el ángulo del sol según la estación.

instinto (instinct): El instinto se refiere a la capacidad de un animal para completar una respuesta estereotipada bastante compleja a un estímulo clave sin tener experiencia previa.

interneuronas (interneurons): Una interneurona es una neurona asociativa, es decir, una neurona que se encuentra ubicada entre una neurona sensorial y una neurona motriz.

ión (ion): Un ión es una partícula con carga eléctrica.

ionización (ionization): Ionización se refiere a todo proceso que resulte en la formación de un ión. Un ejemplo es la formación de iones a partir de moléculas disueltas por la acción de un solvente.

isotónica (isotonic): Una solución isotónica es aquella en que la concentración de solutos en el exterior de la célula es igual a la de la concentración del interior.

isótopo (isotope): Un isótopo es un tipo de elemento que tiene una cantidad determinada de neutrones en el núcleo de cada átomo. Los diversos isótopos de un elemento en particular tienen el mismo número atómico (cantidad de protones) pero distintos números de masa debido a la diferente cantidad de neutrones.

L

lambda (λ) (lambda [λ]): Lambda es la letra griega que se usa para representar la longitud de onda.

lámparas incandescentes (incandescent lightbulbs): Se llama lámparas incandescentes a aquellas que producen luz por la acción de metales muy calientes. El metal de estas lámparas es generalmente tungsteno, y la lámpara se somete a vacío y se llena con un gas inerte como el argón.

leptón (lepton): Un leptón es una de las partículas elementales. Por ejemplo, un electrón es un leptón.

ley (law): Una ley es una explicación aceptada universalmente de algo del mundo natural, cuya veracidad siempre se puede probar bajo condiciones específicas.

ley de conservación de la materia (law of conservation of matter): Esta ley declara que la materia no se crea ni se destruye durante reacciones químicas o físicas comunes.

Ley de Hubble (Hubble's law): Esta ley, descubierta por Edwin Hubble, expresa matemáticamente la idea de que las galaxias más distantes se alejan de nosotros más rápidamente que las galaxias más cercanas.

ley de la inversa de los cuadrados (inverse square law): Toda cantidad que disminuye con el cuadrado aumentado de la distancia entre dos objetos sigue la ley de la inversa de los cuadrados.

línea de contención de incendios (firebreak): Una línea de contención de incendio es una barrera natural o artificial que sirve para detener la propagación del fuego. Puede ser una zona libre de vegetación, una zona de combustible verde de muy lenta combustión o una masa de agua.

lípido (lipid): Un lípido es un tipo de grasa, aceite o compuesto grasoso que generalmente contiene ácidos grasos en su estructura molecular. Son componentes importantes de la membrana del plasma.

litosfera (lithosphere): Se denomina litosfera a la capa exterior, relativamente rígida, de un planeta. Generalmente incluye la corteza y la parte superior del manto.

localización por ecos (echolocation): La localización por ecos se refiere al proceso utilizado por los murciélagos, delfines y otros animales para detectar objetos. Mediante este proceso de tipo sonar el animal emite sonidos altos que se reflejan en un objeto y vuelven a los oídos u otros receptores sensoriales.

longitud de onda (wavelength): Longitud de onda es la distancia entre ondas adyacentes, que generalmente se mide desde una cresta positiva a la otra o desde una cresta negativa a la siguiente. El símbolo para la longitud de onda es la letra griega lambda (λ).

luminosidad (luminosity): Se denomina luminosidad de un objeto a la potencia total de salida de dicho objeto, y generalmente se mide en vatios o en unidades de luminosidades solares ($L_{Sum} = 3.8 \times 10^{26}$ vatios).

M

macromolécula (macromolecule): Una macromolécula es una molécula de gran tamaño compuesta por cientos de miles de átomos. Las proteínas, los carbohidratos y los ácidos nucleicos son macromoléculas.

marco referencial (frame of reference): Una orientación fija en el espacio a partir de la cual se efectúan todas las observaciones. No existe un marco referencial absoluto.

masa crítica (critical mass): La masa crítica es la masa mínima de material fisionable en un reactor nuclear o en una bomba nuclear capaz de mantener una reacción en cadena.

medidor de conductividad (conductivity meter): Un medidor de conductividad mide la capacidad de una corriente eléctrica para pasar a través de un material.

medio (medium): El medio es la materia a través de la cual viaja una onda.

melanina (melanin): La melanina es un pigmento marrón que se halla en la piel y que es producido en los melanocitos.

melanoma (melanoma): Un melanoma es un cáncer de piel que comienza en los melanocitos. Muchas veces produce metástasis y es el tipo de cáncer de piel más grave.

membrana plasmática (plasma membrane): Esta membrana, también llamada membrana celular, rodea a la célula. La membrana plasmática sirve de barrera selectiva para el paso de iones y moléculas.

metabolismo (metabolism): El metabolismo es la suma de todos los cambios químicos que se producen en un organismo.

metástasis (metastasis): Metástasis es la propagación de células cancerosas de una parte del cuerpo a otra.

meteorito (meteorite): Un meteorito es una roca espacial que cae en la Tierra.

mezcla (mixture): Una mezcla es la combinación de dos o más clases de materia que retienen su propia identidad. Una mezcla se puede separar por medios físicos.

mitosis (mitosis): Mitosis es la división de los cromosomas y la producción de dos núcleos en una célula, a lo cual generalmente le sigue la división del citoplasma de la célula.

modelo conceptual (conceptual model): Un modelo conceptual describe un sistema mediante el uso de representaciones simbólicas.

modelo físico (physical model): Se denomina modelo físico a la representación física de un objeto o idea. A menudo estos modelos son más grandes o más pequeños que el original, de tal forma que se los pueda manipular.

molécula (molecule): Una molécula es un grupo neutro de átomos que se mantienen unidos mediante enlaces covalentes.

molécula covalente (covalent molecule): Una molécula covalente es aquella en la cual los átomos se mantienen unidos por enlaces covalentes. Los enlaces covalentes se forman cuando los núcleos de un compuesto comparten electrones casi por igual.

moléculas de carbono (carbon-based molecules): Estas moléculas, también llamadas moléculas orgánicas, están compuestas de carbono y otros elementos.

moléculas orgánicas (organic molecules): Las moléculas orgánicas, también llamadas moléculas de carbono, son aquellas que están compuestas por carbono combinado con otros elementos.

monosacárido (monosaccharide): Un monosacárido es un azúcar simple con una cantidad de tres a siete átomos de carbono en su esqueleto de carbonos.

motivo (motive): Un motivo es una causa o razón por la cual una persona actúa de cierta forma.

multicelular (multicellular): Los organismos multicelulares están compuestos por muchas células.

músculo cardíaco (cardiac muscle): El músculo cardíaco es un tipo de tejido muscular especializado que sólo se halla en el corazón.

músculo esquelético (skeletal muscle): El músculo esquelético es un tipo de tejido muscular que se encuentra adherido a partes del esqueleto y que es responsable de los movimientos musculares voluntarios.

músculo liso (smooth muscle): Este es un tipo de músculo que se halla en las paredes de los órganos internos huecos. Las contracciones del músculo liso son involuntarias.

N

nebulosa (nebula): Una nebulosa es una nube de gas en el espacio, generalmente luminosa.

neurona (neuron): Una neurona es un tipo único de célula que se halla en el cerebro y en el cuerpo y que se especializa en procesar y transmitir información. También recibe el nombre de célula nerviosa.

neuronas motrices (motor neurons): Estas son neuronas especializadas que reciben impulsos del sistema nervioso central y los transmiten a músculos o glándulas.

neuronas sensoriales (sensory neurons): Este tipo de neuronas son las que reciben impulsos de un órgano sensorial o receptor y los transmiten al sistema nervioso central.

neurotransmisión (neurotransmission): La neurotransmisión es el proceso mediante el cual una neurona libera neurotransmisores para comunicarse con otra neurona mediante la sinapsis.

neurotransmisor (neurotransmitter): Un neurotransmisor es un mensajero químico generalmente similar o idéntico a una hormona que transmite un impulso nervioso de una neurona a otra en la sinapsis.

neurotransmisor excitador (excitatory neurotransmitter): Los neurotransmisores excitadores hacen más probable que las neuronas inicien un potencial de acción (impulso nervioso).

neurotransmisor inhibidor (inhibitory neurotransmitter): Un neurotransmisor inhibidor hace más difícil que una neurona inicie un potencial de acción (impulso nervioso).

neutrón (neutron): Un neutrón es una partícula de carga eléctrica neutra que se encuentra en el núcleo de un átomo.

nivel de riesgo (level of risk): El nivel de riesgo indica las probabilidades de que ocurra un suceso indeseable o una enfermedad. El nivel de riesgo puede aumentar cuando se combinan varios factores de riesgo (ver factor de riesgo).

núcleo (nucleus): 1. En los átomos, el núcleo es la parte central, que contiene protones con carga positiva y neutrones generalmente de carga eléctrica neutra. 2. En las células eucariotas, el núcleo es el orgánulo membranoso que alberga el ADN cromosomático.

O

onda de choque (blast wave): Esta es una clase de onda poderosa y compresiva que viaja rápidamente a través de la atmósfera. Las ondas de choque son el resultado de sucesos repentinos, como explosiones, erupciones volcánicas o hasta grandes desprendimientos de rocas.

onda de compresión (compressional wave): *Ver* onda longitudinal.

onda longitudinal (longitudinal wave): Este tipo de onda viaja a través de un medio cuyas partículas oscilan en la misma dirección que la onda. Una onda sonora viaja de ese modo.

onda transversal (transverse wave): Una onda transversal es un tipo de onda que se desplaza por un material cuyo movimiento se realiza en ángulos rectos en la misma dirección en que se desplaza la onda.

ondas electromagnéticas (electromagnetic waves [EM waves]): El término ondas electromagnéticas es un sinónimo de luz, que consta de todas las ondas del espectro electromagnético.

órbita (orbit): Una órbita se refiere a la trayectoria que sigue un cuerpo al moverse alrededor de otro, generalmente de forma circular o elíptica.

orgánulo (organelle): Un orgánulo es una estructura organizada dentro de un célula con una función específica. Por ejemplo, los cloroplastos y las mitocondrias son orgánulos.

osmosis (osmosis): Se denomina osmosis al movimiento del agua a través una membrana de permeabilidad selectiva.

P

palanca (lever): Una máquina simple que consta de una barra que gira en torno a un fulcro colocado en cualquier posición a lo largo de la barra.

paralaje (parallax): Paralaje se refiere al cambio aparente de un objeto cuando se lo observa desde diferentes ángulos.

paralaje estelar (stellar parallax): El paralaje estelar es el cambio de posición aparente de una estrella cercana en relación a un objeto distante, lo cual ocurre cuando vemos la estrella desde diferentes posiciones en la órbita de la Tierra alrededor del Sol.

partes interesadas (stakeholders): Las partes interesadas son aquellos individuos que tienen intereses establecidos en las decisiones que se toman.

patógeno (pathogen): Un patógeno es un agente como un virus, una bacteria o un veneno en el cuerpo que puede provocar una enfermedad o la muerte.

peligros (hazards): Un suceso representa un peligro cuando expone a las personas a lesiones o muerte. Los peligros naturales también dañan o destruyen la propiedad pública o privada.

peligros para la salud (health risks): Cualquier factor o variable que tenga un impacto negativo en un organismo es un peligro para la salud. La combinación de factores de riesgo independientes puede crear niveles totales de riesgo más altos.

periodo (period): 1. Un periodo es el tiempo necesario para completar todo un ciclo o acción de un suceso repetitivo. 2. Las filas horizontales de la tabla periódica también se llaman periodos.

periodo de semidesintegración (half-life): Se denomina periodo de semidesintegración al tiempo que se requiere para que la mitad de los átomos de un isótopo radioactivo de un elemento se desintegre.

permeabilidad (permeability): La permeabilidad se refiere a la capacidad de una membrana u otro material para permitir el paso de una sustancia a través de sí.

permeabilidad selectiva (selectively permeable): La permeabilidad selectiva se refiere a una propiedad de las membranas biológicas que permite que algunas sustancias pasen y otras no.

plasma (plasma): El plasma es el líquido de color claro de la sangre, el cual es aproximadamente 90 por ciento agua. El plasma también contiene proteínas, elementos esenciales, moléculas de alimentos, oxígeno, dióxido de carbono y desechos celulares.

polar (polar): Las partículas polares son las que tienen una distribución de carga desigual.

potencial de acción (action potential): Un potencial de acción es un cambio breve en el potencia eléctrica a través de la membrana de una neurona. Los potenciales de acción son señales eléctricas que viajan a lo largo de una neurona en la forma de un impulso nervioso.

potencial eléctrico (electrical potential): Se denomina potencial eléctrico a la energía generada por una diferencia en la distribución de la carga. En una neurona, la diferencia de la carga pasa a través de la membrana.

presión de turgencia (turgor pressure): Esta es la presión dentro de un célula como resultado del influjo de agua debido a la osmosis.

presión termal (thermal pressure): La presión termal es la presión común en un gas a partir del movimiento de partículas que se debe a la temperatura del objeto.

probabilidad (probability): La probabilidad se refiere a las posibilidades de que un suceso ocurra o no.

productores (producers): Los productores son organismos que fabrican su propio alimento (autótrofos). Todos los consumidores (y descompositores) de la red alimenticia dependen de los productores.

propiedad característica (characteristic property): Este es un tipo de propiedad que se puede usar para identificar el material. No depende de la cantidad de material.

propiedad extensiva (extensive property): Este tipo de propiedad depende de la cantidad de materia presente. La masa es un ejemplo de propiedad extensiva.

propiedad intensiva (intensive property): Este tipo de propiedad no depende de la cantidad de materia presente. La densidad es un ejemplo de propiedad intensiva.

propiedad química (chemical property): La propiedad química se refiere a la capacidad de una sustancia para experimentar un cambio que implique la descomposición o formación de enlaces químicos que la transforman en una sustancia diferente.

proplyd (proplyd): Proplyd es la abreviatura en inglés del término "disco protoplanetario".

proteína (protein): Una proteína es un compuesto orgánico formado por una o más cadenas polipéptidas de aminoácidos. La mayoría de los materiales estructurales y enzimas de la célula son proteínas.

protón (proton): Los protones son las partículas positivas en el núcleo de un átomo o ión. La cantidad de protones de un determinado átomo es igual a su número atómico.

protoplanetas (protoplanets): Se denomina protoplanetas a los planetas en formación.

Q

quántum (quantum): Un quántum es la mínima cantidad de energía que puede ganar o perder un átomo.

quark (quark): Un quark es una de las partículas elementales de las cuales están compuestos todos los protones y neutrones.

R

radiación electromagnética (electromagnetic radiation [EM radiation]): La radiación electromagnética consta de ondas electromagnéticas que se mueven a la velocidad de la luz (300,000 kilómetros por segundo en un vacío).

rayos catódicos (cathode rays): Estos son rayos de electrones de alta velocidad emitidos por un cátodo en un tubo sometido a vacío al cual se ha aplicado corriente eléctrica.

reacción en cadena (chain reaction): Una reacción en cadena es una reacción automantenida que, una vez comenzada, proporciona de forma regular la energía y materia necesarias para continuar la reacción.

reacción nuclear (nuclear reaction): Una reacción que implica al núcleo de un átomo es una reacción nuclear. Entre este tipo de reacciones están la fisión y la fusión.

receptor sensorial (sensory receptor): Un receptor sensorial es una estructura sensorial especializada o un órgano que detecta estímulos.

red alimenticia (food web): Una red alimenticia representa el sistema de relaciones y cadenas alimenticias en un ecosistema. Las redes alimenticias también muestran dónde podría existir competencia por la misma fuente de alimento.

red cristalina (crystal lattice): La red cristalina es una disposición tridimensional de partículas (átomos, iones o moléculas) que se repiten en todo un sólido.

reflejo (reflex): Un reflejo es una reacción involuntaria a un estímulo.

rendimiento mecánico (mechanical advantage [MA]): El rendimiento mecánico es la relación entre la fuerza de entrada y la fuerza de salida de una máquina.

repeticiones en tándem (tandem repeats): En el ADN, las repeticiones en tándem se caracterizan por la ocurrencia de varios nucleótidos dispuestos en un patrón (generalmente cuatro o más) que se encuentran directamente adyacentes el uno al otro.

repolarización (repolarization): La repolarización es un cambio que devuelve a una neurona en reposo su potencial eléctrico tras la despolarización. Después de la repolarización, el interior de la neurona tiene más carga negativa que su exterior.

respiración aeróbica (aerobic respiration): La respiración aeróbica es la respiración celular que requiere la presencia de oxígeno.

respiración anaeróbica (anaerobic respiration): La respiración anaeróbica es la respiración celular que no requiere oxígeno.

respiración celular (cellular respiration): La respiración celular consiste en una serie de reacciones químicas por las cuales una célula viva descompone carbohidratos u otros compuestos orgánicos para liberar energía.

retina (retina): La retina es la capa de tejido sensible a la luz que recubre la parte posterior del glóbulo ocular. La retina envía señales al cerebro a través del nervio óptico.

S

sal (salt): Una sal es un tipo de compuesto formado por iones positivos y negativos. Las sales varían considerablemente en su solubilidad.

sarcómeros (sarcomeres): Los sarcómeros son las unidades básicas de contracción de los músculos esqueléticos y cardíacos.

sinapsis (synapse): La sinapsis es el sitio donde hacen conexión el extremo de un axón y el de una dentrita.

sintético (synthetic): El término sintético se utiliza para describir las sustancias fabricadas por los humanos.

solvatación (solvation): La solvatación es el proceso por el cual una partícula de un soluto es rodeada por moléculas solventes.

solvente (solvent): Un solvente es una sustancia líquida que se utiliza para disolver otra sustancia. Por ejemplo, el agua disuelve la mayoría de las substancias y se la considera el "solvente universal".

sotobosque (understory): El sotobosque es la capa de follaje que se halla debajo de la bóveda forestal. *Ver* bóveda forestal.

sublimación (sublimation): La sublimación se refiere al cambio de estado de un sólido directamente a un gas.

supercúmulos (superclusters): Los supercúmulos constan de muchos cúmulos de galaxias, grupos de galaxias y galaxias individuales, y son las estructuras más grandes conocidas en el universo.

supresión del fuego (fire suppression): La supresión del fuego se relaciona con las normas y decisiones por las cuales todos los incendios se extinguen cuando se descubren. La práctica de supresión del fuego puede resultar en una peligrosa acumulación de combustibles en los bosques.

sustancias puras (pure substances): Estas son sustancias que tienen una composición fija y difieren de las mezclas en el sentido de que cada muestra de determinada sustancia pura tiene exactamente las mismas propiedades características y composición.

T

tabla periódica de los elementos (periodic table of the elements): La tabla periódica de los elementos presenta de forma ordenada los elementos según su números atómicos, de modo que los elementos con propiedades similares estén en la misma columna o grupo.

tasa de mortalidad (mortality rates): La cantidad y frecuencia de muertes en un grupo de organismos durante determinado periodo de tiempo es la tasa de mortalidad del grupo.

tensión superficial (surface tension): La tensión superficial se refiere a la fuerza que se requiere para vencer la atracción intermolecular y atravesar la superficie de un líquido o esparcirlo.

teoría (theory): Una teoría es una hipótesis bien establecida que organiza el conocimiento, incorpora datos existentes, explica cómo se cree que ciertos sucesos o procesos ocurren y predice observaciones futuras satisfactoriamente.

tono (pitch): El tono es la cualidad de un sonido, entre grave y agudo, en relación con la frecuencia de ese sonido.

triángulo del fuego (fire triangle)**:** El triángulo del fuego representa las tres cosas necesarias para iniciar o mantener un fuego: oxígeno, combustible y calor. Si falta cualquiera de las tres, el fuego se apaga.

tubo de elementos o tubo de gases (element tube)**:** Este tipo de tubo se llena con elementos tales como hidrógeno, nitrógeno o neón. Al aplicar electricidad al tubo, se observa la emisión de una luz de color distintivo. El color de la luz es característico del elemento o elementos presentes en el tubo.

tubo fluorescente (fluorescent tube)**:** Este tipo de artefacto de luz consiste en un tubo de vidrio lleno de vapor de mercurio y revestido por dentro con un polvo fluorescente. Cuando se aplica electricidad al tubo, los electrones bombardean el mercurio causando la emisión de luz ultravioleta. Esta luz ultravioleta hace que el polvo fluorescente resplandezca, dando así luz visible.

U

unicelular (single celled, unicellular)**:** Los organismos unicelulares están compuestos por una sola célula.

unidad astronómica (UA) (astronomical unit [AU])**:** Una unidad astronómica es equivalente a la distancia promedio entre la Tierra y el Sol, la cual es de unos 150 millones de kilómetros. Estas unidades se utilizan para medir las distancias dentro del sistema solar.

V

variable (variable)**:** Una variable es una cantidad que puede cambiar o ser alterada durante el curso de una investigación científica.

vatio (watt)**:** Un vatio es la unidad básica de potencia eléctrica, equivalente a 1 julio de trabajo por segundo (1 J/s).

Credits

CHAPTER 1: **Opener** (scientist in the snow) USDA/ARS, (scientist in computer lab) Fermilab, (working with audio equipment) USDA/ARS, (scientists working with map and computer) NASA, (woman holding rabbit) U.S. Fish and Wildlife Service; **1.3** Copyright ORF/Tone Mathis; **1.5a–e** BSCS by David Ball and Sara Krause; **1.5f** The Iceman's Shoes. © Photo Archives of the South Tyrol Museum of Archeology. www.iceman.it; **Mary Leakey** Photo of Mary Leakey with Laetoli Footprints, courtesy of The Leakey Foundation; **Homo havilis Olduvai Skull** The Leaky Foundation; **Laetoli Trackway** The Leakey Foundation; **Laetoli Trackways Map** Laurie Grace; **1.8** Morguefile; **1.10** PhotoDisc; **1.12a** PhotoDisc; **1.12b** Comstock; **1.12c** Salvatore Massaro testing his automatic telescope pointing software; **1.12d** Photo courtesy of Prof. Christina Coughian, Biological Sciences Department, University of Denver; **1.14** EyeWire; **1.15** AP/Wide World Photos; **1.16** Adapted from *Global Tectonic Activity Map of the Earth*, NASA; **1.19** BSCS by David Ball and Juna Kurihara; **1.20** From M. Millard-Stafford, "Water Versus Carbohydrate-Electrolyte Ingestion Before and During a 15-km Run in the Heat," in the *Internal Journal of Sport Nutrition*, 7(1), 26–38. © 1997 by Human Kinetics. Adapted with permission from Human Kinetics (Champaign, IL); **Physical Therapist** PhotoDisc.

Unit 1

Unit Opener iStockphoto.

CHAPTER 2: **Opener** (penguins) Morguefile, (iceberg) iStockphoto, (hot air balloons) Corel, (boy thinking hard) Shutterstock, (messy closet) iStockphoto; **2.2** iStockphoto; **2.4** EyeWire; **2.6** BSCS by David Ball and Rick Simonson; **2.7** iStockphoto; **2.8** Corel; **2.13** Photo by Lars B. Anderson; **2.16** BSCS by David Ball and Rick Simonson; **2.23** iStockphoto; **2.25** Data compliments of the International Gem Society, www.gemsociety.org; **2.30** (clouds) Corel; **2.31** iStockphoto; **2.36** PhotoDisc.

CHAPTER 3: **Opener** (tree being struck by lightning) iStockphoto, (copper wire) Morguefile, (copper pots) iStockphoto, (boys washing a car) Thinkstock Photos, (blob of tar on car) iStockphoto; **3.2** LifeArt; **3.3** (photo) Thinkstock Photos, (blob of tar) iStockphoto; **3.8** ClipArt.com; **Copper Pots** iStockphoto; **Copper Coins** Morguefile; **Copper Wire** Morguefile.

CHAPTER 4: **4.1** Morguefile; **Hummingbird and Flower** Morguefile; **Skiers on Chairlift** iStockphoto; **4.4** iStockphoto; **4.8** PhotoDisc; **Student Thinking about Models of Methane** PhotoDisc; **Student Thinking about Models of Sodium Ion** PhotoDisc; **4.13** Edgar Fahs Smith Collection, University of Pennsylvania Library.

CHAPTER 5: **Opener** (closer view of the "twisters" in the Lagoon Nebula) A. Caulet (ST-ECF, ESA) and NASA, (Herbig-Haro object) Hubble Space Telescope WFPC2 image. Courtesy of Jeff Hester, AZ State U., (nebula) NSSDC, C.R. O'Dell (Rice University), and NASA; **5.6** BSCS by David Ball and Rick Simonson; **Chadwick Experimental Diagram** Adapted from "Discoveries of the Fundamentals of Matter"; **5.20** NSSDC, C.R. O'Dell (Rice University), and NASA; **Herbig-Haro Object** Hubble Space Telescope WFPC2 image. Courtesy Jeff Hester, AZ State U.

Unit 2

Unit Opener (rhino) Comstock, (muscle cells) Comstock, (glucose) Corel, (cross section of muscle cells) Dr. Thomas Caceci, Director, Morphology Research Laboratory, Virginia-Maryland Regional College of Veterinary Medicine, (plant cells) Corel, (teenager) Corbis, (orchid) PhotoDisc, (paramecium) ClipArt.com, (red blood cells) Drs. Constance T. Noguchi and Alan N. Schechter, National Institutes of Health, (anacharis plant) BSCS by Bill Beaudin.

CHAPTER 6: **Opener** (dianthus leaf, trodescontia leaf, radiolaria, human muscle cells) Comstock, (periphyton) National Science Foundation, (paneth cells) Corel; **6.1b** Michael Abbey/Photo Researchers, Inc; **6.1c** Comstock; **6.1d** Dr. Hans-W. Ackermann, Laval University; **6.1e** Copyright Dennis Kunkel Microscopy, Inc.; **Compound Microscope** John Bostrack/Visuals Unlimited; **6.4a,d** Ed Reschke; **6.4b** Corel; **6.4c** Copyright Dennis Kunkel Microscopy, Inc.; **6.8** Copyright Dennis Kunkel Microscopy, Inc.; **6.15** Copyright Dennis Kunkel Microscopy, Inc.; **6.17a** Drs. Constance T. Noguchi and Alan N. Schechter, National Institutes of Health; **6.17b** Dr. Thomas Caceci, Director, Morphology Research Laboratory, Virginia-Maryland Regional College of Veterinary Medicine; **Hooke's Cork Cells and Schwann's Animal Cells** The Linda Hall Library of Science, Engineering, and Technology; **6.26a** Courtesy of Stephen Durr; **6.28** BSCS by David Ball and Rick Simonson; **Water Balance in Plants** Courtesy of Michael W. Clayton; **Water Balance in Salmon** U.S. Fish and Wildlife Service Digital Library; **6.33** Andrew S. BAJER, DSc. Prof. of Biol. Emer., Center for Ecology and Evolutionary Biology, University of Oregon; **6.37** The Linda Hall Library of Science, Engineering, and Technology; **6.38** The Linda Hall Library of Science, Engineering, and Technology; **6.39** Image courtesy of Celestron; **6.40a-b** Copyright Dennis Kunkel Microscopy, Inc.; **6.41** Dr. Zhifeng Shao; **6.45b** ClipArt.com.

CHAPTER 7: **Opener** (clouds and sun, salmon, rice plants, salmon fillet, green beans, rice bowl) iStockphoto, (copepod) U.S. Fish and Wildlife Service, (teen reading) Corbis; **7.2** BSCS by Bill Beaudin; **7.3** BSCS by Carlye Calvin; **7.5** iStockphoto; **7.6a** iStockphoto; **7.6b** Dr. Lewis Kay Shumway, Blanding, Utah; **Sea Lettuce** iStockphoto; **Mixed Algae** Copyright Dennis Kunkel Microscopy, Inc.; **Kelp** iStockphoto; **Diatoms** Courtesy of Michael W. Clayton; **Purple Bacteria** Image derived from Sarah Boomer's NSF-Microbial Observatory Project, Red Layer Microbial Observatory (RLMO) Curriculum Project, http://www.wou.edu/~boomers/research/MMLID/MMLID.htm; **Aerobic Exercise** Shutterstock; **Mitochondrion** Copyright Dennis Kunkel Microscopy, Inc.; **7.14a** ClipArt.com; **7.14b** G. E. Grant/60south.com; **7.16** Based on data gathered by H. T. Odum from a river ecosystem in Silver Springs, Florida; **7.17** (photos of leaf & monkeys) Comstock.

CHAPTER 8: **Opener** (at the starting line) iStockphoto, (runners in a race) Image Ideas, (the brain) Corbis; **8.1** iStockphoto; **8.3** Shutterstock; **8.4** (guppy habitat) Helen Rodd; **8.6** iStockphoto; **8.7a** PhotoDisc; **8.7b** iStockphoto; **8.7c** Corel; **8.8** Heather Angel/Natural Visions; **8.9** iStockphoto; **8.10** Shutterstock; **8.12** iStockphoto; **8.13** data source: Kluger, M. J. et al. (1975) *Science, 188*, p. 166; **Chimps Grooming** Corel; **Lions Eating** Corel; **Ostriches Running** Corel; **Eurasian Lynx Kittens** Corel; **Colorado Potato Beetles** Corel; **Dog Panting** Corel; **Golden-Mantled Ground Squirrel** iStockphoto; **8.16** iStockphoto; **8.17** PhotoDisc; **8.21** (grasshopper, teenager, fish) iStockphoto, (ape) PhotoDisc; **8.28** BSCS by David Ball and Rick Simonson; **8.33** BSCS by David Ball and Rick Simonson; **8.34** BSCS by David Ball and Rick Simonson; **8.36** BSCS by David Ball and Rick Simonson; **8.38** BSCS by David Ball and Sara Krause; **8.39a** Copyright Dennis Kunkel Microscopy, Inc.; **8.39b** Eric V. Grave/Photo Researchers, Inc.; **8.40** Morguefile; **8.41** BSCS by David Ball and Juna Kurihara; **8.42** ClipArt.com; **8.43** iStockphoto.

CHAPTER 9: **Opener** (arm flex, lifting weights, doing pushups, pulley) iStockphoto, (cross section of muscle cells) Dr. Thomas Caceci, Director, Morphology Research Laboratory, Virginia-Maryland Regional College of Veterinary Medicine; **9.1a,c** Shutterstock; **9.1b** iStockphoto; **9.2** (carrying heavy backpacks) iStockphoto; **9.3** (seagull) U.S. Fish and Wildlife Service; **9.10** Shutterstock; **9.13** iStockphoto; **9.15a** Dr. Don W. Fawcett/Visuals Unlimited; **9.15b-c** Copyright Dennis Kunkel Microscopy, Inc.; **9.16** BSCS by David Ball and Juna Kurihara; **9.22** BSCS by David Ball and Juna Kurihara; **9.23** Image Ideas; **Gecko on Ceiling** iStockphoto; **9.25** Brand X Pictures; **9.26** Corel; **9.28** BSCS by David Ball and Rick Simonson.

Unit 3

Unit Opener (ring galaxy, full HST ACS Image of AM 0644-741) Image Credit: NASA, ESA, and The Hubble Heritage Team (AURA/STScI). Acknowledgment: J. Higdon (Cornell U.) and I. Jordan (STScI); (whirlpool galaxy) Image Credit: NASA and The Hubble Heritage Team (STScI/AURA). Acknowledgment: N. Scoville (Caltech) and T. Rector (NOAO).

CHAPTER 10: **Opener** (globular cluster in Hercules) Canada-France-Hawaii Telescope/J.-C. Cuillandre/Coelum, (Earth at night) Data courtesy of Marc Imhoff of NASA GSFC and Christopher Elvidge of NOAA NGDC. Image by Craig Mayhew and Robert Simmon, NASA GSFC, (stars) Corel, (spiral galaxy NGC 3949) NASA, ESA and The Hubble Heritage Team (STScI/AURA); **10.1** NASA; **10.3** *The Stars A New Way to See Them*, H. A. Rey, © 1980 Houghton Mifflin Company; **10.4** *The Stars A New Way to See Them*, H. A. Rey, © 1980 Houghton Mifflin Company; **Earth at Night** Data courtesy Marc Imhoff of NASA GSFC and Christopher Elvidge of NOAA NGDC. Image by Craig Mayhew and Robert Simmon, NASA GSFC; **Source of Light Pollution** Image provided courtesy of the International Dark-Sky Association. http://www.darksky.org; **10.7** Adapted with permission from Terry Herter, Cornell University, Department of Astronomy; **Monster Truck** iStockphoto; **10.8b,d** Comstock; **10.8c** ClipArt.com; **10.9** EyeWire; **10.10** NASA, ESA and H.E. Bond (STScI); **10.11** (stopwatch) ClipArt.com; **10.17** iStockphoto; **10.18** (galaxy) Corel, (Earth) Comstock; **10.19** iStockphoto; **10.23** NASA, ESA and The Hubble Heritage Team (STScI/AURA); **10.24** Bob McBroom of www.kansaswind-power.net; **Leavitt** Courtesy of the American Association of Variable Star Observers (AAVSO); **10.31** NOAO/AURA/NSF; **10.35** ClipArt.com.

CHAPTER 11: **Opener** (Eagle Nebula) Jeff Hester and Paul Scowen (Arizona State University), and NASA, (Hubble telescope) NASA, (astronaut servicing Hubble Space Telescope) STS-103 Crew, NASA, (Spitzer space telescope) NASA/JPL-Caltech, (galaxies collide) Debra Elmegreen & the Hubble Heritage Team (AURA/STScI/NASA); **11.1** © 1986 Alan Bean, *The Hammer and the Feather*; **11.2** Canada-France-Hawaii Telescope/J.-C. Cuillandre/Coelum; **11.3** NASA/JPL-Caltech/W. Reach (SSC/Caltech); **11.6** NASA/JPL-Caltech/R. Hurt (SSC-Caltech); **11.7** iStockphoto; **11.9** ClipArt.com; **11.10** Science Museum/Science and Society Picture Library; **11.13** BSCS by David Ball and Rick Simonson; **11.15** Anglo-Australian Observatory/David Malin; **Bright Light from Supernova** Courtesy of Tunç Tezel; **Cave Drawing of Supernova** Copyright Doak Heyser 2005; **Crab Nebula** (optical) NASA/CXC/SAO; **11.17** Jon and Bryan Rolfe/Adam Block/NOAO/AURA/NSF; **Astronaut Servicing Hubble Space Telescope** STS-103 Crew, NASA; **11.18** NASA; **11.19** After de Lapparent, Geller & Huchra 1986 (Astrophysical Journal Letters). Graphics by Michael Kurtz. © 1987 Smithsonian Astrophysical Observatory; **11.20** 2dF Galaxy Redshift Survey Team; **11.21** NASA/WMAP Science Team; **11.22** Caltech/David Malin Images; **Cat's Eye Nebula, NGC**

6543 Credit: NASA, ESA, HEIC, and The Hubble Heritage Team (STScI/AURA). Acknowledgment: R. Corradi (Isaac Newton Group of Telescopes, Spain) and Z. Tsvetanov (NASA); **Charles Messier** Courtesy of Owen Gingerich; **11.23** Anglo-Australian Observatory/David Malin; **11.24** NASA and The Hubble Heritage Team (STScI/AURA); **11.25** Adam Block/NOAO/AURA/NSF; **11.26** Anglo-Australian Observatory/David Malin; **11.27** Image Credit: NASA, ESA, and The Hubble Heritage Team (STScI/AURA). Acknowledgment: M. Tosi (INAF, Observatorio Astronomico di Bologna); **11.28** Image Credit: NASA, ESA, and The Hubble Heritage Team (AURA/STScI). Acknowledgment: J. Higdon (Cornell U.) and I. Jordan (STScI); **11.29** NASA, N. Benitez (JHU), T. Broadhurst (Racah Institute of Physics/The Hebrew University), H. Ford (JHU), M. Clampin (STScI), G. Hartig (STScI), G. Illingworth (UCO/Lick Observatory), the ACS Science Team, and ESA; **11.30** Anglo-Australian Observatory/David Malin; **11.31** Robert Williams and the Hubble Deep Field Team (STScI) and NASA; **Images of Crab Nebula** NASA/CXC/SAO; **11.33–11.36** GRACE Master Teachers, Texas Space Grant Consortium; **Hubble Deep Field South** R. Williams (STScI), the HDF-S Team, and NASA; **Spitzer Space Telescope** NASA/JPL-Caltech; **11.41a** Larry and Judy Patterson/Adam Block/MOAO/AURA/NSF; **11.41b** Brad Whitmore (STScI) and NASA; **11.42** Debra Elmegreen & The Hubble Heritage Team (AURA/STScI/NASA).

CHAPTER 12: **Opener** (group of galaxies) Credit: NASA, ESA, J. Blakeslee and H. Ford (John Hopkins University); **12.6** Wesley R. Hitt/Mira.com; **12.12** NASA; **Jet Breaking Sound Barrier** Ensign John Gay, USS Constellation, US Navy; **12.17** NASA; **12.18** NOAO/AURA/NSF; **12.19** Courtesy, Carnegie Observatories, Carnegie Institution of Washington; **12.20** (galaxies) NASA/IPAC Infrared Science Archive, (spectra) 2dFGRS Image Gallery; **12.23** Adam Block/NOAO/AURA/NSF; **12.24** NASA; **12.25** Jeffrey Newman (Univ. of California at Berkeley) and NASA; **12.29** BSCS by David Ball and Rick Simonson; **12.30** Reprinted with permission of Lucent Technologies Inc./Bell Labs; **12.31** NASA/WMAP Science Team; **12.32** NASA/WMAP Science Team; **The Future of the Universe** Adapted from NASA and A. Feild (STScI), BSCS by David Ball and Rick Simonson; **12.34** Courtesy of the Fisher Collection, Chemical Heritage Foundation Collections, Philadelphia, PA.

CHAPTER 13: **Opener** (star-forming region) NASA/JPL-Caltech/S.Carcy (Caltech), (early Earth) © 2000 Don Dixon/cosmographica.com, (nebula NGC 3603) Wolfgang Brandner (JPL/IPAC), Eva K. Grebel (Univ. Washington), You-Hua Chu (Univ. Illinois Urbana-Champaign), and NASA, (dust and rock in cloud) Painting by William K. Hartmann; **13.1** NASA/JPL-Caltech/S. Carey (Caltech); **13.2** Wolfgang Brandner (JPL/IPAC), Eva K. Grebel (Univ. Washington), You-Hua Chu (Univ. Illinois Urbana-Champaign), and NASA; **13.3** NASA, ESA, D. R. Ardila (JHU), D. A. Golimowski (JHU), J. E. Krist (STScI/JPL), M. Clampin (NASA/GSFC), J. P. Williams (UH/IfA), J. P. Blakeslee (JHU), H. C. Ford (JHU), G. F. Hartig (STScI), G. D. Illingworth (UCO-Lick) and the ACS Science Team; **13.4** NASA/JPL-Caltech/T. Pyle/ssc; **13.7** Painting by William K. Hartmann; **13.9** Painting by William K. Hartmann; **13.10** Painting by William K. Hartmann; **13.11** Courtesy of NASA; **13.13** NASA Kennedy Space Center; **13.14a** Mark Sterkel/Odessa American; **13.14b** Photo courtesy of Michael E. Zolensky. NASA JSC; **13.14c** Photo courtesy of Robert Bodnar, Virginia Polytechnic Institute. NASA JSC; **13.15** Captain Budd Christman, NOAA Corps; **13.16** NASA; **13.17** Courtesy of NASA JPL; **Maatmons on Venus** JPL Multimission Image Processing Laboratory, NASA, and the NSSDC; **Ulysses Patera on Mars** Copyright © Calvin J. Hamilton; **Volcano on Io** Galileo Project, JPL, NASA; **13.18** © 2000 Don Dixon/cosmographica.com; **13.19** Photo courtesy of Institute of Meteoritics, University of New Mexico; photographer Ken Nichols; **Diamond** Comstock; **13.22** NASA/USGS; **13.23** Photo courtesy of Institute of Meteoritics, University of New Mexico; photographer Ken Nichols; **13.24** Photo courtesy of Adrian Brearley, University of New Mexico; **13.25** Naval Research Laboratory; **13.28a–c** Courtesy of Michael W. Clayton; **13.28d** Visuals Unlimited; **13.29** J. W. Schopf, UCLA; **13.31** Marjory Martin and Judith Kinnear; **13.32** © Dr. Alan Jay Kaufman. Reprinted with permission; **Vent of Superheated Water** OAR/National Undersea Research Program (NURP), NOAA; **13.33** Painting by William K. Hartmann; **13.34** David Crisp and the WFPC2 Science Team (Jet Propulsion Laboratory/California Institute of Technology), and NASA; **13.35** NASA/JPL/Malin Space Science Systems; **13.36** NASA.

Unit 4

Unit Opener (aerial photo of Earth, micrograph of hair, child in field, red fibers) iStockphoto, (aerial image of Colorado) image from ARC Science Simulations Inc.'s "Face of the Earth" produced on UNAVCO's map server http://jules.unavco.org.

CHAPTER 14: **Opener** (investigators taking photos of evidence) Brand X Pictures, (two people wearing police gear) Shutterstock, (police tape at crime scene) iStockphoto; **14.2** Reprinted with permission from the WGBH Educational Foundation; **14.6** iStockphoto; **14.12** Data source: Cobert Associates, Inc.; **14.13** Data source: Cobert Associates, Inc.; **14.19** Phillip B. Danielson; **14.20** Phillip B. Danielson; **World Trade Center** Corel; **Wooly Mammoths and Horses on Tundra** All rights reserved, Image Archives, Denver Museum of Nature & Science; **14.22** Courtesy of Dr. Richard Hallick, The Biology Project, DNA Forensics Activity, University of Arizona, http://www.biology.arizona.edu; **14.23** iStockphoto; **14.35** Data source: Cobert Associates, Inc.; **14.37** Phillip B. Danielson.

CHAPTER 15: **Opener** (destruction from Loma Prieta, CA earthquake) USGS, (volcano) USGS/Cascades Volcano Observatory, (tornado) iStockphoto, (sunburn, smoking, eating junk food) iStockphoto, (heart disease map) Cardiovascular Health Branch, Centers for Disease Control and Prevention; **15.1** iStockphoto; **15.2** iStockphoto; **15.3** iStockphoto; **15.9** Adapted from data from the EPA's Sunwise Program; **15.10** Adapted from NOAA data; **15.11** Adapted from NOAA data; **15.13** Cardiovascular Health Branch, Centers for Disease Control and Prevention; **15.14** National Cancer Institute; **15.15** National Cancer Institute; **15.17** (epidermis image) © Dr. James Little; **15.18** Morguefile; **Lead in Gasoline Graph** Data source: Nriagu, 1989; **Kestrel and Vole** iStockphoto; **Male Blue Tit** John Foxx; **15.22** Leonard Von Matt/Photo Researchers, Inc.; **15.23** Corel; **15.24** USGS/Cascades Volcano Observatory; **15.25** USGS/Cascades Volcano Observatory; **15.26** USGS; **15.28** Adapted from Myers, USGS/CVO, 2000; **Volcanic Bombs** (volcano) Corel; **Trees Toppled by Volcanic Blast** USGS/Cascades Volcano Observatory.

CHAPTER 16: **Opener** (smoldering trees) iStockphoto, (fire on hillside above houses) Shutterstock, (small fire in forest) iStockphoto, (man setting grasses on fire) Fermilab, (Earth view) iStockphoto; **16.1** The name and character of Smokey Bear are the property of the United States, as provided by 16 U. S. C. 580p-1 and 18 U. S. C. 711, and are used with the permission of the Forest Service, U.S. Department of Agriculture, and the Smokey Bear Licensing Program; **16.2** © David J. Strohmaier; **16.3** The name and character of Smokey Bear are the property of the United States, as provided by 16 U. S. C. 580p-1 and 18 U. S. C. 711, and are used with the permission of the Forest Service, U.S. Department of Agriculture, and the Smokey Bear Licensing Program; **16.5** USDA Forest Service photograph 86476 by W. J. Lubken; **16.6** USDA Forest Service, photograph by W. J. Reich; **16.7** Shutterstock; **16.8** Langston, N. (1995). *Forest dreams, forest nightmares: The paradox of old-growth in the inland West.* University of Washington Press, Seattle; **16.9** USDA-ARS; **16.10** Adapted from USDA Forest Service RMRS-GTR-91; **16.11** FEMA; **16.12** The name and character of Smokey Bear are the property of the United States, as provided by 16 U. S. C. 580p-1 and 18 U. S. C. 711, and are used with the permission of the Forest Service, U.S. Department of Agriculture, and the Smokey Bear Licensing Program; **Tree Rings** Dr. Henri Grissino-Mayer, Department of Geography, University of Tennessee; **Tree Rings with Fire Scars** Dr. Henri Grissino-Mayer, Department of Geography, University of Tennessee; **Debris and Charcoal Flow** Grant A. Meyer, Ph.D.; **Alluvial Fan Record: Northeast Yellowstone National Park** Grant A. Meyer, Ph.D.; **16.14** Data source: Smith, J. K., + McMurray, N. E. 2000 FireWorks Curriculum featuring ponderosa, lodgepole, and white bark pine forests. (General Technical Report RMRS-GTR-G5). Fort Collins, CO: U. S. Department of Agriculture, Forest Service, Rocky Mountain Research Station, 270 p.; **Aerial View of 2003 Cone Fire** Adapted from a photo by Larry Hood, U. S. Forest Service Fire and Fuels Specialist; **Cone Fire as Crown Fire in Unthinned Forest** Martin Ritchie, USDA Forest Service; **Cone Fire in Unprescribed and Prescribed Burn Plots** USDA Forest Service; **16.15** (fox, rabbit) iStockphoto, (raspberry) Shutterstock; **16.17** (backdrop) Mr. Jack Alves, (stellar's jay, ponderosa pine cone, northern goshawk, ants) iStockphoto, (kaibab squirrel) Digital photograph courtesy William Herrera, Colorado Springs, CO, (beetle, red squirrel) Corel, (Kaibab plateau shaded DEM with inset map) Study Area map adapted from The Effects of Forest Management of the Biology and Population Ecology of Northern Goshawks on the Kaibab Plateau, Arizona. By R. T. Reynolds, S. Bayard de Volo, S. M. Joy, S. R. Salafsky, J. D. Wiens, et al. USDA Forest Service, Rocky Mountain Research Station, Fort Collins, CO, (northern flicker) Digital Vision; **16.18** Adapted from USDA Forest Service RMRS data; **16.19** Adapted from USDA Forest Service RMRS data; **16.20** Mr. Jack Alves; **16.22** © Dr. Kimberlyn Williams; **16.23** (backdrop) Mr. Jack Alves, (cooper's hawk, quail, gray fox, lizard) Corel, (road runner, gopher snake, rabbit) iStockphoto, (coyote) Shutterstock, (scrub oak) W. L. Wagner © USDA–NRCS–PLANTS Database; **16.24** Data source: "Role of Fire in Regeneration from Seed" by Keeley, J. E., & Fotheringham, C. J. (2000). In M. Fenner (Ed.), Seeds: *The Ecology of Regeneration in Plant Communities* (2nd ed.). United Kingdom: CAB International. Photos: Jay Sullivan; **16.25** California Conservation Corps.

Index

Page numbers in bold print indicate item was in bold in the text; italic indicates a chart, table, graph, or illustration.

Biomechanics, 44, 439–440

Biosphere, **654–655**

Biosynthesis, 344, 350–354

Biotic environment, **802, 804**

Black dwarf stars, 235

Black-headed gulls, 372

Black holes, 237

Black powder, 157

Blacks Mountain Experimental Forest, Susanville, California, 799–800

Blast wave, of volcanoes, **770**

Blood, 707–720; confirmation of, 710–712; observation of, 708–709; probability and, 718–720; supply of, 415; typing of, 713–717, 729

Blueshift, in spectra, **584–585, 594**

Body maintenance behaviors, 374

Bohr, Niels, 176–180, 217

Bohr atomic model, 176–180

Bonds, 51, 86; charges and, 98–99; chemical, 184; covalent, 132, 138, 189; definition of, 101; ionic, 133; of metals, 138–139; nuclear reactions and, 203; polar covalent, 132, 136; predicting, 188–189; types of, 125

Bones, vitamin D and, 759–760

Brain, 396, 399. *See also* Nervous system

Brainstorming, 311, 441

Breakdown, as cellular process, 350–354

Breathing rate, 415

Brightness, apparent, of stars, **490, 496, 498**

Bronchus cancer, 751

Brown algae, 335

C

Caffeine, 19, 140–143

Calcium, 266, 431

California; Blacks Mountain Experimental Forest in, 799–800; chaparral ecosystem of, 814–821; forest fires in, 789

Calories, 415

Calorimeters, 349

Cancer, 304, 747–755

Canopy of forest, **787**

Capitan Mountains, New Mexico, 782

Captions, 494

Carbohydrates, **19, 267**

Carbon; in cells, 252, 264, 266–268, **267;** in dipoles, 123; early life and, 646–650; photosynthesis and, 330–333; radioactively labeled, 354–355; in star formation, 234

Carbon dioxide; cellular membranes and, 294; in cellular respiration, 345; for decaffeination, 143; dissolved, 322; for drycleaning, 146; in early Earth atmosphere, 650; experiment

with, 84; as fire product, 85, 191, 785; model of, 142; phases of, 210; in photosynthesis, 332

Carbonic acid, 322

Cardiac muscle, **426**

Carnivores, 348

Cascade Volcanic Arc, 768–769

Catalysts, **331**

Catapults, 416, 428

Cataracts, of eyes, 754

Cathode rays, **170**

Cause-and-effect relationships, **748,** 758

Cavendish, Henry, 530, 559–560

Cell(s), 252–313. *See also* Cancer; Crime science; cell theory and, 278–279; describing, 254–255; division of, 297–303; DNA in, 702; eukaryotic, 272–277, 280; growth of, 304; molecules in, 264–271; elements of, 264–269; proteins and amino acids in, 269–271; movement through membranes of, 281–296; active *versus* passive transport in, 294; environment and, 281–283; model of, 283–287; molecular exchange in, 287–293; osmosis in, 296; muscle, 429–431; observing, 256–262; onion example of, 262–264; prokaryotic, 272–273; red blood, **714;** technology to see, 305–310; white blood, **714;** writing about, 310–314

Cell bodies, in nerves, 389–390

Cell cycle, **298**

Cell phones, 487

Cell processes, 314–355; biosynthesis and breakdown in, 350–354; energy and matter flow in, 347–350; overview of, 320–321; photosynthesis, 327–337, **328;** in algae, diatoms, and bacteria, 335–336; ATP and, 330–333; carbon compounds from, 330–333; energy for, 327–329; plant gas exchange, 321–325; plant starch storage, 325–327; radioactive tracing of, 354–355; respiration, 337–346; ATP in, 340–341, 343–346, 415; description of, 340–343; exercise and, 345–346; yeast experiment on, 337–340

Cell theory, 613

Cellulose, 267, 332

Cell walls, 275–276

Celsius temperature scale, 509

Centers of mass, **556–558**

Central nervous system, 396. *See also* Nervous system

Centrioles, 274, 276

Cepheid variable stars, **498,** 500–501, 548, 590, 594, 599–600

Cerebrum, of brain, 399

Chaco Canyon National Historical Park, New Mexico, 540

Multicellular animals. *See* Behavior

Multicellular organisms, 252, **272**

Murray meteorite, 643

Muscular system, 408–447. *See also* Exercise; ATP in, 431; biomechanics and, 439–440; design based on, 441–447; energy for, 414–416; as force to work, 417–421; mechanics of, 421–424; muscle cells in, 277, 429–431; muscle loss and, 434–435; nerve signals to, 410; power of, 435–438; skeletal system and, 421–428

Myofibrils, of muscles, 429

Myosin protein, 429, 431

N

NADH (nicotinamide adenine dinucleotide), 341–342

National Aeronautics and Space Administration (NASA), 542, 660–663

National Science Foundation's Young Investigator Award, 147

National Zoo, Washington, D.C., 782

Nature *versus* nurture argument, 378–381

Nebulae, 234, 237, 523–524, **536**, 549, 554, 590

Nebular theory of solar system formation, 630–631

Negative charges, 118, 120, 127

Nematodes, 401

Nerve cells, 276–277

Nerve impulse, **391**

Nervous system; description of, 387–389; eyes and, 400; in learning and memory, 399; muscle response to, 410; neurotransmitters in, 392–393; in response to stimuli, 395–397

Net charge, across membranes, 294

Neurons, in nerves, **386**, 388–390, 392, **395**, 400

Neurotoxins, 336

Neurotransmission, **390**

Neurotransmitters, 392–393

Neutral charges, 115, 127

Neutrinos, 219

Neutrons, 166, 216, **218**, 604

Neutron stars, 237

Nevado del Ruiz volcano, Colombia, 766

New General Catalogue (Dreyer), 549

New Mexico, 540, 782

Newton (N, force unit), 437

Newton, Sir Isaac, 529, 547, 559

Newton's second law, 32

Nitrogen, 123–124, 266

Nobel Prize, 218

Noble gases, 153, 180–187

Nociceptors, 397

Nocturnal species, 376

North Carolina Governor's Award for Excellence, 147

North Pole, magnetic, 118

Notebook, science, 5

Novelty-seeking behavior, 362–364

Nuclear power plants, 226, 228

Nuclear reactions, 198–243, **220**; definition of, 203; fission, 228–229; fusion, 221–224; of gases, 209–212; of hydrogen, 204–208; isotopes and, 213–221; Chadwick and, 217–218; hydrogen and helium as, 213–216; nuclear particles and, 219; symbols for, 220; radioactive decay and, 225–227; stars and, 229–240; density and, 241–243, in early universe, 238–239; experiment on, 229–233; high-mass, 235–237; low-mass, 233–235

Nucleic acids, **267**, 270–271

Nucleus; of atoms, **165**, 183; of cells, 272, **274–275**, 702

Nutritionists, 44

O

Oberlin College, 500

Observations, in scientific inquiry, 28, 30, 64

Observatories, 512–515

Olduvai Gorge, Tanzania, 14–15

Olympics, 44

Olympus Mons, Mars, 640

Omega-3 fatty acids, 268

Omega-6 fatty acids, 268

Omnivores, 348, 365

Onion, as cellular example, 262–264

Orbits, **178**, 575

Organelles, 272, **274–275**, 280

Organic molecules, **267–268**

Organizing information, 515–517. *See also* Classification; Periodic Table of the Elements

Osmosis, 252, **292**, 294, 296

Outermost shells, of atoms, 184

Outgassing, **639**, 651

Oxygen; burning and, 85, 785, 791; in cells, 266; cellular membranes and, 294; in cellular respiration, 340, 343, 345, 432; diffusion of, 290; in early Earth atmosphere, 650–652, 656; extremeophiles and, 657; hemoglobin for, 714; in red blood cells, 276; in water, 123–124, 136

Ozone, 758

P

Paint thinner, 88

Paper, charged, 115–116

Paper chromatography, 685–691

Paraffin, 66

Parallax angle, **468**

Parkinson's disease, 393

Particle model of matter, 57. *See also* Matter

Particles; alpha, 164, 225–226; beta, 226; charge development in, 126–128; electron sharing by, 131–135; gamma, 226; ionization *versus* dissociation in, 129–131; isotopes and, 219; nuclear, 219

Passive transport, 294

Pasteur, Louis, 278

Patent fingerprints, 680

Pathogens, **714**

Patterns. *See also* Crime science; constellations as, 458; of gravity, 528; in Periodic Table of the Elements, 193–197; in properties, 509–510; in star properties, 509–511

Pauling, Linus, 132

Peebles, P. J. E., 607

Pensias, Arno, 606

Performance, 42–43

Period, of variable stars, **498**, 548

Periodic Table of the Elements, 51, 127, 148–197, **192**, 212; Bohr atomic model and, 176–180; color and, 154–157; massive-star supernova explosions and, 237; metals in, 139; Noble gases in, 180–187; organizing principles of, 188–193; overview of, 150–151; patterns in, 193–197; Rutherford conceptual atomic model and, 162–170; Rutherford mathematical atomic model and, 171–175; spectra and, 158–162, **159**

Peripheral nervous system, 396. *See also* Nervous system

Permeability, selective, 252, **391**

pH, 323–324, 403

Phases of matter, 87–90, 136, 210, 228

Phospholipids, 293, 352

Phosphorus, 266

Photons, 604, 609

Photoreceptors, 397

Photosynthesis, 280; in algae, diatoms, and bacteria, 335–336; ATP in, 330–333; by bacteria, 335–336, 400; as biosynthesis, 350; carbon compounds from, 330–333; in chloroplasts, 319; concept map for, 334; early Earth and, 651–654, 656; energy for, 327–329

Physical models, **166**, 173

Physical properties, 62, 101. *See also* Density

Physical therapists, 44

Pillan Patera, Io (moon of Jupiter), 641

Pitch, **479**, 577–576, 580–581

Pivot point, of levers, 410

Planarians, 387

Planetary geologists, 637

Plants, behavior of, 401–404. *See also* Photosynthesis

Plasma, in blood, **714**

Plasma membranes, 275–276

Plastic fingerprints, 680

Plate tectonics, **33**

Plato, 79

Play behaviors, 375

Pleura cancer, 751

Plinian eruptions of volcanoes, **762**–764

Pliny the Younger, 762, 765

"Plum pudding" atomic model, 171

Plus charges, 120

Polar covalent molecules, 123–124, 132, 136

Polarity, chromatography and, 685

Polar molecules, **121**–122, 293, 392

Pollution, light, 463–464, 554

Polyunsaturated fats, 268

Pompeii, Vesuvius volcano and, 762–763

Positive charges, 118, 120, 127

Potassium, 22, 266, 390

Potassium chlorate, 157

Potential energy, 417

Power, muscle, 435–438

Predators, 373, 375, 400

Predictions, in scientific inquiry, 28

Prescribed burns, in forests, **800**

Presidential Green Chemistry Challenge Award, 147

Pressure; density and, 84; of ocean, 657; thermal, **532**–533; turgor, 296, **403**

Princeton University, 607

Principles of Chemistry (Mendeleyev), 191

Probability, 718–721

Producers, in ecosystems, **802**

Product labels, 37–38

Prokaryotic cells, 272–273, 280, 297

Properties; characteristic, **70**, 203; chemical, 81, 104–108; extensive, **75**; intensive, **75**; of matter, 51, 58–61, 90–95; patterns in, 509–511; physical, 62, 101

Proplyd (protoplanetary disk), **626, 631,** 634

Prosthetic limbs, 410, 433, 439

Proteins, **267, 269**–271, 293, 294, 429, 431, 714–715

Protons, **165**–166, 183, 215, 218, 220, 342, 604

Protoplanetary disk (proplyd), **626, 631,** 634

Protostars, 233, 235

Prototypes, 443

Protozoans, 401

Proxy variables, 415

Psychology, 399

Puebloan (Anasazi) people, 539

Pulleys, 422

Pupil, of eye, 400

Pure substances, **79**

Purple bacteria, 280, 336

Pyroclastic flow, from volcanoes, 765–766

Pyrotechnicians, 157

Pyruvate, 341

Q

Quantum of energy, **178**

Quarks, 166, **219**

Questions, testable, 5, 17–18

R

Radcliffe College, 500

Radiation, 217–218; electromagnetic, 578, 606, 740, 757–758; experiment on, 736–737; skin cancer and, 747–755; SPF test for, 744–746; ultraviolet, 741–744; visible, 737–741; vitamin D and, 759–760

Radioactive decay, 203, **225–227**

Radioactive wastes, 229

Radioactivity, 354–355

Radio waves, 485–486

Random samples, 525

R&D 100 Award, 147

Readings, 5

Reasonable doubt, 718

Receptors, sensory, **396–397**, 400

Recessional velocity, 593, 595–597, 599, 610

Recipes, 65

Red algae, 335

Red blood cells, 276, **714**

Red giant stars, 233–**234**

Redshift, in spectra, **584**–585, 592, 596, 599

Red tides, 336

Reflex actions, **395**

Rehabilitation, 435

Relative data, 107

Relative hardness testing, 108

Relative melting points, 109

Relative solubility testing, 109

Repelling charges, 115

Repolarization, **391**

Reporting results, 445–447

Reproduction. *See* Cells

Reproductive behaviors, 375

Resistance training, 434

Resolution, microscopic, 307

Respiration, cellular, 337–346, **340**; ATP in, 340–341, 343–346, 415; as breakdown reaction, 350; description of, 340–343; energy from, 319; exercise and, 345–346, 415; in muscles, 431; yeast experiment on, 337–340

Retention factor, in chromatography, **688**

Retina, of eye, 400, **754**

Revolution, of Earth, **575**

Rh antigens, 714

Rhythmic behaviors, 376

Ribonucleic acid (RNA), 271, 645

Ring galaxies, **551**

Risk factors, **747**

Risks and hazards, 730–773, **761**; in communities, 771–773; lead poisoning, 756–757; radiation, 736–755; volcanoes, 761–771; Cascade Volcanic Arc, 768–769; Herculaneum, 765–766; models of, 770–771; Mount St. Helens, 764; Vesuvius, 762–764, 767–768

RNA (ribonucleic acid), 271, 645

Robots, 439

Rods, of eye, 400

Rotation, 238, 574

Russia, 191

Rutherford, Ernest, 177, 217; conceptual atomic model of, 162–170, 214, 225; mathematical atomic model of, 171–175

S

Sagan, Carl, 604

Saltwater, 144

Sarcomeres, of muscles, **429–431**

Saturated fats, 268

Scaled physical models, 173

Scanning electron microscope (SEM), 308

Scanning probe microscope (SPM), 308

Scatter plots, **381**

Schleiden, Matthias, 278

Schwann, Theodor, 278

Scientific inquiry, 2–47; conducting, 664–667; controlled experiments in, 26; definition of, 27–29; evidence in, 8–10, 35–37, 39–41; features of, 30–34; in human evolution studies, 14–17; Iceman example of, 11–13; product labels from, 37–38; sports drinks example of, 18–19, 45–47; sports medicine example of, 44; study reports from, 42–43; testable questions in, 17–18; testing in, 20–25

Scoring rubrics, 5, 91–95, 145, 194, 310, 354, 441, 664

Scott, Dave, 522

"Sea of electrons" model, 139

Second-class levers, 422